To Clarence E. Mickel
who, fortunately, wouldn't let me
forget I had suggested writing this.

A. Glenn Richards

June 1, 1951.

THE INTEGUMENT OF ARTHROPODS

Signed by Author

The Integument of ARTHROPODS

The Chemical Components and Their Properties, the Anatomy and Development, and the Permeability

A. GLENN RICHARDS

PROFESSOR, DIVISION OF ENTOMOLOGY AND ECONOMIC ZOOLOGY, AND DEPARTMENT OF ZOOLOGY, UNIVERSITY OF MINNESOTA

UNIVERSITY OF MINNESOTA PRESS, MINNEAPOLIS
London, Geoffrey Cumberlege, Oxford University Press

PRINTED AT THE NORTH CENTRAL PUBLISHING COMPANY, ST. PAUL

"An author never finishes a book; he merely abandons it."

PREFACE

The present book is intended primarily for entomologists and other invertebrate zoologists, but it is hoped that it may also serve as a useful compilation for chemists. My aim has been to cover the available literature and to synthesize this, as far as possible, into a coherent picture of the arthropod integument as one of the primary organ systems of this phylum of animals. Otherwise stated, the aim has been to give a documented statement of present knowledge that will be self-sufficient and adequate for most workers — both biologists and chemists — and to include in the documentation a bibliography for ready reference when more detail about past work is needed. With this objective in mind, major headings have been treated in considerable detail, while less directly concerned topics (e.g., pigments, sense organs) have been treated incompletely and only to round out the main picture.

In attempting to make the volume "self-sufficient" — an obvious impossibility if interpreted literally — background material has been written into the text when feasible. One of my friendly critics has told me that I have made parts of the text too elementary and taken space to explain things "that everyone knows"; another, that I have written on too high a level and am "talking over the heads" of many potential readers. I can only hope this means that the text will prove to be an acceptable compromise.

In general the coverage is to the end of the year 1949. A few items from 1950 have been included (mostly from prepublication information), but no attempt has been made to keep the manuscript up to date while in the course of publication.

The bibliography accompanying this volume is voluminous. I hope it is adequate, but it is by no means complete even for those topics which are treated in detail. Much of the literature of the nineteenth century furnishes only further specific examples for the general applicability of the simplified description given in the introductory chapter. Similarly, literally hundreds of anatomical papers, and for sculpturing and setae thousands of taxonomic papers, mention the integument incidentally. Many of these data, especially from the older papers, cannot be fitted into current terminology without reinvestigation or presumptive reinterpretation of them in terms of current knowledge. But a great deal was seen by workers in the nineteenth century, and an attempt will be made to cite the historically important papers and to indicate the names associated with particular discoveries.

The author is an entomologist, and so the other classes of arthropods get less complete coverage. But it should be remembered that more work has been done with insects. The current trend is to interpret the integument of other arthropods in terms of known insectan structure. This is a practice, however, that may be badly misleading if carried too far.

The bibliography contains a good many references not primarily concerned with the integument. Many of these are only casually cited in the text to note similarities (either to other animate or to inanimate phenomena) or to illuminate some point by calling attention to the existence of seemingly relevant literature. The author has repeatedly disavowed the view, commonly held among entomologists (at least in the United States), that insects are a world unto themselves that may be studied without regard to other animals or other phenomena.

Citations in the text are related to the subject where cited. This does not, however, necessarily mean that the citations say or conclude the same thing as the text, or even that they necessarily treat directly the statement made. Any attempt to give full details of all the various papers would be prohibitively voluminous (as well as of dubious value). Citations have been made primarily for documentation and for cataloguing the literature that bears both directly and indirectly on the point. Instead of a separate author index, which would be of little value for authors who are quoted frequently, page references have been placed after each entry in the bibliography.

The author is deeply indebted to the University of Minnesota for the facilities, time, and encouragement to complete this monograph. Acknowledgment is also due to the Medical Division of the Army Chemical Center and to the Surgeon General's Office of the U.S. Army for encouragement provided by research contracts. For critical reading of all or part of the manuscript I owe thanks to Dr. Fred Smith of the Division of Biochemistry; Mr. R. E. Snodgrass of the Bureau of Entomology; Dr. G. Fraenkel of the University of Illinois; Dr. C. M. Williams of Harvard University; Dr. H. T. Spieth of the College of the City of New York; and Dr. H. S. Mason of the National Institute of Health. For information about and permission to utilize findings from current work that has not yet appeared in print, thanks are due to Dr. M. F. Day, Dr. R. Dennell and his students Mr. Krishnan and Miss Sewall, Dr. G. Fraenkel, Dr. L. E. R. Picken, Dr. W. A. Riley, Dr. K. M. Rudall, Dr. C. M. Williams, and Dr. M. V. Passonneau. Further thanks are due to Dr. Williams for supplying me with a copy of his translation of the article by Hamamura *et al.* Thanks are also due for permission to use illustrations as acknowledged under the individual figures. Original photographs were made by Mr. V. P. Hollis of the University Photographic Laboratory. And last but not least, thanks are due to my wife, Sally Richards, for typing much of the manuscript and polishing up at least some of the rough spots in my use of the English language.

In closing, somewhat philosophically, it might not be amiss to mention that one sometimes hears that the most crucial points needing elucidation in the arthropod cuticle are within the province of physical chemists, not within the province of biologists. In a sense this is indeed true, but history anyone can observe in other fields of biology makes it seem highly unlikely that physical chemists will seriously interest themselves in the problem of an arthropod's skin. My own opinion is that advances in the study of arthropod cuticle, including the physical chemistry thereof, will not come from chemists themselves but from biologists who take the trouble to master the necessary techniques or, for the more difficult and specialized ones, induce persons with the necessary training to collaborate with them.

A. GLENN RICHARDS

TABLE OF CONTENTS

LIST OF FIGURES

THE INTEGUMENT OF ARTHROPODS

CHAPTER 1

Introduction

The integument is one of the primary organ systems of an animal. The term can be restricted to the tissue and tissue products forming the outer surface of the body or it can be used in a broader sense, as in this book, for the external covering tissue and structures which are derived from it and have a similar general structure. Epithelial tissue, derived from the embryonic ectoderm and having a structure fundamentally similar to that of the body wall, lines the fore-gut and hind-gut, the tracheae of the respiratory system, most of the reproductive ducts and the glands associated therewith, muscle apophyses and apodemes, and numerous glands (silk, salivary, etc.). In arthropods the integument is characterized by being formed from a single layer of nonciliated epithelium that deposits on its outer surface an acellular cuticle, the characteristic structure of which will be given in detail in subsequent chapters. The cuticle, and in fact the entire integument, show a fundamental similarity throughout the phylum despite the presence of secondary calcification in certain groups.[1] The cuticle itself may vary in thickness from a small fraction of a micron to several millimeters. It is extremely durable except for digestion by specific enzymes. It has been identified chemically from moderately old fossil remains and is recognizable after passage through a mammalian gut and after treatment with solutions of alkali or weak mineral acids. A large part of this durability is due to the presence of a polysaccharide called chitin, but chitin itself is not distinctive of arthropod cuticle because it is found in skeletons of several other groups of animals as well as seemingly being absent from some parts of arthropod integumental structures.

The typical or generalized structure of an arthropod cuticle is

[1] The Onychophora, which will be treated subsequently, are now generally recognized as a distinct phylum. Perhaps some aberrant and little-known classes of the Arthropoda such as the Linguatulida may have to be listed as exceptions when more thoroughly studied, but the better-known groups fit the above generalization.

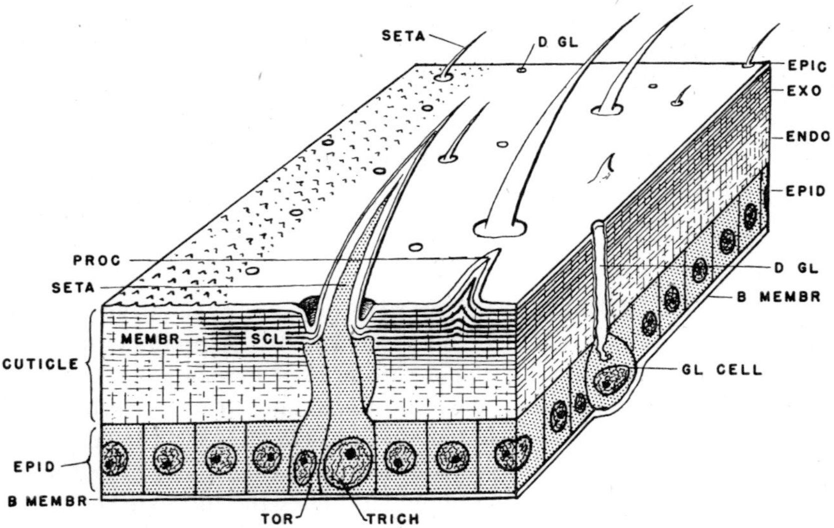

Figure 1. Diagrammatic reconstrutcion of a block of integument to show the general organization. Drawn at boundary between a sclerite and membrane to show fundamental similarity of soft and hard cuticles.

B MEMBR = basement membrane; D GL = duct of unicellular gland; ENDO = endocuticle, or soft inner portion of procuticle; EPIC = epicuticle (the subdivisions of this not indicated); EPID = epidermal cell layer; EXO = exocuticle, or hard and usually darkened outer portion of procuticle; MEMBR = membrane; PROC = a type of immovable, noncellular process; SCL = sclerite, or hardened and darkened area of cuticle; SETA = the commonest type of movable (tactile) projection; TOR = tormogen, or socket-forming cell; TRICH = trichogen, or seta-forming cell.

shown in Figure 1. A continuous single layer of epidermal cells secretes or deposits a comparatively thick cuticle on its outer surface, and is separated from the body cavity by a thin membrane called the basement membrane. The cuticle consists of two major subdivisions: a relatively thick inner or lower layer containing chitin, and a thinner outer layer which is negative to chitin tests. Both of these are further subdivisable in most cases. The hardening and darkening processes giving rise to sclerites (sclerotization) involve both the inner portion of the outer layer (epicuticle) and the outer portion of the inner layer (exocuticle). At intervals socketed setae and other sense organs are found. Typically the cuticle is also penetrated by ducts of integumentary glands whose secretion is concerned with development of the cuticle. Glands producing other secretions are also sometimes found. Other components, such as oenocytes, may be present.

Commonly the arthropods are referred to as possessing a chitinous exoskeleton. To a certain extent this is a misnomer because arthropod cuticles are known which lack or at least have no detectable chitin (Forbes 30, Richards 47a, b). Arthropod skeletons do almost always contain chitin, and if the designation "chitinous exoskeleton" is used simply to indicate that the chemical chitin is normally one of the components present, it is justifiable. However, we do not know of any cuticle which consists only of chitin; ordinarily only one quarter to one half of the dry weight of the cuticle is due to chitin.

The chemical chitin constitutes only one of the components in cuticle (as pointed out by Odier in 1823), but the term chitin is, unfortunately, in common use both for the polysaccharide of that name and for the entire cuticle. This dual usage of the word chitin persists, especially in the German literature, and in many cases it is difficult to determine which usage an author means. Since the term cuticle is employed throughout the animal kingdom, the term hoplin (Campbell 29) was proposed, as a name lacking chemical significance, for use in connection with arthropod cuticle; it is still available but has not been adopted. In most literature prior to 1930, and in some of it since then, the word chitinized has been used incorrectly to indicate a hard portion of cuticle; since the hardness is not due to the presence of chitin, the term sclerotized has replaced it (Ferris & Chamberlin 28, Fraenkel & Rudall 40, Snodgrass 35).[2]

The arthropod exoskeleton is fundamentally an elongate, hollow, continuous ellipsoid modified by complex invaginations and evaginations (Maloeuf 35a). As with any exoskeleton, solutions for the problems of growth, sensation, and movement are required. Growth within a rather tight box is made possible by periodic shedding of the cuticle and development of a new and larger one. Sensations are readily received by having the sense organs, in effect, project through small holes in the thick cuticle, and, when chemoreception is involved, having the sensillae covered by only a thin and presumably highly permeable cuticle. The phenomenon that appears to be of major importance for the remarkable evolutionary development of arthropods is the specific method adopted for locomotion. Instead of retaining a soft cuticle, or a hard cuticle with locomotory appendages projecting from it, the arthropods have developed an exoskeleton of alternately hard and soft areas. Thereby levers and hinges are provided which

[2] Incidentally it is commonly said that chitin is secreted only by the ectoderm and ectodermal derivatives. Modern concepts of embryology, which no longer uphold the sanctity of the germ layers, would consider the production of chitin by ectoderm merely a by-product of specific differentiation of this tissue.

permit development of elaborate and complicated muscular systems (Maloeuf 35a) and also great superficial diversification (Kennedy 27). Some authors have indeed gone so far as to say that the usual short life, usual small size, and even cold-bloodedness of arthropods are due to the exoskeleton (Kennedy 27) – an oversimplification in a complex of phenomena.

For entomologists and invertebrate zoologists whose background in physics and chemistry may be no more than that received by the author when he was a student, numerous background references are available. Among the more readable are Astbury (33, 43) and Mark (43) for fiber structure; Frey-Wyssling (38, 48) and Picken (40) for the ultrastructure of biological systems; and standard references such as Baldwin (47), Burk and Grummitt (43), and Needham (42) for biochemistry.

Numerous general books are available for entomology, but few of these contain much material useful as background for the present book. Chemists and others desiring additional information on insect structure and development are referred to Snodgrass (35), H. Weber (33), and Wigglesworth (39). Corresponding treatments of the entire phylum Arthropoda or of the classes other than Insecta are not available except for the commonly inaccessible series of volumes (in German) by Kukenthal and Krumbach (26–30) and by Bronn (1866–1948).

A number of technical reviews have been written on the arthropod integument (or that of insects alone), beginning with the one by Straus-Durckheim in 1828. Useful treatments to consult now begin with the monumental treatise by Biedermann (14a) and include those by Deegener (28), Kühnelt (28c), H. Weber (33), Snodgrass (35), Wigglesworth (39, 48b), the relevant sections of Kukenthal and Krumbach (26–30), and some of the more recently written sections of Bronn's still unfinished series.

Section I

THE CHEMICAL COMPONENTS, THEIR COMBINATIONS, THEIR PROPERTIES

CHAPTER 2

Glucosamine, N-acetylglucosamine, Chitobiose, and Chitin

How many polysaccharide derivatives should be discussed in this section seems an open question (Haworth 46). Some would probably limit it to a discussion of the polymer called chitin, which, it is now established, is a polyacetylglucosamine, or at most, they would mention those units which have led to the identification of the polymer unit. However, if we adopt the current point of view, which seems to be gaining general acceptance, that chitin does not occur naturally as a distinct and separate chemical entity in the cuticle but is always found as one component in a chitin-protein complex, then it follows that chitin is no more a "natural" compound than are the various degradation products that can be prepared from it. The fact that chitin can be separated from the chitin-protein complex with relative ease, whereas the subsequent breakdown of the chitin chains themselves requires more drastic treatment, means only that bonding energies of different magnitudes are involved in different linkages within the complex. Accordingly a fairly complete listing of chitin derivatives and chitin compounds will be given, even though some of this material has no obvious biological significance.

The most readily obtained derivative of chitin is glucosamine (Fig. 2). In 1843 Payen reported that chitin differs from cellulose in containing nitrogen, and as early as 1876 Ledderhose obtained from the acid hydrolysis of chitin (lobsters and May beetles) a crystalline product which differed from glucose in having an amine group in place of one hydroxyl. He named this product glucosamine. Further, he found that the hydrolysis of chitin not only gave glucosamine but also acetic acid (1878/79, 81). He did not recognize that the glucosamine and acetic acid were produced in equimolar amounts. These results were shortly confirmed by Tiemann and Landolt (1886) and

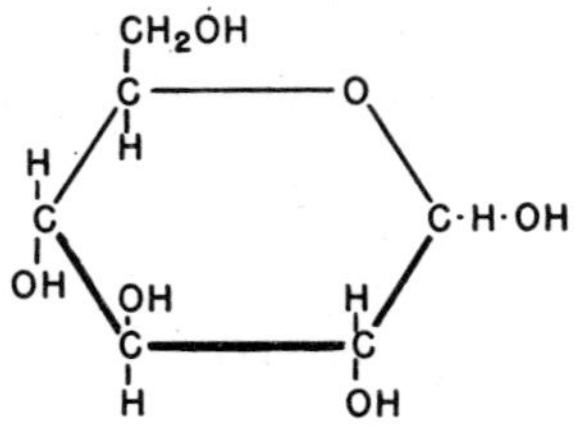

D-GLUCOSE

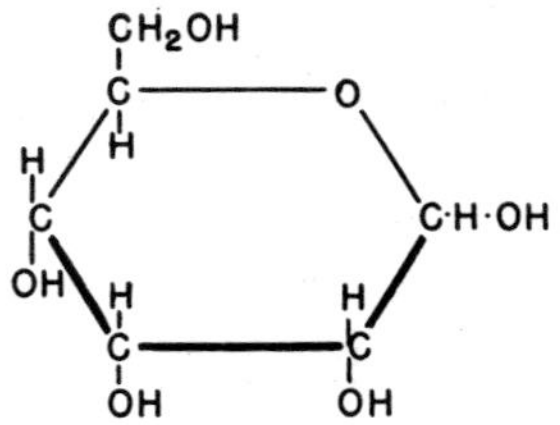

D-MANNOSE

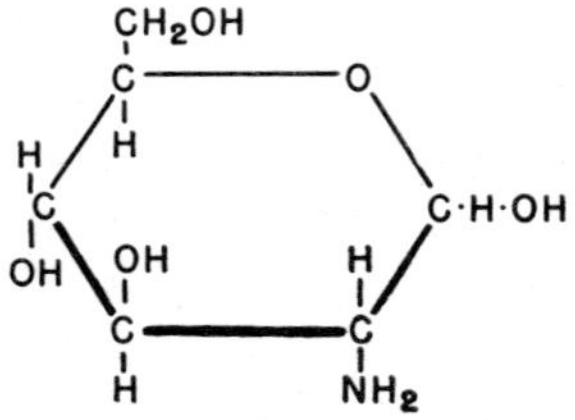

GLUCOSAMINE

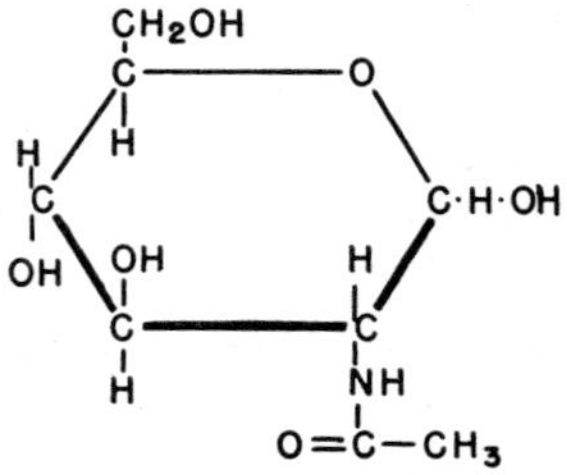

N-ACETYLGLUCOSAMINE

Figure 2. Pyranose ring formulae of Haworth for d-glucose, d-mannose, glucosamine, and N-acetylglucosamine.

extended to the chitin from fungal cell walls by Winterstein (1893–99).

From these early data and the ever present tendency to compare chitin with its better-known relative cellulose (Fig. 4),[1] the idea crept into the literature as far back as the nineteenth century that chitin was a polymer of acetylglucosamine residues. This assumption early gained popular acceptance despite the fact that some authors insisted, quite correctly, that the compound in arthropod cuticle should be called chitosamine, at least until it could be verified that the natural unit was glucosamine and not mannosamine (Fig. 2) which underwent a Walden inversion to give glucosamine during hydrolytic degradation (Levene 21). The X-ray diffraction patterns by pioneer workers (Herzog 24, Kurt Meyer & Mark 28b, and Kurt Meyer & Pankow 35) showed considerable similarity to patterns from

[1] A good and readable review of cellulose chemistry is the one by Ott (43). Other good treatments, some exhaustive, are by Preston (39), Wergin (43), Marsh and Wood (45), Pigman and Wolfrom (45), and Haworth (46). Some of the similarities and differences between chitin and cellulose will be cited during the treatment of chitin properties.

cellulose and strengthened but did not prove the case in favor of glucosamine. It was not until Karrer and Mayer in 1937 and Haworth, Lake, and Peat in 1939 isolated glucosamine from chitin under conditions which precluded the Walden inversion, and the latter group of workers obtained appropriate chemical reactions, that the case in favor of glucose rather than mannose became really strong.

Glucosamine (Fig. 2) has the typical pyranose ring structure (Bergmann *et al.* 34; Cox & Jeffrey 39) and belongs to the monoclinic sphenoidal group; the six atoms of the pyranose ring are nearly coplanar, the O atom being slightly displaced out of the plane of the C atoms (Cox *et al.* 35).

Many other references to glucosamine can be found in the literature (e.g., Fränkel & Jellinek 27, Karrer & Smirnov 22, Bergmann *et al.* 31, etc.). For the quantitative determination of glucosamine, in pure form or in the presence of other sugars, various methods are available, including iodometric titration and colorimetric methods using Ehrlich's reagent (Aminoff & Morgan 48, Dumazert & Lehr 42, Elson & Morgan 33, Hahn 46, Zuckerkandl & Messiner-Klebermass 31). Chromatographic separation is also feasible (Freudenberg *et al.* 42, Hough *et al.* 48).

The powerful acid hydrolysis of chitin usually leads to the removal of the acetyl group from the molecule, giving thereby both glucosamine and acetic acid. Early evidence indicated that the acetyl group was attached to the amine (Brach & von Fürth 12, Fränkel & Kelly 01, 02, Kotake & Sera 13), and this has been subsequently verified by studies on the isolated N-acetylglucosamine (= chitosamine) prepared both by less destructive chemical procedures (Bierry *et al.* 39, Zechmeister & Tóth 31) and by enzymatic action (Karrer *et al.* 22–37).

Karrer (29) and his colleagues have obtained as high as an 80% yield of normal acetylglucosamine from the enzymatic breakdown of chitin. They obtained no more than a trace of glucosamine. This agrees with other data indicating that most if not all the glucosamine residues in a chitin chain are acetylated. However, apparently the molecular structure does not prevent the occurrence of acetyl groups in other linkages, for a number of authors have prepared acetylchitins and various acetylglucosamines (Bergmann & Zervas 31; Bergmann *et al.* 31a, b; Bertho *et al.* 31; Cutler *et al.* 37; Cutler & Peat 39; Kurt Meyer & Wehrli 37; Schmiedeberg 20; Shorigin & Hait 35). Also, chitin that has been deacetylated and then reacetylated can have the nitrogen split off quantitatively, yet retain 12% of the acetyl groups (Karrer & White 30). There is no evidence that acetyl groups occur other than on the amine groups in normal chitin; conceivably such groups could be a factor causing discrepancies in the nitrogen values and in the unrecognized carbohydrates which will be discussed subsequently.

N-acetylglucosamine can be estimated chemically by methods similar to those used for glucosamine (Aminoff & Morgan 48, Morgan & Elson 34).

OTHER SOURCES OF GLUCOSAMINE AND ACETYLGLUCOSAMINE

It might not be amiss to mention that both glucosamine and N-acetylglucosamine may be obtained from a variety of sources other than from chitin. Seemingly the natural compounds contain N-acetylglucosamine, but owing to the ease of removing the acetyl group, glucosamine is commonly found. Probably the least surprising source is the isolation of the phenylisocyanate of glucosamine from fossils, where presumably it was present in the highly durable chitin (Abderhalden & Heyns 33). Either or both of these products have been obtained from or determined in the exuvial or molting fluid of silkworms (Hamamura *et al.* 40), from a protein fraction in the blood of crabs (Roche & Dumazert 40), from the entasternite of an arachnid (Halliburton 1885a, b), from the hydrolysate of the fibroin of Tussah silk (Abderhalden & Heyns 31), and from the hydrolysate of the salivary gland secretion of Drosophila (Kodani 48).

In occurrence these compounds are not limited to arthropods and other forms of life with chitin but can be obtained from a wide variety of sources. Among the many sources we might mention streptococcic bacteria (Kendall *et al.* 37), casein (Nilsson 36), egg white (Nilsson 36), hyaluronic acid (Humphrey 46), and various mucoids where the glucosamine can be associated with either mannose or galactose or both (Haworth 46, Hewitt 38, Iseki 34, Karlberg 36, Karl Meyer *et al.* 34, Ozaki 36, Schmiedeberg 1891, Stacey 43). In some cases the percentage is fairly high: thus it is said that 10% of the weight of purified ovomucoid is N-acetylglucosamine (Iseki 34). Komori (26) claimed that there were some differences between glucosamine from chitin and from ovomucoid, but this has not been confirmed by subsequent work and would seem to be erroneous.

It would be of interest to know the manner of linking N-acetylglucosamine to protein molecules in albumen, mucoid, etc., but the literature does not seem to contain any significant data on this point (Bendich & Chargaff 46, Karl Meyer 38).

LOW MOLECULAR WEIGHT POLYMERS

N-acetylglucosamine chains of various lengths have been obtained by a number of workers, but the majority of these polymers have not been studied in any detail. It is well established that a so-called solution of chitin in concentrated mineral acid begins to degenerate rather rapidly, shorter and shorter chains being produced with time (Clark & Smith 36). Certainly the most interesting of the low molecular weight polymers is chitobiose (Fig. 3), which was first isolated

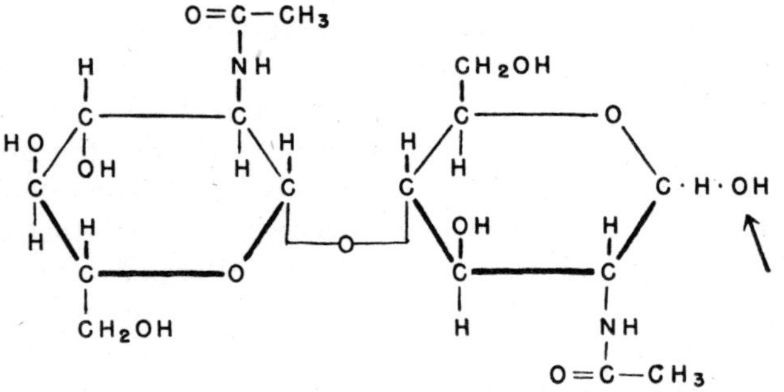

Figure 3. Configuration of a chitobiose molecule. This is identical with the cellobiose molecule except for the substitution of acetylamine groups for the hydroxyl group on carbon atoms no. 2. The arrow indicates the single reducing group (or potentially aldehydic group) present in the molecule.

as an octacetate by Bergmann, Zervas, and Silberkweit (1931a, b). Six of the acetyl groups can be removed by treatment with dilute alkali, leaving two presumably on the nitrogens. The diacetylchitobiose so formed has one reducing or potentially aldehydic group and is joined by a linkage between carbon atoms nos. 1 and 4. Tests on this biose show that it conforms to the structure previously calculated by Kurt Meyer and Mark (28b) on the basis of X-ray analysis. Shortly thereafter, the postulated β-glycosidic linkage (Fig. 4) was confirmed by appropriate chemical tests (Zechmeister *et al.* 32, Zechmeister & Tóth 33), and chitobiose, originally isolated from lobster shells, was isolated from beetles, snail radulae, and fungi (Tóth 40, Zechmeister & Pinczési 36, Zechmeister & Tóth 34).

Useful as chitobiose may be in the study of chitin chemistry, it should not be assumed that the biose has any more physiological significance than other chain numbers. Zechmeister and Tóth (31, 32) have not only isolated the readily obtained monose (= N-acetylglucosamine) but also both the biose and triose. The biose contains a complete unit only in the sense that it portrays the repeating unit of a chitin chain. It is, however, no more readily obtained from chitin than the triose, and much more difficult to obtain than the monose. As far as we know, it represents only the length that is necessary to portray all the features of the completed chain. Of course, if someone were to isolate chitobiose as a chitin precursor, then this unit would take on physiological significance. It might be of some interest in this connection to note that chitobiose has not yet been recognized as the product normally arising from the enzymatic breakdown of chitin (Karrer 30). Chitobiose, however, does not portray all the properties of the chitin micelle or of chitin in bulk; see p. 22.

Details of the physical and chemical properties of the above compounds can be found in references already cited. The one additional point that seems of possible interest here is the fact that chitobiose decomposes at temperatures above 185° C. (Bergmann *et al.* 31b).

Chains longer than three N-acetylglucosamine residues have been recorded by a number of workers but not studied in any detail except for empirical analyses of the conditions required in processing chitin for use as an industrial chemical (p. 28). As already noted, a number of workers have recorded that so-called acid solutions of chitin degenerate, giving rise to products of shorter average chain length (Clark & Smith 36, Zechmeister & Tóth 31). The groups working with enzymes have sometimes used one of these shorter chains, which they have named chitodextrin, but which has been characterized only in terms of the enzyme conglomerate that will act upon it (Grassmann *et al.* 34, Karrer & Hoffmann 29, Zechmeister *et al.* 32).

CHITIN

As everyone likely to use this treatise probably already knows, the polysaccharide we now call chitin was discovered by Braconnot in fungi in 1811 and named by him "fungine." The name chitin which is now universally used was proposed by Odier in 1823 for what has subsequently been found to be the same compound in insects.[2]

[2] Other names which have been proposed but have not gained acceptance and are now largely forgotten include metacellulose (Fremy), pilzcellulose or fungal cellulose (de Bary), mycetin (Ilkewitsch), entomeiline (Packard), and entomaderme (Lassaigne). Perhaps Griffith's term pupine is also a synonym.

Originally defined as the cuticular material insoluble in hot concentrated alkali solution, chitin is now known to be a high molecular weight polymer of anhydro-N-acetylglucosamine residues joined by ether linkages of the β-glycosidic type between carbon atoms nos. 1 and 4 of adjacent residues (Fig. 4). The molecular chains are very long, seemingly at least several hundreds of the N-acetylglucosamine residues linked together into one long molecule, and, as far as known, show no branching.

As usually prepared for chemical study (most chemical work has been done with chitin purified from the shells of lobsters and crabs), chitin is a colorless, superficially amorphous solid which is insoluble in water, alcohol, ether, dilute acids, alkalies, and most other solvents. It is dissolved by concentrated mineral acids at room temperatures, but promptly begins to undergo a rather slow degradation, which is principally a shortening of the average chain length (Clark & Smith 36). Whether or not this also occurs in the reported solutions in anhydrous formic acid is unknown (Schulze & Kunike 23). Some authors have succeeded in dissolving their preparations of chitin in concentrated solutions of lithium iodide and lithium thiocyanate (Von Veimarn 26a, b, 27a, b, 28), but certain other workers have been unsuccessful in making their samples disperse in solutions of lithium salts. X-ray diffraction analyses of chitin dissolved in solutions of lithium salts showed no evidence of hydrolysis even after several months (Clark & Smith 36). Although chitin is not dissolved by even rather lengthy treatment with hot concentrated alkali solution, a portion of the acetyl groups are removed, giving rise to a derivative called chitosan, which will be discussed subsequently. Chitin is decomposed by Na hypochlorite solutions (Looss 1885, Ito 24, Campbell 29), but seems to be unaffected by many oxidizing agents (H_2O_2, $KMnO_4$, ClO_2 in acetic acid, etc.). Summarizing, the glycosidic linkage is more readily attacked by acid, the acetyl bond is more readily attacked by alkali, and solution known to be without degradation has been accomplished only with hot solutions of neutral salts that are capable of strong hydration and eventually bring about so much swelling that solution occurs. Actually it is an open question whether chitin is soluble in any solvent; perhaps, like cellulose (Ott 43), chitin is truly insoluble, and only its reaction complexes go into solution.

The many earlier papers by Bütschli, Krawkow, Fränkel and Kelly, Morgulis, Rothera, Offer, Leuckart, von Fürth and Russo, Brach,

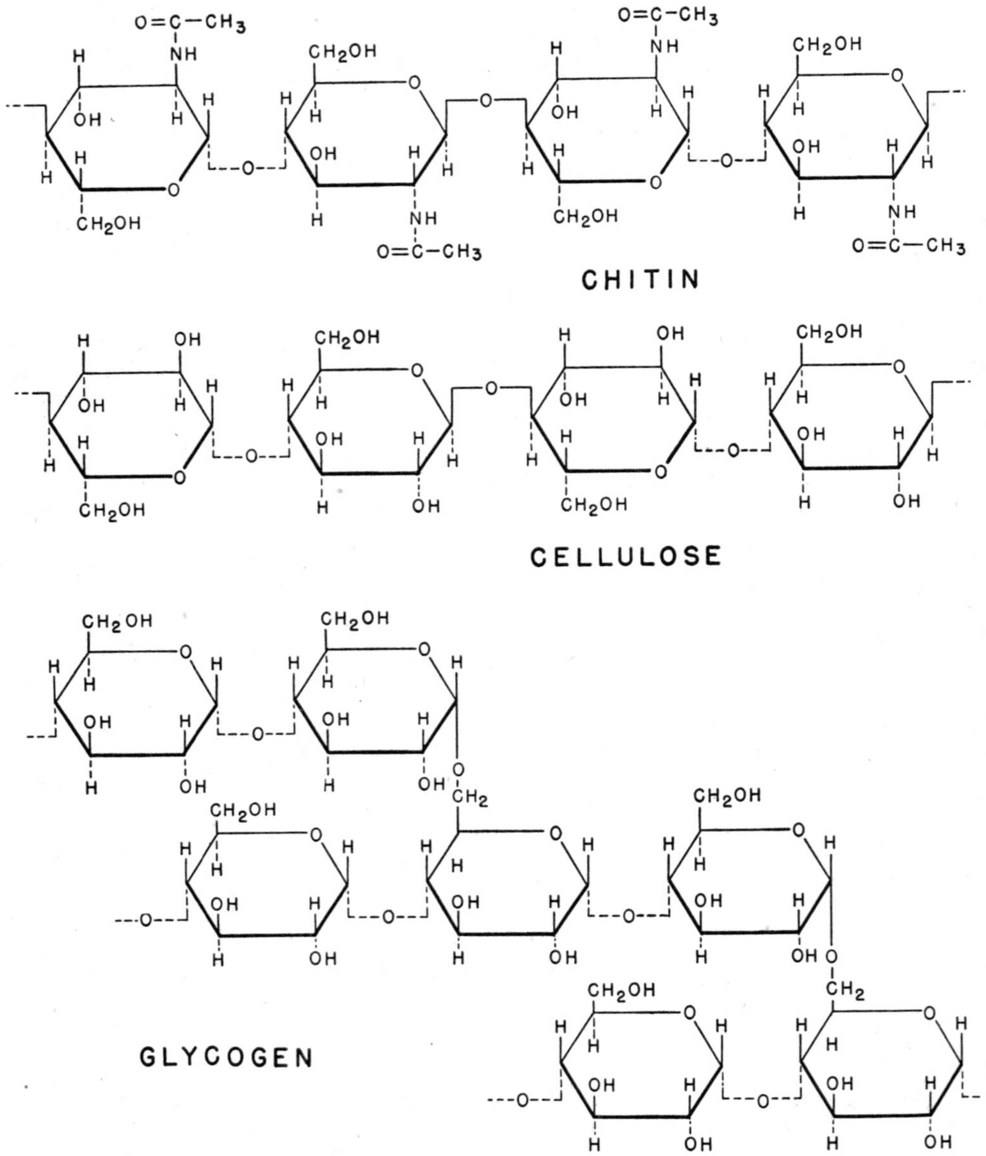

Figure 4. Steric configuration of portions of chains of chitin, cellulose, and glycogen. Chitin and cellulose have the β-glycosidic linkage between residues, as shown; glycogen has the α-glycosidic type of linkage. The glycogen formula also shows the method of formation of branched chains.

Städeler, Schmiedeberg, Krukenberg, Sundwik, etc., are now of only historic interest. The papers by Rosedale (45a, b) seem uninterpretable. Among the more useful reviews of chemical literature we might mention for older literature the ones by Biedermann (14a) and Wester (09), and for more recent literature the papers by Karrer (30), Clark and Smith (36), Kurt Meyer and Wehrli (37), and Worden (40–41), the last named being a review of only the patent and technical literature.

In purified chitin the molecular chains are, at least usually, associated together in a highly ordered manner. This may be shown by examination of the birefringence (Fig. 24) or by observation of the micelles with an electron microscope (Fig. 8), but is best studied by X-ray diffraction (Fig. 6).[3]

Following some examinations made earlier (Gonell 26, Herzog 24, Katz & Mark 24, Khouvine 32), Kurt Meyer and Mark (28b) were led to point out the great similarity to the better-known molecular structure of cellulose, as has already been noted. Later Kurt Meyer and Pankow (35) made a more detailed analysis, which is the basis of the currently accepted structure. Using crustacean chitin, they recorded a rhombic cell with the dimension $a = 9.40$ Å, $b = 10.46$ Å, $c = 19.25$ Å[4] (Fig. 5). As can be seen from the figure, the *b* axis is the fiber or chitin molecular chain dimension. They also pointed out that the analysis showed an alternation of the acetylamine groups from one side of the molecule to the other between adjacent residues, and that the rows of alternate chains of molecules

[3] The analysis of X-ray diffraction patterns is a time-consuming and highly technical procedure. As a simple generalized statement we might say that series of rings (Fig. 6B) give data on molecular spaces within powdered or randomly oriented material, whereas rings of spots (Fig. 6A) show the same spacing in more or less highly oriented (= crystalline) material and so give a clue to the types of crystal structure involved. Rings, then, represent an infinite series of spots such as shown in Figure 6A. In general, the amount of information obtainable is a function of the number of rings or spots that are recognizable (Fourier analysis is used). The actual spacings shown, commonly referred to as lattice unit dimensions, are not to be confused with molecular dimensions; they represent the distances in the lattice between similarly placed atoms or groups of atoms. In other words, if we drew planes through the material in the direction of these three axes, the same atomic groups would appear at regular intervals along a line within that plane at the distances which are called the lattice unit dimensions (Fig. 5). These dimensions are sometimes referred to by the descriptive term "repeat distances." The distances stated for the *a* and *c* axes are greater than the actual molecular dimension because they include both the dimension of the molecule and the space between molecular chains.

[4] Å = an Ångström unit = 0.0001 micron. It is the unit standardly used for molecular dimensions.

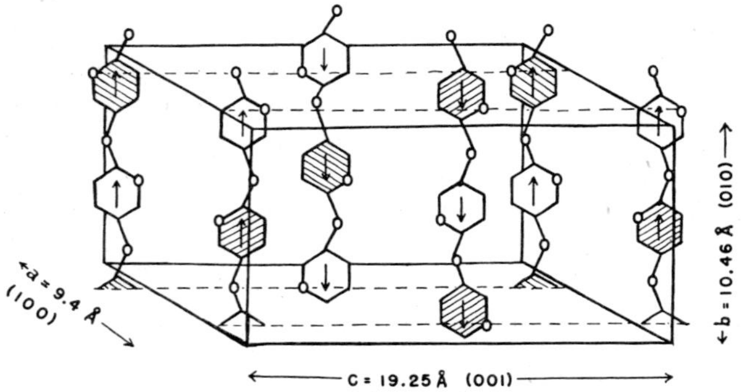

Figure 5. The chitin unit cell or space lattice as determined by Meyer and Pankow. Arrows indicate the alternation in direction of chains in successive rows (which is also indicated by the small circles which show the position of the oxygen molecules in the pyranose rings).

ran in opposite directions, as is indicated by arrows in Figure 5. Clark and Smith (36) obtained similar results, but state the dimension of the *a* axis as 9.25 Å. Lotmar and Picken (50) give $b = 10.27$ Å. Heyn (36b, c) states dimensions of $a = 9.70$, $b = 10.4$, $c = 4.6$ Å for fungal chitin, but adds that the diagrams obtained are almost the same as those from control chitin from cockroaches; other authors have not accepted this value for the *c* axis (Astbury & Bell 39). Similar X-ray patterns have now been recorded from chitin in plant cell walls (Heyn 36a, b, c, van Iterson *et al.* 36, Khouvine 32), in insects (Lotmar & Picken 50, Fraenkel & Rudall 40, 47), and in the peculiar arachnoid *Limulus* (Lotmar & Picken 50, Richards 49).

Since the above was written, Lotmar and Picken (50) have reported finding a new crystallographic type of chitin in chaetae of the polychaete worm *Aphrodite* and in the "pen" of the mollusc *Loligo*. This has a unit cell with dimensions of $a = 9.32$, $b = 10.17$, and $c = 22.15$ Å, and density data indicate that this cannot be derived from the form found in Arthropoda by swelling along the *c* axis. This new type they term the β form; the type found in arthropods and at least most fungi they call the α form.

The unit cell (Fig. 5) represents a space lattice unit, but does not represent an ordinary molecular unit. This is obvious from the fact that it contains parts, but only parts, of a number of molecular chains and the spaces between them. The actual molecular chain unit or molecular length has as yet to be accurately defined. On the basis of X-ray patterns it has been stated by several authors to be at least one hundred and probably several hundred N-acetylglucosamine residues (Alsberg & Hedblom 09, van Iterson *et al.* 36, Kurt Meyer & Wehrli 37). Estimates of chain length are, however, among the less accurate of the things that can be learned by X-ray diffraction methods in solid structures, and in any event represent an average chain length, with little idea being given of how far different chains deviate from the average. Statements that the average chain length

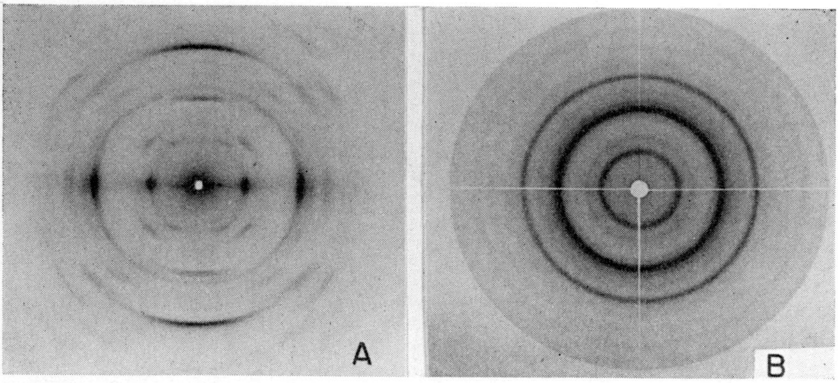

Figure 6. X-ray diffraction diagrams of purified chitin, from a blowfly, *Sarcophaga falculata.* (After Fraenkel and Rudall.)

A. Larval cuticle stretched 40% and purified in hot 5% KOH; washed and air-dried. Beam parallel to surface and perpendicular to axis of stretching.

B. Comparison quadrants of randomly oriented chitin prepared from "white pupae" with hot 5% KOH (top right and bottom left) and from puparia with Diaphanol (top left and bottom right).

in chitin molecules is similar to that in cellulose would seem reasonable. This would mean that chain length might reach some hundreds of units or even conceivably exceed a thousand. Restating this in dimensional units more familiar to a biologist, a chain one hundred residues long would be approximately 0.1 micron, and a chain a thousand residues long would be over one micron.

The nature of the associations of chitin chains with adjacent, presumably parallel chains in the normal cuticle is a little-known subject that will be discussed later (p. 22). In partially or well purified chitin long chains of molecules come together, in the manner illustrated in Figure 5, to form larger units, termed micelles or crystallites, diagrammed in Figure 7.

The idea of micelles' being present in biological materials is a fairly old one. It grew out of the necessity of finding an explanation for the

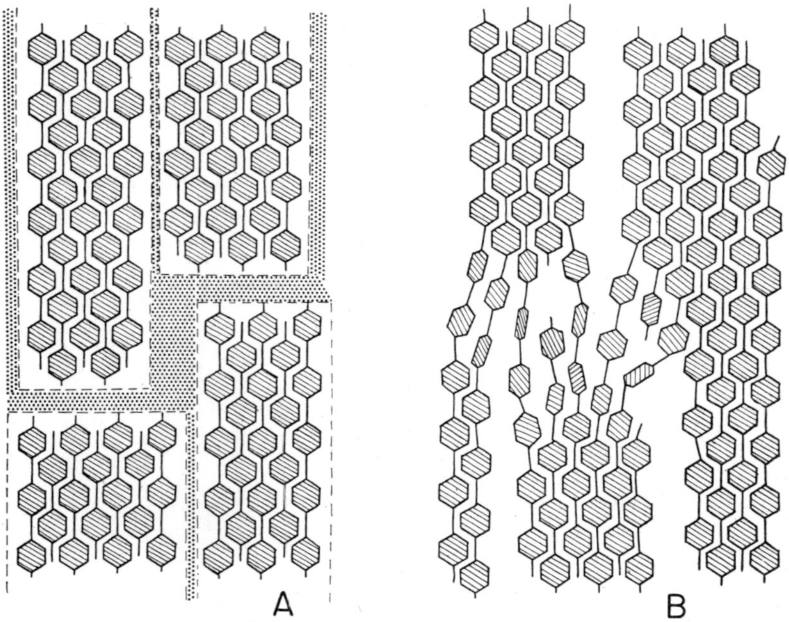

Figure 7. Diagrammatic presentation of the old idea of micelles (A) as brick-shaped units separated by "amorphous material" and the modern view of micelles (B) as regions of a high degree of orderliness separated by, but connected through, regions of more randomly oriented units.

phenomenon of form birefringence (p. 131). Analyses showed that the optical phenomena could be accounted for by assuming that the molecular chains were associated together into larger units separated by material differing in optical properties, the units having at least one dimension considerably longer than the others. The original concept then visualized the structure as due to molecular aggregates of oblong shape fitted together like bricks in a wall (Fig. 7A); or, to use more technical language, they are oblong particles (aniso-diametric) possessing a recognizable degree of internal structural regularity. Recent concepts, which are more consistent with the phenomena observed, view micelles as less discrete entities which represent really the average dimensions of regions of a high degree of regularity separated by areas of lesser regularity (= of greater randomness), as shown in Figure 7B (Mark 43). Another way of saying the same thing is that micelles are due to more or less regularly repeated regions of disorganization of molecular chains along a continuous fiber. The latter point of view is the one consistent with the fact that chitin micelles, like those of cellulose (Kinsinger & Hock 48, Preston *et al.* 48), have been observed in electron micrographs to extend without interruption for several or many microns (Richards & Korda 48). It is also consistent with the report of a mixture of isotropic and anisotropic areas in *Donacia* cocoons (Picken *et al.* 47).[5]

It happens that the *b* repeat axis in the X-ray diffraction diagram is virtually identical with the long direction of the chitin molecular chains and therefore with the fiber axis in micelles. But it should be noted that the relative dimensions of micelles are different from those of the unit cells in the space lattice. In the theoretically perfect micelle each of the three dimensions would be some multiple of the unit cell dimension. It follows from this that different numbers of units must be involved in the three dimensions of the micelle to give a structure of different relative proportions (Fraenkel & Rudall 40).

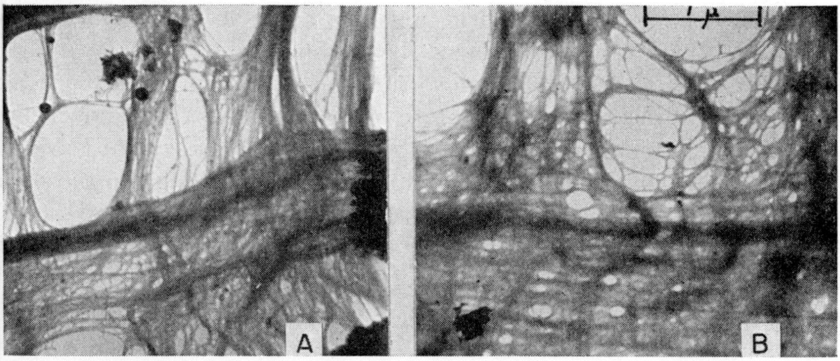

Figure 8. Electron micrographs of chitin microfibers which presumably represent chitin micelles. Chitin prepared from large tracheae of a cockroach, *Periplaneta americana.* (After Richards and Korda.)

A. Purified with 5% NaOH at 20° C. for 9 days; washed in alcohol.

B. Purified with 10% pepsin at 36° C. for 1 day; washed in water (and manually separated from the undigested epicuticle).

Chitin microfibers, which presumably represent the micelles, have been observed by electron micrography (Fig. 8). These microfibers have diameters of 100–300 Å (= 0.01–0.03 micron) – values which presumably represent dimensions of the *a* and *c* axes and which agree rather closely with values for cellulose microfibers (Kinsinger & Hock

[5] Parallel micelles are readily demonstrated by birefringence in tendons (Fig. 24, Clark & Smith 36), Balken (p. 192, Biedermann 03, Gonell 26), and taenidia (p. 256, Richards & Korda 48); randomly arranged micelles require electron microscopy (Richards & Korda 48).

48). Although many thousands of these microfibrils were examined and many of them could be followed uninterruptedly for several microns, no indications of interruption or end along this fiber axis ($=b$) were observed (Richards & Korda 48). The continuity of these microfibrils is excellent evidence in favor of the view (Mark 43) that the chitin fibers are continuous over long distances, conceivably even for the entire macroscopic dimensions of an anatomically coherent structure. The electron micrographs do not show the molecular chains themselves, although they do, by the continuity of the fibrils, show that the chains do not all end in one region without overlapping (Fig. 7B). The X-ray data calling for chitin chain lengths of a few microns or a fraction of a micron must be explained by the fact that one chain ends at one region, another at another region, etc.

The fibrous type of chitin micelles discussed above seems reasonably well established, although there are numerous details that need clarification. The fiber is held together along its long axis by the extremely strong ether linkages. Its resistance to dispersion (Clark & Smith 36) shows that it must also be rather strongly attracted to the adjacent chains, but the nature of this binding is not known. Perhaps a large number of hydrogen bonds would be adequate (Mooney 41).[6] Presumably the random orientation of chitin chains in the plane of the cuticle surface provides, on paralleling, a statistically equal number faced in each direction and so permits the alignment of alternate chains in the crystal lattice in opposite directions (Fig. 5). The greater lateral cohesion (resistance to swelling) of chitin in contrast to cellulose must be attributed to the one difference in the chain, namely, the substitution of an acetylamine group for a hydroxyl group; but whether this is to be taken as indicating a stronger bond or a better steric fit between adjacent chains is not clear.

Larger fibrils, visible with the light microscope, have been recorded by numerous investigators, but the relationship between these and the much smaller fibrils seen in electron micrographs is not known. Thus one can tease from the tendons of lobsters fibrils of approximately one micron diameter (Clark & Smith 36); less clear-

[6] Darmon and Rudall (50) have now recorded hydrogen bonds between some (presumably half) of the CO-NH groups of the aminoacetyl side chains. They think that the remaining acetyl groups are probably joined by CO · · · HO bonds. In chitosan, with progressive deacetylation, OH · · · OH bonds are formed (similar to those in cellulose). Of most interest is the demonstration that there are indeed two types of acetyl groups in the micelle, and that one of these is more readily removed than the other (as postulated by Löwy in 1909).

cut cases are afforded by, for instance, ribbed setae in which a single rib shows optical properties such as might be expected from a rather large fibril (Lees & Picken 45), and by reports of even larger fibrils in the elytra of beetles and in other arthropods (Fig. 24). Perhaps some of these larger fibrous structures when examined by electron microscopy will be found subdivisible into smaller fibrils of micellar dimensions, as the taenidia of tracheae have been (compare Figures 8 and 54) (Richards & Korda 48).

In addition to the linear or fibrous micelles, there are also laminar or plate-like micelles (Picken 40, W. J. Schmidt 42a), but the analysis of these is even less far advanced. Presumably, linear micelles represent those in which the *a* and *c* axes are not greatly different, laminar micelles those cases in which there is a very great difference. The reasons behind such a difference in micellar growth are not at all understood, especially since in at least the best studied cases the micellar growth seems to occur subsequent to secretion and to be beyond direct influence of the secreting cells. Possibly the thin sheet intimately associated with tracheal micelles (Richards & Korda 48) may represent a coexistence of laminar and fibrous micelles.

The so-called "film structure" of chitin micelles in the egg shell of *Ascaris* may not be a different type of structure, but simply an arrangement of fibrous micelles in superimposed concentric layers (W. J. Schmidt 36b); but the peculiar optical properties of this chitin require explanation. There were several types of membrane from which Richards and Korda (48) were unable to obtain micellar fibrils. As far as could be determined from their electron micrographs, there was no trace of fibrous structure in the purified chitin from, for example, very thin wing membranes. They speculated that lateral linkages between chitin chains must vary considerably in different cuticular membrane. This is no more than another way of saying that the fibrillar type of chitin micelle is not the only method for association of chitin chains.

Somewhat of a variant of the micelle idea is the hypothesis of "macromolecules,"[7] which has found favor with certain chemists (Clark 34) but which has not seemed to most biologists to fit the microscopically observable facts. Actually it seems to be no more

[7] The term macromolecule has a vague, broad meaning adequately stated by the word itself. In the present connection it refers to the idea that N-acetylglucosamine units are put together *inside* the epithelial cells into microscopically visible particles, and that these particles are secreted by the cells and fit together to form the cuticle. There is no question that particles can be seen in the cytoplasm of

than a variant of the old brick-micelle idea, which has been discarded, with the additional complication that the large particles are formed inside the secreting cells. How such large particles are to get outside of the cells in which they are found has not been explained (though they would not have to get outside if one adopts the view that the distal end of the cell becomes "chitinized"). The idea can be found expounded vigorously in the papers by Farr and her associates (Farr & Eckerson 34a, b, Farr & Sisson 34). An equally vigorous refutation of at least a part of this work dealing with chitin is given by Castle (45). (See also Clausen & Richards 51.)

Thus far we have treated chitin as though it were a single substance in which the molecular chains differ only in the manner and degree of orientation into micelles, and presumably also in chain length, although no accurate data are available on this point. Older literature claiming that more than one type of chitin existed (Dous & Ziegenspeck 26, Krawkow 1892) has been discredited and need not be discussed in this place. The recent report of another crystallographic form of chitin in worms and molluscs has already been mentioned. Although other polysaccharides are known in the covering or skeleton of other groups of animals (cellulose in the Tunicates, an unidentified substance in the cuticle of Bryozoa, etc.) there appear to be no important exceptions remaining within the phylum Arthropoda. The last outstanding exception within this phylum, the king or horseshoe crab, *Limulus,* has recently been reported as giving an X-ray diffraction powder pattern indistinguishable from that given by Crustacea (Lotmar & Picken 50, Richards 49). Disparities are found in the degree to which different membranes containing chitin resist the action of hot alkali solutions (Richards 47b, Richards & Korda 48), but the significance of this awaits clarification.

Another tacit assumption up to this point has been that the chemist has had available for study pure samples of chitin and that no other carbohydrate is involved, at least in the phylum Arthropoda. Other possible carbohydrates will be mentioned separately in a subsequent section devoted to unrecognized components. Meanwhile, although it may add little to our understanding, it should still be pointed out that all claims to having studied pure chitin are little more than gratuitous assumptions, and the evidence, such as it is, suggests that

epidermal cells, but calling them macromolecules of chitin or cuticle is presumptuous and gratuitous. Any such hypothesis will remain without factual foundation until (and unless) the cytoplasmic granules referred to are isolated and positively identified as chitinous.

some impurities are always present (Richards 49). The best evidence comes from the diversity of nitrogen values that have been reported in the literature. The theoretical nitrogen content of chitin is 6.89%. Yet Fraenkel and Rudall (47), because of the constancy with which they obtained the value, have come to use 6.45% as the standard for chitin. Rammelberg (31) obtained approximately the same value for chitin from both crab shells and fungal walls. Clark and Smith (36) and Lafon (41–48) obtained somewhat higher values. Thor and Henderson (40) obtained 6.59% N for pure chitin flakes and were able to raise this to 6.7% N on reprecipitation from alkali solution, but it is not clear whether the increase is due to further purification or a partial deacetylation. Other values in reasonably recent literature range from 2% to 6.7% (Behr 30, Dous & Ziegenspeck 26, Fränkel & Jellinek 27, Norman & Peterson 32, Proskuriakow 25). A number of these authors record a small amount of ash, ranging from 0.1 to several per cent. Also several record that more exhaustive extraction methods lead to higher values (Fraenkel & Rudall 47, Rammelberg 31, Richards 49). The nature of these impurities is unknown, but it does not seem safe to assume that they are without significance for chitin structure.

CHAPTER 3

Chitin Derivatives and Metabolic Sources

CHITOSAN

When chitin is fused with alkali or treated with concentrated alkali solutions at rather high temperatures (160–180° C. is the customarily used range), it undergoes a variable amount of deacetylation to give a product that has been termed chitosan (Hoppe-Seyler 1895). The product formed is soluble in dilute acids, as was recorded by Rouget in 1859. As far as is known, chitosan does not occur naturally in arthropod cuticle. Its importance for biology lies in the fact that the conversion of chitin to chitosan does not involve changes in gross structure and that chitosan gives a distinctive violaceous color with iodine and acid in contrast to the nondistinctive brownish color given by chitin treated with iodine, as Rouget also recorded. Chitosan then forms the basis of the qualitative color test for chitin detection, which will be discussed subsequently (p. 32).

Chitosan, however, is not a single chemical entity, but rather a family of chitin derivatives, despite the essential agreement of elementary analyses (Araki 1895, Kotake & Sera 13, Löwy 09, Proskuriakow 25). This is conclusively demonstrated by the diversity of X-ray diffraction patterns obtained (Clark & Smith 36, Kurt Meyer & Wehrli 37). The reaction is not a precisely predictable one since the same diffraction pattern is not always produced by the same procedure. Part but presumably not all of the diversity is due to the rupture of variable numbers of glycosidic linkages, which results in a reduction in chain length to some 20–30 residues (Kurt Meyer & Wehrli 37).

Chitosan can be reacetylated more or less satisfactorily to give products that may be similar to chitin except for a greatly shortened chain length (Araki 1895, Karrer 30, Karrer & White 30, Kurt Meyer & Wehrli 37). The reacetylation, which may be accomplished with acetic anhydride plus acetic acid and zinc chloride, may result in simply the reacetylation of the amine groups (Kurt Meyer & Wehrli

37) or in the addition of acetyl groups presumably in place of some of the hydroxyls (Karrer & White 30). Or one may substitute formyl, proprionyl, butyryl, or benzoyl groups to form the correspondings chitosans (Karrer & White 30).

Chitosan, like chitin, gives low nitrogen values in a Kjeldahl analysis. It has been suggested that this may be partly due to the hydrolysis of some of the amine groups to hydroxyls during the preparation of chitosan (Clark & Smith 36), but it is also partly due to the fact that only approximately half of the acetyl groups are hydrolyzed off (hence the suggestion that chitosan is a monoacetyldiglucosamine) (Clark & Smith 36, Karrer 30, Löwy 09). This is strikingly demonstrated by the fact that chitinase acting on chitosan gives both N-acetylglucosamine and glucosamine (Karrer 30).[1]

Chitosan is soluble in dilute acid (Araki 1895, Löwy 09, Rouget 1859) but is insoluble in or precipitated from solutions by concentrated acids, heavy metals, alkalies, alcohol, acetone, etc. (Brown 37, Clark & Smith 36, Löwy 09, Rigby 36). Like chitobiose, it begins decomposing at temperatures of approximately 184° C. (Hoppe-Seyler 1894, 95), but as far as superficial appearances and the ability to apply the chitosan color test are concerned, chitosan may commonly be heated for a short time to temperatures considerably in excess of 200° C. Almost certainly the destructive effect of alkali is a function of time as well as of temperature (Richards 47b, Richards unpubl.). Like alkaloids, chitosan solutions form crystalline salts with acids: HCl, HBr, HNO_3, H_2SO_4, H_3PO_4, H_2CrO_4, and organic acids such as tartaric, oxalic, malic, citric, and acetic (Brunswick 21, Clark & Smith 36, von Fürth & Russo 06, Löwy 09, Kurt Meyer & Wehrli 37). Also, addition compounds may be formed with NaOH and lithium thiocyanate (Clark & Smith 36). The chitosan chains are said to have a more restricted orientation than those of chitin and to be arranged in an orthorhombic cell with the dimensions $a = 8.9$, $b = 10.25$, and $c = 17.0$ Å (Clark & Smith 36).

Attempts have been made to use the crystalline salts of chitosan, especially chitosan sulphate, as microchemical methods of determination. Despite the fact that the best sphaerocrystals obtained are not notably distinctive (round, elliptical, or tetragonal), several authors have reported what they considered satisfactory results with the

[1] Since the above was written, further substantiation of the idea of monoacetyldiglucosamine has been obtained by infrared absorption studies (Darman & Rudall 50). But apparently the situation can be more complex, for they suggest that the chitosan curve in Figure 22 may represent completely deacetylated chitin.

method (Brunswick 21, Campbell 29, Kotake & Sera 13, Löwy 09, Proskuriakow 25), but other authors have not been able to obtain consistent results or to feel that the positive results when obtained were good evidence (Richards 47b). Presumably, halfway satisfactory results are obtained with some species or mixtures of chitosans and not with others.

Since a portion of the amine groups are exposed in chitosan, it is not surprising that weak but positive ninhydrin tests are given (Richards & Korda 48, Rouget 1859).

The name mycosine was proposed for these compounds at about the same time as the name chitosan (Gilson 1895b, c), but like the alternative names for chitin has never come into general usage.

OTHER CHITIN DERIVATIVES

Numerous derivatives of chitin have been mentioned in the preceding pages, and it is probably not desirable to attempt listing all of the chemicals that can be located in the voluminous chemical literature. A few additional ones might, however, be mentioned. One can make glucosaminic acid and various derivatives thereof (Bergmann *et al.* 31c, 34, Levene & Christman 37). Starting with glucosamine-HCl a sizable list of substituted compounds have been made (Bertho *et al.* 31). Methyl derivatives have also been prepared (White 40).

Among possible derivatives of longer chain lengths, several different nitrates have been made (Clark & Smith 36, von Fürth & Scholl 07, Kurt Meyer & Wehrli 37, Shorigin & Hait 34), also xanthates (Thor 39, Thor & Henderson 40), methylchitins (Shorigin *et al.* 35), and various regenerated chitins. Sodium has been substituted for one or more hydrogen atoms, with a resulting product which is soluble (Schmid *et al.* 28).

The term chitose which may be found in the literature refers to the anhydro sugar formed by the deamination of glucosamine (Armbrecht 19, Shorigin & Makorowa-Semljanskaja 35, Wiggins 46).

Phosphoric esters, which might be of considerable interest in the metabolism of chitin, appear to have been seldom studied (Karrer *et al.* 43).

THE COMMERCIAL USES OF CHITIN

It will probably come as a surprise to most entomologists, as it did to the author, to find that there are a rather extensive technical literature and a good many patents dealing with the use of chitin. The literature seems worth reviewing briefly because of the stress it places on certain of the properties of chitin. Several reviews that go into the technical points of the preparation of chitin for industrial use are available (Knecht & Hibbert 26, Nasmith 26, Tsimehc 38, Worden 41).

In general the chitin is prepared by acid and alkali purification from the shells of larger crustaceans and then, with or without deacetylation, degraded (= chain length shortened) just enough to get the material into solution. The viscous solution may be spun into threads by extrusion and hardened with agents such as phenol or formaldehyde (Nastyukov & Nikol'skii 35, Nikol'skii 36) to give fibers with a tensile strength considerably greater than that of artificial silk prepared from cellulose (Herzog 26, Kunike 26a); or the chitin suspension may be mixed with viscose material to increase the strength of artificial fibers made from fish protein (Tadokoro & Nisida 40). Films or sheets may also be rolled (Thor 39, Thor & Henderson 40).

The more interesting part of the technical literature involves the use of deacetylated chitin as a cement or sizing agent (Merrill 36, Patterson & Peterson 36, Rigby 36, Sadov 41, Viktorov & Maiofis 40). The principal factor that is said to make chitin valuable in the production of such nonacademic products as washable wall papers, colored fabrics resistant to laundering, and washable printer's ink is that (presumably) one side of the chitosan chain lies against the underlying cellulosic material forming an excellent fit and perhaps actually a portion of the space lattice thereof, while leaving free amine groups projecting out on the other side; these amine groups then serve to bind down pigments or waterproofing materials (e.g., chinawood oil) which do not adhere well to cellulose. Of the advantages of chitin over cellulose, Tsimehc (38) lists the greater stability to hydrogen ions and heat, greater resistance to water, better intermiscibility, better adhesiveness, and certain other points of less interest here.

Sulfuric acid esters of chitin have been recommended as having desirable properties for making synthetic anticoagulants (Astrup *et al.* 44, Piper 46).

Despite the advantages that chitin has in industrial chemistry because of its strength, adhesiveness, and resistance to water, it is used today practically not at all. Ironically, when the shrimp-packing houses (the chief source of raw material) awakened to the fact that chemical companies were buying their odorous trash piles by the ton, they raised the price so much that the companies could no longer afford the raw materials. And so the waste piles at the packing houses have reverted to the status of being a source of fertilizer for the local farmers.

THE METABOLIC SOURCE OF CHITIN

Nothing at all is known on the subject of chitin precursors, and the literature is not even sufficiently definite to warrant speculating as to whether the syntheses involve one of the well-known phosphorylation mechanisms or one of the less well known nonphosphorylation mechanisms. The old arguments as to whether chitin is secreted around cytoplasmic filaments, as suggested by Leydig (1864), Braun (1875), and numerous more recent investigators, or deposited within the epidermal cells which thus become transformed into cuticle (Chatin 1892a, b, Schlottke 38a, Vitzou 1881), is immaterial to the question of the nature of chemical synthesis involved.

The one suggestion commonly found in the literature is the inadequately documented one that chitin arises from the transformation of glycogen (Fig. 4). The best-documented reports are those based on the fact that the glycogen content of crustacea temporarily decreases during molting, coincidently with the formation of chitin (Drach 39, von Schönborn 11, Verne 24), or decreases permanently coincidently with chitin formation in insect eggs (Tichomiroff 1885, Tirelli 31). The glycogen reserves referred to are located elsewhere than in the integument (Kirch 1886, Vaney & Maignon 05, Wigglesworth 42b, 48b) and are presumed to be mobilized for the formation of chitin, but glycogen granules are also recorded in epidermal cells (Farkas 14, Malaczynska-Suchcitz 49, Wigglesworth 48b). In some species there is a cycle of glycogen deposition in the oenocytes or certain blood cells correlated with molting (Deevey 41, Pardi 39). Quantitative comparisons of the amount of glycogen lost in comparison to the amount of chitin formed do not agree closely, but this is probably to be expected in an actively metabolizing animal. Numerous other papers also suggest that glycogen may be the source of carbohydrate for the formation of chitin (Babers 41, Fauré-Fremiet 12, 13, Hill 45, Mirande 05a, b, Paillot 38, 39, Wottge 37). The most that can be said is that the literature contains the reasonable suggestion that there is a greater or lesser amount of interchange between free sugars and higher carbohydrates (Hill 45) and that this might reasonably be expected to include the change from one polysaccharide to another. Probably no one visualizes the direct change of a branched polymer such as glycogen [2] directly into a straight chain polymer such as chitin, especially since glycogen has α-glycosidic linkages whereas chitin has β-glycosidic linkages (Fig. 4). At most, then, it would seem that glycogen might be the most common storage sugar which after breaking down could be rebuilt into the straight chain polymer chitin.

A number of authors have suggested that chitin might arise from protein (Pardi 39, Weinland 09). The older authors were, very likely, erroneously led to this view by the presence of nitrogen in the chitin molecules (Kirch 1886). Abderhalden (25) has recorded that Dermestid beetles, pests notorious for their ability to live on restricted diets, can grow on silk threads which are free from both fat and carbohydrate, but recent studies in insect nutrition lead to questioning this report. Proteins commonly contain carbohydrate groups, and this seems a likely source (e.g., in blood-sucking insects). At least it does seem true that some but not all species of beetles can develop without having any *free* carbohydrate in their diet (Fraenkel & Blewett 43).

Similarly cellulose has been suggested as a possible source of precursors (le Goffe 39).

Certainly there must be a very active system both for the synthesis and for the destruction of chitin in arthropods because not only do the relative and absolute volumes of chitin change during the life of the animal (Lafon 43c), but the cuticle is largely digested, reabsorbed, and then formed anew at each molt. It is not surprising that the resting O_2 consumption nearly doubles at the time of molting (cockroach), but more information is required before this can be interpreted (Gunn 35). (See section on molting.) Perhaps the most definite thing that can be said is that there appears to be no insulin or adrenaline mechanism in the arthropods (Roche & Dumazert 40).

Incidentally, glucosamine has a nutritive value for rats that is lower than the values of sucrose, glucose, maltose, and dextrin, but about equal to those of fructose and mannose, and higher than those of galactose, lactose, xylose, and arabinose (Ariyama & Takahasi 29).

[2] Branched glycogen chains are formed by the coexistence of linkages between carbon atoms nos. 1 and 4 and carbon atoms nos. 1 and 6 (Fig. 4). Other polysaccharides may show branching, owing to different linkages. See Bell's review (48).

CHAPTER 4

The Detection and Estimation of Chitin

The demonstration of the presence of chitin in a structure is still on a relatively crude qualitative basis. For strong pieces of membrane the iodine-chitosan color test is, as far as we know, completely valid when positive; negative results, however, are open to serious question, as cases are known where positive tests are obtained only a small percentage of the time (Richards 47). The other tests that will be outlined appear to be either less specific or less reliable or are not feasible for general use. The situation is even less satisfactory when one desires quantitative results, either relative or absolute. I doubt that any of the reputable workers today would claim more than that their best results are semiquantitative.

The chitosan-iodine color test. Pure chitin, like many other substances, is colored brown by iodine, but chitosan in an acidified medium is colored violet or a reddish violet. Since few organic substances will stand the alkali treatment necessary to convert chitin to chitosan, few substances remain to interfere. The color reaction was first recorded by Rouget in 1859, and its application to chitin detection in various plants and animals was elaborately developed in the series of papers by van Wisselingh. Some modification and a detailed critical analysis are given in the well-known paper by Campbell (29). There are analyses also in a number of others (C. Koch 32, Kühnelt 28b, Kunike 25, Richards 47b, van Wisselingh 14, 25, Zander 1897).

Campbell's method consists of taking a small piece of cuticle, freeing it from adhering tissues as far as possible (to minimize the concentration of hydrolyzed tissue and so facilitate preparation of clean specimens), placing it in a test tube or other container with a few ml. of KOH solution saturated at room temperature, closing the tube with a Bunsen valve,[1] and placing the tube in a beaker containing

[1] A 5–10 cm. piece of rubber tubing is sealed at one end with a glass rod or clamp, perforated with a longitudinal slit ½ to 1 cm. long at its middle, and connected to the vial at its open end either directly or through a rubber stopper. This allows for escape of excess pressure.

glycerine. The glycerine bath is then slowly heated (15–20 min.) to 160° C. and held at this temperature for about 15 minutes. The container is then removed, cooled to room temperature, and examined. If no recognizable pieces remain, the test is said to be negative; i.e., no chitin is present (but see below). If, however, some recognizable material remains, it is transferred to water through a graded series of alcohols (or if obviously sturdy may be placed directly in water), after which it is ready for testing and should be divided into several pieces. If the residue consists entirely of chitin which has been transformed into chitosan, it should give the following reactions. One of the pieces placed in 3% acetic acid should pass slowly into solution, from which solution a white precipitate may be obtained by the addition of a drop of 1% sulfuric acid. Another piece covered with a drop of 0.2% iodine in potassium iodide solution should turn brown rapidly. On removal of the excess iodine solution and replacement with 1% sulfuric acid, the piece should immediately become a reddish-violet color of variable intensity (black if quite thick). On removal of the dilute acid and replacement by 75% sulfuric acid, the color should disappear as the object goes slowly into solution. Sometimes if the slide is set aside in a humid atmosphere for a few hours or days and then washed with a stream of distilled water, a cloudy film of colorless spherical crystals will be found where the drop was. If sufficiently large, these crystals show a dark cross in a polarized light microscope. They also stain with acid dyes. If the conversion into chitosan has been incomplete, the color reaction will be obtained, but the material will only partly go into solution in the 3% acetic acid.

According to Campbell, a solution of KOH saturated at room temperature can be raised to 160° C. without boiling. This is not always true, presumably owing to variations in room temperature and in the composition of different samples of alkali. In such a case one has either to treat at a lower temperature for a longer time, or to add some solid alkali which will precipitate out when the solution is cool, or to resort to the older sealed-tube method. Commonly any one of these alternatives will produce satisfactory results (in fact, some workers have expressed a preference for boiling their solution in open vessels even to the point of complete evaporation) (Kunike 25, P. Schulze 22b, Spek 19, Vouk 15). Other workers have preferred to go back to the old van Wisselingh method of using sealed tubes, despite the danger of explosion from a defectively sealed tube (Castle 45, Kühnelt 28b, Richards 47b). The sealed-tube method does have the advantage of maintaining equal pressure and minimized internal expansion, but however important this may be with tubular fungi, it does not seem to matter significantly with ordinary pieces of arthropod cuticle. Incidentally, because of the differences in power of hydrolizing off the acetyl group, KOH solutions are usually used for the preparation of chitosan, whereas NaOH solutions are used for the purification of chitin itself.

Both the van Wisselingh technique and the Campbell modification of it claim that the complete dissolution of the specimen being examined demonstrates the absence of chitin,[2] and that other organic substances which might interfere with the color test are removed at least to an adequate extent by the treatment in alkali. Unfortunately neither of these statements is completely true. As far as I am aware, no one has ever examined the solution to see if he could detect possible chitin derivatives that had gone into solution as a result of this particular treatment with alkali, but there are a number of common cuticular structures which are usually completely dispersed by treatment with hot concentrated alkali (some butterfly scales, the peritrophic membrane of certain species) and yet which when not dispersed or only partly dispersed will give a positive chitosan color test (Richards 47b). Also some very soft membranes, such as that around the base of the caudal spine of the horseshoe crab *Limulus*, will withstand quick conversion to chitosan and give a positive test, whereas it may rather readily be completely dispersed by slightly prolonging the treatment (Richards unpubl.). Quite likely sufficiently prolonged treatment with hot alkali solution will disperse any membrane of chitin, but this is of no great moment to us. The important point is that there appear to be certain structures which give a positive chitosan color test when not dispersed, and therefore lead to questioning the validity of using dissolution in alkali as proving absence of chitin.

The second point, elimination of other organic substances associated with chitin, is in practice less serious. Failure to remove all of the associated compounds is presumably one of the reasons why Krawkow (1892) reported that there are several kinds of chitin. He based his claim on the fact that he sometimes obtained violet, sometimes violet-brown, color tests. Some authors have preferred using more dilute alkali solutions on the grounds that they remove associated substances more effectively (Kunike 25), and the present au-

[2] Van Wisselingh (10) has recorded preventing dissolution of fly tracheae by treatment with chromic acid and then obtaining positive chitosan tests. Pretreatments deserve more study.

thor has sometimes succeeded in adequately decolorizing heavily melanized butterfly scales by treating first with dilute alkali and then with concentrated alkali, whereas they were not decolorized adequately by the treatment with concentrated alkali alone. The majority of these associated substances which are less readily removed with alkali, principally pigments, can be removed rather effectively by treating with a 0.1–1.0% solution of $KMnO_4$ solution, followed by a reducing agent such as Na bisulfite or other oxidizing agents such as hydrogen peroxide or Diaphanol.[3] Bleaching with an oxidizing agent is more necessary with certain of the Crustacea and Arachnoids. Within the author's experience the cuticle of scorpions has been found most difficult to purify with alkali solution (Kunike 25), and in fact decolorization was not obtained until after the use of oxidizing agents.

Several authors have reported that the color produced by iodine staining can be augmented by the use of the correct concentration of certain salts (Nasse 1886, Zander 1897). NaCl, $ZnSO_4$, alum, Na acetate, $ZnCl_2$, and NH_4Cl have been recommended, but apparently one needs to experiment to obtain the correct concentration for a particular structure. However, if one has obtained an adequate conversion into chitosan, accentuation of color is not necessary. Considering the mechanisms likely involved in the iodine color reaction, it is not surprising that salts have a distinct effect, but to date the mechanism of the iodine color reaction has not been investigated at all with chitin. That the situation is probably complex may be gathered from a consideration of the literature on the staining of starch and glycogen (Gilbert & Marriott 48, Mooney 41, Stein & Rundle 48).

Only passing reference need be made here to the rather elaborate analysis of chitosan salts that might be used for the microchemical detection of chitin; for details see Brunswick's paper (21). Brunswick studied eleven different chitosan salts and recommended the use of the sulfate because of its relative ease of preparation, its insolubility, and its supposedly characteristic sphaerocrystals. As already mentioned in the section on chitosan, these so-called crystals do not have truly distinctive characteristics for identification, and though they are sometimes produced readily, they are not obtained consistently. Perhaps they depend on obtaining a particular species of chitosan, but this is something we have not yet learned how to control (Clark &

[3] A 50% solution of glacial acetic acid saturated with chlorine dioxide. This reagent is not highly stable but can be kept for some time in a tightly stoppered dark bottle in the refrigerator.

Smith 36). My own opinion is that these chitosan salts have little to offer in the field of chitin determination at the present time.

The chitosan color test is the most reliable known today,[4] but it still has rather severe limitations. When the specimen is adequately resistant to the action of hot alkali solution (p. 34), one may say that the lower limit is the size which is positively recognizable by some anatomical feature and large enough to give a clear color reaction (make visible). However, there are two additional limitations which cannot be circumvented by the chitosan method. The severe alkali treatment completely destroys all cells and cell processes, thereby preventing direct observation of cuticle-cell relationships, and furthermore the chitin chains undergo more or less extensive reorientation (Fraenkel & Rudall 40, Richards & Korda 48). Accordingly the method does not permit any precise histochemical localization. A workable compromise is to use the chitosan color test for identification and one of the other coloring methods to obtain cytological details (Dennell 46).

The Diaphanol-iodine-zinc chloride test. The fact that mixtures of iodine and zinc chloride give blue or violaceous colors with chitin has been known for nearly a hundred years (Ambronn 1890, Radlkofer 1855, Rouget 1859, Zander 1897); its serious application for the detection of chitin, however, dates from 1921 (P. Schulze 21), and its use has been limited largely to the papers by P. Schulze and his students. Apparently the technique was adapted from a botannical procedure (E. Schmidt 31, E. Schmidt & Graumann 21). The method consists of treating the specimens with a saturated solution of chlorine dioxide in 50% acetic acid (Diaphanol) for some minutes, hours, or days until the cuticle is decolorized and shown by subsequent testing to be capable of giving the color reaction. This solution is a strong oxidizing agent, and if renewed and if the treatment is continued for some weeks, a pure sheet of apparently undegraded chitin is left (Fraenkel & Rudall 40). Short periods such as are usually used in performing this test may be quite satisfactory for the test, but certainly do not result in the complete purification of chitin, despite the unsupported claims of Schulze and his students. Since the solution is a strong acid, it removes the lime when present as well as the protein, pigment, etc. After treatment with the Diaphonal solution, the excess chlorine may, if wished, be removed by treatment with a solution of

[4] It is even recorded as having given positive results with fossil specimens (Kraft 23).

Na bisulfite. After being washed in water, the specimen is treated with a freshly prepared solution of the iodine zinc chloride.[5] After some minutes in this solution the specimen is removed, and upon being washed in water develops a violet color. It is said (C. Koch 32) that if the color does not develop immediately, it can be made to do so by repeated transferal of the specimen from water to the zinc-chloroiodide solution and back again.

The method has been severely criticized, especially for its non-specificity (Campbell 29, Kraft 23, Kühnelt 28b, van Wisselingh 25), but has been passionately supported in a most remarkably irrational paper by one of Schulze's students (C. Koch 32). There are not many papers resulting from use of this technique (W. Braun 39, Jacobs 24, Kunike 25, P. Schulze 21–26). In a few cases, authors have made the mistake of reporting membranes of pure chitin, basing their claim on the fact that they obtained a coloring by zincchloroiodide without pretreatment in Diaphanol (Jacobs 24).

Actually this method does have one decided advantage over the chitosan test. The chitosan test involves destruction of all cells associated with the cuticle and allows no more than a minimum to be seen about its structure. The Diaphanol-iodine-zinc chloride method does not involve destruction of the cells and in fact can be performed on histological sections (Glick 48, C. Koch 32, Lison 36). When the chitosan color test is used to confirm the presence of chitin, this color test and some to be mentioned subsequently are valuable for assisting in seeing minute details (Dennell 46). Quite likely the Schiff reaction will replace the Schulze zincchloroiodide method for this purpose.

It is interesting that although Kunike (25) used the Diaphanol technique, his reports on the absence of chitin from certain phyla of animals were almost always based on solubility in KOH.

The Schiff polysaccharide reaction. This is a recently described general polysaccharide reaction which will not distinguish chitin from other polysaccharides but which will give brilliant staining in sectioned material (Hotchkiss 48). When accompanied by chitosan tests or other means of demonstrating that chitin is the polysaccharide concerned, it would seem that this will be the best of histochemical differential staining methods. The general nature of the reaction is that the chitin chains are oxidized by periodic acid to give corresponding polyaldehydes; treatment with Schiff reagent (fuchsin-sulfite) then

[5] Two stock solutions are prepared. One contains 1.6 g. iodine, 10 g. KI, and 14 ml. water. The other contains 60 g. ZnCl and 14 ml. of water. Equal quantities of these two solutions are mixed fresh and filtered through glass wool for use.

gives rise to colored compounds. Soluble polysaccharides are either eliminated or retained, depending on whether or not a step is inserted for their precipitation. Like other histochemical procedures involving the Schiff reagent (the Feulgen reaction so commonly used in chromosome studies) the method requires some experience but once learned, gives consistent results. Preliminary studies in this laboratory have not been encouraging owing to the relatively light staining of cuticle and to the discovery that chitin is negative if it has been dried.

Other color reactions. The α- and β-naphthol tests (Schulze & Kunike 23), the thymol test (Kraft 26), the dubious pyrogallic acid test (Racovitza 19), the Prussian blue test with ferrocyanide, and a number of other color reactions (van Wisselingh 14, 25) are sometimes useful as stains, but for the detection of chitin are less good than the preceding, if indeed not worthless. Surely, reporting chitin present when the iodine tests are negative is inexcusable (Kudo 21, von Lengerken 23).

Enzymatic methods. The suggestion that enzymes might be used for the detection of chitin is an old one (Tower 03b), but the use of conglomerate mixtures such as the contents from a snail's stomach is of no value for the determination of any specific compound. Also studies in the fractionation of the enzyme systems involved suggest that the system will not be simple (Grassman *et al.* 34, Zechmeister & Tóth 39a, b) and lead one to wonder if a practical enzyme test will ever be available to entomologists.

Chemical analyses as means of detection. The isolation and identification of glucosamine has been used by a number of authors for the detection of chitin (e.g., Halliburton 1885b), but the method is time consuming, needs an expert chemist, requires a rather large amount of material, and even so does not determine chitin but rather one of the components of a chitin molecule (Lafon 43c, Richards 47b, Roche & Dumazert 40). Actually the method is worthless unless one demonstrates that the glucosamine determined originated from chitin rather than from some other molecule (p. 12).

The isolation of chitobiose derivatives is good evidence (Zechmeister & Pinczési 36, Zechmeister & Tóth 31, 34), but aside from requiring expert chemical technique, is limited to application on a macro scale since the yield obtained is less than 2%. In a few special cases, such as the analysis of fossil remains which are refractory to other methods, the isolation of some of these chemical derivatives is worth while (Abderhalden & Heyns 33). Similarly, when it is difficult to separate small or delicate pieces from contaminating material, such as the contents of a gut, chitosan can be prepared, dissolved, concentrated, and reprecipitated for subsequent testing (Brown 37).

Physical methods of detection. Relatively few attempts have been made to develop methods for chitin detection by means of physical properties. It has been suggested that optical rotation (Irvine 09) and density (Sollas 07) might be used, but these call for preceding purification and solution. Some have cited birefringence as supporting evidence (e.g., Picken 49, Castle 45), and others have cited fluorescence, although this last seems decidedly questionable (Metcalf 45); see Chapter 15. In a few special cases where purification difficulties are encountered (Richards 49), and for a comparison of chitin from such diverse sources as fungi and insects, X-ray diffraction methods are of assistance, but these are not applicable to extremely minute structures (Fraenkel & Rudall 47, Heyn 36, van Iterson *et al.* 36, Khouvine 32, Lotmar & Picken 50, Richards 49).

Conflicting and confusing contaminants. It has already been mentioned that a reasonable degree of purification is required prior to the satisfactory application of tests for chitin detection. Numerous authors have discussed various facets of this problem (Campbell 29, Kunike 25, Norman 37, van Wisselingh 25).

Another possibility is that particles of cellulose may be present as contaminants. It is generally agreed today that cellulose does not occur in the cuticle of any arthropod, despite the old claims of Ambronn (1890) and others, but sometimes a piece of lint or other cellulosic fragment becomes inadvertently included with the specimen being tested. Usually such fragments are recognizable by their gross structure, but when there is occasion for doubt any of several tests which will distinguish between cellulose and chitin may be applied (Campbell 29, Kunike 25, E. Schmidt 31, van Wisselingh 25, Zander 1897). Unlike chitin or chitosan, cellulose is dissolved by solutions of cupric ammonium hydroxide, but is not dissolved by dilute organic acids (formic and acetic) or by hot concentrated nitric acid. Cellulose is not colored by the iodine-acid mixture used in the chitosan test, but after application of this reagent it swells and turns blue on the addition of 75% sulfuric acid. It is reported that cellulose gives a violet color with β-naphthol, whereas chitin gives a yellow color (Kunike 25), but the reliability of this test is open to question.[6] Cellulose is stained by lead acetate; chitin is not.

[6] A key for the supposed separation of chitin, cellulose, spongin, cornein, conchiolin, scintillin, and keratin is given by P. Schulze & Kunike (23). More recent advances make such simple distinctions of questionable value.

The quantitative estimation of chitin. Quantitative estimates are based on weights to which one may apply a correction factor based on a nitrogen determination and a value for residual ash.

The majority of quantitative determinations of chitin are based on purification with 5–20% NaOH at 60–100° C. for some hours, followed by washing in water and dilute acid;[7] then the material is treated with an oxidizing agent such as 0.1% $KMnO_4$, followed by a solution of $NaSO_3$ to effect oxidation of the more alkali resistant components, followed by thorough washing with water and passing through alcohol to ether, from which it is dried. Alternatively, prolonged treatment with repeated changes of Diaphanol for 6–10 weeks gives comparable results. A variant is to consider chitin as the ashable fraction of the alkali-insoluble residue (Pepper & Hastings 43). The method starting with superheating in alkali solutions and determining the quantity of chitin from the weight of residual chitosan (Tauber 34) needs careful study. Offhand one would suspect that it would be liable to various sources of error that would make the data inaccurate even for relative figures, but if adequate correction factors could be demonstrated, it would certainly be a simple method. Chitin is somewhat hygroscopic and so must be dried before being weighed; lower values are obtained if the drying is performed in a vacuum oven.

Quantitative estimates are subject to three sources of error which we are not ready to evaluate. These are, first, a complete ignorance of the amount of chitinous material that may be removed during the purification procedure, unless we are to define chitin as the amount of the polymer remaining after some selected standard treatment. Second, there is a greater or lesser uncertainty concerning the degree of purity of the material being weighed. That impurities are present is clearly shown by the presence of recognizable quantities of ash. It is probably also indicated by discrepancies between theoretical and actual nitrogen values (Richards 49). Third, we cannot be absolutely sure that the purification treatment has really altered 0% of the acetylglucosamine residues (Thor & Henderson 40). Perhaps the third of these points is negligible, but the first two are not. Until we are more certain on these points, it seems that even the best figures given in the literature should be viewed as probably only rough approximations (Campbell 29, Evans 38b, Fraenkel & Rudall 47, Lafon 41a, 48).

[7] Alkali is so strongly sorbed by chitin that it is not removed by simple washing. Even repeated changes of the washing water prolonged over several weeks is not adequate to remove all traces. Alkali washes out of chitosan relatively quickly and easily.

CHAPTER 5

The Distribution of Chitin in the Animal and Plant Kingdoms

It was originally intended to bring together for purposes of ready reference all the seemingly authentic records of the presence of chitin. Collation had not proceeded far before it became clear that this aim was not feasible, partly because many of the references are simply inserted in taxonomic monographs or morphological papers where they are not readily located, and even more because in a considerable percentage of the references, other than those specifically dealing with this point, it is not possible to tell whether the author is recording the result of a test he performed or simply stating what is generally true for the group with which he is working. An abbreviated table is given to provide some starting references for the various groups, and, incidentally, to document the statement that a wide variety of forms have been tested.

In a compilation of this sort one is immediately faced with the question of what is to be expected as an adequate demonstration of the presence or probable presence of chitin. We will ignore the old usage of chitin and chitinized as indicating the hard or sclerotized part of the cuticle rather than the polysaccharide chitin (Forbes 30), and we can also ignore the cases where the word chitin is used to indicate the entire cuticle, despite the fact that in numerous papers it is difficult to tell how the author is using the term. Since adequate chemical analyses are available for only a few species, we must perforce for the present accept the chitosan color test. Actually, as far as we know, the chitosan color test when positive is valid. An important part of any working definition, then, is that the material be insoluble in hot concentrated KOH. This eliminates those reports where a structure that is soluble in KOH none the less gives a positive I + ZnCl test (Machatoschke 36) or gives glucosamine on hydrolysis (Halliburton 1885, Mathews 23). However, it does not seem advisable at the present time to discard all the reports based on color reactions with zincchloroiodide, and so some of these are included (with a question mark).

That chitin is the same in the plant and animal kingdoms, wherever found, is a statement commonly seen. As long as the definition of chitin is kept sufficiently broad to include the differences that seemingly must be invoked at the polymer chemical level to account for some of the known differences between membranes (Richards & Korda 48), this statement seems likely to remain true. Seriously critical comparisons involve only the crustacea, the insects, and certain fungi. For these the comparison by use of the chitosan color test (P. Schulze 24, van Wisselingh 1898) is supported by some critical chemical analyses, including both elemental analyses and isolation of octaacetylchitobiose (Diehl 36, E. Gilson 1895a, Rammelberg 31, Scholl 08, Winterstein 1895–99, Zechmeister & Tóth 34), and a similarity of X-ray diffraction patterns (Heyn 36, van Iterson *et al.* 36, Khouvine 32, Picken 49). Perhaps the Mollusca should be added to this list since octaacetylchitobiose has been prepared from snail radulae (Tóth 40).

General reviews and extensive series of tests through a long range of forms of animals are given in the papers by Leuckart (1852), Krawkow (1892), Zander (1897), Wester (10), Biedermann (14a), Wettstein (21), P. Schulze (24), Kunike (25), Campbell (29), C. Koch (32), and Wigglesworth (48b). The most comprehensive papers for the plant kingdom are those by van Wisselingh (1898, 25) and von Wettstein (21). The monumental treatise by Biedermann covers all types of skeletal tissue and seems to the author the most valuable single compilation available.

Commenting briefly on the various groups of animals: (Table 1) The Protozoa, like their relatives the flagellated algae, seem to lack chitin entirely, although Lacroix's (23) data on foraminifera, if verified, would indicate some chitin in these calcified shells. Awerinzew (07) coined the term "pseudo-chitin" for the organic material in Rhizopod shells, having performed rather extensive tests showing it is not chitin but probably protein. The reports on the occurrence of chitin in spores of *Nosema* are not convincing, though one may argue that it is logical for such forms to have chitin considering their habitat (Koehler 21, Kudo 21).

The Porifera in general lack chitin, but it is said that some is to be found in the gemmulae of certain forms.

Table 1. An Abbreviated Résumé of Reports on the Occurrence of Chitin
More important references are indicated by an asterisk (*), especially ones involving better chemical documentation. Works cited in text as comprehensive are indicated by author's name only.

Phylum and Subgroup	Part	Report	Authority
Protozoa			
All		Absent	Wester, Kunike, Awerinzew 07
Porifera			
Most		Absent	Wester, Kunike
Spongilla	Gemmulae	Little present	Wester, Kunike
Coelenterata			
Hydromedusae	Perisarc [a]	Present	Wester, Kunike, Richards & Cutkomp 46, etc.
Hydromedusae without perisarc [b]		Absent	Same as above
Graptozoa (fossil)	Perisarc	Present	Kraft 23, 26
Syphomedusae		Absent	Wester, Kunike
Anthozoa		Absent	Wester, Kunike
Ctenophora			
All		Absent	Wester, Kunike
Platyhelminthes			
All [c]		Absent	Wester, Kunike, Voigt 1886, Grana & Oehninger 44
Nematoda			
All [d]	Body wall	Absent	Wester, Kunike, Chitwood 38, Lassaigne 1843a, Krawkow 1892, W. J. Schmidt 36b
All [e]	Egg shell	Present	Krawkow 1892, W. J. Schmidt 36b, Chitwood 38, Wottge 37, Faure-Fremiet 13, Deschiens & Pick 48
Gordiacea	Body wall	Absent	Von Ebner 10
Chaetognatha			
Sagitta	Hooks	?	W. J. Schmidt 40
Acanthocephala			
Macracanthorynchus . . .	Body wall	Absent	Von Brand 40
Macracanthorynchus . . .	Egg shell	Present	Von Brand 40

[a] Genera tested include *Antennularia, Obelia, Campanularia, Tubularia, Pennaria, Cordylophora, Plumularia, Sertularia, Hydrallmania.*
[b] Genera tested include *Hydra, Hydractinia.*
[c] Genera tested include *Planaria, Distomum, Taenia, Branchiobdella, Dendrocoelum, Echinococcus.*
[d] Genera tested include *Ascaris, Toxocara, Trichuris, Spironura, Strongylus, Agamermis, Theristus, Rhabditis, Oncholaimium, Heterodera, Ditylenchus.*
[e] Genera tested include *Ascaris, Dioctophyma, Heterodera.*

TABLE 1 *continued*

Phylum and Subgroup	Part	Report	Authority
Rotifera			
All [f]		Absent	Wester, Kunike
Chaetopoda (= Annelida)			
Polychaeta [g]	Body wall	Absent	Wester, Kunike, Mau 1882, Timm 1883
Polychaeta	Jaws, bristles, gut lining	Present	Wester, Kunike, Picken 49, Lotmar & Picken 50 *
Oligochaeta [h]	Body wall	Absent	Wester, Kunike, Reichard 03, Goodrich 1896, Sukatschoff 1899, Reed & Rudall 48,* Richards & Cutkomp 46, Timm 1883
Oligochaeta (*Lumbricus*)	Setae, gut lining	Present	Wester, Sollas 07, Goodrich 1896
Hirudinae		Present? Absent	Reichard 03 Kunike, Wester, Voigt 1886, Sukatschoff 01
Mollusca			
Cephalopoda [i]	Dorsal shield	Present	Kunike, Krukenberg 1885a, van Wisselingh 1898, Schulz 1900, Wester, Lotmar & Picken 50 *
Amphineura	"Some parts"	Present	Kunike
Gasteropoda [j]	Radula, jaws	Present	Wester, Kunike, Spek 19,* Sollas 07, Pantin & Rogers 25, Tóth 40 *
Lamellibranchiata [k]	Shell	Present? or absent	Wester, Sollas 07, Tóth 40
Gephyreae			
Sipunculus	Body wall	Absent	Wester
Phoronidea			
Phoronis		Present Absent	Kunike Wester

[f] Genera tested include *Rotifer.*

[g] Genera tested include *Eunice, Aphrodite, Glycera, Lepidonotus, Arenicola, Pectinaria, Nais, Scoloplos.*

[h] Genera tested include *Lumbricus, Aeolosoma, Vermiculus, Enchytraeus, Phreoryctes.*

[i] Genera tested include *Sepia, Loligo, Nautilus.*

[j] Genera tested include *Helix, Arion, Aphysia, Patella, Haliotus, Notica, Conus, Buccinus, Littorina, Tergipes.*

[k] Reported to be present in the following genera tested: *Anodonta, Mya, Cymbulia, Pecten;* reported absent from *Petricola, Tapes, Mytilus.*

TABLE 1 *continued*

Phylum and Subgroup	Part	Report	Authority
Polyzoa (= Bryozoa)			
Most Entoprocta [1]	Operculum	Present	Wester, Kunike, Zander 1897
Bugula	Operculum	Absent [m]	Richards & Cutkomp 46
Borentsia	Operculum	Absent	Kunike
Brachiopoda			
Terebratula		Absent	Wester, Kunike
Lingula	Shell	Present	Wester
Echinodermata		Absent	Wester, Kunike
Tunicata		Absent	Wester, Kunike
Chordata		Absent	Wester, Kunike
Bacteria		Absent	See van Wisselingh
Fungi			review 25,* Proskuria-
Myxomycetes			kow 25, Rammelberg
Most		Absent	31, Norman & Pe-
Plasmodiophora		Present	terson 32, Khouvine
Zygomycetes		Present	32,* D. E. Johnson
Phycomycetes		Present	31, M. Schmidt 36,
Ascomycetes		Present	Heyn 36,* Zechmeis-
Oomycetes		Absent	ter & Tóth 34,* van
Basidiomycetes		Present	Iterson *et al.* 36, Rip-
Lichens (most)		Present	pel 37, Hilpert *et al.*
Algae			37, Castle 38a, 45,*
Most		Absent	Bucherer & Schmidt-
Geosiphum		Present	Lange 40, Diehl 36,
Pteridophyta		Absent	Thomas 42, Locquin
Flowering plants		Absent	43,* Nabel 39, Har-
			der 37

[1] Genera reported positive include *Plumatella, Cristatella, Bugula, Zoobotryon, Flustra, Therme, Pedicellina, Pectinella.*

[m] See text.

In the Coelenterata, those hydroids that possess a perisarc (= periderm) give a strong chitin reaction for this covering, but those genera without a perisarc are entirely negative for chitin. The other classes of the Coelenterata (Anthozoa, Syphozoa), and also the Ctenophora, are negative to the chitosan test, but Kunike says that some Anthozoa give a positive zincchloroiodide test.

In the Nematoda and Acanthocephala there is a situation the reverse of that found in arthropods. The cuticle over the outside of the body is entirely negative to all forms of chitin tests; it appears to be a protein mixture. Yet the egg shell of the four genera tested contains chitin. In *Ascaris* the egg shell is said to consist of three layers: a protein layer secreted in the ovary, a chitinous layer secreted by the egg after fertilization but before the maturation divisions, and an inner striated nonchitinous layer secreted somewhat later (Wottge 37). W. J. Schmidt (40) has suggested that the hooks of *Sagitta* (a Chaetognath) might contain chitin, but his optical data are inconclusive. Numerous genera of Platyhelminthes have been tested and found negative.

Not all of the small invertebrate phyla have been tested, but the Rotifera, most Polyzoa, the Echinodermata, and the Tunicata have been reported as completely negative. Incidentally, the tunicates are the one group of animals said to possess cellulose (= tunicin). The Vertebrata and other Chordata are negative for chitin. In the Brachiopoda, *Lingula* is said to have a "little" chitin, whereas *Terebratula* is said to have none.

The situation in the phylum Bryozoa is not clear. Some authors say they possess chitin in the covering over the stalks, others that they possess a chitin-like material. Unquestionably at least some of them give a typical positive chitosan color test, but in the genus *Bugula* it is reported that the material after treatment with hot concentrated alkali solution is not dissolved by dilute acetic acid and gives, with iodine and dilute sulfuric acid, a greenish-brown instead of a violet color (Richards & Cutkomp 46). It does not seem likely that impurities could make a violet appear green.

The Mollusca present a varied picture which certainly deserves more serious study than it has received. Ever since the work by Krukenberg in 1885 it has been agreed that the cephalopods have chitin. It is also rather generally agreed that the jaws and radula of snails contain chitin, and strong support for this is given by the recent isolation of octaacetylchitobiose (Tóth 40). Numerous other chemicals are associated with the radula, but the interrelationships of these is completely unknown. In the shells of bivalves some authors record a little chitin ($<1\%$), but this needs verification. (See also p. 116.)

In the Annelida chitin is found in the jaws, bristles, and restricted parts of the gut of various Polychaetes and Oligochaetes but is said to be never present in the cuticle of the body wall. The presence of chitin in the bristles of *Aphrodite* has, indeed, recently been confirmed by X-ray diffraction patterns (Bobin & Mazoué 46, Picken 49), and surprisingly is found to be crystallographically different from that of arthropods (p. 18). The chitinous setae give strong Millon and xanthoproteic reactions, indicating the presence of protein; and positive argentaffin, Nadi, and Diaphanol reactions indicate a sclerotization comparable to that found in arthropod cuticles (Dennell 49b, Picken & Lotmar 50, Schepotieff 03). It is interesting in this connection that electron microscopy has revealed microfibrils occurring naturally in the protein cuticle of earthworms, whereas microfibrils are not found in the chitin-protein cuticle of insects (Reed & Rudall 48, Richards & Korda 48). The earthworm cuticle is said to be a collagenous protein.

In the Arthropoda, chitin is found in the body wall of every species in which tests have been reported — and this includes representatives of all the major and most of the minor subgroups — with the exception of the dubiously included Tardigrada. (See Table 2.) The same

TABLE 2. AN ABBREVIATED RÉSUMÉ OF THE PAPERS DEALING WITH CHITIN IN ARTHROPODS
More important references are indicated by an asterisk (*).

Class, Order, and Subgroup	Part	Report	Authority
General	Body wall	Present	Wester 10, 13, Kunike 25, Krawkow 1892, Kühnelt 28b,* Campbell 29,* Wigglesworth 30b, Fraenkel & Rudall 47,* Lafon 43b, Zander 1897
	Gut lining	Present	Yonge 32, Wigglesworth 30b, Campbell 29, Wester 10
Onychophora			
Peripatus	Body wall	Present	Kunike 25, Richards unpubl., Lotmar & Picken 50 *
Tardigrada			
Echiniscus	Body wall, claws	Absent	Marcus 27, 28, 29
Chilopoda [a]	Body wall, tracheae	Present	Kunike 25, Krawkow 1892, Richards & Korda 47, Lafon 43b, Wester 10, Zander 1897
Diplopoda [b]	Body wall, tracheae	Present	Wester 10, Zander 1897, Sollas 07, Kunike 25, Krawkow 1892, Lafon 43b
Linguatulida			
Armillifer	Body wall	Present	Kunike 25, Richards unpubl.

[a] Genera tested include *Scolopendra, Scutigera, Lithobius, Cryptops, Geophilus.*
[b] Genera tested include *Julus, Glomeris, Ophistreptus, Pachylobus, Oxydesmus.*

TABLE 2 *continued*

Class, Order, and Subgroup	Part	Report	Authority
Arachnida			
Xiphosura			
Limulus	Body wall	Present	Von Fürth & Russo 06, Sollas 07, Wester 13, Kunike 25, Krawkow 1892, Lafon 43a,* Richards 49,* Fränkel & Jellinek 27, Lotmar & Picken 50 *
Eurypterida			
Pterygotus	Fossil	Present?	Rosenheim 05, von Lengerken 23
Scorpiones [c]	Body wall	Present	Krawkow 1892, Sollas 07, Wester 13, Kunike 25, Fraenkel & Rudall 47,* Lafon 43b
Araneae [d]	Body wall	Present	Zander 1897, Wester 13, Kunike 25, Sollas 07, Browning 42, Krawkow 1892, Lafon 43b
Pseudoscorpiones . . .	Body wall, tracheae	Present	Richards unpubl.
Opiliones			
Phalangium	Body wall, tracheae	Present	Krawkow 1892, Richards unpubl.
Acari [e]	Body wall, tracheae	Present	Van Wisselingh 1898, Wester 10, Kunike 25, Falke 31
	Egg shell	Absent	Lees & Beament 48
Crustacea			
Branchiopoda [f]	Body wall	Present	Krawkow 1892, Kunike 25, Lafon 43b, Richards & Cutkomp 46
Cladocera [g]	Body wall	Present	Zander 1897, Wester 10, Kunike 25
Copepoda [h]	Body wall	Present	Zander 1897, Wester 10
Cirripedia [i]	Body wall	Present	Zander 1897, Wester 10, Prenant 25, Lafon 41a, 43b
Mysidacea			
Mysis	Body wall	Present	Zander 1897

[c] Genera tested include *Scorpio, Buthus, Opisthophthalmus, Pandinus.*

[d] Genera tested include *Epeira, Gonatum, Heteropoda, Lycosa, Mygale, Tegenaria.*

[e] Genera tested include *Acarus, Oribata, Boophilus, Ixodes.*

[f] Genera tested include *Apus, Artemia, Triops.*

[g] Genera tested include *Daphnia, Leptodora.*

[h] Genera tested include *Cyclops, Lernaeopoda.*

[i] Genera tested include *Balanus, Lepas.*

TABLE 2 *continued*

Class, Order, and Subgroup	Part	Report	Authority
Isopoda [j]	Body wall	Present	Zander 1897, Sollas 07, Wester 10, Lafon 41a, 43b, 48,* Koch 32, Richards & Korda 50
Amphipoda [k]	Body wall	Present	Wester 10, Kühnelt 28b
Decapoda [l]	Body wall, gills, gut, setae, egg shell	Present	Krawkow 1892, Zander 1897, van Wisselingh 1898, Sollas 07, Wester 10, 13, Kunike 25, Kühnelt 28b,* Rammelberg 31, Johnson 32, Yonge 32, 35, Khouvine 32, Zechmeister & Tóth 34,* Castle 36, Clark & Smith 36,* van Iterson *et al.* 36,* Rigby 36, Fraenkel & Rudall 40, 47,* Lafon 41a, 43b, 48,* Drach & Lafon 42, Richards & Cutkomp 46, Lotmar & Picken 50 *
Hexapoda (Insecta)			
General	Body wall	Present	As under phylum
General	Tracheae [m]	Present or absent	Richards & Korda 48, 50, Campbell 29, van Wisselingh 1898, 10, Wester 10
General	Peritrophic membrane [n]	Present	Wigglesworth 30b, Brown 37, Richards & Korda 48, Kusmenko 40, Campbell 29

[j] Genera tested include *Asellus, Ligia, Oniscus, Armadillidium, Porcellio.*

[k] Genera tested include *Caprella, Gammarus.*

[l] Genera tested include *Astacus, Cambarus, Cancer, Carcinides, Carcinus, Crangon, Emerita, Eupagurus, Galathea, Hippolyte, Homarus, Hyas, Maia, Nephrops, Pagurus, Palaemon, Palinurus, Portunus, Potamobius, Xantho.*

[m] Positive chitosan tests recorded for larger tracheae of *Periplaneta, Blatta, Galleria, Calandra, Dytiscus, Melolontha, Culex, Aedes, Phormia* (larva), *Neodiprion.*

Dissolution in hot alkali recorded in *Apis, Sciara, Musca, Drosophila, Phormia* (adult), *Rhodnius, Xenopsylla,* and tracheoles and commonly smaller tracheae of all species tested. However, van Wisselingh (10) has recorded success in preventing the dissolution of *Musca* tracheae by pretreatment with dilute chromic acid, and then obtaining a violet color with $I + H_2SO_4$.

[n] Genera tested include *Anopheles, Culex, Aedes, Sciara, Rhyphus, Telmatoscopus, Lucilia, Glossina, Bombus, Apis, Sitotroga, Ephestia, Cheimabacche, Ceratophyllus, Hemerobius, Aeschna, Melanoplus, Blatella, Forficula, Tenebrio, Cicindella.*

TABLE 2 *continued*

Class, Order, and Subgroup	Part	Report	Authority
General	Egg shells [o]	Absent	Wester 10, Campbell 29, Slifer 37, Slifer & King 34, Jahn 35b, Tichomiroff 1885, W. J. Schmidt 39a, Beament 46b *
General	Ootheca	Absent	Campbell 29, Pryor 40a *
Thysanura			
Lepisma			Richards 47b
Orthoptera [p]			Krawkow 1892, Campbell 29,* Heyn 36, C. Koch 32, Richards & Anderson 42a, Richards & Korda 48,* Sollas 07, Lafon 43b, 48,* Tauber 34, Fraenkel & Rudall 47,* Ichikawa 38, Zander 1897
Isoptera			
Queen termite ...			Campbell 29
Dermaptera			
Forficula			Krawkow 1892
Ephemerida [q]			Zander 1897, Zaitschek 04
Odonata [r]			Zander 1897, Kunike 25, Lotmar & Picken 50 *
Hemiptera [s]			Wigglesworth 33, Kunike 25, Lafon 43b, P. A. Buxton 32a
Homoptera [t]			Zander 1897, Lafon 43b
Coleoptera [u]			Krawkow 1892, Zaitschek 04, Wester 10, Kunike 25, Campbell 29, C. Koch 32, Zander 1897, Zechmeister & Pinczési 36,* Lafon 41a, b, 43c, 48, Fraenkel & Rudall 47,* Picken *et al.* 47, P. Schulze 27

[o] Genera tested include *Bombyx, Gastropacha, Malacosoma, Harpyia, Antheraea, Platysamia, Smerinthus, Philosamia, Bombus, Melanoplus, Periplaneta, Pediculus, Rhodnius.*

[p] Genera tested include *Periplaneta, Blatta, Melanoplus, Locusta, Dixippus, Gryllus, Gryllotalpa, Decticus, Bacillus.*

[q] Genera tested include *Ephemera, Palingenia.*

[r] Genera tested include *Aeschna, Libellula.*

[s] Genera tested include *Rhodnius, Pyrrhocoris, Nepa, Cimex.*

[t] Genera tested include *Cicada, Cercopis.*

[u] Genera tested include *Calosoma, Carabus, Cicindela, Donacia* (cocoon), *Dytiscus, Dorcus, Geotrupes, Goliathus, Leptinotarsa, Lucanus,* "May beetles," *Melolontha, Melasoma, Lytta, Necrodes, Osmoderma, Oryctes, Platyderma* (cocoon), *Staphylinus, Sylpha, Telephorus, Tenebrio.*

TABLE 2 *continued*

Class, Order, and Subgroup	Part	Report	Authority
Hymenoptera [v]			Van Wisselingh 1898, Wester 10, Kunike 25, Campbell 29, Jacobs 24, (Aronssohn 10), C. Koch 32, Krawkow 1892, Lotmar & Picken 50 *
Lepidoptera [w]			Krawkow 1892, von Fürth & Russo 06, Sollas 07, Wester 10, Kunike 25, Campbell 29, Kühnelt 28b, C. Koch 32, Pepper & Hastings 43, Richards 47b,* Fraenkel & Rudall 47,* Lafon 43b,
Diptera [x]			Van Wisselingh 1898, Krawkow 1892, Wester 10, Kunike 25, Campbell 29, C. Koch 32, Richards 47b, Richards & Korda 48,* P. A. Buxton 32a, Lafon 41c, 48, Fraenkel & Rudall 40, 47,* Dennell 46
Siphonaptera			
Pulex			Kunike 25

[v] Genera tested include *Apis, Cynips, Vespa, Xylocopa, Chlorion, Bombus, Pomphilus, Sirex.*

[w] Genera tested include *Bombyx, Deilephila, Galleria, Phalera, Smerinthus, Harpyia, Vanessa, Hyloicus, Gastropacha, Pieris, Loxostege, Sphinx.*

Wing membranes and attached scales of 109 species, of 103 genera, representing 45 families, have been tested. The membranes were always positive, the scales usually so (iridescent blue scales of *Morpho, Atlides, Erasmia,* etc. were outstanding exceptions) (Richards 47b).

[x] Genera tested include *Culex, Aedes, Tipula, Musca, Phormia, Lucilia, Calliphora, Sarcophaga, Drosophila.*

may be said for the lining of the gut and for the invaginations (apophyses) which serve for the attachment of muscles. The peritrophic membrane which lines the mid-gut has been shown to contain chitin in a large number of diverse forms (Wigglesworth 30b). Likewise the tracheae usually contain chitin, but in some cases the tracheae and in all cases the tracheoles disintegrate in hot alkali (Richards & Korda 50). In most but not all cases the scales on insect wings contain chitin (Picken 49, Richards 47b). It is reported that the rhabdom of the arthropod eye contains chitin, but this is based on the fact that it stains with zincchloroiodide; it disintegrates under treatment with alkali (Debaisieux 44, Machatoschke 36, Richards unpubl.).

As for strictly internal tissues, the entasternite of arachnids (Mathews 23, Richards unpubl.) and the neural lamella of insects (Richards 44a), both of which superficially look like cuticle, are dispersed by alkali solutions.[1] The intracellular concretions, recorded as chitinous, in fat cells of *Branchipus* (Alverdes 12) require reinvestigation because the tests used were inconclusive. The insect egg shell has always been reported negative for chitin, although the grasshopper embryo does secrete a chitinous layer beneath the true egg shell (Slifer 37), and the crustacean egg, like that of round worms, also secretes an inner chitin-containing layer (Yonge 35, 38b). Spermatophores have been recorded as possessing chitin (Petersen 07), but more recent tests have shown them soluble in alkali (Khalifa 49a, Richards unpubl.,[2] Weidner 34). It is commonly stated that parasites within insects may become chitinized, but the term appears to have been presumptively applied without adequate tests (Brug 32, Hollande 20).

Scar tissue lacks chitin (Bordage 01, Campbell 29, Thorpe 36, Wigglesworth 37), but when induced by parasites may be resistant to alkali (Marshall & Staley 29), although it resembles a type of connective tissue in appearance (Boese 36).

No attempt will be made to review in detail the occurrence of chitin in the plant kingdom because of the extensive reviews by van Wisselingh (25) and Harder (37). In the fungi the list of forms tested reads like a catalogue of the fungi of the world. As a general summary, it may be said that chitin apparently is absent from bacteria, Actinomycetes, Oomycetes, and most Myxomycetes. Chitin is present in Basidiomycetes, Ascomycetes, Phycomycetes, Lichens, and perhaps some Myxomycetes. The diverse bacterial polysaccharides will not be discussed (Norman 37). The most extensive chemical work has been done with the genera *Aspergillus, Agaricus, Boletus,* and *Phycomyces.* As with some arthropods, high nitrogen values are

[1] The neural lamella resembles cuticle in histological appearance and in being laminated (Richards 44a, Scharrer 39), but the arachnid entasternite bears little resemblance to cuticle histologically – it is more reminiscent of vertebrate cartilage (Lankaster 1884, Schlottke 34).

[2] In the author's laboratory complete dissolution in hot alkali (both concentrated and dilute) was obtained for spermatophores of the field cricket (*Gryllus assimilus*) and of sphingid and noctuid moths (*Chromis erotus, Catocala ilia, Graphiphora c-nigrum*).

obtained only with exhaustive purification involving both KOH and $KMnO_4$ (Proskuriakow 25).

Three special points seem worth recording here. First, although fungi usually contain either chitin or cellulose, there are three cases where both cellulose and chitin have been reported in the walls of a single fungus, presumably actually associated together (Locquin 43, Nabel 39, R. C. Thomas 42). Second, in fungi, chitin, like cellulose, apparently is laid down in intimate association with the protoplasm in definite fibrous form, in contrast to the secretion and subsequent reorientations at a distance from the cells such as occur in insects and other arthropods (Castle 38a, 42). And third, while percentages are seldom given, chitin has been recorded as being only a minor component of the cell walls (Proskuriakow 25, Takata 29); in other words there is no record of the occurrence of chitin in anything approaching pure form in fungal walls, just as there is no record of chitin in anything approaching pure condition in animal cuticles. Whether this is interpreted as reflecting difficulties in purification or indicating a mixture of polysaccharides (Norman 37) does not affect the statement that chitin is only one of the components in the fungal wall complex, as also in arthropods.

CHAPTER 6

The Decomposition of Chitin and Cuticle in Nature

It seems self-evident that cuticle would have to be decomposed or its accumulation would represent a serious depletion of available carbon and nitrogen reserves. It has been estimated that the copepod crustacea alone produce several billion tons of chitin annually (Johnstone 08); probably several times this amount is produced annually by other marine crustacea and by terrestrial arthropods. And yet no great accumulation results, despite the fact that, as far as we know, the system does not decompose spontaneously. Also, relatively delicate laboratory measurements of electrical properties and examination by electron microscopy of cuticles kept under favorable conditions have not revealed any spontaneous changes (Richards & Fan 49, Richards & Korda 48, Ricks & Hoskins 48). It is easy to alter or remove some of the components with heat or extraction methods (Fraenkel & Rudall 47, Richards & Korda 48), but the chitin persists, and chitin is extremely durable, having even been identified in fairly old fossil remains (Abderhalden & Heyns 33, Kraft 23, von Lengerken 22, 23, Rosenheim 05). Also it is well known that chitin resists solution and is not attacked by mammalian digestive enzymes (Richards & Korda 48, Wolff *et al.* 1876, Zaitschek 04), though it decomposes in water, as was recorded by Schlossberger in 1856.

The answer is that many bacteria produce enzymes that will digest chitin as well as other components of the cuticle. For some reason this literature appears to be unknown to most entomologists and chemists; at least current textbooks in entomology and biochemistry are content to cite the one old classical paper by Benecke (05) with the implication that a single bacterium, *Bacillus chitinovorus*, is responsible for all the decomposition of chitin in nature. The fact is that many species of bacteria are concerned, although most of them have not yet been given technical scientific names.

Bacteria have been isolated in Russia, Germany, and the United States from fresh water, salt beds, sea water of the Atlantic and Pacific Oceans, from the gut contents of marine, fresh water, and terrestrial animals, from mud and soil, from decomposing manure—in short, from every habitat in which they have been sought (Table 3). In the ocean they have been dredged from distances up to two hundred miles from the nearest land and two thousand meters deep (Zobell & Rittenberg 37), and they occur in numbers up to one thousand per gram of sediment. Much greater numbers are found in decomposing arthropods. The majority of the bacterial strains studied[1] have been aerobic, but anaerobic forms are known (Aleshina 38, Rittenberg *et al.* 37). Most of the forms are gram negative, motile rods of different dimensions, but coccus, vibrio, and myxobacterial forms are known. Even among the bacilli the various types or strains may be markedly dissimilar, giving colonies, for instance, which are yellow, orange, pink, brown, or colorless. Thus Zobell and Rittenberg think that their thirty-one types represent thirty-one new species of bacteria, but in view of the taxonomic difficulties in this group, refrain from assigning them each a Latin name. Certainly there is little overlapping between these thirty-one types and the types worked on by Benton, Hock, Stuart, and others. Most of the bacteria routinely used in bacteriological laboratories have, however, proved to be negative when tested for chitin digestion (Benecke 05).

The decomposition of cuticle in water was noted as long ago as 1856 by Schlossberger and since then has been repeatedly mentioned, especially in connection with soil chemistry (Bucherer 35, Jensen 32, Shorey 30). Presumably the decomposition in nature is rather slow; at least in the laboratory, in synthetic culture media, decomposition requires from two to ten days, or even months (Hock 41, D. E. Johnson 31, Zobell & Rittenberg 37). The decomposition can be accelerated considerably by the addition of other nutrients (glucose and peptone). None of the forms studied so far have been obligate chitinovores, but at least those studied by Hock, by Stanier, and by Zobell and Rittenberg are unable to utilize cellulose. An important ecological fact is that some of these bacteria act quite satisfactorily at low temperatures, some of the marine forms being active at 0–4° C. and probably even at temperatures slightly below zero (Zobell & Rittenberg 37).

[1] The techniques used for isolation of cultures have favored the detection of aerobic forms. Anaerobic forms may be much more common than shown by the studies made to date.

TABLE 3. ORGANISMS RESPONSIBLE FOR THE DECOMPOSITION OF CHITIN AND CUTICLE IN NATURE

Organism	Source	Products	References
Bacteria			
Reduce sulfate anaerobically	. . .	NH_3	Aleshina 38
Bacillus chitinovorus	Sea water		Benecke 05
B. chitinovorus?	Sea water		Rammelberg 31
B. chitinovorus?	Soil		Folpmers 21
250 cultures of 17 types	Water, soil, carcasses, and guts of birds, fish, bats, frogs		A. G. Benton 35
Bacillus chitinophilum (5 strains)	Marine sand, mud, sea water, rotting *Limulus*, and guts of oysters, squid, fish	NH_3 organic acids, and reducing substances	Hock 40, 41
Bacillus chitinochroma	Same as above	Same as above	Hock 40, 41
31 cultures of 14 types	Marine sediments, animals, sea water	NH_3 or acids	Zobell & Rittenberg 37
"Myxobacterium"	Corn and oat smut (fungi)		D. E. Johnson 31
Cytophaga johnsonae	Soil and mud		Stanier 47
Serratia salinaria? (5 strains)	Solar salts, world wide		Stuart 36
Sarcina littoralis? (3 strains)	Solar salts, world wide		Stuart 36
Snail			
Helix pomatia	Digestive fluids or hepatopancreas	Various	Karrer 30 Karrer & François 29 Karrer & Hoffman 29 Karrer & White 30 Yonge 32
Fungus			
Penicillium	Culture		Benecke 05

Zobell and Rittenberg coined the term chitinoclastic for any bacterium which is capable of altering the chitin molecule. They point out that some bacteria dissolve and derive their nourishment from chitin (= chitinovore), whereas others derive nourishment but require supplementary C or C + N sources, whereas still others attack only the side chains of the chitin molecule and apparently derive no nourishment at all. An interesting but unexplained relationship which they observed and called symbiosis is that certain mixtures of their cultures were capable of attacking chitin, although none of the component bacteria in pure culture had any effect on chitin.

The halophilic bacteria are said to lose their chitinase power after growing on agar (Stuart 36), but at least many of the marine forms can be cultured without chitin for years and yet remain chitinovores (Zobell & Rittenberg 37).

A pH optimum of 7.5 has been recorded for the bacterial disintegration of chitin, but since the decomposition requires days or weeks, it is not clear whether this is an optimum for the enzyme concerned or for the growth of the bacteria (Rammelberg 31).

Parasitic chitinovorous bacteria have been recorded on lobsters (Hess 37), and it would certainly seem that some of the fungi which are parasitic on arthropods would have to have chitinase power, although this appears not to have been actually demonstrated (Steinhaus 49, von Zopf 1888). Chitinases from snails have also been used in studying chitin chemistry (Karrer 30), and snail digestive juices have been shown to be capable of dispersing lobster cuticle (Yonge 32), but one would suspect that these play only a minor role in the large job of decomposing chitin in nature.[2]

Most of these authors have used purified chitin, but some of them mention—and all imply—that the intact cuticle and other cuticle components are capable of being digested (Dutt 36, Hock 41). Presumably the digestion of sclerotized cuticle will be found to involve some additional factor, but no ideas have been advanced.[3] The diges-

[2] It has recently been reported that the cellulase in the digestive juices of a snail, *Helix pomatia,* come from a symbiotic bacterium living in the gut and hepatopancreas (Florkin & Lozet 49). This possibility should be checked for snail chitinases.

[3] The additional factor is not necessarily another enzyme. It might not be irrelevant to recall that larvae of the clothes moth first reduce keratin with a thiol-like compound and then can and do digest it with ordinary proteinases (Linderstrom-Lang & Duspiva 35); also that interfering molecular configurations can be broken mechanically, as shown, for instance, by the fact that silk and keratin are attacked by ordinary proteolytic enzymes provided they are first finely ground (C. L. A. Schmidt, 1944, p. 1099).

tion of beeswax by larvae of the wax moth is said to be due to the presence of a symbiotic bacterium in the gut (Florkin *et al.* 49), and clearly the epicuticle is relatively resistant to enzymatic decomposition (Dennell 50).

Here is a picture of tremendous variability in nature. Many species, many habitats, many reactions — and just enough information to document the diversity. Surely this is a subject deserving serious consideration by ecologists.

CHAPTER 7

Proteins

ARTHROPODIN AND OTHER CUTICULAR PROTEINS

When Odier discovered chitin in the elytra of May beetles in 1823, he recognized that this represented only about 30% of the weight of the cuticle and that the remainder of the material was mostly protein. Since then a large number of workers have recognized the presence of protein by qualitative color tests. It is, however, only in the papers by Trim (41a, b) and by Fraenkel and Rudall (40, 47) that some information concerning the nature of this particular protein group is to be found.

In soft cuticles a large portion of the protein can be removed by water, especially hot water, while a smaller additional portion is removed by 5% KOH. In hard cuticles, while the total amount of protein may be approximately the same as in soft cuticles, a small percentage is removed by water and a large percentage by alkali or acid. We can then recognize a water-soluble fraction and a water-insoluble fraction, the latter being soluble in alkali or acid solutions. Since water-soluble protein fractions with the same general characteristics have been isolated from the cuticles of various insects, crustaceans, and a scorpion, Fraenkel and Rudall (47) have proposed the name arthropodin "on account of its universal occurrence among arthropods and because its presence is responsible for the free movability of the limbs." The water-insoluble proteins, or at least the common type thereof, have been termed sclerotin by Pryor (40a, b).

Arthropodin is characterized by its failure to coagulate in hot water and by being soluble in hot but not cold 10% trichloracetic acid. It is precipitated from aqueous solution by ethyl alcohol in concentrations above 45%, by half-saturated $(NH_4)_2SO_4$, and by saturated NaCl solutions. It is remarkable in that after precipitation by either trichloracetic acid or alcohol it is readily redissolved by warm water. X-ray diffraction studies give evidence that this protein exists natu-

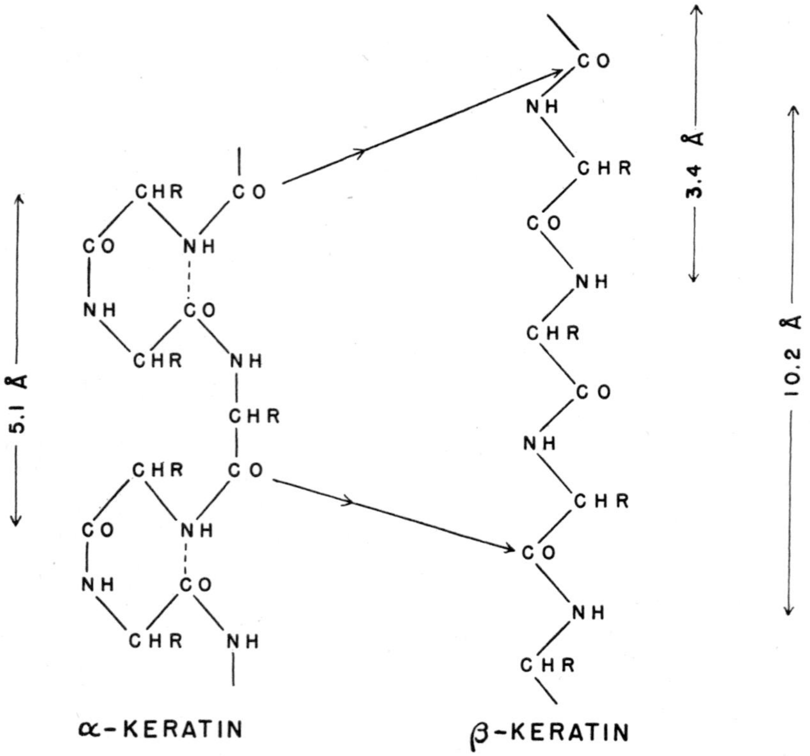

Figure 9. The idea of folded and extended configurations for fibrous proteins as illustrated by Astbury's scheme for α- and β-keratin. (Redrawn after C.L.A. Schmidt.)

rally in the fully extended or β configuration (Fig. 9).[1] Boiling produces the molecular configurations of denaturation (Astbury & Lomax 35), but nevertheless the protein remains soluble in water. The heating does alter the reaction to quinones, as will be discussed later. Of unquestionably great importance for the development of the cuticle is the fact that the molecular spacings of this extended protein agree with those of chitin (Fig. 10); that this permits the ready formation of mixed lattices can scarcely be doubted. Arthropodin is tanned by quinones to give hard insoluble materials, but for reasons not yet understood this reaction does not necessarily proceed in the same manner with the isolated proteins as when the protein is in po-

[1] This is an unusual configuration. Most structural proteins occur naturally in the α-configuration (Rudall 47). The biological importance of this is that it is only the β-configuration which has lattice dimensions agreeing with those of chitin.

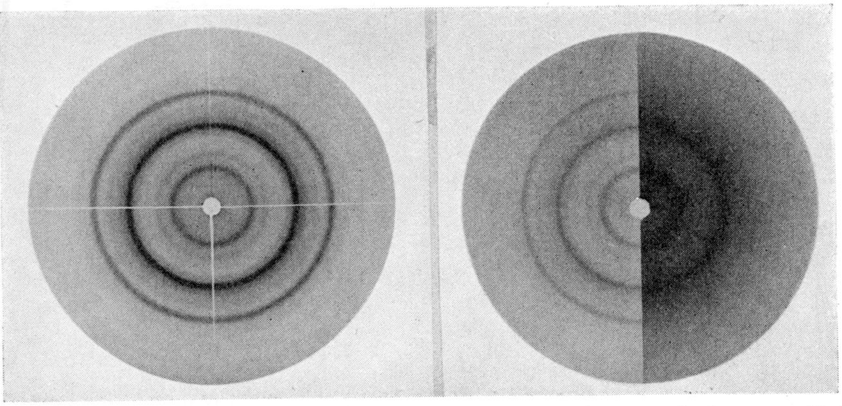

Figure 10. A. X-ray diffraction patterns showing identity of chitin purified from soft and from sclerotized cuticle (purification with Diaphanol). Top right and bottom left from soft "white pupa" cuticle; top left and bottom right from hard, dark puparium. (After Fraenkel and Rudall.)

B. Comparative X-ray diffraction patterns of chitin and arthropodin showing the identity of the lattice spacings. The identity of these lattice spacings, presumably permitting ready mixed crystallization, is almost certainly of great importance for cuticle development. (After Fraenkel and Rudall.)

sition within a cuticle. X-ray studies also show that the quinones affect the side chains of the molecule (Fraenkel & Rudall 47). If one accepts at face value the data from these impure preparations, then arthropodin shows unique properties, unlike those of any other known protein, but the important distinctions are physical rather than chemical.

Trim (41a, b) has performed the one partial analysis of the composition of arthropodin. The values he determined are given in Table 4 along with values derived from egg shells, various kinds of silk, and the salivary secretion of *Drosophila* larvae and the royal jelly of honeybees. Values for a few of the typical and better-known proteins are also given to facilitate ready comparison. Like silk fibroin and egg shells, arthropodin has a rather high tyrosine content, but unlike these is extremely low in glycine. Also, it is reported to have none of the amino acids which contain sulfur (cysteine, cystine, taurine, methionine). Trim considers arthropodin distinct from all previously known proteins but most nearly similar to sericin (silk gelatin), with which it agrees rather well in content of ammonia N (6.2–9.5 vs. 10–12%), basic N (18–23 vs. 16–18%), monoamino N (68–75 vs. 69–70%), tyrosine, and tryptophane. It is however quite different from

Table 4. Percentage of Amino Acids Found in Proteins from arthropod cuticle, egg shells, various silks, and salivary secretion, with comparative values from some typical proteins. The methods used for these determinations were various, and the original papers should be consulted for details.

Material Studied	Simple							Phenyl	
	Glycine	Alanine	Serine	Threonine	Valine	Norvaline	Leucine & Isoleucine	Tyrosine	Phenylal-anine
Arthropodin (Trim)	0.6–1.3	. . .	4–5?	1.8–2.5	. . .	. . .	. . .	5–12 [a]	. . .
Egg shell (Tomita)	13.7	3.8	1.1	. . .	0.28	. . .	1.7	11.2	0.7
Spider silk (Fischer)	36.0	23.4	. . .	. . .	. . .	. . .	1.75	8.2	. . .
Tussah silk (Abderhalden & Heyns)	++++	++++	. . .	. . .	. . .	++	. . .	++	. . .
Silk – *Bombyx mori*									
Sericin (silk gelatin)									
Alders	. . .	. . .	. . .	. . .	. . .	. . .	. . .	6.89	. . .
Ito & Komori	. . .	. . .	. . .	. . .	. . .	. . .	. . .	. . .	. . .
Nicolet & Saidel	. . .	. . .	33.9	8.9	. . .	. . .	. . .	. . .	. . .
Lang "A"	1.5	. . .	++	++	. . .	. . .	. . .	4.65	. . .
Lang "B"	1.65	. . .	++	++	. . .	. . .	. . .	6.25	. . .
Fibroin									
M. Bergmann & Niemann	43.8	26.4	. . .	. . .	. . .	. . .	. . .	13.2	. . .
Cohn & Edsall	43.8	26.4	13.6	1.4	. . .	. . .	2.5	13.2	1.5
C. L. A. Schmidt 44	40.5	25.0	1.8	. . .	. . .	. . .	2.5	11.0	11.5
Polson *et al.*	42.4	34.0	11.9	. . .	5.7	. . .	2.5	8.3	0.0
Coleman & Howitt	42.3	24.5	12.6	1.5	3.2	. . .	0.8	10.6	. . .
Levy & Slobodiansky	42	28	9.24	. . .	. . .	. . .	. . .	. . .	. . .
Salivary gland – *Drosophila* (Kodani) [b]	+++	+++	++++	++++	+++	. . .	+++	trace	trace

[a] 5%–6% in *Sarcophaga* and lobster; 12% in *Sphinx*.

[b] Estimates on size and intensity of spots on paper chromatograph.

TABLE 4 *continued*

Material Studied	Simple							Phenyl	
	Glycine	Alanine	Serine	Threonine	Valine	Norvaline	Leucine & Isoleucine	Tyrosine	Phenylal-anine
Royal jelly – honeybee (Pratt & House)									
Free	+	+	+	—	+	. . .	+	+	—
Combined	+	+	+	+	+	. . .	+	+	+
Gelatin (= collagen)	25.5	8.7	0.4	. . .	0.0	. . .	7.1	0.0	1.4
Wool (= keratin)	0.6	4.4	2.9	. . .	2.8	. . .	11.5	4.8	. . .
Casein	0.5	1.9	0.5	. . .	7.9	. . .	9.7	6.6	3.9
Egg albumen	0.0	2.2	. . .	. . .	2.5	. . .	10.7	4.2	5.1

Material Studied	Heterocyclic				Dicarboxylic		Diamino		With S		
	Histidine	Tryptophane	Proline	Hydroxyproline	Aspartic acid	Glutamic acid	Arginine	Lysine	Cystine	Methionine	Taurine
Arthropodin (Trim)	. . .	1.4	low	. . .	. . .	. . .	. . .	. . .	0.0	0.0	0.0
Egg shell (Tomita)	++	. . .	2.2	. . .	0.37	4.16	0.19	0.39	0.0	. . .	. . .
Spider silk (Fischer)	. . .	. . .	3.7	. . .	. . .	11.7	5.2?	. . .	. . .	. . .	. . .
Tussah silk (Abderhalden & Heyns)	. . .	. . .	. . .	. . .	++	. . .	. . .	. . .	. . .	. . .	. . .

TABLE 4 *continued*

Material Studied	Heterocyclic: Histidine	Heterocyclic: Tryptophane	Heterocyclic: Proline	Heterocyclic: Hydroxyproline	Dicarboxylic: Aspartic acid	Dicarboxylic: Glutamic acid	Diamino: Arginine	Diamino: Lysine	With S: Cystine	With S: Methionine	With S: Taurine
Silk – *Bombyx mori*											
Sericin (silk gelatin)											
Alders	0	1.02	. . .	. . .	. . .	. . .	5.14	1.0	1.04	. . .	. . .
Ito & Komori	2.7–3.8	. . .	. . .	. . .	. . .	. . .	9.1–9.6	4.7	0.0	. . .	. . .
Nicolet & Saidel	. . .	. . .	. . .	. . .	. . .	. . .	. . .	. . .	. . .	. . .	. . .
Lang "A"	1.0	0.0	0.0	. . .	++	++	4.4	++	. . .	. . .	. . .
Lang "B"	0.0	1.1	3.0	. . .	++	++	5.2	++	. . .	. . .	. . .
Fibroin											
M. Bergmann & Niemann	0.07	. . .	. . .	. . .	. . .	. . .	0.95	0.25	. . .	. . .	. . .
Cohn & Edsall	0.1	. . .	1.0	. . .	. . .	. . .	0.76	0.25	. . .	2.6	. . .
C. L. A. Schmidt 44	0.1	. . .	1.0	. . .	. . .	. . .	0.7	0.3	. . .	. . .	. . .
Polson *et al.*	. . .	. . .	trace	. . .	. . .	. . .	0.8	. . .	0.0	0.0	. . .
Coleman & Howitt	0.45	. . .	1.5	. . .	. . .	. . .	1.05	0.44	. . .	. . .	. . .
Levy & Slobodiansky	. . .	. . .	. . .	0.05	1.54	1.07	. . .	. . .	. . .	. . .	. . .
Salivary gland – *Drosophila* (Kodani)[b]	. . .	0.0	+	. . .	++	++++	++	++	++	+	. . .
Royal jelly – honeybee (Pratt & House)											
Free	—	—	+	—	+	+	+	+	–	+	+
Combined	—	—	+	—	+	+	+	+	–	+	. . .
Gelatin (= collagen)	1.0	0.0	9.5	14.1	3.4	5.8	8.2	5.9	0.2	0.0	. . .
Wool (= keratin)	0.7	1.8	4.4	. . .	2.3	12.9	7.8	2.3	13.1	. . .	. . .
Casein	2.5	2.2	9.0	0.2	4.1	21.8	3.8	6.0	0.3	3.4	. . .
Egg albumen	1.4	1.3	4.2	. . .	6.1	14.0	5.2	6.4	1.3	4.6	. . .

[b] Estimates on size and intensity of spots on paper chromatograph.

sericin in content of β–hydroxy–α–amino acids, especially serine. It might be worth noting that the tyrosine content of moth larvae is approximately twice that of the larvae of blowflies and lobsters.

In addition to the work on arthropodin, Trim made a few analyses on the protein fraction extractable from the cuticles of moth larvae by 5% KOH solution. This fraction is not yet well enough characterized to postulate whether it is a derivative of arthropodin or an entirely distinct protein. It differs in having a considerably lower nitrogen content and, more interestingly, contains approximately 0.5% sulfur and about 3% carbohydrate. It is not certain whether the carbohydrate exists as a polysaccharide or in combination with the protein, but the fact that analyses of partial fractionations show the sulfur present in the carbohydrate-rich fraction suggests that the carbohydrate may be present as a prosthetic group on the protein molecule. It will bear repeating that though sulfur is present in the alkali-extractable fraction, the sulfur-containing amino acids are recorded as absent. Trim also records tests showing that the sulfur is not present as an ethereal sulfate, a sulphydryl, or as inorganic sulfur.

As previously mentioned, arthropodin is tanned to give rise to a derivative that has been named sclerotin, but a discussion of this will have to be deferred until after consideration of the other chemical components present in cuticle (p. 185).

It might also be remarked that Trim feels his determinations show specific differences for the protein. This seems quite reasonable but must await further study for confirmation.

The series of papers by Lafon contain numerous determinations of the percentage of protein present in the cuticles of various arthropods, and, in addition, several points of confirmatory interest here. In the elytra of beetles he records (41b) the presence of 1.3% sulfur, a figure not too far from that given by Trim. More recently Lafon has recorded the percentages of water-soluble (arthropodin) and water-insoluble proteins for a variety of crustacea, both calcified and noncalcified (48).

Nothing is known about the metabolic development of the cuticular proteins other than the balance-sheet determinations by Evans (32, 38a, b) which show, as one would expect, that concomitant with an increase in skeletal nitrogen there is a decrease in nonskeletal nitrogen, especially soluble protein nitrogen.

It may perhaps be of some metabolic interest that injuries leading to the formation of scars or scabs become covered with a cuticle which, at least at first, contains no chitin, but is positive for protein tests (Campbell 29, Thorpe 36, Wigglesworth 37).

The egg shell of insects has long been recognized as lacking chitin and being positive for protein tests (Beament 46b, Farkas 03, Jahn 35b, Pantel 19, Tichomiroff 1885, Tomita 21). Perhaps one might expect the egg shell to resemble tanned arthropodin, but the one amino acid analysis reported (Tomita 21) – while abundantly distinct from sericin and silk fibroin and perhaps similar to arthropodin in many respects – is very high in both glycine and tyrosine content (Table 4). It seems hardly likely that such discrepancies can be encompassed within the definition of arthropodin.

There is a recent short paper (Wheeler 47) reporting that 85% of radioactive iodine fed to *Drosophila* larvae becomes localized in the cuticle. Since the radioactivity is removed by treating the cuticle with KOH solution, the author assumes that the iodine is attached to cuticular proteins, probably in a manner comparable to the addition of iodine to tyrosine to form thyroxine. Since the paper seems neither convincing nor consistent, the significance of the data is not clear.

The term trachein, proposed for the material composing the tracheal walls of insects, may profitably be forgotten (von Frankenberg 15).

SILK

Silk is not strictly speaking a part of arthropod cuticle, but it is produced by cells of ectodermal origin (with the questionable exception of the Malpighian tubules) which are homologous with the epidermal cells that secrete the cuticle. Also the silk of commerce has been studied so intensively that a consideration of this literature seems worth while. No attempt will be made to cite all the papers dealing with silk chemistry.

Silk, in the sense of a hard, rather strong filament spun by a living arthropod, is produced by a wide variety of species scattered throughout the phylum (Lesperon 37). In addition to spiders and the silkworm moth of commerce, silk is said to be produced by cutaneous glands in certain species of terrestrial Isopoda (Collinge 21, Huet 1883), pseudoscorpions (Barrows 25, Kew 29), Acarina (Blauvelt 45, Ewing 12), Symphyla (Michelbacher 38), and by representatives of at least the majority of orders of insects. It is spun from the maxillary (= labial, = salivary) glands by many larvae of Lepidoptera, Trichoptera, Siphonaptera, Hymenoptera, and by some species of Coleoptera, Corrodentia, Diptera, and Homoptera; it is spun from the

Malpighian tubules through the anus or from accessory genital tubules in certain species of Neuroptera and Coleoptera; and is spun by special glands on the tarsi by members of the peculiar little order Embiidina.

Diverse as the above sounds, it seems unquestionably incomplete (Packard 1898); for instance, an old paper records seven different types of silk glands in spiders (Apstein 1889, Millot 26a, b). Incidentally, it is not safe to assume that the possession of a cocoon necessarily means that the larva spins silk, for evidence has been presented suggesting that filaments in the cocoons of certain beetles may be derived from fungal hyphae incorporated into the cocoon (P. Schulze 27); neither is it safe to assume that a cocoon signifies threads are spun or even that these are nonchitinous (Picken *et al.* 47). A modern survey of silk-producing organs throughout the phylum is needed. Modern electron microscopy would probably be helpful but the early cursory examination of spider threads revealed only multiple cables, the individual strands having diameters of some hundreds of Ångstrom units (Anderson & Richards 42a).

Naturally the vast majority of chemical data deal with the silk of commerce, which is spun by larvae of the moth *Bombyx mori* (di Tocco 27). Raw silk as it is spun by the insects consists of approximately 75% fibroin and 25% sericin or silk gelatin (Abderhalden & Behrend 09, Balli 34). In processing for commerce, the water-soluble sericin is removed, leaving essentially pure fibroin. The material is spun by the insect in the form of a filament composed of two strands of fibroin cemented together by sericin (Frey-Wyssling 38, Ohara 33a, b). Each strand is continuous, fine, smooth, irregularly oval in cross section, and usually with faint longitudinal striations (Chamot & Mason 44, Ochmann 33). In the reservoir of the gland (seripterium) the components occur as a reasonably homogeneous colloidal solution which is soluble in hot water, 5–20% NaCl, and 5–10% Na_2CO_3.[2] It is nondialyzable and not coagulated by heat. Examination with an ultramicroscope reveals particles of various sizes. On standing, the solution gelatinizes, but does not spontaneously coagulate (Foa 12). Also the material does not show a crystalline X-ray diagram until after solidification (Brill 30, Ho *et al.* 44). Natural solidification occurs virtually instantaneously during spinning, but

[2] Injection of glycine and alanine labeled with radioactive carbon can be followed by the spinning of radioactive silk within 24 hours, but it is uncertain whether this represents true synthesis of fibroin or an exchange phenomenon (Zamecnik *et al.* 49).

apparently is not due simply to exposure to air or drying (van Lidth de Jeude 1878). The data, while not conclusive, suggest that stresses and shearing forces operate to distort and perhaps activate the molecules to give steric configurations necessary for these reactions (Foa 12, Ramsden 38). In line with this, it has recently been suggested that the water-soluble form is the native protein and that this becomes denatured by opening of the coiled molecules and by their subsequent aggregation in a β-keratin pattern (Fig. 9) (Coleman & Howitt 47).[3] (See also Kratky *et al.* 50.)

Sericin, which has no commercial value, has been studied less intensively than fibroin. As mentioned in the section on proteins, sericin is water soluble and characterized by the extremely high content of hydroxy amino acids, especially serine (Table 4). A recent study reports it as composed of two separable albumens which differ in physical and chemical properties (Ito & Komori 39, O. Lang 48a, b).

Fibroin is characterized chemically by its high content of glycine, alanine, and tyrosine (Table 4). No differences are shown by different races of *Bombyx mori,* but Tussah silk is different (Goldschmidt *et al.* 33). Fibroin is noteworthy as being a simple protein filament which gives the X-ray pattern of a fully extended polypeptide chain. The unit cells have eight amino acid residues, and dimensions of $6.46 \times 7.2 \times 15.43$ Å, with 4.4–6.1 Å between the chains (Kurt Meyer & Mark 28a, 30). A rather general X-ray scattering, however, shows that much amorphous material must be present in addition to the highly crystalline fraction (Goldschmidt & Strauss 30, Mark 43). Perhaps the amorphous material has the same chemical composition but a greater degree of disorder.

The highly crystalline fraction is largely composed of alternating glycine and alanine residues. Several arrangements have been suggested (M. Bergmann & Niemann 38, Levy & Slobodiansky 48). For instance:

$$-G-A-G-T-G-A-G-Ar-G-A-G-X-G-A-G-X-$$

or

$$-G-X-A-G-A-G-X-,$$

where G = glycine, A = alanine, T = tyrosine, Ar = arginine, and X = any other amino acid. In a space formula these chains fit to-

[3] It is tempting to speculate on the fact that arthropodin is found in the extended or β-configuration, whereas silk attains this only after being spun; but it should be remembered that whereas silk is known both before and after spinning, arthropodin is known only after solidification (or after extraction from a solidified condition).

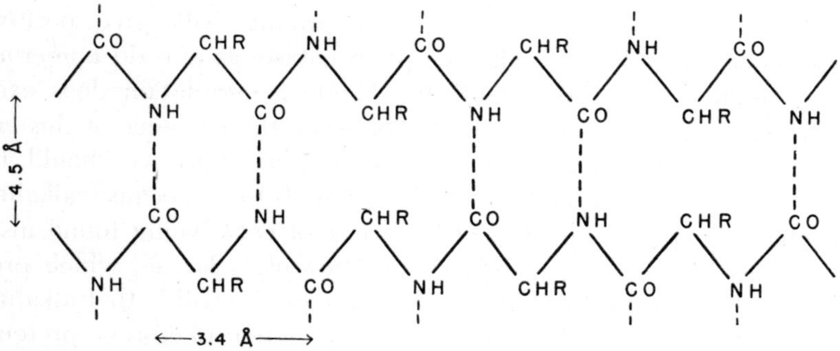

Figure 11. The configuration of silk fibroin according to the scheme proposed by Meyer and Mark. The R groups, which represent either $-CH_3$ or $-CH_2C_6H_4OH$, are to be visualized as extending in a plane perpendicular to that of the paper. The C=O bonds extend perpendicular to the fiber axis as shown by absorption of polarized infrared light.

gether in the simple manner shown in Figure 11. In contrast to other well-known fibrous proteins the side chains are of relatively little significance (Astbury & Bell 39). Fibroin is dissolved by cupriethylenediamine (Coleman & Howitt 47).

Several authors have pointed out the considerable degree of similarity among the simple X-ray diagrams given by cellulose, chitin, and silk (Herzog 24, Kurt Meyer & Mark 28a, 30, Trim 41b, Trogus & Hess 33). Trim (41b) suggests, that the sericin-fibroin complex of silk is analogous to the arthropodin-chitin complex of arthropod cuticle. If this were accepted, it would follow that structurally speaking, fibroin and chitin are interchangeable—a situation which would go far toward explaining those cases (especially tracheae) where structurally similar membranes may occur either with or without chitin. However, the suggestion is premature and likely oversimplified.

Great diversity is shown in the several estimates reported for the size of a silk fibroin molecule. The molecule is variously reported as consisting of at least forty amino acid residues (Kurt Meyer & Mark 28a), of having a molecular weight of 7,000 to 33,000 (Coleman & Howitt 47), or consisting of 1292–2592 residues with corresponding weights of approximately 108,500 to 270,700 (M. Bergmann & Niemann 38). All of the authors prefer the higher range in their estimates and think shorter chains are partially degraded. Treatment of a number of other properties of silk proteins is given in the recent papers by Bath and Ellis (41) and by Coleman and Howitt (47) (titration values, UV and infrared absorption, reducing activity, optical rotation, tryptic hydrolysis, etc.).

The secreting margins of cells that produce silk give positive histochemical reactions for alkaline phosphatase, as also do numerous other secretory cells (Bradfield 46). While a correlation does exist in both vertebrates and invertebrates between the presence of this enzyme and the secretion of fibrous proteins, it seems we should be conservative in interpretation at the present time because alkaline phosphatases are present in such a variety of cells, being found also, for instance, in the salivary glands of *Drosophila* larvae, which produce no silk (Krugelis 46). It is, of course, quite possible that alkaline phosphatases may be concerned in the production of fibrous proteins without necessarily any macroscopic fiber being produced.

CHAPTER 8

Polyphenols and Enzymes

POLYPHENOLS

Polyphenols and their corresponding quinone derivatives have recently come into great prominence following the demonstration by Pryor (40a, b) of their role in hardening as well as darkening of the cuticle. That they played a role had been suggested earlier by Schmalfuss and Barthmeyer (31). Orthodihydroxyphenols are readily demonstrated in arthropod cuticle by the nonspecific but convenient argentaffin reaction[1] or more specifically by the ferric chloride test.[2] The argentaffin test (Fig. 64) has now been applied to a wide variety of insects (Broussy 33, Dennell 46, 47b, Kuwana 40, Lafon 41b, c, Wigglesworth 45, 47a, b, 48b) as well as to crustacea (Dennell 47b) and ticks (Lees 47). It seems reasonably safe, then, to predict that this reaction will be generally found positive throughout the Arthropoda.

Since the reaction involves the deposition of metallic silver, it results in a brown or black deposit (depending on the strength of the reaction), which may be visible either microscopically or macroscopically. In some cases where only a diffuse light browning is visible under the light microscope, the electron microscope reveals microdeposits (Fig. 64B) which are beyond the resolving power of the

[1] The argentaffin reaction involves the reduction of metallic silver from the complex ammoniacal silver nitrate (Lison 36). The reagent is prepared by adding dropwise a solution of NH_4OH to a 5% solution of $AgNo_3$ until a cloudy precipitate just begins to form. More of the 5% $AgNo_3$ solution is then added, sufficient just to dissolve the precipitate. The ammonia should be added carefully because only a rather small amount is required. Specimens are treated for some hours or days, with or without previous fixation in one of the usual histological fluids. Thorough washing should be given in distilled water after treatment. Specimens may be counterstained with dyes of contrasting color. In addition to polyphenols, the test may be positive for urates, some aldehydes, and adrenalin (Gomori 50).

[2] This test is not so readily obtained. The material, preferably an extract, when treated with a dilute solution (e.g., 1%) of $FeCl_3$ turns green; on addition of a dilute solution of Na_2CO_3 the green turns to red (Lison 36).

light microscope (Richards unpubl.). The reaction is not well enough understood to say whether or not this is to be interpreted as meaning that the enzyme reaction is restricted to equally minute, closely spaced, centers.

At least in blowfly larvae the polyphenol appears to be derived from tyrosine of the blood. This is suggested, for instance, by the rise in tyrosine content of the blood just prior to pupation and its subsequent decrease at pupation, when considerable amounts of polyphenol are being added to the cuticle (Dennell 47a, Fraenkel & Rudall 47). Dr. Fraenkel has given me permission to say that he has similar data for adult *Tenebrio* (unpublished). Quite likely this will be found to be the general source, although one can hardly rule out the tyrosine of the cuticle itself. An older paper (Broussy 33) records o-dihydroxyphenol granules in the epidermal cells of a cricket (the author considering them melanin precursors).

Tyrosine, which is p-hydroxyphenylalanine, is capable of being oxidized through a series of intermediate steps to 3, 4-dihydroxybenzoic acid (protocatechuic acid) presumably through the series of stages shown in Figure 12. The first of these, 3, 4-dihydroxyphenylalanine ("Dopa"), was postulated by Onslow (23, 25) and isolated by Schmalfuss *et al.* shortly thereafter (Przibram & Schmalfuss 27, Raper 26, Schmalfuss *et al.* 26, 29, Spitzer 26). The same group later isolated the acetic acid derivative (Schmalfuss *et al.* 33, 35), and the other stable intermediates have recently all been isolated and identified (Hackman *et al.* 48, Pryor *et al.* 46, 47). Isolation and identifications were made from extracts of cuticle of beetles, grasshoppers, and flies, as well as moth cocoons (Brecker & Winkler 25, Przibram 22, 24, Sciacchitano 33, Spitzer 26), but no one source has yet supplied more than two of the stages.[3] Presumably the entire series of stages will be passed through by those species possessing the benzoic acid derivative, but there is at present no reason to assume that the reactions proceed as far as this in all species, or even that it must proceed in the manner diagrammed in Figure 12.

Although tyrosine and tyrosinase are both present in insect and spider blood (Dennell 47a, Millot & Jonnart 33), and give rise to the blackening that occurs on exposure to air, they do not normally react until the ontogenetically correct time. The reasons for this are an

[3] These compounds are highly unstable and react with proteins readily. Accordingly only minute amounts are to be expected to be present at any particular moment, and no significance is to be attached to the fact that the entire series has not been isolated from one species yet.

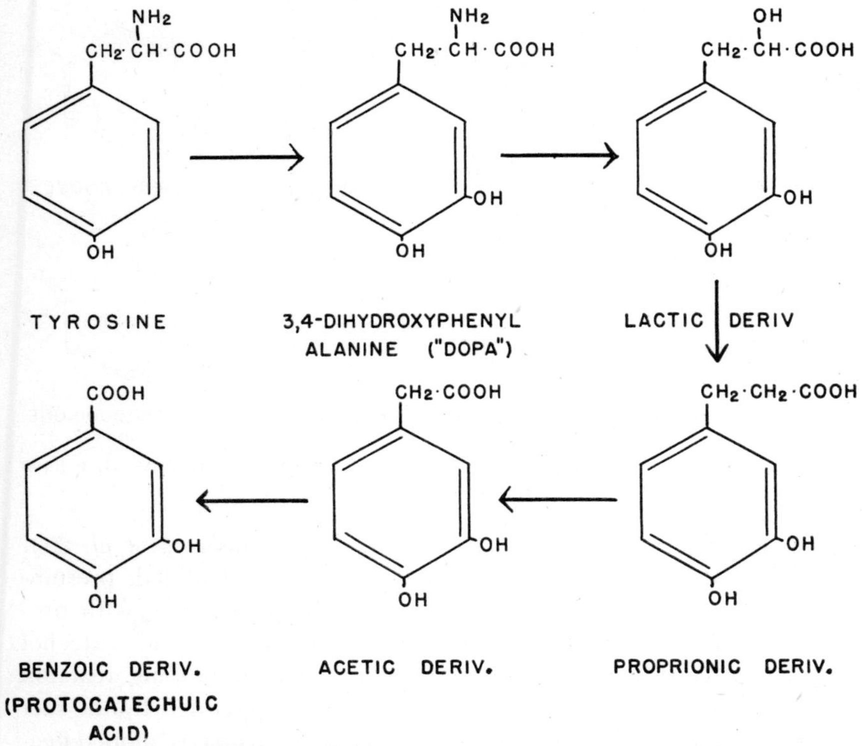

Figure 12. Structural formulae for tyrosine and the series of stable derivatives which have been found in arthropod cuticles.

interesting problem in metabolism. Dennell (49a) has recently obtained evidence that tyrosinase is inhibited by a dehydrogenase system which acts by lowering the redox potential below the point at which tyrosinase can act. An escape from this inhibition (= lowering of the reducing power of the blood) by release of the puparium-formation hormone automatically results in initiation of this oxidation sequence. The observation that hardening and darkening is inhibited by enforced physical exertion (digging) could be reconciled with this hypothesis (Fraenkel 35a).

The dihydroxyphenols require oxidation to the corresponding quinones before reacting with the protein chains to harden and darken the cuticle (Pryor 40a, b). Presumably this would involve a stepwise oxidation through corresponding semiquinones [4] with molecular oxy-

[4] A simplified treatment of two-step oxidation involving semiquinones is given by Michaelis (46b, 49). More technical treatments are also available (LuValle & Goddard 48, Michaelis 46a, Roman 38).

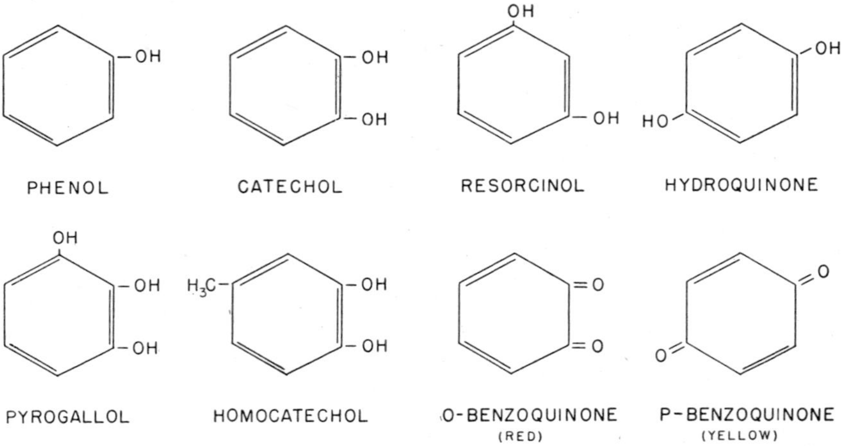

Figure 13. Structural formulae for some of the artificial substrates that have been used or tested in studies on sclerotization.

gen being utilized (Gortner 11a, Onslow 16, Schmalfuss *et al.* 39). The effective quinone has not been isolated and identified, presumably because it promptly becomes bound through reacting with protein chains. However benzoquinone, hydroquinone, and catechol (Fig. 13) have been used to simulate the normal tanning reaction (Fraenkel & Rudall 47). Specific differences are suggested by the fact that while benzoquinone is generally effective, Dopa is more effective with some species and catechol with others (Fraenkel & Rudall 47, Gomori 50). It is interesting in this connection that certain species of beetles actually secrete either benzoquinone or ethylbenzoquinone (Alexander & Barton 43, Hackman *et al.* 48, Moreau 31), and an old paper records the secretion of quinones by a millipede (Phisalix 00).

TYROSINASE

The best known of the enzymes found in arthropod cuticle is the tyrosinase system associated with the hardening and darkening processes. The enzyme system is found in high concentration in the integument of various arthropods, in mushrooms, and in higher plants. The concentration is much lower in other invertebrate animals, and very low in vertebrates and certain invertebrates (Bhagvat & Richter 38). Most of the chemical work with arthropod material has been done with preparations from beetle larvae and grasshopper eggs. As far as one can determine from the existing data, essential similarity exists between the enzymes from plants and arthropods; accordingly it is expedient to consider data derived from the more commonly used plant sources.

Unfortunately the enzyme chemists are not in agreement. Two divergent schools of thought exist.[5] One of these, favored in the United States, thinks that there is a single copper protein entity or complex which has at least two separate activities: (1) the oxidation of monohydric phenols to o-dihydric forms, and (2) the oxidation of these o-dihydric phenols to corresponding quinones. A current theory in relation to this point of view is that tyrosinase catalyzes the oxidation of monohydric phenols only when activated by simultaneously oxidizing an o-dihydric phenol (Behm & Nelson 44). Perhaps the same enzyme system accomplishes the deamination of tyrosine and the stepwise replacement of the alanine group by a carboxyl group, but no relevant data are available for arthropods. The other view, favored in England, is that there are at least two distinct enzymes: (1) tyrosinase, which acts on monohydric phenols, and (2) polyphenol oxidase, which performs the second step in the oxidation sequence (Keilin & Mann 38). Both views are presented and critically discussed in the review by Nelson and Dawson (44). One of the reviews giving more historical coverage is that by Franke (40). Actually, whichever of these points of view is accepted seems to the present author to make little difference for the analysis of available data on arthropods. For convenience, the arthropod data will be treated here under a single heading.[6]

Tyrosinase is a copper-protein compound which is inhibited by copper poisons (KCN, CO, phenylthiourea, diethyldithiocarbamate, etc.) (Allen & Bodine 41). At least in the grasshopper eggs it is said to exist in or arise from an inactive form called protyrosinase (Allen *et al.* 42, 43, Bodine *et al.* 41a, b, 43, 44, 45). This inactive system can be activated by heat, mechanical shaking, certain concentrations of the salts of heavy metals, detergent solutions, etc., and the method of activation has some effect on at least the heat stability of the enzyme formed. Also tyrosinase from genetically different beetles (*Tenebrio*) produces somewhat different pigments with the same substrate (Schuurman 37), but the significance of this is open to

[5] Danneel (43, 46) recognizes three separate enzymes, but there are good reasons for thinking that at least a third enzyme is unnecessary (Mason 48a, b).

[6] Phenol oxidases can be localized by histochemical tests with the "Nadi" reagent (Dennell 47a). This reagent consists of a solution of dimethyl-p-phenylenediamine and α-naphthol. On oxidation it gives indophenol blue (Lison 36). Adequate controls with appropriate enzyme inhibitors are required for interpretation because other oxidases and even o-quinones give a positive reaction.

question because of the possible influence of contaminants (Nelson & Dawson 44). Tyrosinase is said to act upon adrenalin, tyrosine, phenol, catechol, m-cresol, p-cresol, homocatechol, pyrogallol, and Dopa. It does not act on hydroquinone (p-dihydroxyphenol), resorcinol, etc. (Fig. 13). As a general statement, tyrosinase acts on mono and ortho-dihydroxy phenols, but not on meta or para forms. The pH optimum lies between 6 and 8. Various other chemical properties are treated in the reviews cited above.

The distribution of tyrosinase within arthropod bodies has not been well investigated. It is present in blood, especially the blood cells (Bhagvat & Richter 38, Dennell 47a, Pinhey 30), in viscera (whatever is meant by that term), in the inner epicuticle (Dennell 47a, Wigglesworth 47b, 48b), and in the serosa of grasshopper eggs (Bodine & Allen 41b). By some mechanism, seemingly involving redox potential, the enzyme is prevented from working until the proper time (E. Becker 41, Dennell 47a, 49a, Heller 47, Kuwana 37, Robinson & Nelson 44).

The brown and black pigment patterns in arthropods are at least partly produced by tyrosinase activity. An extremely interesting point is that the enzyme appears to be distributed generally over the cuticle, and the localization of the melanization to be due to the local distribution of substrate (Danneel 43, Dennell 47a, Gortner 11b, Graubard 33, Henke 24, H. Onslow 16, Schlottke 38b, Tower 06b). This is the reverse of the usual reason for localized enzyme action. In some cases the resulting melanization is diffuse, perhaps to be interpreted as suggesting diffusion of substrate through the cuticle matrix; in other cases intensity around the pore canals suggests passage through those ducts (Fig. 40) (Kühn & Piepho 38). Experiments on wound healing support the logical assumption that local distribution of substrate is controlled by the underlying cells (Wigglesworth 40).

The picture of concomitant hardening and darkening presented above is the general one for noncalcified cuticles. Hard beetle elytra that are uncolored have been shown to be deceptive; the cuticle of the upper surface is soft and colorless, that of the lower surface is hard and dark (Pryor 48). However, at least as far as can be determined by superficial inspection, hard but uncolored cuticles occur, e.g., *Dixippus* and *Buthus* (Fraenkel & Rudall 47). The nature of this hardening remains to be investigated.

There are many older references, now of only historic interest, reporting that Dopa reactions are involved in the development of arthropod color pattern (Biedermann 1898, Dewitz 02a, b, c, 16, 21, Gessard 04, H. Onslow 16, Tower 06a).[7]

OTHER ENZYMES

It seems reasonable to suppose that there must be at least four important enzyme systems, which are responsible for the production respectively of chitin, arthropodin, waxes, and the phenol-quinone hardening system. The phenol-quinone system has already been treated, and no information at all is available concerning the steps leading to the production of arthropodin and waxes, not even on the question of whether the major stages occur in the epidermal cells or whether some fraction of the enzymic synthesis occurs in the cuticle after secretion from the cells.[8] The little information available on chitinases can be summarized rather briefly.

The data on chitinases all deal with the digestion of chitin or some of its degradation products. Since chitin and cellulose are both glycosides, and since β-glycosidases show less specificity than α-glycosidases (Fig. 3), it has been suggested that chitinase and cellulase may be identical (Baldwin 47). This view does not seem to be in agreement with existing data. Digestive fluids from snails will digest both cellulose and chitin (Karrer 30, Karrer *et al.* 29, 30), but these conglomerate digestive mixtures can be fractionated either by chemical means (Grassman *et al.* 34) or by chromatographic adsorption (Zechmeister *et al.* 38, 39a, b, c) to give components with enhanced activity on one or another of the substrates employed. At least two enzymes have been shown: (1) a true chitinase which is not adsorbed on bauxite columns and which attacks chitin and a partial degradation product called chitodextrin, and (2) a chitobiase which is adsorbed on a bauxite column and which attacks only low molecular weight substrates. The preparation with greatest activity on chitodextrin is almost inactive toward cellulose and cellodextrin. Also many of the chitinovorous bacteria (p. 55) are inactive against cellulose (Hock 41, Stanier 47, Zobell & Rittenberg 37).

The enzymes in snail digestive fluids have a pH optimum of 5.2 when acting on chitin and 4.4–4.5 when acting on chitosan (Karrer

[7] Tower (06b) proposed the term chitase for the enzyme responsible for development of pigmentation. The term was never adopted by other workers.

[8] For waxes, the cytological evidence (p. 166) suggests synthesis in the cytoplasm of dermal or tegumental glands and subsequent pouring out over the surface of the cuticle, but the available cytological data cannot be interpreted in any precise chemical terms.

& Hoffman 29). The enzymes in this snail juice will attack chitin, chitosan, and reacetylated chitosan, but show specificity to the extent that they will not attack the formyl, proprionyl, butyryl, or benzoyl derivatives (Karrer & White 30). The bacterial enzymes have not been fractionated, but it is recorded that the bacterial action yields NH_3, organic acids, and reducing substances (Hock 41).

There are papers in the literature dealing with the metabolic fate of glucosamine and acetylglucosamine in vertebrates (Kawabe 34, Watanabe 36). There are also papers dealing with the enzymic decomposition of glucosamine, notably its deamination (Lutwak-Mann 41) and the splitting into two 3-carbon fragments (Kawakami 34).

A review of the occurrence of cellulase and chitinase in the digestive fluids of invertebrates is given by Yonge (38a). (See also Chapter 6.)

Only one paper has been found dealing with the enzymic properties of exuvial fluid;[9] this deals with the silkworm (Hamamura *et al.* 40). Since this paper is written entirely in Japanese, it may profitably be abstracted in some detail even though the present author was not particularly impressed. Finding it difficult to obtain exuvial fluid directly, these authors extracted shed skins with water and assumed that they thereby obtained the material that composes the exuvial fluid. Tests on their extracts are said to demonstrate the presence of a protease (casein substrate), amylase (starch substrate), and invertase (sucrose substrate). They report negative results in tests for lipase and tyrosinase. In a second section they report the identification of glucosamine in their extracts, and on a basis of increasing glucosamine concentration with time, report the presence of chitinase which they say has a pH optimum of 8.5 and a temperature optimum of 50° (not clear whether F. or C.). A better job than this is clearly needed.

PHOSPHATASES

One would very much like to know whether phosphorylation is involved in the production of cuticle, especially the polymerization

[9] This is the fluid found between the old and new cuticle of an arthropod approaching a molt. It presumably contains the digestion products from the major portion of the old cuticle plus the enzyme mixture that brought about this digestion. Dr. C. M. Williams informs me (in correspondence) that they have data showing that chitinase and proteinase are present in the exuvial fluid only rather late in the molting cycle. Clearly, this fluid is being secreted and resorbed more or less continuously (p. 230); accordingly it is not surprising that its composition varies with stages of the cycle.

of chitin. Phosphorus is absent from arthropodin (Trim 41b), and has seldom been mentioned in papers dealing with the chemistry of noncalcified cuticles. Perhaps one should not expect phosphorylation to be involved in the polymerization forming chitin – at least, the well-known phosphorylases are active with α-glucose-1-P, but inactive with β-glucose-1-P (Fig. 3).

It has been suggested that the alkaline phosphatase demonstrated histochemically (Gomori 50) in the salivary or silk glands is related to the production of fibrous protein (moth larva and spider) (Bradfield 46, Day 49b). This would not be surprising. However, there is a recent paper which requires confirmation and explanation. In the crayfish a strong histochemical phosphatase reaction is reported in the outer part of the soft cuticle (= insect exocuticle), and this is more intense in premolt specimens than in those at the time of molting (Kugler & Birkner 48). No reaction is obtained in the thick inner parts of the cuticle, and owing to sectioning difficulties no data were obtained for the period when the cuticle was calcified.[10] Even if this paper is correct, it still contains no suggestion as to the role the enzyme may be playing. Only negative tests for alkaline phosphatases have been obtained from insectan cuticles (8 genera in 6 orders) (Day 49b, Richards unpubl.).

CARBONIC ANHYDRASE

One might reasonably suppose that carbonic anhydrase could be involved in calcification. Perhaps it is, but at least in the lobster this enzyme is no more abundant in cuticle than in internal tissues and shows no changes in concentration correlated with the molting cycle (Maloeuf 40).

[10] Perhaps to be related to the presence of a phosphatase is the report that phosphorus is found in *Carcinus* cuticle in relatively higher concentration during the period of active cuticle deposition (80% inorganic) (Robertson 37).

CHAPTER 9

Mixed Polymers

There is nothing novel in the idea that mixed polymers occur in arthropod cuticle, but there are still so few significant data that even speculative discussion should be kept conservative. In a sense a protein molecule could be called a mixed polymer since it is composed of different amino acid residues. The term mixed polymer, however, is usually restricted to polymeric molecules containing more than one type of organic chemical, such as lipoproteins or glycoproteins. Since there are strong indications that mixed polymers are of considerable significance in arthropod cuticle, the subject will be discussed briefly in terms of the available data and the suggestions that have been made.

Pryor's (40a, b) scheme for the tanning of arthropodin by an orthoquinone to give rise to primary aromatic cross linkages, presumably between amino groups of adjacent protein chains (Pryor *et al.* 47), has been quite generally accepted (Fig. 14). The isotropy of the tanned protein, which he terms sclerotin, in the cockroach ootheca may mean that there are no parallel protein chains, but isotropy alone does not prove this. The absence of swelling or disruption in LiI and Na sulfide at pH 10 is evidence in favor of primary cross valences without sulfur bridges. Pryor also demonstrated that reactions comparable to those in the ootheca take place in insect cuticle, presumably implying that the cuticle consists of a simple mixture of chitin chains and tanned protein chains. However, other evidence indicates that linkages between chitin and protein molecules do actually occur, although we have as yet little idea about the nature of bonding involved. The process of hardening and darkening of insect cuticle is not yet known in precise chemical terms; accordingly it seems preferable to treat these phenomena in the section on developmental histology (p. 185).

The old view that arthropod cuticle is a chitinous matrix impregnated with other materials is gradually giving way to the view that

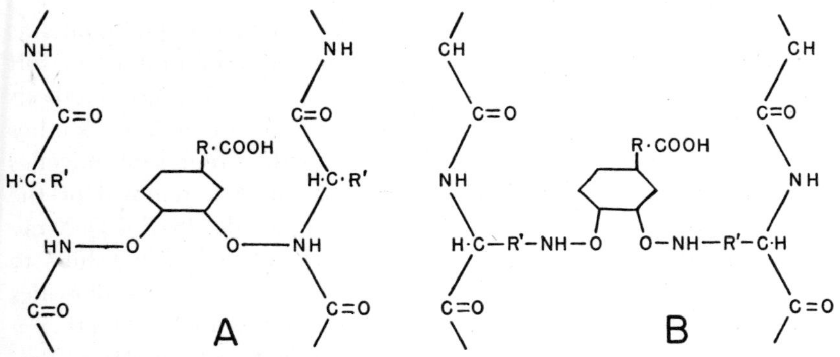

Figure 14. Pryor's two suggested schemes for possible methods of reaction in the sclerotization process.

A. Reaction of the quinone groups with imino groups of the main chain of adjacent protein molecules.

B. Reaction of the quinone groups with amino groups of side chains from adjacent protein molecules.

the cuticle is a mucopolysaccharide, that is, a glycoproteid resulting from the chemical combination of chitin and protein. This is not a new idea. A somewhat similar view was expressed by Berthelot in 1859 and is to be found in some other papers of the nineteenth century; it is also more or less implied in several later papers (Campbell 29, Evans 38b), and has recently been recognized in classifications by chemists (Karl Meyer 38, Stacey 43).

Three views of chitin-protein associations have been advanced in the past decade. Perhaps no one of these is correct, and certainly no one of them in unmodified form is adequate to cover all the diversities known. They do indicate trends of thought. Trim (41a, b) suggested, but without any real evidence, that possibly chitin crystallizes within a protein matrix from a homogeneous, fluid, polysaccharide-protein complex in a manner analagous to the crystallization of fibroin within a sericin matrix in silk (see p. 67). Richards (47) emphasized the important role of the protein component, which may or may not have chitin intimately associated with it. And Fraenkel and Rudall (47) suggested that the percentages of chitin and protein in soft cuticles were consistent with the view of alternating monolayers of chitin and protein.[1]

[1] Fraenkel and Rudall seem to postulate these alternating monolayers as successive secretion stages in which the postulated chitin monolayer acts as a mold or template for the deposition of a postulated protein monolayer, which in turn serves as a template for another chitin layer, etc. It is difficult to see how this could be rationalized with known cases of cuticle deposition at a distance from the secreting cells (blowfly larva, p. 185; *Donacia* cocoon, p. 175; etc.).

Looking over these and other papers, we can select four points as at least highly suggestive: (1) The vast majority of protein in soft cuticles can be separated from the chitin by relatively gentle methods (Fraenkel & Rudall 47). (2) Extensive electron microscope studies have showed that microfibers which presumably represent micelles are discernible only after treatments which effect a removal of the majority of the protein (Fig. 8) (Richards & Korda 48).[2] (3) X-ray diffraction patterns reveal a 33 Å spacing which on wetting shifts to 44 Å (Fraenkel & Rudall 47). And (4) the puparium of blowflies can be dispersed in LiCNS and reprecipitated without effecting a separation of the chitin and protein components (Trim 41b). Perhaps one should add here the recent report (Picken & Lotmar 50) that protein, as well as chitin, is oriented (rather than amorphous) in annelid chaetae.

Other points seem questionable, irrelevant, or beyond explanation at present. Thus it has been suggested both that there is a definite and important percentage relationship between chitin and protein (Fraenkel & Rudall 47) and that there is no constant percentage relationship, the chitin percentages ranging from zero to 60% (Richards 47b). Also it is recorded that while most of the protein is readily removed from soft cuticle by hot water, a certain percentage requires moderate treatment with hot alkali solutions, but it is not indicated by this alone whether the insolubility of the minor protein component is due to chitin-protein linkages or to a greater insolubility of this protein fraction (Trim 41b). Similar uncertainty is met in interpretation of the fact that whereas sclerotized bristles break irregularly, the same bristles split cleanly into fibrils after removal of the non-chitinous components by Diaphanol (Lees & Picken 45). The fact that benzoquinone will tan the protein in intact cuticles, but not extracted arthropodin, is provocative, but of uncertain significance (Fraenkel & Rudall 47). The role of sulfur bridges requires more study, but clearly the amount of S present is inadequate (Trim 41b) except possibly in *Limulus* (Lafon 43a). And, finally, points such as the diversity of chitin patterns seen by electron microscopy (Richards & Korda 48) and the low nitrogen values given by purified chitin (Fraenkel & Rudall 47, Lafon 43a, Richards 49, Thor & Henderson 40), are completely beyond satisfactory explanation at the present time. In a descriptive sense, Wigglesworth (48b) aptly suggests that

[2] Seemingly the fibrous felt of the "white cuticle" secreted as an inner egg shell by the embryonic serosa of grasshoppers will be an exception (Schutts 49), but this is scarcely to be called a typical cuticle.

the function of sclerotin in cuticle is to bind the chitin chains laterally, but this comparison to commercial plastics (Smith 43) may be only superficial.

Concerning the four selected points: X-ray diffraction studies show that treatment of the soft cuticles of blowflies with mild heat[3] or grinding induces reorientation in the sense of a great increase in the crystallinity of the chitin fraction (Fraenkel & Rudall 47). The visible microscopic changes seen in sections of soft cuticle of beetle larvae after cauterization (Lazarenko 28) suggest effects that may be entirely similar. One would not expect a mild heat treatment to affect a chitin micelle, and indeed electron microscope studies show that partly or more or less completely purified chitin matrices exhibit no effect from considerably greater heat treatments than the above (Richards & Korda 48). The simplest explanation appears to be that the chitin micelles offer a much more stable configuration, but that the cuticle is laid down in the relatively unstable chitin-protein association. When by mild heating the chitin-protein bond is broken or the chitin molecule sufficiently activated to escape from this bonding, the more stable chitin micelle is formed. One of the probable explanations of the 33 Å spacing observed in cuticle is that it represents the chitin-protein unit (Fraenkel & Rudall 47).

The electron microscope data on chitin micelles (Richards & Korda 48) can be rationalized in identically the same manner. These lines of evidence suggest a very weak bonding, such as one would expect from a moderate number of hydrogen bonds distributed along the molecules.

The fourth point, dispersion in LiCNS and reprecipitation without separation of the chitin and protein (Trim 41a, b), suggests a much stronger bond. In fact, one would expect this lithium salt at 170° C. to disrupt any bond less strong than a primary cross valence. The first three points were based on data derived from studies of soft cuticle; this fourth point is derived from data on a hard, sclerotized cuticle. Incidentally, in hard cuticles comparable to that of a puparium the formation of discrete chitin micelles was not found by electron microscopy (Richards & Korda 48). Also protein is not readily removed from sclerotized cuticles (Fraenkel & Rudall 47). The simplest tentative assumption appears to be that there is a weak bonding between chitin and protein chains in soft cuticle, but a very

[3] That is, mild heating in the sense a chemist would use the term. It is still heating beyond the thermal death point and accordingly does not represent a phenomenon that can occur in a living animal.

strong bonding in sclerotized cuticle. In both cases, some degree of chitin-protein bonding seems required to explain the available data.

There is another source of data commonly used in discussions of this subject, namely optical analyses. However, these seem to the present author ambiguous. It is routinely assumed that the increased birefringence attendant on purification of material such as chitin is due to the removal of materials which interfere (Lees & Picken 45). The nature of the interference is not known. Some authors have held the view that the nonchitinous components merely increase the randomness of chitin orientations and so result in an approach to statistical isotropy; removal of these components then leads to increased crystallinity and therefore to increased birefringence (Castle 36). Some other authors have preferred the view that the interstices between the chitin micelles are completely filled with another substance of similar refractive index (W. J. Schmidt 37a). The situation is further complicated by the fact that there is another possible interpretation which to the best of my knowledge has not appeared in the literature, namely, that the postulated chitin-protein polymer has only a low order of birefringence and that on removal of the protein the strong birefringence of the chitin micelles is substituted. Whatever is the correct explanation, there certainly seems to be too much ambiguity to draw deductions on this subject from optical data at the present time.

Nonchitinous membranes. Some mention should be made of those membranes that appear structurally similar to chitinous membranes and yet are consistently negative to chitin tests (Richards 47a, b). If we accept the tests as valid—which is not entirely certain—we have to face the fact that membranes, e.g., of tracheae, may appear similar by both light and electron microscopy and yet possess or not possess chitin (or have only a few per cent of chitin, Pepper & Hastings 43). Recalling that the crystal lattice spacings of chitin and arthropodin have been shown by X-ray diffraction studies to be nearly identical (p. 60) (Fraenkel & Rudall 47), one possibility is that a silklike crystallization (Trim 41b) occurs in cuticle with or without, or with only a little, chitin being present to be incorporated in the lattice. Alternatively, the chitin might be conceived as dispersing under the treatments employed, a view that violates our concept of chitin. Obviously only a beginning has been made in analyzing cuticle, and only enough of a beginning to indicate a system of great complexity and diversity.

Lipoproteins. The fact that the lipid epicuticle consists of a layer of presumably highly oriented wax molecules attached to the underlying protein layer and overlain by numerous layers of free wax molecules seems well established (Beament 48b, Dennell 45, Lees 47, Pryor 40b, Wigglesworth 47b). This apparently includes the "cuticulin layer" of Wigglesworth. The nature of the bonding involved is unknown, but seems probably diverse (Dennell 45). The evidence consists of identification of extracted waxes plus demonstration that treatment of cuticles with the wax solvents used for extraction does not prevent a surface layer from staining with black sudan B or giving globules with a mixture of concentrated HNO_3 plus $KClO_3$. Some deductions can also be made from permeability data (see p. 300). Data cover various insects (Beament 48b, Dennell 45, Pryor 40b, Wigglesworth 48b), ticks (Lees 47), and decapod crustacea (Lafon 48). If it is true that spiders lack a waxy epicuticle, they would presumably have no lipoprotein layer (Browning 42) but this report has been contested (Cloudsley-Thompson 50a, Sewell unpubl.).

Calcified cuticles. A number of authors have suggested that the calcium in calcified cuticles is partly present in complex organic associations, but no strong evidence is to be found in support of this suggestion (Biedermann 01, Drach & Lafon 42, Pantel 19). The subject warrants further study because of biological interest in the report that the first part of calcareous cuticles is a chitin-protein complex comparable to that in insects but that subsequent development represents the simultaneous secretion and polymerization of chitin, lime, and lower amounts of protein (Dennell 47b, Lafon 43b). (See p. 105.)

CHAPTER 10

Pigments

For various reasons the subject of pigment chemistry is going to receive only restricted treatment here. Even if the author had adequate background to treat this subject critically, which he certainly does not have, there is still considerable uncertainty in many of the papers as to whether the pigment dealt with is located in the cuticle or located in some internal organ and seen through the cuticle. With very few exceptions the older papers are of only historic interest now, and even many of the recent ones seem of questionable value. Certainly we can add only hearty agreement to Uvarov's (48) rebuke: ". . . it is to be hoped that such research will be undertaken by highly trained biochemists in well equipped laboratories. Attempts made by entomologists at identifying pigments by a few simple reactions, followed by giving them long but meaningless names, should be discouraged as they are more likely to introduce confusion than clarity." One does not have to read many papers before realizing how this condemnatory remark came to be made.

There are a number of reviews, the older ones cited only for historic interest, which should be consulted for comprehensive treatment of the literature: Hagen (1883), von Fürth (04), Tower (06b), Biedermann (14b), Verne (23, 26), Prochnow (27), Balss (27), Lederer (35, 40), Becker (37a), Brecher (38), F. Mayer and Cook (43), Timon-David (47), and Wigglesworth (49). The recent review by Timon-David seems good, but in using it one needs to watch for typographical errors, especially in the structural formulae. For a comprehensive bibliography the above reviews should be consulted; only a selected few references will be cited below.

MELANINS

In a broad sense, the term melanin is used for any dark brown or black pigment which is amorphous, highly stable, and insoluble in the usual solvents. Transmission curves are nearly straight lines for both the granular vertebrate melanins and the diffuse, or perhaps continuous, insect melanins; in other words, the pigment absorbs comparable percentages of all wave lengths (colors) (H. S. Mason 48b, Merker 39, Sumner & Doudoroff 43). Several classifications of this heterogeneous assemblage have been proposed (Jacobsen 34, Mason 48a). In Mason's classification the melanin pigments in arthropod cuticles would have to go under the heading of native animal melanins. These are noncarotenoid, nonhemic, nonfuscinoid, and capable of being decolorized by hydrogen peroxide. Mason (in correspondence) feels that all melanins form a melanoprotein section under the chromoproteins. However, melanin from other sources such as skin, hair (Einsele 37), and the ink sac of squids occurs in or from intracellular granules, whereas the brown or black pigments of arthropod cuticle are, at least usually, dispersed or continuous throughout the cuticle matrix.[1]

Perhaps the difference between granular and dispersed melanin is a fundamental one, but the present author is inclined to think not. Selecting from accepted data, we can list that (1) synthetic and cuticular melanins are nongranular, whereas cellular melanins are granular; (2) melanins are insoluble and so would be expected to stay where they are formed; (3) cellular enzyme reactions are commonly associated with or at the surface of granules (Danielli 45); (4) the cuticular components are secreted from the epidermal cells and then melanin is formed as part of the sclerotization process; and (5), more specifically, the oxidase enzyme system involved in sclerotization is distributed over the entire cuticle surface, and local action producing sclerites is due to the localization of substrate (Danneel

[1] Granules of guanine have been recorded in some cuticles (Frick 36), various pigment granules in crustacean cuticles (Balss 27), and unidentified granules in *Dixippus* (Fraenkel & Rudall 47). But the common "melanin" of arthropod cuticles is not detectably granular whether examined by ordinary microscopy or by special methods such as phase-contrast, dark field, polarized light, or electron microscopy. One can find numerous reports of melanin granules (in the epidermal cells or cuticle), but the identification is at least usually presumptuous and seems never to have been convincingly demonstrated. Thus Broussy (33) and Paillot and Noël (26) recorded specifically staining granules in epidermal cells of a caterpillar; Dennell (47a) has recorded granules in puparia in addition to the continuous colored matrix; Goldberg and de Meillon (48) have recorded melanin granules as being normally present in mosquito larvae but absent from individuals reared on a diet deficient in tyrosine and phenylalanine; Kühn and Piepho (38) found both granular and continuous pigment in "pupation spots" resulting from hormone experiments on ligatured larvae (Fig. 36); etc. Modern chemical work is needed.

43, Dennell 47a, Gortner 11b, Graubard 33, Henke 24, H. Onslow 16, Schlottke 38b, Tower 06a, b).

On the basis of the above five points, the author accepts the hypothesis, already proposed by Kopac (48) for vertebrate melanins, that the granularity of melanin, when found, is a by-product of the melanin granules being formed on or in cytoplasmic granules, where presumably the enzyme is located, whereas dispersed enzymes give nongranular melanin. However, there is no proof of this hypothesis, and other differences make alternative hypotheses possible. Tyrosine is not only oxidized to a quinone but is also deaminated prior to its participation in the sclerotization process in arthropods (Fig. 12). This is well shown by the fact that addition of the tanning agent does not add nitrogen to the cuticle (Fraenkel & Rudall 47). At least some of the better-known synthetic melanins involve a condensation through the amino group to give an indole ring (Fig. 15) (Fox 47, H. S. Mason 48b). These indole forms can then polymerize to give melanin pigments which are soluble in ethylene chlorhydrin (Lea 45). In arthropods the deaminated tanning agents cannot form indole rings;[2] they react with protein chains (and conceivably chitin chains) to give rise to a hardened and darkened matrix. An attempt to isolate an unchanged melanin pigment from this complex has not met with success (Fraenkel & Rudall 47), but it does not seem safe to assume that no indole melanins are present; there might be some "true melanin" in addition to "sclerotin" (Waddington 41).

One thing is clear: Unlike most of the compounds treated in preceding sections, there are good reasons for saying that melanins are not the same throughout the animal kingdom. What to call a melanin in arthropods is an open question. One could readily define the term in such a way as to eliminate the dark brown pigments associated with sclerotization. If the diffuse brown and black colors found in various groups of arthropods are to be called melanins, as the present author is inclined to call them, then the definition of melanin must include polymers formed from enzymic derivates of polyphenols combined with protein chains. As such the melanin is an integral part of the cuticle rather than a pigment found in the cuticle.

From discussions with various biologists and chemists I know that some will accept the point of view expressed above but others definitely will not. An obvious alternative is to distinguish between those

[2] Since the above was written, Kikkawa (50) has reported that indoles injected into moth pupae can be recovered as such; they are not converted to chromogen.

melanins that do and those that do not contain indole rings, and perhaps further between those that are polymerized indoles and those that are chromogens linked with protein. There simply are not yet enough data to say what view will most satisfactorily classify the melanins of arthropods (and other animals).[3] It would seem that chemical studies on cuticles such as those obtained in hormone studies by Kühn & Piepho (38) might be illuminating; as perhaps a nutritional approach might be (Goldberg and de Meillon 48). Studies such as those by Hasebroek seem to be unhelpful (21–26).

NONMELANIN PIGMENTS

It does not seem entirely certain that all of the pigments to be mentioned below actually occur in cuticle. With butterfly and moth scales one can be sure the pigment is either in the cuticle of the scale or in the specialized epidermal cell that forms the scale, but when, as commonly happens, one extracts a pigment in small quantity from whole wings, it is not really known that the pigment even comes from some part of the integument. Presence of the pigment in exuvia is presumptive evidence (Chauvin 39b) but should be verified. Caution is called for in accepting recorded localizations.

Carotenoids. Various derivatives of carotene form yellow or red pigments in arthropods. They are commonly called lipochromes because of their solubility in fat solvents, and considering this solubility it is not surprising that they may appear granular. A-carotene differs from β-carotene in the position of one double bond (Fig. 15), γ-carotene differs in the opening of one of the terminal rings, lycopene differs in having both rings open, luteine differs in having an hydroxyl group on each ring (Fig. 15). Astaxanthin is a common carotenoid of arthropods; it differs from β-carotene in having two keto groups (one on the bottom carbon of each ring as drawn in Figure 15) and two hydroxyl groups (on carbon atoms adjacent to the keto groups); therefore it is 5-5′ dihydroxy–4-4′ diketo-β-carotene. On oxidation,

[3] Tyrosinase in insect blood is normally held in check by the low redox potential (Dennell 49a), but on exposure to air gives darkening. It is not safe to assume that the chemical steps involved in melanization of blood are the same as or even similar to those involved in melanization of cuticle. For instance, there is good evidence for saying tyrosine is deaminated as well as oxidized to give o-dihydric phenols for cuticle tanning, but it is not known what happens to tyrosine in blood melanization. If the tyrosine were not deaminated, it might condense to give indole rings which polymerize to black pigments, or it might form melanin in other ways. No more than a warning to be cautious seems possible at present.

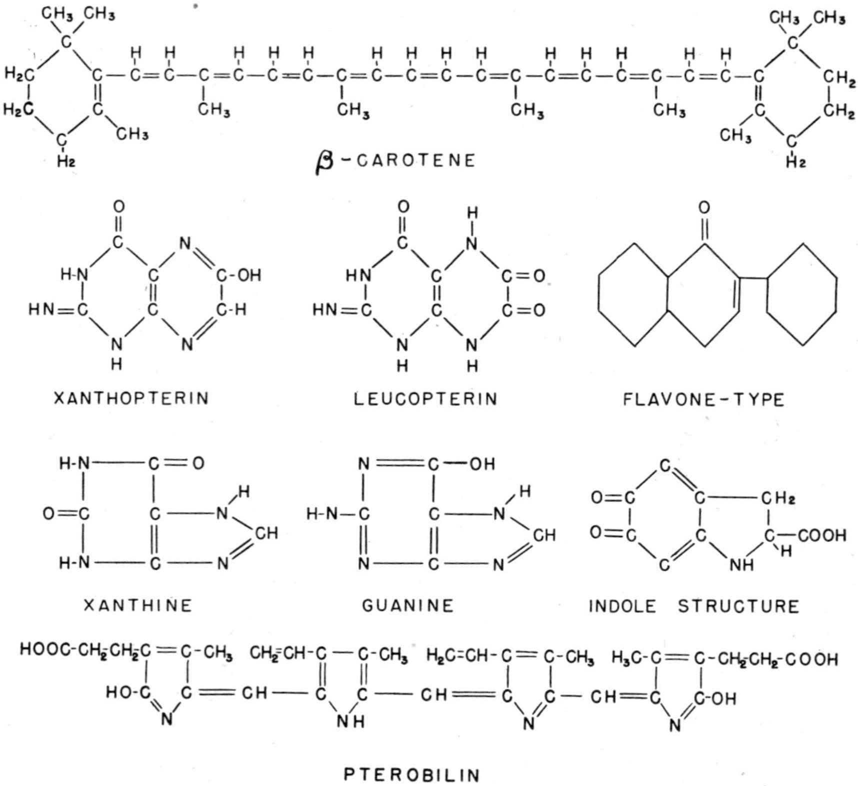

Figure 15. Structural formulae for some representative pigments recorded from arthropod cuticles.

the blue astaxanthin is changed to the red astacin by oxidation of the hydroxyl groups to give tetraketo-β-carotene (as occurs when a crab or lobster turns red on being cooked). The carotenoids have been reviewed in considerable detail by Lederer (35), by F. Mayer and Cook (43), and by Fox (47). More than sixty carotenoids have been described; these belong to four general types: hydrocarbons (carotene), ketonic or hydroxylic derivatives (xanthophylls), carotenoid acids, and xanthophyll esters.

It is presumed that in at least most cases the carotenoids are derived from plant sources (but the food may contain carotenoids without the animal's having these pigments [Beatty 49]). Thus grasshoppers are reported to have normally both β-carotene and astaxanthin (Goodwin 49, Goodwin and Shrisukh 49, Manunta 42b,

Okay 49), but to have no carotenoids if reared on a diet free of carotenes (Chauvin 39a). However, the astaxanthin must be synthesized or at least produced from another carotenoid because it is not a normal constituent of the diet (Goodwin and Shrisukh 48). The relative percentages of β-carotene and astaxanthin vary at different stages of the life cycle (perhaps related to nutrition), and some specimens have only astaxanthin (Goodwin 49, Grayson & Tauber 43). Parasitized individuals also have only astaxanthin.

Astaxanthin has also been recorded from a grass mite (Manunta 39, 48), in addition to being very common in higher crustacea. True carotenes, so common in insects, are sometimes found in crustacea (Beatty 49, F. A. Brown, Jr., 34, Verne 23). It is scarcely surprising that carotenoids are found in cocoons of the silkworm (Jucci 36, Oku 35) and in bugs that feed on plants (Henke 24). A predaceous bug, *Perillus,* is said to derive the carotene found in its cuticle from blood of the Colorado potato beetle, which in turn gets it from the potato plants (Palmer and Knight 24a).

Carotenoid-albumens. According to recent papers, several different carotenoids can serve as prosthetic groups with either albumens or globulins to give blue or green chromoproteins (Danielli 45, Junge 41, Okay 47a, 49). Perhaps this is quite common (Goodwin and Shrisukh 49).

Anthoxanthines and anthocyanins. These flower pigments, which have a flavone-type structure (Fig. 15), supply the red or white pigments for a number of insect groups (dos Passos 48, Ford 41, Glaser 18, Palmer & Knight 24b). It is said that white anthoxanthines turn reversibly yellow when exposed to ammonia vapors, and that this can be used as a test even in old museum specimens.

Pterines. The pterines are fluorescent pigments with a structure similar to that of purines. A detailed review is given by Becker (37a) as well as by Timon-David (47). These pigments are found in various insect groups, but are best known and have been most studied in the wing scales of Pierid butterflies. Red, orange, yellow, and white pterines are known, the lighter colors being thought to be oxidized forms of the darker ones. Xanthopterin (yellow) and leucopterin (white) have been isolated and identified (Fig. 15). Erythropterin (red) and chrysopterin (yellow-orange), as well as some greyish white pigments, have not been determined structurally. Until recently, especially when they were still considered urates, these wing pigments were thought of as a type of storage excretion (see Hirata *et al.* 50).

In recent years, with their discovery in other groups of animals, as well as in bacteria, and particularly with the demonstration of a relationship between pterine metabolism and folic acid, more interest has developed in them.

It is reported that some pterines can be demonstrated by their turning purple on exposure to chlorine vapors for a few days (Ford 47a, b, Leclercq 50), but fluorophotometry is to be preferred when it can be used. As with the carotenes, chromatographic separation is feasible (Good and Johnson 49).

Purines. In a few cases xanthine, hypoxanthine, guanine (Fig. 15), isoguanine, and allantoin have been reported from arthropods, but it does not seem entirely certain that these were extracted from the integument except in the case of guanine granules in the cuticle of copepods, spiders, and ticks (Frick 36, Millot 26b, W. J. Schmidt 26). A review covering the animal kingdom is given by Peschen (39).

Pterobilin. Early workers, even in the nineteenth century, recognized that the wings of Pierid butterflies contained, in addition to the pterin pigments, a very small amount of a green pigment (assumed to be in the scales). This has been identified only recently—approximately 1,000,000 butterflies having been used for extraction (Fig. 15). This green pigment turns out to be related to biliverdin, one of the bile pigments resulting from the breakdown of haemoglobin in vertebrates (Wieland & Tartter 40). Its metabolic source is unknown.

Various other pigments recorded for arthropods. Flavins, anthraquinones, pyrroles, and kynurenin (tryptophane derivative found in eye pigments [Kikkiwa 41]) seem not to have been positively recorded from the cuticle or epidermal cells, although injection of kynurenin into pupae of genetically unpigmented *Ephestia* can result in adults whose progeny have pigmented integuments (Caspari 49). And several pigments have been recorded, some certainly from the integument, but not identified (Ford 42, 44a, b, Metcalf 43, W. J. Schmidt 41a).

Incidentally, pigmentary colors may develop or change after emergence of the adult (E. D. Burtt & Uvarov 44, Hamilton 36, Hammond 28, Uvarov 33).

Cellular pigments. Numerous authors have recorded the presence of cytoplasmic granules of various colors in epidermal cells (Broussy 33, Browning 42, Chauvin 41, Franceschini 38, Hollande 43, Knight 24, P. Schulze 13c, Wigglesworth 33, 48b); also a number of authors have recorded granules in the cytoplasm of cells which secrete the tracheal lining (H. J. A. Koch 36, Kolbe 1893, Purser 15, Remy 25a, Riede 12, Wolf 35), in some cases even postulating that these subserve a respiratory function.[4] In a few insects the pigment granules in the epidermal cells are capable of being moved under hormonal influence to produce transient color changes, or altered by pigment replacement (Giersberg 28, Janda 36, Priebatsch 33, Przibram & Brecher 22, Schleip 10), but this type of color change is known only in the phasmids among insects. In a few cases these have been identified as carotenoids; in other cases the identification is unknown or uncertain.

A separate and voluminous literature deals with the chromatophores of crustacea. Various pigment granules in these cells are capable of being moved under hormonal control. However, the chromatophores are subepidermal and accordingly not a part of the integument. For details consult the reviews by Fuchs (14), Kleinholz (42), and F. A. Brown, Jr. (44). Some authors have referred to chromatophores in insects (Dupont-Raabe 49, Hadorn & Frizzi 49, W. J. Schmidt 20), but the subject has not elicited much interest.

[4] It is only in the paper by H. J. A. Koch (36) that evidence is presented for the power of reversible oxidation and reduction of these cellular granules. This property, while interesting, does not prove a respiratory function.

CHAPTER 11

Lipids

The cuticular lipids, or at least those about which chemical information is available, are all waxes,[1] but there is some evidence for the presence of sterols. That insects produce wax in the sense of secretion, for instance, beeswax, has been known since antiquity. However, the fact that waxes form an important part of arthropod cuticle is a fairly recent finding. It was recognized in the nineteenth century (Odier 1823) that the outermost layer of arthropod cuticle is a thin sheet of highly refractile material, but the lipid nature of this thin layer was not convincingly demonstrated until the work of Kühnelt (28a, c). Since then waxy layers at or near the outer surface of the cuticle have been recorded from an extremely wide assortment of arthropods, including insects, crustacea, and some arachnids (Alexander *et al.* 44a, b, Dennell 46, Eder 40, Kuwana 40, Lafon 41b, c, 48, Lees 47, Ludwig 48, Rosedale 46, W. J. Schmidt 39b, Schulz 30, Schulz & Becker 31a, b, Thomas 44, Wigglesworth 33, 42c, 45, 48b, Yonge 32). The waxes may be either white or yellow and may or may not give good crystals. As some of these surveys cover many species, obviously wax layers are to be expected in the majority of arthropods. In locusts, cockroaches, and ixodid ticks, the wax is replaced by a grease which has not been studied chemically (Beament 48b, Dusham 18). Positive Liebermann-Burchardt reactions, indicating the presence of sterols, have been obtained for a number of insect species (Dennell 46, Kühnelt 28a, Bergmann 38). In a very few cases no lipid has been found: the larvae of the fly *Bibio* (Wigglesworth 45), a spider, *Tegenaria* (Browning 42), and the remarkable larvae of the petroleum fly, *Psilota petrolei*, which breeds in open oil pools in

[1] The term wax as used in chemistry does not refer to a material of lipid composition, which is solid at ordinary temperatures. The term fat is used for esters of fatty acids with glycerol. The term wax refers to esters in which the glycerol is replaced by some other alcohol. Paraffin hydrocarbons may also be included.

petroleum fields (Crawford 12, Pryor 40b, Thorpe 30b, 31). It seems probable that a sizable list of exceptions will be found.

All of the information concerning chemical structure deals with insect waxes, and almost all of it with waxes which are secreted in bulk rather than incorporated as a layer of the cuticle. The techniques available for studying wax chemistry prior to about 1930 are now known to have been so unreliable that earlier papers had best be forgotten (Schulz 22, Sundwik 1893–1911, etc.). As shown in the data

TABLE 5. COMPOSITION OF INSECT WAXES

Source	Composition (Saponified)	Authority
Bombyx mori (exuvia)	$C_{27} - C_{31}$ paraffins + $C_{26} - C_{30}$ esters of alcohols and acids	Bergmann 38
Adelges strobi (Chermes wax)	17-keto-n-hexatriacontanol and 11-keto-n-triacontanoic acid	Blount *et al.* 37
Coccus cacti (Cochineal wax)	15-keto-n-tetratriacontanol, n-triacontanoic acid, 13-keto-n-dotriacontanoic acid	Chibnall *et al.* 34
Coccus ceriferus (Chinese insect wax)	C_{26}, C_{28}, C_{30} alcohols and acids	Same as above
Psylla alni (Psylla wax)	Mixture acids and alcohols	Same as above
Beeswax	Even-numbered $C_{24}-C_{34}$ primary alcohols + N-fatty acids	Same as above
Wild beeswax (*Melipona*)	Even-numbered $C_{24}-C_{30}$ alcohols	Same as above
Apis dorsata (Ghedda wax)	Even-numbered $C_{24}-C_{30}$ alcohols + $C_{24} - C_{34}$ acids	Same as above
Bombus lapidarius (Bumblebee wax)	Uncertain mixture alcohols + paraffins	Same as above
Lac wax	Even-numbered $C_{26}-C_{36}$ primary alcohols + esters of $C_{30} - C_{34}$ n-fatty acids with $C_{30}-C_{36}$ primary alcohols	Same as above
Pemphigus xylostei	Mixture C_{33} acid + C_{34} alcohol	Schulz & Becker 31b
Apple wax	N-nonecosane, n-heptacosane, d-10-nonacosanol, n-hexacosanol (C_{26}), n-octacosanol (C_{28}), n-triacontanol (C_{30})	Chibnall *et al.* 31
Grass wax	Mostly hexacosanol (C_{26}), 1% tetracosanol	Pollard *et al.* 31

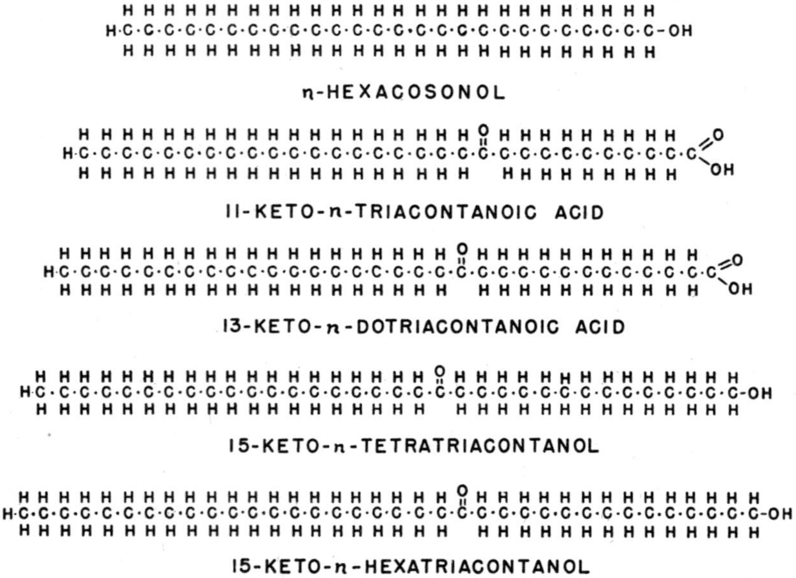

Figure 16. Structural formulae for alcohols and acids obtained from insect waxes (see Table 5).

summarized in Table 5, these insect waxes are usually esters of even-numbered primary alcohols with normal fatty acids, both of which have chain lengths of from C_{24} to C_{34-36} (Fig. 16). In a few cases paraffins are recorded. Ketonic alcohols, generally considered uncommon, have been found in several insect waxes. These determinations are not particularly different from ones made on plant waxes, a few values for which are also given in the table for comparative purposes.

In the one set available, the values for waxes extracted from the shed skins of silkworms, and so certainly representing true cuticular waxes rather than some more gross secretion product, are reported to be somewhat but not strikingly different: the differences are not greater than those among gross wax secretions from different insects. A mixture of even-numbered C_{26}–C_{30} esters of alcohols and acids is found mixed with odd-numbered C_{27}–C_{31} paraffin hydrocarbons (Bergmann 38).

These insect waxes are soluble in CCl_4, $CHCl_3$, and at least sometimes in xylol and benzene. They are at least largely insoluble in alcohol, ether, and acetone (Beament 45a, Gabreil 03, Schulz & Becker 31b, Slifer 48). They form a layer with an average thickness

Table 6. Comparison of the Transition Points of Waxes from Various Species of Insects

Measured by various methods. Temperature in degrees centigrade for change in properties.

Species	Melting Point	Optical Changes	Spreading on Water	Contact Angle	Film Permeability: On Tanned Gelatin	Film Permeability: *Pieris* Wing On Membrane	Film Permeability: In Vivo	Reference
Nematus, larva	36–42, indefinite	30	29	37	32	34	35	Beament
Calliphora, puparium	Indefinite	. . .	26	36	29	37	35	Beament
Calliphora, pupa	50–55	36–46	43	44	42	49	52	Beament
Pieris, larva	57, sharp	46–54	41	42	46	46	42	Beament
Tenebrio, larva	57–59	51–53	55	53	. . .	53	52	Beament
Rhodnius, adult	60.5, sharp	56–58	55	58	58	57	57.5	Beament
Rhodnius, egg	. . .	. . .	. . .	. . .	. . .	. . .	42.5	Beament
Pieris, pupa, white	67, sharp	59	60	62	. . .	63	60	Beament
Pieris, pupa, yellow	No change to 100°	54	52	. . .	. . .	. . .	. . .	Beament
Melanoplus, egg	60–65 or 70	. . .	. . .	. . .	. . .	. . .	. . .	Slifer 48
Ixodid ticks	. . .	. . .	. . .	. . .	. . .	. . .	32–45	Lees
Ixodid eggs	. . .	. . .	. . .	. . .	. . .	. . .	35–44	Lees & Beament
Argasid ticks	. . .	. . .	. . .	. . .	. . .	. . .	63–75	Lees
Argasid eggs	. . .	. . .	. . .	. . .	. . .	. . .	45	Lees & Beament
Beeswax	62–64	57–58	60	56	56	57	. . .	Beament
Chinese insect wax	80	. . .	. . .	. . .	. . .	. . .	. . .	Chibnall *et al.* 34
Psylla wax	96	. . .	. . .	. . .	. . .	. . .	. . .	Chibnall *et al.* 34
Pemphigus wax	108–9	. . .	. . .	. . .	. . .	. . .	. . .	Schulz & Becker 31b

of 0.1–1 micron (Beament 45). A wax layer is also present in the egg shell, but here it is usually found on the inside rather than the outside (Beament 46a, 48a, b, Lees & Beament 48, Ongaro 33, Slifer 48).

Physical properties of the waxes depend greatly on the species of arthropod from which they are extracted. The softening and melting points range from fairly low temperatures to considerably above 100° C. (Table 6). Within any one species, however, there is reasonably good agreement among such things as melting point, contact angle, spreading on water, and permeability of the membrane on which the waxes lie. The great biological importance of this will be discussed in a subsequent section (p. 299). As one would expect, the waxes increase in hardness and crystallinity with increasing melting point. As found on an insect, the wax layer will average some thirty monolayers in thickness, the innermost layers being better oriented and apparently attached to the underlying protein molecules.

Some of the data from synthetic and nonarthropod waxes cover points almost certainly of interest to our subject, since similar data may be expected from arthropod waxes. Thus X-ray diffraction analyses have shown that paraffins are packed as long chains in an extended planar zigzag configuration (Alex Müller 28). At higher temperatures these paraffin chains can rotate around their long axes. Although possible biological significances are not known, it is well to hold in mind that various physical properties for odd-numbered and even-numbered waxes may differ considerably (Alex Müller 29). Under the heading of dimensions, a C_{30} hydrocarbon is approximately 40×3–4 Å, and an average wax molecule has a length of approximately 100 Å, with side spacings of 3.7–4.1 Å, which change to 4.6 Å at close to the melting point (Alex Müller 30). For comparison of data from chemically pure substances with the more or less impure mixtures usually extracted from biological sources, it might be well to hold in mind that waxes can show more than one temperature transition point and that the lower one of these is much influenced by impurities (Piper *et al.* 31, 34). Presumably no difficulty is to be anticipated in the formation of films from natural waxes, since it has been shown that fatty acids longer than C_{12} have adequate lateral adhesion for film formation (Schofield & Rideal 26).

Almost nothing is known concerning the metabolism and secretion of arthropod waxes. It is sometimes assumed that they are derived from plant sources, and to a certain extent this is supported, for instance, by the fact that the bug *Trialeurodes* does not secrete wax except when it is feeding on a plant (H. Weber 31). On the other hand, (1) insect waxes do not appear to be identical with the common plant waxes, though they are reasonably similar, and (2) insects reared on synthetic diets, containing only known ingredients and no waxes, none the less possess waxes on the cuticle. The route for these syntheses is unknown, but a scheme has been suggested whereby they all might be derived from unsaturated fatty acids (Chibnall & Piper 34). The waxes produced by young and by old adult honeybees are indistinguishable (Jordan *et al.* 40), but waxes from *Rhodnius* and tick eggs and adults have different transition points (Beament 46a, Lees & Beament 48). The wax layer on the epicuticle is secreted fairly early in cuticle development, but it can be added to, replenished, and even repaired by additional secretion (Wigglesworth 45). Curious growth forms have been recorded for wax deposits forming over abrasions on ticks (Lees 47); since these are influenced by atmospheric humidity, it has been suggested that this is evidence of the waxes' being secreted in an aqueous medium. More recently, it has been shown that the wax for tick eggs is secreted as a watery refractile liquid said to contain wax precursors (Lees & Beament 48).

CHAPTER 12

Inorganic Constituents and Calcification

Ashing of any intact cuticle shows a few per cent of ash. Of particular interest is the small percentage of sulfur, but unfortunately little is known about it other than its presence (Lafon 43a, Trim 41b). However, in the crustacea, the organic matter may account for anywhere from $< 1\%$ to $> 99\%$, the remainder of the substance being referred to as lime or calcareous material. Calcareous skeletons are also found in many Diplopoda. Calcareous deposits are found on a few dipterous larvae and in the egg shells of phasmids, but in these insects do not form true calcareous skeletons. The puparium of *Rhagoletis* is an exception that seems unique (p. 107). Reviews of various aspects of this topic are given by Clarke and Wheeler (22), M. Prenant (27b), and Robertson (41).

The vast majority of available data deal with crustacea. Here, large or significant amounts of calcium, phosphorus, magnesium, aluminum, iron, silicon, and sulfur are found (Tables 7 & 8). Calcium is by far the commonest of these, and at least in a good percentage of cases is known to be present as $CaCO_3$. The percentage of Ca carbonate and Ca phosphate in crustacean cuticles is comparable to the percentages found in molluscan shells; both contrast with bone and dentine where $Ca_3(PO_4)_2$ is the dominant constituent (Cartier 48, Dallemagne & Melon 46a, b). The salts formed by the other elements are not so well known because they are not found in crystallographically recognizable units. It is usually assumed that they occur in molecules, listed in Table 8, but the evidence for this is not strong, and certainly the figures in the table must err by whatever amounts of these elements are present in organic combination.

In addition to the references cited in Tables 7 and 8, there are a considerable number of papers which contain additional figures for the total mineral content of crustacean cuticles (Drach 35a, 37a, b, c, 39, Drach and Lafon 42, Gautrelet 02, Gicklhorn 25, Lafon 43b, 48, Mann & Pieplow 38, Numanoi 34b, 37, 43, M. Prenant 27a), Diplop-

TABLE 7. SELECTED VALUES FOR THE PERCENTAGE COMPOSITION OF CALCAREOUS MATERIAL IN ARTHROPOD CUTICLES

Genus	$CaCO_3$	$Ca_3(PO_4)_2$	Organic	Reference
Crustacea				
Lepas	95.3	0.7	4.0	C. Schmidt 1845a
Balanus	38.7	2.6	58.7	Schlossberger 1856
Potamobius	48	6.8	40.6	Balss 27
Astacus	47.3	5.2	44.7	Chevreul 1820
Astacus	48.5	6.1	45.4	Kelly 01
Astacus	47.5	6.7	40.6	Bütschli 08
Astacus	40.3	9.5	48	Drach & Lafon 42
Cancer	62.8	6.0	28.6	Chevreul 1820
"Edible crab"				
Outer part	78.8	1.2	20.0	Irvine & Woodhead 1889
Inner part	65.0	1.0	34.0	Same as above
Homarus	33–45	7–11	38–52	Herrick 1896
Squilla	19.5	17.7	62.8	C. Schmidt 1845a
13 genera [a]	16–60	4–17	29–78	Clarke & Wheeler 22
Diplopoda				
Julus	49.0	7.3	43.7	Kelly 01
Ophistreptus	64	5	31	Lafon 43b

[a] *Callinectes, Chloridella, Crago, Eriphia, Grapsus, Homarus, Libinia, Lithodes, Munida, Pagurus, Pandalus, Panulirus,* and *Tryphosa.*

oda (Kelly 01, Lafon 43b, Rossi 02, Silvestri 03), probably in Trilobites (Cayeux 33), and a few insects which will be discussed later. The most interesting feature in these general percentages is that the amount of calcification stands in inverse relationship to the amount of protein present in the cuticle (Lafon 43b). In species that are not calcified, in areas that are not calcified on otherwise calcified individuals, and in the new cuticle of crustacea prior to calcification, there are roughly comparable quantities of chitin and protein. With calcification the quantity of protein added to the cuticle decreases greatly. We can say, then, that calcification takes the place of a large portion of the protein that would otherwise be needed for hardening of the cuticle, or vice versa (Dennell 47b, Fraenkel and Rudall 47, Lafon 43b, Reid 43). (See also Cloudsley-Thompson 50b.)

Calcium carbonate exists in several distinct crystallographic forms — calcite, aragonite, vaterite — and perhaps also in an amorphous form (M. Prenant 27b). Of these, aragonite, which is the common form in molluscan shells, is the only one not recorded for arthropod cuticle. Vaterite is rare, but has been identified by X-ray diffraction patterns (Dudich 31). Calcite may occur in either micro or macro

TABLE 8. SELECTED SETS OF VALUES FOR THE COMPOSITION OF CRUSTACEAN CUTICLES
(From Clarke & Wheeler 22.)

	Actual Analytical Values in Percentage of Cuticle								
Genus	SiO_2	$(Al,Fe)_2O_3$	MgO	CaO	P_2O_5	SO_3	Ignition	CO_2 Needed	Organic
Lepas anatifera	0.04	0.19	1.14	52.3	trace	...	49.5	48.4	2.13
Balanus niveus	1.99	0.68	0.73	50.1	trace	...	44.8	40.2	4.68
Libinia emarginata	2.61	0.78	2.81	32.8	2.73	0.49	57.9	26.1	31.0
Tryphosa pinguis	0.62	0.37	1.27	28.6	4.56	0.23	64.7	19.5	45.2
Munida iris	0.32	0.16	2.58	31.3	1.87	0.47	62.3	25.4	36.9
Panulirus argus	0.16	0.13	3.15	25.6	2.09	0.41	66.7	21.2	45.5
Homarus americana	0.00	0.21	2.35	31.4	3.04	0.45	61.8	24.1	37.7
Chloridella empusa	0.02	0.17	2.60	15.4	7.75	1.07	72.4	7.2	65.2
Eriphia sebana	trace	4.82	1.19	34.2	3.38	trace	53.9	25.0	28.9

	Calculated Values Assuming Salts Listed, in Percentage of Inorganic Material					
Genus	SiO_2	$(Al,Fe)_2O_3$	$MgCO_3$	$CaCO_3$	$Ca_3(PO_4)_2$	$CaSO_4$
Lepas anatifera	0.04	0.20	2.49	96.7	trace	...
Balanus niveus	2.12	0.72	1.63	95.5	trace	...
Libinia emarginata	3.82	1.14	8.65	76.4	8.7	1.22
Tryphosa pinguis	1.12	0.67	4.84	74.6	18.0	0.71
Munida iris	0.52	0.27	8.71	82.6	6.6	1.29
Panulirus argus	0.31	0.25	12.6	76.8	8.7	1.31
Homarus americana	0.00	0.34	8.02	79.5	10.9	1.23
Chloridella empusa	0.06	0.50	16.0	28.5	49.5	5.33
Eriphia sebana	trace	7.02	3.65	78.6	10.7	trace

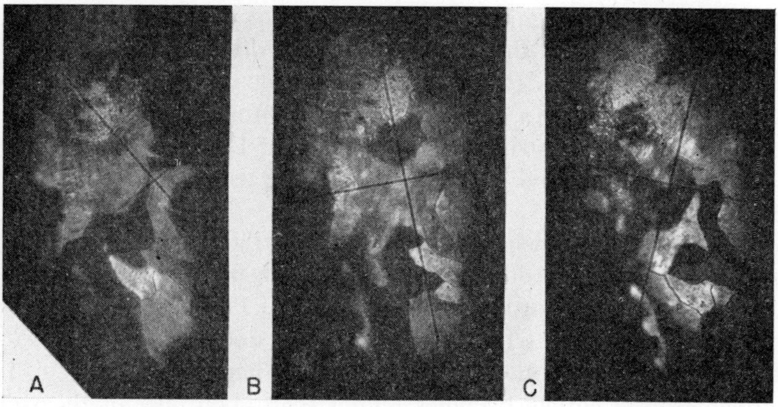

Figure 17. Illustration of mosaic calcification in cuticle of a terrestrial isopod, *Trachelipus* sp. All three pictures are photographs of the same small fragment. The pictures are mounted so that the position of the specimen remains constant; the orientation of the Nicol prisms is shown by the cross hairs. These pictures show both that the orientation of calcification is different in different adjacent areas and that it may be different at different levels in the same area. (Original.)

crystals which are granular, platelike, or show circular symmetry, or in crystal aggregates in a disclike sphaerite, or in a hidden or cryptocrystalline condition (Dudich 29). Quite commonly, especially in platelike crystals, the orientation in different adjacent areas is different, with the resulting production of what is called a mosaic pattern (Fig. 17).

The origin of this mosaicism is the fact that while the optic axes of the separate crystal plates lie parallel to the surface, they may be at an angle to one another in the plane of the surface. This seems certainly due to the fact that crystallization begins independently at various loci, and extends, filling out the crystal lattice until prevented from further growth by abutting against another crystal (Drach 39, Dudich 31). Examination by dark-field microscopy shows lines between the different calcified areas and therefore indicates there is no intimate fusion of crystallites as they grow up against one another. In embryological terminology each crystal would be considered a self-differentiating unit beginning at a particular locus. The distribution of these loci commonly results in the repeated production in one species of the same general type of mosaic, and accordingly a correlation with taxonomic groupings, which in some cases give generic characters, in others family or other higher group characters. Twenty types have been recognized by Dudich, ten of these found only in the Isopoda. Translating the above biological description into the language of petrography, these mosaic elements are xenomorphs which begin as idiomorphic sphaerites and pass through hypidiomorphic to panallotriomorphic structure. Incidentally Dudich's larger paper (31) is beautifully and copiously illustrated, as are also the books by W. J. Schmidt (24).

It seems to be generally assumed that the so-called amorphous calcification (which does show very weak birefringence) is pure $CaCO_3$. This is seriously questioned by M. Prenant's demonstration (27a) that the crystallinity of $CaCO_3$ is definitely related to the relative amount of phosphorus present. When the weight of P_2O_5 derived from a cuticle becomes higher than about 10% of the weight of the CaO from the same cuticle, an amorphous calification results, irrespective of whether we are dealing with different species or different areas on the same specimen. If we change these figures from a weight to a molar basis, then a few per cent of phosphate ions are adequate to inhibit the crystallization of calcium carbonate. The degree of intimacy of the mixed crystallization which results when more phosphate ions are present remains to be elucidated. Actually one would probably expect more conflict from the presence of Mg because the common mineral dolomite is a mixed Ca-Mg carbonate, but Prenant found no fixed relationship between the percentage of magnesium and crystallization. In general, when crystallinity is high, Mg is also high, but the crystals formed appear to be calcite.

As one would probably guess, there is more Mg in the cuticles of marine species than in those from fresh water (Clarke & Wheeler 22). However, one would not guess that Mg, P, and S all increase with age. In the lobster P and S nearly double from youth to old age, Mg increases only some 5–10%, while Ca remains relatively constant. Also the percentages of Mg, P, and S are considerably higher in the claws of lobsters than in the carapace. The significance of these relative differences in concentration of various elements is not understood. More study is needed on the state called amorphous calcification.

Once calcification begins, it proceeds fairly rapidly, in some cases beginning at the free margins of the shell and progressing inwards, in other cases spreading from more generally distributed loci (Dudich 29, Fassbinder 12, Hay 04, Olmsted & Baumberger 23, Paul & Sharpe 16, Reid 43). In a few cases calcification may begin before molting, but it usually begins shortly thereafter. A soft-shelled crab is not completely helpless; it can walk and even swim if necessary (Hay 04). In *Gammarus* the calcification is complete in less than 24 hours as far as one can determine from observation of the crystal optics (Reid 43). In *Carcinides* and *Cancer* calcification of the outer layer takes place in 24–48 hours, but takes days or weeks in some parts (Drach 37a, b). In the Decapoda, Drach (39) says that the epicuticle is calcified first, then successively lower laminae are, with the calcification spreading in each lamina from crystallization centers. After calcification, the coloration may appear much dimmer (Hay 04).

It is interesting that while molting itself is under hormonal control, the calcification process is not (Kleinholz 41). The independence of the calcification process from other aspects of cuticle development is strikingly illustrated by the fact that there is no relationship between mosaic elements and ommatidia in the compound eye; the platelike crystals cut across ommatidia at all angles and end where they meet another crystal, irrespective of the position relative to the visual elements (Dudich 31, Wolsky 29). Of potentially considerable interest is the fact that whereas this initial calcification represents impregnation of a previously developed chitin-protein cuticle, subsequent secretion of cuticle represents simultaneous deposition of both calcium salts and organic components with the crystallization being much slower (Drach 37a, c, Drach & Lafon 42, Mann & Pieplow 38). Drach and Lafon not only point out that the calcium salts largely replace the protein, but suggest that the calcium salts enter into combination with the organic molecules in place of the protein which they replace.[1] If this is substantiated, it will represent another difference between cuticle and bone, for it seems now established that in bone the phosphate particles are simply surrounded by organic matter without there being any chemical bond (Dallemagne & Melon 46a, b). Again we must say that more study is needed on so-called amorphous calcification.

There is a sizable literature on the resorption of Ca from the old cuticle into the blood at the time of molting and its subsequent excretion or storage. This literature has been ably reviewed by Robertson (41) and continues to be actively studied by crustacean physiologists (Drach & Lafon 42, Kleinholz 41, Maloeuf 40, Numanoi 43). In some species a part of the calcium may be stored in a structure

[1] There is an interesting recent paper on calcification in molluscan shells (Bevelander & Benzer 48) which reports that first an organic matrix is laid down and then Ca phosphate is formed; the Ca phosphate is then said to be changed to Ca carbonate (organic intermediates being postulated).

called a gastrolith, on the side of the stomach, whence it is dissolved and used for calcification of the new cuticle; in other species all the calcium is excreted. In Isopods it may be deposited as plates between the old and new cuticles and lost with the shed skin (Herold 13, Nicholls 31a). In either event additional calcium has to be absorbed from the environment for calcification. Naturally, blood calcium percentages vary in correlation with this movement and may rise to five times the normal level. Authors have suggested that this large amount of calcium might be carried in the blood either as $CaCl_2$ (Dambovičeanu 30) or as a salt of a fatty acid (Paul & Sharpe 16) or as a proteinate (Numanoi 43). It has been claimed that an enzyme is involved in its deposition (Cantacuzene & Damboviceanu 32). One might expect carbonic anhydrase to be involved, but at least in the lobster there is no change in concentration of this enzyme correlated with the molting cycle (Maloeuf 40).

There is one recent paper recording the presence of alkaline phosphatase in the cuticle of crayfish, but there is as yet no indication of the role it may be playing there (Kugler & Birkner 48).

The formation and molting of calcified cuticles in the Diplopoda has not been studied intensively, but it is reported that decalcification of the ventral, but not of the harder dorsal, cuticle occurs during molting of *Nopoiulus* (Verhoeff 01b, 19, 39, 40). (See Cloudsley-Thompson 50b.)

In the insects there are only a few scattered cases of calcification. Certain aquatic dipterous larvae belonging to the families Stratiomyidae and Psychodidae have long been known to have calcareous deposits or nodules (Krüper 30, Leydig 1860, G. W. Müller 25, Vaney 02, Viallanes 1882). The inorganic material appears to be composed of only $CaCO_3$. The situation is altogether different from that found in the crustacea and diplopods in that rather than the calcification of the cuticle, we have a deposition of lime in more or less definite form on the outside surface of the cuticle (and reaching a maximum of three times the weight of the cuticle). Krüper's (30) figures both of entire larvae and of sections show clearly that the lime is deposited on the outer surface. In Psychodid larvae the lime is mostly located on the spines, which become heavily incrusted with an amorphous appearing precipitate. In Stratiomyid larvae (11 genera examined) the deposit is in the form of a definite nodule with a canal through the center, which connects with the duct of a gland in the cuticle. The appearance of the published figures suggests that lime is de-

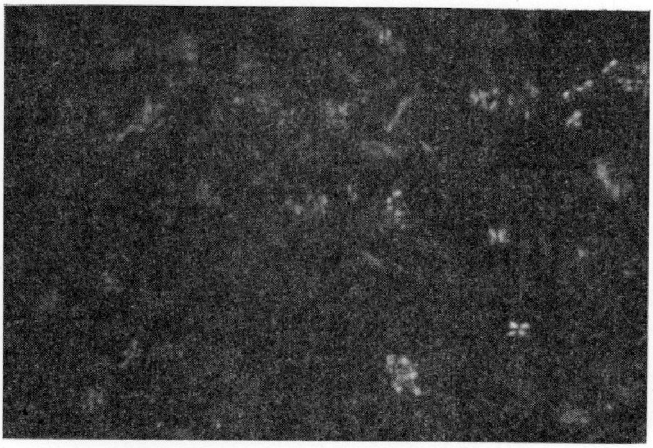

Figure 18. Picture in polarized light of the weakly birefringent needle crystals and more strongly birefringent sphaerites obtained by crushing a KOH-cleaned egg shell of a phasmid, *Diapheromera femorata.* (Original.)

posited as a result of diffusion outwards of CO_2 into a calcium-rich water.

The egg shells of various genera of phasmids (*Dixippus, Bacillus, Diapheromera, Donusa*) have large amounts of $CaCO_3$ and Ca oxalate and smaller amounts of Al, Mg, and K (Kühnelt 28c, Moscona 48, Pantel 19, Richards unpubl., Robertson 41). The ash may account for as much as 38% of the dry weight of the egg shell, and the Ca alone for 23%. The $CaCO_3$ is located principally in a crystalline layer over the inner surface of the egg shell, and staining reactions suggest that the crystal form is that of aragonite (Pantel 19); but the purity of the deposit is questioned by the presence of both crystals and rather indefinite sphaerites (Fig. 18). Moscona reports that a large portion of this inorganic material is transferred from the shell to the embryo during development.

In some insects the shed skin is more or less covered on its inner surface with a deposit of Ca salts. These are not a part of the cuticle proper, but originate from excretory materials that are secreted by the Malpighian tubules and then spread over the body in the space between old and new cuticles prior to molting (Keilin 21, Kiyomizu —, Shimizu 31, Wiesmann 38). A modification of this phenomenon seems to represent the origin of the one exception to the fact that lime is absent from insect cuticles. In larvae of the fly *Rhagoletis cerasi* the

Ca salts are eliminated from the Malpighian tubules before loosening of the cuticle (Wiesmann 38). They then pass out through the epidermis to become deposited *in* the cuticle in a *granular* form. With transformation of the larval cuticle into a puparium, the granules of $CaCO_3$ remain in what is then the outer portion of the procuticle of the puparium (and may account for more than half the weight thereof).

CHAPTER 13

The Percentages of Cuticular Components

A tabular presentation of the percentages of various inorganic constituents and the percentage of inorganic in relation to organic compounds has already been given in the preceding chapter (Tables 7 & 8). In the present section consideration will be limited to the percentages of organic components; for calcified species the percentages given are in relation to the organic content after removal of the mineral salts. The difficulties in the quantitative estimation of organic components are considerable (Campbell 29, Fraenkel & Rudall 47, Richards 47b). However accurate some of the more recent reports may be, it certainly seems safest to assume that these are approximations which depend so much on technique that a comparison of data from different authors is to be made only with caution (Tables 9 & 10).

At the time of molting, the cuticle is commonly very thin and may then represent only a fraction of 1% of the total weight of the animal. In actual dimensions the thickness of the cuticle may vary from a fraction of one micron to several millimeters. In general, larger animals may be said to have thicker cuticles, but there is no approximation to a ratio between body size and cuticle thickness. Within a single species the thickness of the cuticle may increase during the entire intermolt period (Dennell 46, Kuwana 33), and at least in blowfly larvae this increase is not accompanied by any relative change in the major organic components (Fig. 19).[1] No such smooth curve, however, would be shown by calcified cuticles, where first there is an organic skeleton, which subsequently becomes impregnated with mineral salts, and which later is added to by the simultaneous deposition of organic and inorganic constituents (Lafon 43b, Drach & Lafon 42). In some species there are definite periods of

[1] An exception is the ptilinum of higher Diptera, which decreases in thickness and apparently also in material in the adult after its function is completed (Laing 35).

Table 9. Recorded Amounts of Cuticle and Chitin in Various Arthropods Expressed as a Percentage of Body Weight

Figures in parentheses are certainly too low because of the technique employed.

Genus	Cuticle		Chitin		Reference
	Wet Wgt.	Dry Wgt.	Wet Wgt.	Dry Wgt.	
Crustacea					
Nephrops	. . .	. . .	. . .	6.96	J. A. Meyer 14
Carcinus	. . .	. . .	. . .	8.29	J. A. Meyer 14
Crangon	. . .	. . .	. . .	5.78	J. A. Meyer 14
Carcinus	. . .	. . .	0.4–3.3	. . .	Von Schönborn 11
Insecta					
Periplaneta	. . .	. . .	(2.01)	. . .	Tauber 34
Periplaneta	. . .	(11.6)	. . .	. . .	Buxton 32a
Schistocerca	. . .	. . .	2–4	. . .	Millot & Fontaine 38
Locusta	. . .	. . .	to 3.4	4.7–10.2	Rotman 29
Rhodnius	. . .	(10–11)	. . .	. . .	Buxton 32a
Cimex	. . .	(17.5)	. . .	. . .	Buxton 32a
May fly	. . .	. . .	. . .	8.14	Zaitschek 04
Beetles (38 species) . .	. . .	. . .	5–15	. . .	Bounoure 12
Tenebrio	. . .	(8.2)	. . .	. . .	Buxton 32a
Tenebrio	7.6	17.4	2.13	4.89	Lafon 43c
Dytiscus	. . .	*ca.* 45	. . .	. . .	Lafon 43c
Melolontha	. . .	*ca.* 45	. . .	. . .	Lafon 43c
May beetle	. . .	. . .	. . .	16	Zaitschek 04
May beetle	. . .	. . .	. . .	16	Wolff *et al.* 1876
Culex	. . .	(13)	. . .	. . .	Buxton 32a

Table 10. Amounts of Organic Components in the Cuticle of Various Arthropods Expressed as a Percentage of Dry Weight of the Organic Fraction of the Cuticle

Differences in technique make figures by different authors only roughly comparable. (See also Tables 7 and 9.) For convenience, the percentage of water in the fresh cuticle is added when known.

Genus and Type	Water	Chitin	Extractable Protein, Etc.[a]	Reference
Arachnida				
Buthus (scorpion)	. . .	31.9	68.1	Fraenkel & Rudall 47
Buthus (scorpion)	. . .	32.6	67.4	Lafon 43b
Pandinus (scorpion)	. . .	30.2	69.8	Lafon 43b
Mygale (spider)	. . .	38.2	61.8	Lafon 43b
Damon (phalangid)	. . .	38.2	. . .	Lafon 43b
Limulus	. . .	24.5	high	Lafon 43a
Limulus	. . .	28	. . .	Richards 49

[a] Values by Lafon (43b) are usually minimal protein values determined by calculation from nitrogen analyses. Values by other authors mostly indicate amount of material extractable by alkali treatments.

TABLE 10 *continued*

Genus and Type	Water	Chitin	Extractable Protein, Etc.[a]	Reference
Crustacea				
Branchiopoda				
Triops	...	61.4	...	Lafon 43b
Isopoda				
Ligia	...	78.5	9.5	Lafon 41a, 43b
Cirrepeda				
Lepas	...	58.3	19	Lafon 41a, 43b
Decapoda				
Cancer	...	71.4	13.3	Lafon 43b
Carcinides				
Noncalcified	...	61.7	38.3	Lafon 48
Calcified	...	80.2	19.8	Lafon 48
Carcinus	...	64.2	16.4	Drach & Lafon 42
Crangon	...	69.1	30.9	Lafon 48
Eupagurus				
Noncalcified	...	48.2	51.8	Lafon 48
Calcified	...	69.0	31.0	Lafon 43b, 48
Galathea	...	74.2	25.8	Lafon 48
Homarus				
Noncalcified	...	77.0	23.0	Lafon 48
Noncalcified	...	60.8	39.2	Fraenkel & Rudall 47
Calcified	...	85.0	15.0	Lafon 48
Maia	...	72.5	16.3	Lafon 43b, Drach & Lafon 42
Nephrops	...	76–77.5	13.7	Lafon 41a, 43b
Palaemon	...	60–65	14–15	Lafon 41a, 43b
Portunus	...	69–73	13–16	Drach & Lafon 42
Xantho	...	74.6	10.6	Drach & Lafon 42
Chilopoda				
Scolopendra	...	31	high	Lafon 43b
Lithobius	...	31	high	Lafon 43b
Diplopoda				
Ophistreptus	...	68.1	22.5	Lafon 43b
Oxydesmus	...	76.6	22.6	Lafon 43b
Pachylobus	...	76.8	26.4	Lafon 43b
Insecta				
Orthoptera				
Periplaneta	...	22–60,av.35	...	Campbell 29
Periplaneta	...	18–37,av.29.6 [b]	...	Tauber 34
Periplaneta	...	48.6	51.4	Lafon 48
Periplaneta	...	38	...	C. Koch 32
Locusta, wings	53	23.7	76.3	Fraenkel & Rudall 47

[b] These values are clearly too low because they represent chitosan.

TABLE 10 *continued*

Genus and Type	Water	Chitin	Extractable Protein, Etc.[a]	Reference
Locusta, abdomen	30	31.8	68.2	Same as above
Locusta, femora	15	36.9	63.1	Same as above
Grasshopper	. . .	20	. . .	Kunike 26b
Dixippus, thorax	37.5	36.5	63.5	Fraenkel & Rudall 47
Dixippus, abdomen	50	42.5	57.5	Same as above
Bacillus	. . .	32.5	. . .	Lafon 43b
Hemiptera-Homoptera				
Pyrrhocoris, wing	35.6	27	28.7	Lafon 43b
Cercopis, wing	43	25	. . .	Lafon 43b
Cicada, pupa	. . .	37	. . .	Komori 26
Coleoptera				
Carabus, elytra	31.8	36.1	. . .	Lafon 41b, 43b
Dytiscus, elytra	35.9	34.5	. . .	Lafon 43b
Dytiscus, elytra	. . .	37.4	62.6	Fraenkel & Rudall 47
Leptinotarsa, elytra	29.6	33.2	37.5	Lafon 43b
Lucanus, elytra	27–35	40	25.8	Lafon 43b
Melolontha, elytra	44	33.9	27	Lafon 43b, c
Melolontha, elytra	. . .	48	. . .	C. Koch 32
Melolontha, larva	. . .	33.5	. . .	Lafon 43b, c
Telephorus, elytra	55	26.8	36.2	Lafon 43b
Tenebrio, elytra	42.7	29	. . .	Lafon 43b, c
Tenebrio, larva	. . .	28	34.4	Lafon 43b, c
Tenebrio, larva	37.5	31.3	68.7	Fraenkel & Rudall 47
Lepidoptera				
Bombyx, larva	. . .	44.2	55.8	Fraenkel & Rudall 47
Bombyx, exuvia	. . .	30	. . .	Hamamura *et al.* 40
Galleria, larva	. . .	33.7	36.7	Lafon 43b
Loxostege, larva	. . .	1.4–2.3	82.9–93.7	Pepper & Hastings 43
Pieris, larva	. . .	64	. . .	C. Koch 32
Sphinx, larva	. . .	50.3	49.7	Fraenkel & Rudall 47
Diptera				
Calliphora, larva	. . .	54.8	31.8	Lafon 43b
Calliphora, puparium	13.3	32.5	35	Lafon 43b
Phormia, larva	67.6	59.5	40.5	Fraenkel & Rudall 47
Sarcophaga, larva	70	60	40	Same as above
Sarcophaga, puparium	20–40	47	53	Same as above
Sarcophaga, larva	55	42	. . .	Dennell 46

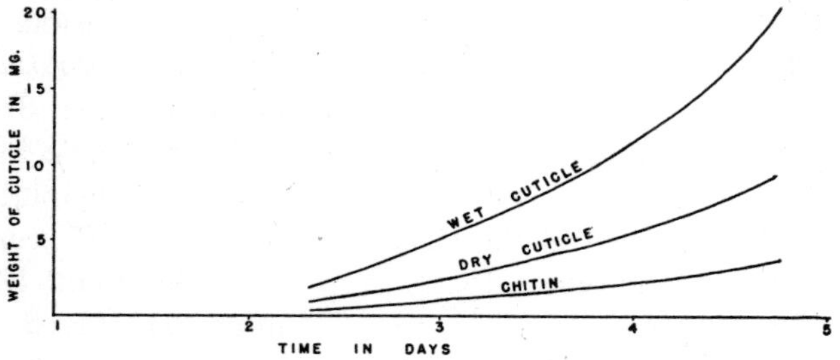

Figure 19. Curves for the growth of the larval cuticle of a blowfly, *Sarcophaga falculata.* The curves show that the percentage composition remains constant during the growth of the larva. (Redrawn from Dennell.)

secretion, followed by resting periods until the next molt (Browning 42, Zschorn 37). Numerous papers deal with the increase of cuticle with age, especially increase in thickness or in the amount of chitin present (Bounoure 13, Dennell 46, Evans 38a, b, Kuwana 33, Lafon 43c, Millot & Fontaine 38, Pepper & Hastings 43, Rotman 29, von Schönborn 11). The only paper giving age variations for all organic components deals with the larva of a moth (Pepper & Hastings 43). In this case, *Loxostege,* on a dry-weight basis, the fat content is said to decrease from 11.7% to 0.2%, protein to increase from 82.9% to 93.7%, chitin to increase from 1.4% to 2.3%, and ash to increase from 0.23% to 0.31% over a period of three instars, including the mature larva.

There appears to be no relation between percentages of cuticular components and the systematic position of the species even within a single order of insects (Lafon 41b). As anyone would probably predict, there tends to be more water in soft cuticles than in hard ones, but no quantitative relationship between water content and hardness is apparent. Incidentally, cuticles imbibe water so readily that considerably higher percentages are obtained when cuticles are dissected free in water than when they are dissected in oil (Dennell 46). It is also recorded that the percentage of chitin is higher in phytophagous beetles than in carnivorous species (Bounoure 13), but even if this report were confirmed, its significance would still be obscure. In view of the difference in size of the reproductive organs, it is not surprising that commonly there is a higher percentage of chitin in males than in females (Bounoure 11).

While a number of papers record determinations on several types of cuticle from a single species, there has been only one paper systematically covering the amount of chitin found in various parts of the body (Tauber 34). In a cockroach, *Periplaneta fuliginosa,* Tauber gives the following chitosan percentages: dorsal abdomen 37.65, ventral abdomen 37.11, metathoracic legs 35.55, mesothoracic legs 33.28, prothoracic legs 32.24, pronotum 31.55, head 31.07, genitalia 29.28, dorsal thorax 29.07, ventral thorax 28.33, antennae 27.77, cerci 25.65, fore wing 19.99, hind wing 18.22, crop 18.69, hind-gut 18.15, and tracheae a trace. Unfortunately the technique employed involved conversion to chitosan, and accordingly, although we can be sure the figures are all too low, we do not know how much to raise the figures to obtain the true values for chitin. Also it would seem at the present time a gratuitous and dubious assumption to think that all the values contain the same percentage of error. In contrast, values for the elytra, pronotum, metasternum, and abdominal stermites of *Tenebrio* adults, obtained without conversion to chitosan, are all said to lie in the range of 28.8%–29.4% (Lafon 43c).

The percentage of ash present in noncalcified cuticles is seldom given (Fraenkel & Rudall 47, Lafon 41b, c, 43a, Pepper & Hastings 43, Trim 41b). Figures for the intact cuticle lie in the range of 0.2%–3% except for some determinations based on beetle elytra where the cuticle was not separated from underlying epithelial cells. The content of sulfur is decidedly low (Lafon 41b, Trim 41b) except in *Limulus* (Lafon 43a).

Percentage variations are inherent in the report that insect tracheae and the wing scales of many butterflies and moths may give strong, weak, or negative chitosan tests (Richards 47b), but quantitative determinations are not available.

In addition to the data cited in Tables 9 and 10 there are a number of other, mostly older, papers recording certain percentage figures (Beauregard 1890, Beguin 1874, Bialaszewicz 37, Chevreul 1820, Miall & Denny 1886, Odier 1823).

CHAPTER 14

Unknown Chemical Components

Remarks on the occurrence of unknown components are found scattered throughout the preceding sections. It might be worth while to bring these together into a single section, although little more than a listing can be given. The significance of the several per cent of ash found in insect cuticles, and probably to be found in other noncalcified cuticles, is not known. Probably much of it is simply contaminant salts which have diffused in from underlying tissues and play no real role in the cuticle itself. But this is not necessarily true, and the data seem to indicate clearly that sulfur is definitely of interest for cuticle formation (Lafon 43a, Trim 41b). Trim records that 0.57% of the water-insoluble, alkali-extracted material of blowfly larvae is sulfur, and his data imply that perhaps this is involved in chitin-protein linkages. Lafon found a much higher amount (2.85%) in the cuticle of *Limulus,* and although he has no real data as to the role this is playing, he compares it with the amount of S found in keratin.[1]

It is certainly desirable to identify the nonchitin carbohydrate reported by Trim (41b), especially if it should be found to be neither a chitin precursor nor a chitin degradation product. All that is known is that a substance giving a general carbohydrate reaction is present in the less readily removed protein fraction, and that the sulfur tends to go with the carbohydrate in preliminary fractionations. The reducing activity of certain cuticles (Dennell 47a, Kühnelt 49, Mirande 05a, b) is important in sclerotization (p. 187), but its identity is unknown.

The significance of the trace of ash found by various workers in samples of purified chitin is open to several possible interpretations.

[1] The presence of sulfur, e.g., in keratin, has led to use of the vague term "vulcanized protein." The term has recently been used to describe the fertilization membrane of insect eggs (Beament 49). The topic of vulcanization, however, covers a considerable range of linkage phenomena, and may or may not involve sulfur. The present author does not find the introduction of the term vulcanization sufficiently specific to be helpful.

Since the trace of ash persists despite exhaustive washing, it is commonly assumed to be a cuticle component rather than to be derived from some of the chemicals used in the treatment procedures (Richards 49). This is not proved. Correlated with, but not necessarily related to, the trace of ash is the low nitrogen value recorded by many authors (p. 25). This can be interpreted as indicating an impurity that has not yet been identified (Richards 49). To a biologist the fact that chitin may not have been prepared in absolutely pure form is of no great importance. But if these values are to be interpreted as indicating that other components are present, it is of biological interest to have these components identified and their role in cuticle formation elucidated (Norman 37).

The occasional reports of arthropod membranes which are resistant to hot KOH and yet negative to the chitosan test are of unknown significance (for instance in the cockroach ootheca, Campbell 29). Conversely, those membranes which sometimes give positive chitosan tests but usually are dispersed by hot alkali solutions lead one to wonder about the basic definition of chitin as an alkali-insoluble compound. Chitin from diverse sources needs to be studied chemically instead of using only chitin from sturdy alkali-resistant structures, and full satisfaction will not be obtained before a qualified chemist includes consideration of the composition of the material removed by alkaline solutions and routinely discarded.

For chitin chemistry in general outside of the phylum Arthropoda, it is desirable to have an identification of the compounds giving peculiar color reactions in certain Bryozoan skeletons (Richards & Cutkomp 46) and an elucidation of the nature of the "chitins A and B" in snail radulae (Pantin & Rogers 25).

The nature of the so-called cuticulin, polyphenol, and cement layers is largely unknown (Aronssohn 10, Blunck 10, Frey 36, Kühnelt 28c, Plateau 76, Wigglesworth 47b). Under the general heading of obvious lacunae concerning components, properties and processes, we can also list several of considerable biological interest. Of primary importance are such items as the nature of the deamination of tyrosine; the nature of hardening that occurs without distinct darkening in some noncalcified cuticles (e.g., *Dixippus,* Fraenkel & Rudall 47); a satisfactory explanation of amorphous calcification in cuticles and its possible relation to other components; an elucidation of the nature of the chitin-protein associations and protein-polyphenol linkages that seem necessitated but not explained by existing data, especially in order to be in a better position for interpreting data obtained from studies on the more or less purified components; an interpretation of the development and role of laminae in the chitin-protein portion of cuticles; and a simple, fool-proof test for chitin, preferably quantitative and adaptable to histochemical work. Of great biological importance, but of lesser chemical interest, are a broad study of the role of stresses and plastic states in cuticle development and an adequate treatment of elasticity, the importance of which has been suggested in a number of papers (Fraenkel & Rudall 40, Lees & Picken 45, Richards & Korda 50). It seems much too early to suggest more sweeping analyses, such as a treatment of the thermodynamics of cuticle production.

CHAPTER 15

The Physical Properties of Cuticle and Cuticular Components

There have been relatively few studies on the physical properties of cuticle, partly, at least, because of the large range of variation in those of considerable biological interest, such as elasticity and hardness. Perhaps the chief function of Table 11 will be to emphasize the paucity of quantitative data that are available. Some properties have already been treated in the preceding sections on chemistry and will not be repeated here, namely, solubilities, melting points, molecular weights, and lattice structures. Discussion of the production of physical colors and of permeability will be deferred until after treatment of cuticle morphology. No data at all appear to be available on viscosity, thermal properties, or electrical properties (other than the fact that insect cuticle, like hair and feathers, belongs to the electropositive group of substances, usually carries a positive charge, and properly insulated specimens may have developed on them charges ranging from 17 to 163 volts [Heuschmann 29]).

DENSITY

The only figure for the density of chitin is fairly low, lower than recent determinations on the density of cellulose (Hermans 46), and in view of technical difficulties involved in determination it seems best considered uncertain. Density is closely dependent on both moisture content and on closeness of packing. Thus silk fibroin, which has a density of 1.353 when dry, has an apparent density of 1.426 in water (Goodings & Turl 40). Similarly, cellulose shows a density range of 1.5–1.64, depending on source and moisture (Hermans 46).

Two biologically important facts are known about cuticular densities, even though the data are only qualitative. Hardening and darkening of the cuticle, most readily studied in the puparia of flies, involves considerable dehydration with consequent increase in density (Dennell 47a, Fraenkel & Rudall 40). Both hard and soft cuticles show laminations parallel to the surface of the cuticle, and electron microscope pictures (Fig. 20B), which are essentially pictures of differential density, show that these represent alternating layers of greater and lesser density (Richards & Anderson 42a). The same interpretation can be given to the persistence of laminae in the exuvial space (Fig. 45). In fact, the laminar structure may be entirely due to this differential density as will be discussed subsequently (p. 140).

TENSILE STRENGTH

Purified chitin fibers are very strong, stronger than hair, silk, or "cellulose" (Herzog 26, Homann 49). The considerable difference between the sets of figures cited in Table 11 may well be real and if so indicate the considerable difference to be expected with different sources of material and different methods of preparation. Chitin shows the strength typical of a fibrous material rather than of a rubbery or plastic material, and high as the values for tensile strength may seem, they are still lower than would be expected on a basis of the ether linkages in the molecular chains. It seems necessary to assume that breaking is due to a slipping of molecular chains past one another rather than to actual breakage of chains (Mark 43, Kurt Meyer & Wehrli 37).

Anyone who has dissected a few arthropods is aware that the tensile strength of cuticle varies from area to area and species to species independently of thickness; also that strength as well as brittleness increases on drying (Thor & Henderson 40). There is an obvious qualitative correlation with the degree of sclerotization, but quantitative figures are not available. A beginning in this direction has been made with the chitinous walls of certain fungi (Castle 37a).

ELASTICITY

This is a property of inestimable biological importance, and yet almost no quantitative data are available. Numerous actions, for instance, movements of certain parts of the feeding apparatus of various insects, are supplied with muscles for movement in one direction and depend on the elasticity of the cuticle for return to the original position (J. B. Schmitt 38, Wallengren 14). It is well known that ticks are capable of great distention on engorgement, and the cuticle of the abdomen of spiders is extended approximately 15% after feeding (Browning 42).

TABLE 11. SOME PHYSICAL PROPERTIES OF CUTICLE FRACTIONS AND COMPONENTS

Property	Epicuticle	Exocuticle	Endocuticle	Chitin	Silk	Other	Reference
Density	. . .	. . .	. . .	1.393–1.408; av. 1.398	. . .	. . .	Sollas 07
Density	. . .	. . .	. . .	1.41–1.42	. . .	. . .	Lotmar & Picken 50
Density	Wax 0.96	. . .	. . .	. . .	. . .	. . .	Lewkowitsch & Warburton 21
Density	. . .	. . .	. . .	. . .	1.353	. . .	Goodings & Turl 40
Tensile strength, dry	. . .	. . .	. . .	58 kg./mm.^{2}	35.6 kg./mm.^{2}	. . .	Herzog 26
Tensile strength, dry	. . .	. . .	. . .	35 kg./mm.^{2}	. . .	. . .	Kunike 26a
Tensile strength, dry	. . .	. . .	. . .	9.5 kg./mm.^{2}	. . .	. . .	Thor & Henderson 40
Tensile strength, wet	. . .	. . .	. . .	1.8 kg./mm.^{2}	. . .	. . .	Thor & Henderson 40
Elasticity	. . .	. . .	. . .	1.3%	13.5%	. . .	Herzog 26
Refractive index	. . .	. . .	. . .	1.525	. . .	. . .	Becking & Chamberlin 25
Refractive index	. . .	. . .	. . .	1.52	. . .	. . .	Castle 36
Refractive index	. . .	. . .	. . .	1.550–1.557	. . .	. . .	Sollas 07
Refractive index	. . .	. . .	. . .	1.61	. . .	. . .	Möhring 22, Picken 49
Refractive index	1.56–1.57	. . .	1.52–1.53	. . .	. . .	. . .	Dethier 42, 43
Refractive index	. . .	. . .	. . .	. . .	. . .	1.54 [a]	Tshirvinsky 26
Refractive index	1.594	. . .	1.50–1.52	. . .	. . .	. . .	C. W. Mason 27b
Absorption curves							
Ultraviolet	. . .	. . .	2500 Å	. . .	. . .	. . .	Durand *et al.* 41
Ultraviolet	. . .	To opaque	See separate table	Decreases with λ	. . .	. . .	Merker 29a, 39
Ultraviolet	. . .	. . .	. . .	. . .	2600 Å +; near 2900 Å	. . .	Coleman & Howitt 47
Visible light	. . .	To opaque	75%	. . .	. . .	. . .	Portier & Emmanuel 32
Visible light	. . .	. . .	Between 2500 + 7200 Å	. . .	. . .	. . .	Weiss 44, 46, Merker 39
Infrared	. . .	Various	. . .	. . .	Various	. . .	Coblentz 12, Bath & Ellis 41, Stair & Coblentz 35

[a] Scales from wings of butterflies and moths.

TABLE 11 *continued*

Property	Epicuticle	Exocuticle	Endocuticle	Chitin	Silk	Other	Reference
Fluorescence	. . .	Bluish-white	Bluish-white	. . .	. . .	. . .	Beer 31a, b, c, Merker 29a, b, 31, Metcalf 45, Salfi 37, Stübel 11
Fluorescence	. . .	Bluish-white	Bluish-white	Very weak	. . .	. . .	Richards unpubl.
Phosphorescence	. . .	. . .	Short-lived	. . .	. . .	. . .	Giese & Leighton 37
Birefringence	. . .	Strong	. . .	Absent	. . .	. . .	Lafon 43a
Birefringence	. . .	Absent	Present	. . .	. . .	. . .	Pryor 40b
Birefringence	. . .	. . .	Moderate	Strong form, weak intrinsic	. . .	. . .	Castle 36, Browning 42, Lees & Picken 45, Möhring 26, W. J. Schmidt 29, 34a, b, 36a
Birefringence	. . .	. . .	. . .	. . .	$\epsilon = 1.59+$; $\omega = 1.54$	. . .	Chamot & Mason 44
Pleochroism	. . .	. . .	. . .	. . .	. . .	Strong, weak, or absent [a]	Tshirvinsky 26
Isoelectric point	pH 5.1	(pH 3.5)	pH 3.5	. . .	. . .	. . .	Yonge 32
Isoelectric point	pH 5.0	(pH 3.4–3.5)	pH 3.4–3.5	. . .	. . .	. . .	Thomas 44
Isoelectric point	pH 5.1–5.3	pH 3.4	pH 3.4–4.3	. . .	. . .	. . .	Dennell 46
Isoelectric point	. . .	pH 6.0–6.8	pH 4.0–4.8	. . .	. . .	. . .	Kuwana 40
Isoelectric point	. . .	. . .	pH 5.0–5.6	. . .	. . .	. . .	Browning 42
Isoelectric point	. . .	. . .	. . .	(pH 2.6)	. . .	. . .	Pantin & Rogers 25
Isoelectric point	. . .	. . .	. . .	. . .	pH 2.0–2.2	. . .	Harris & Johnson 30
Isoelectric point	. . .	. . .	. . .	. . .	. . .	pH 2.1 [b]	Jahn 35a
Heat on ignition	. . .	. . .	. . .	4650 cal./g.	. . .	. . .	K. Farkas 03
Activation heat for hydrolytic degradation	. . .	. . .	. . .	29,500 cal./mol.	. . .	. . .	Kurt Meyer & Wehrli 37
Swelling (H_2O)	. . .	. . .	. . .	. . .	43.2%	. . .	Goodings & Turl 40
Surface plane	. . .	1%–2%	7.4%	. . .	. . .	. . .	Fraenkel & Rudall 47
Normal to surface	. . .	30%–40%	56%	. . .	. . .	. . .	Fraenkel & Rudall 47

[a] Scales from wings of butterflies and moths.
[b] Grasshopper egg shell.

The value of 1.5% given by Herzog may be quite accurate, but is deceptive because it is based on fibers with a very high degree of orientation. A distinct and biologically important correlation exists between elasticity and the degree of orientation. The higher the degree of crystallinity as shown either by birefringence or X-ray diffraction, the lower, in general, the elasticity. Elastic membranes, in the sense of membranes that can be stretched, are those with a random arrangement of chitin micelles in the plane of the membrane; stretching probably involves an increase in the orderly arrangement of micelles in the direction of stress rather than any extension of the micelles themselves. Another way of expressing this, to the present author less descriptive, is to say that elasticity involves the presence of a considerable percentage of amorphous intermicellar material (Mark 43). Soft cuticles greatly stretched (40%) show little or no return, i.e., are inelastic (Fraenkel & Rudall 47), which means that internal yield values have been exceeded and the micelles permanently displaced by overstretching.

Biologically important activities involving elasticity are commonly concerned with bending rather than stretching. No quantitative data on bending values appear to be available, but the fact that threads with little longitudinal elasticity can be manufactured and woven into cloth is indicative. Plasticity is thought to enter into the development of micellar orientations found in cuticle (Fig. 24B) (Lees & Picken 45, Richards & Korda 50), and might well occur under sustained loads or by overstretching in imperfectly sclerotized cuticles (Maloeuf 35a, Thompson 29), but the usually rapid or relatively rapid movements of a living arthropod almost certainly involve a considerable amount of elastic bending and a smaller amount of elastic stretching.

Silk is more elastic than chitin fibers (Table 11), and perhaps this is why Fraenkel and Rudall (47) in proposing the term arthropodin state that it is responsible for the free movability of arthropod appendages. Whatever the reason for this statement, it seems to lack documentation and to be, to the present author, a questionable assumption. Incidentally there is an old paper reporting that spider silk is somewhat less strong than the silk of commerce (Benton 07).

The present author feels that accurate quantitative determination of the various elastic properties of cuticle would be of more interest to the biologists who study arthropods than data on any other physical properties except those concerned with permeability.

HARDNESS

Everyone is aware that calcified and sclerotized cuticles are hard, whereas intersegmental membranes and various other membranes are soft, but the terms "hard" and "soft" are only relative and are without quantitative meaning. It seems likely that all cuticles, even calcified cuticles, are soft in terms of a mineralogical scale. Whatever is the degree of hardness of the hardest arthropod cuticles, general qualitative observations suggest a complete range of hardnesses from this maximum down to highly viscous solutions. Considerable literature exists in connection with the abrasion of arthropod cuticles by dust particles (Alexander *et al.* 44a, b, Chiu 39, Germar 36, Lafon 48, Lees 47, Wigglesworth 44a, b, 45, 46, 47a), but it does not seem possible to interpret these data in terms of hardness other than as very rough approximations, because of the indirect nature of the tests, uncertainty as to what components of the cuticle are being scratched, and the complication introduced by adsorption on the surface of the particles being used (Dennell 45).

REFRACTIVE INDICES

All layers of the cuticle and also purified chitin have fairly high refractive indices (Table 11). The values lie in the range of 1.5–1.6. In general, softer and more hydrated cuticles have lower refractive indices, and the highest values are given by the waxy epicuticle. However, it seems that the values given should not be interpreted as more than first approximations because the lower values are obtained by the Becke line technique and the higher values from minima of birefringence curves (Fig. 25), both of which involve immersion in media of various refractive indices. This method is thoroughly reliable only when the immersion medium does not penetrate the specimen and introduce any change therein (Castle 36). Such a condition does not appear to be met in cuticle work. Similar difficulties are encountered with cellulose and silk, where the Becke line technique does not give the same value as the minimum in a birefringence curve (Frey-Wyssling 38). Nevertheless it seems that the values stated are approximations and that the epicuticle and sclerotized cuticle have higher refractive indices than soft cuticle. Calcified cuticles presumably can approach the higher refractive indices of calcite.

Of more biological interest than the absolute values of refractive index, is the fact that successive laminae in the chitin-protein portion of the cuticle (data pertain to noncalcified cuticles) have consider-

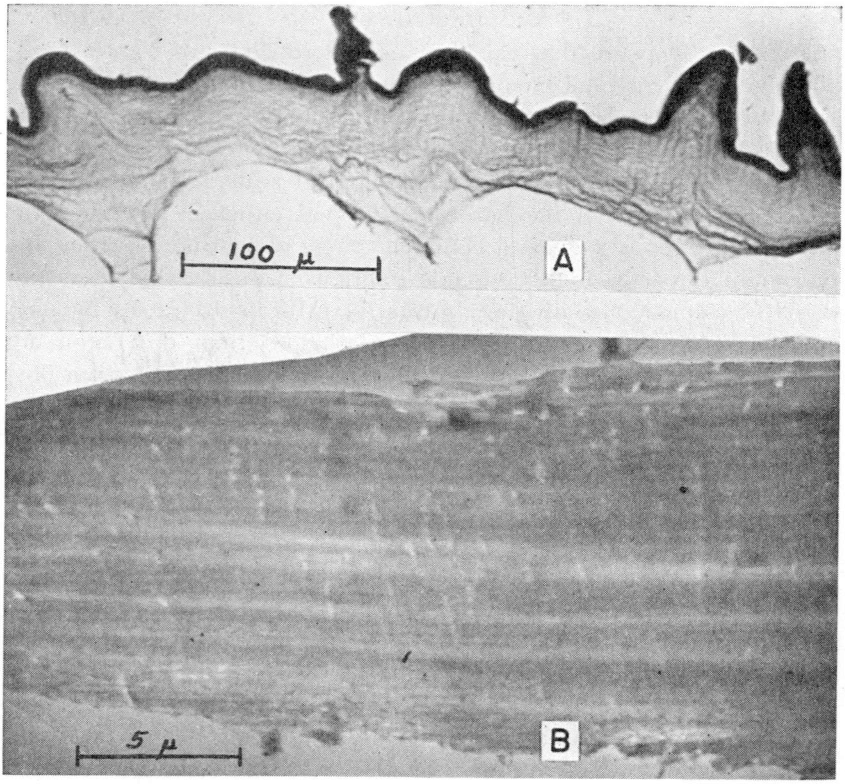

Figure 20. A. Light microscope picture of a section of the larval cuticle of a blowfly, *Phormia regina*, after soaking in water for several days. The laminations, visible because of differences in refractive index, are especially distinct in the swollen inner (= lower part of the picture) region. (After Richards and Fan.)
B. Electron microscope picture of a very thin section of the pronotum of a cockroach, *Periplaneta americana*. The thin laminations here are made visible because of differences in density. Incidentally, the vertical rows of lighter spots represent holes due to nearly longitudinal sections of the helical pore canals (see Figure 34). (After Richards and Anderson.)

ably different refractive indices (Fig. 20).[1] This is correlated with and probably directly related to the density differentiation of laminae already treated (p. 119). In fact, the best evidence suggests that laminae in the sense of discrete superimposed layers are nonexistent (Richards & Anderson 42a). The data are more consistent with the view that the laminar appearance is an illusion due to periodic dif-

[1] Mason (27b) has suggested values of 1.59 and 1.50–1.52, based on the cuticle of the iridescent beetle *Euphoria*, but careful measurements on a variety of species are desirable.

ferences in density distribution and consequently in refractive index (see p. 140).

ABSORPTION SPECTRA

Cuticular absorption curves are of interest primarily in delimiting the range of radiations that may be seen by an arthropod and in showing the degree of protection the cuticle may afford against the injurious photodynamic action of sunlight. The major cuticular components do not show sharp absorption peaks, which would be of assistance in identification, except perhaps in the inadequately studied infrared region. Chitin, silk, and cuticle all show high transparency for visible light, almost equally high transparency for the longer ultraviolet, and complete or nearly complete opacity for wave lengths shorter than 2500 Å (Fig. 21). For chitin there is apparently a gradually increasing absorption with the shorter waves of ultraviolet, although the determination covers only the bright lines of the mer-

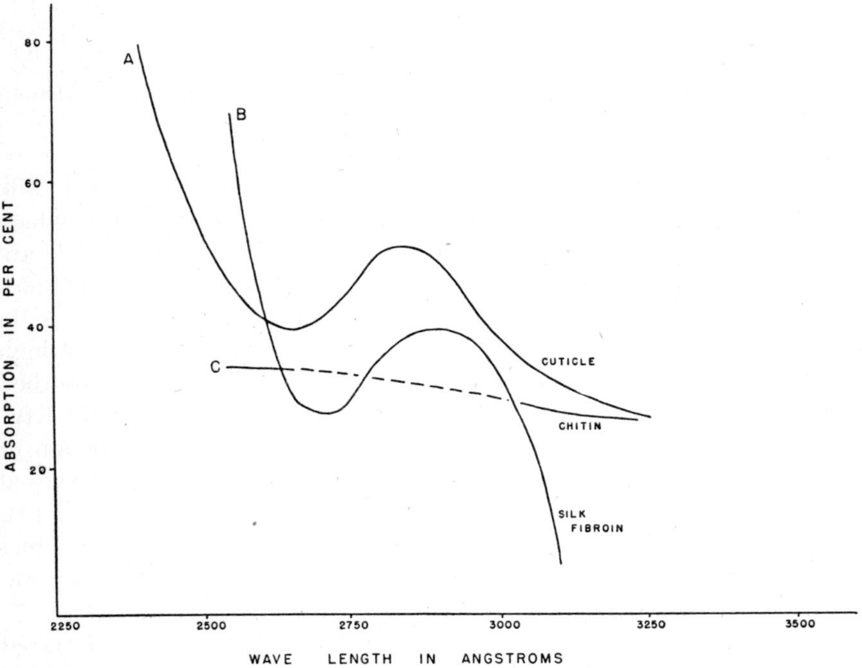

Figure 21. Ultraviolet absorption curves for cuticle, chitin, and silk fibroin. Unfortunately the data for chitin cover only the bright lines of the mercury spectrum and accordingly miss the interesting region which is given as a broken line. (Redrawn from published data: cuticle by Durand, Hollander, and Houlahan; chitin by Merker; silk fibroin by Coleman and Howitt.)

TABLE 12. PERCENTAGE OF LIGHT TRANSMITTED THROUGH CUTICLE
Values for only bright lines of mercury spectrum. (After Merker 39.)

Species	Thickness in Microns	Wave Length in Millimicrons						
		Blue	Violet	Ultraviolet				
		436	405	366	313	303	265	254
Epineuronia popularis, ommatidia	21	61.5	55.7	53.0	36.3	32.5	22.7	22.3
Apis mellifica, ommatidia	37	40.2	35.1	31.5	16.1	13.0	7.0	6.7
Dytiscus marginalis, ommatidia	98	9.5	6.0	4.7	0.8	0.6	0.12	0.09
May beetle elytron (pigmented)	120	0.4	0.3	0.05	0.04	0.02	0.00	0.00
May beetle elytron (bleached)	100[1]	34.0	28.3	18.5	12.1	9.6	5.6	5.0
Chitin film, crab (colorless)	20	61.5	55.7	53.0	36.3	32.5	22.7	22.3
Chitin film, crab	40	36.6	31.5	28.5	12.5	10.2	4.2	4.0
Chitin film, crab	60	23.2	17.3	14.9	4.8	3.4	1.2	1.1
Chitin film, May beetle	100	8.8	5.4	4.2	0.6	0.4	0.1	0.1

[1] Elytron bleached with Diaphanol. The thickness stated is that of the elytron; the effective thickness of chitin is not known, but is certainly much less.

cury spectrum rather than a continuous spectrum (Table 12). Silk fibroin has an increase in absorption in the range 2800–3000 Å, which presumably corresponds to a similar hump in the normal cuticle absorption curve. Presumably this lump is to be assigned to the arthropodin component of the cuticle. As shown by the two curves in Figure 21, transparent and lightly colored cuticles do transmit a high percentage of the longer ultraviolet rays, which are highly absorbed by underlying epithelial cells and internal organs. This would have to be true to allow the use of ultraviolet light for the production of mutations (Eloff & Bosazza 38) as well as for the reception of visual stimuli (Brecher 24, Hase 29, W. N. Hess 22, Merker 39, Weiss 46). Ultraviolet photomicrographs of sections of the cuticle of the bug *Aphelocheirus* show the epicuticle more transparent than the exocuticle (Thorpe & Crisp 47).

The picture concerning the transmission or absorption of infrared rays is not clear. Numerous attempts have been made to control insects by the heating effects of infrared and longer types of irradiation (Leao 41, MacLeod 41) without determination of which rays were penetrating or, indeed, what passed beyond the cuticle. Infra-

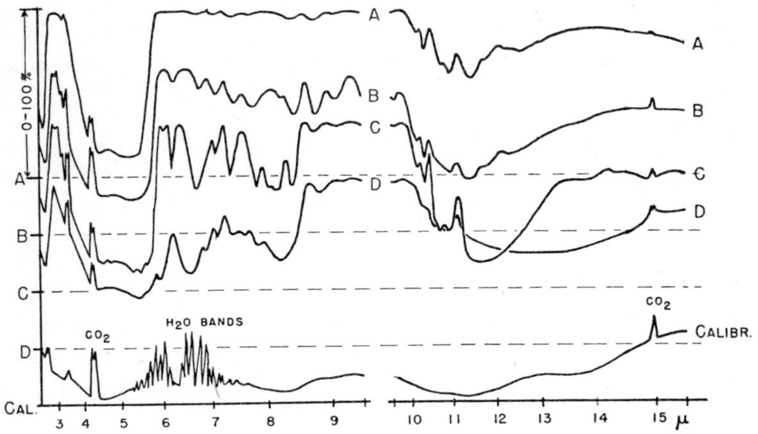

Figure 22. Infrared absorption curves from pronota of a cockroach, *Periplaneta americana.* All curves have the same values for ordinate and abscissa, but to keep them distinct have been drawn at different but overlapping levels. Thus, curve A has its zero base line at the level marked "A" on the left margin and extends to complete absorption in the distance labeled "0–100%". Curves B, C, and D similarly have their zero base lines at the levels indicated. At the bottom is a calibration curve showing the bands due to CO_2 and H_2O vapor. All curves were made under the direction of Dr. B. L. Crawford, using a Perkin-Elmer recording spectrometer, model 12-C, with a rocksalt prism.

A. Normal, fully pigmented pronotum. Cleaned by gentle rubbing in distilled water (3–4 changes over period of an hour); air-dried. Epidermal layer completely removed by the treatment.

B. Normal, unpigmented pronotum (specimen just molted). Cleaned as preceding.

C. Purified chitin. Pronotum treated with 6 changes of 10% NaOH at 100° C. over period of 8 hours; washed in acidified water overnight; air-dried.

D. Chitosan. Pronotum treated with conc. KOH at 160°–180° C. for half an hour; then fully decolorized by treatment with 10% KOH at 100° C. for an hour; then given a second half-hour treatment with conc. KOH at 160°–180° C.; washed in several changes of distilled water with constant stirring for about 2 hours; passed through acetone into ether, from which air-dried.

red irradiation may be presumed to penetrate better than visible light; and this is supported by the report that visible light results in more heating of dark cuticles than infrared light produces (Duspiva & Cerny 34). However, the relatively high percentage of reflection of infrared (about twice that of frog and lizard skins) is unexplained (Rücker 34), as is also the fact that reflected light may be circularly polarized (Gaubert 24).

Several absorption curves for the infrared region have been pub-

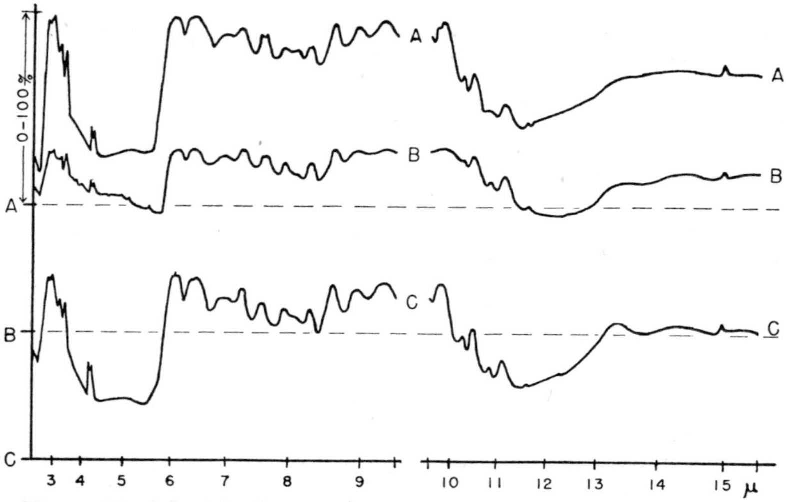

Figure 23. Infrared absorption curves for larval cuticle of a blowfly, *Phormia regina*. Explanation as for Figure 22.

A. Normal larval cuticle. Cleaned by gentle rubbing in distilled water (as for Figure 22A–B).

B. Chitin from larval cuticle. Treatment as for Figure 22C. The sheet shrank on drying, with resultant increase in thickness and in optical density.

C. Larval cuticle air-dried, then refluxed with boiling $CHCl_3$ for 2 hours; air-dried.

lished (Coblentz 12, Stair & Coblentz 35), but it is not clear whether these authors were dealing with cuticle, body wall, or an even more heterogeneous assemblage. Accordingly, some curves were made here from membranes whose composition was known in relation to the terminology employed in the present volume. In Figures 22–23, absorption curves are given for the range of 2.5 to 15 μ wave length. Four curves for the cockroach pronotum (plus a calibration curve) are given in Figure 22. The fully pigmented pronotum, *A*, is too nearly opaque except in the region 3.5–6 μ and above 10 μ to show anything of interest. The unpigmented pronotum, *B*, shows many clear peaks, as also do the curves for chitin, *C*, and chitosan, *D*. The normal cuticle shows all the chitin peaks, naturally, but additional absorption at about 6.5, 6.9, 8.1, 11.6, and 12.1 μ. The extra absorption at 11.6 and 12.1 μ may perhaps be related to the phenolic constituents, but it is not advisable to assign definite interpretations on the basis of available data. The chitosan curve is strikingly different from that of chitin in the regions 3.0–3.5, 6.0–6.8, 7.6, 8.3, and 13–14.3 μ; the first two might be related to the suggestion by Clark and Smith

(36) that some deamination is involved in the routine preparation of chitosan, but the last three are of completely unknown significance.[2]

The three curves from blowfly larvae (Fig. 23) are surprising in that no significant differences are shown; in other words, all show essentially the same peaks as the curves obtained from cockroach chitin – there is no indication of peaks at points where the normal cockroach cuticle differs from chitin. Quite likely the phenolic content of blowfly cuticles (at this age) is too low to show, but one would expect a protein such as arthropodin to show definite differences from chitin.

It is not desirable to attempt detailed interpretation of these infrared curves at present (see recent analysis by Darmon & Rudall 50). Comparison with the infrared absorption curve for silk is not possible because the only published data for silk cover the range 1.5–2.5 μ (Bath & Ellis 41), whereas our data for chitin and cuticles cover only longer wave lengths. However, all the curves are relatively rich in absorption peaks, and when the chemistry of cuticle and of chitin is better understood, the method may provide a useful and profitable tool.

FLUORESCENCE AND PHOSPHORESCENCE

Fluorescence is the emission of visible light by an object when it is irradiated by waves of shorter length (the longer ultraviolet rays are usually used); phosphorescence is the same phenomenon, but with a continuation of the emission of visible light for a sensible period after cessation of the irradiation. Both involve the absorption of some part of the shorter irradiation; they differ only in the speed with which the excited longer irradiation is emitted. The cuticle of crustacea and insects fluoresces a whitish or bluish white or greyish white, which is hardly to be considered distinctive since similar fluorescences are given by albumens, gelatin, keratin, tyrosine, glycogen, and a number of other compounds (Merker 31, Stübel 11). Obviously the several papers which report or imply that finding this

[2] Since these data have not been published and since it is not possible to read with precision from the small reproductions in Figures 22 and 23, it might be of use to have a listing of the values for the peaks shown. Using wave numbers (reciprocal to wave length), the normal cockroach cuticle, *B*, shows peaks at 3400, 3300, 3100, 2950, 1660, 1540, 1450, 1380, 1320, 1240, 1210, 1160, 1120, 1080, 1030, 975, 950, 895, and 825; chitin, *C*, shows peaks at 3450, 3300, 3100, 2920, 2880, 1660, 1630, 1570, 1420, 1380, 1315, 1260, 1207, 1160, 1120, 1070, 1020, 975, 950, 920, 895, 755, and 703; chitosan, *D*, shows peaks at 3400, 2860, 1700, 1600, 1460, 1420, 1380, 1320, 1300, 1260, 1155, 960, 950, and 895.

fluorescence in an arthropod structure indicates the presence of chitin are wrong, for the fluorescence is not at all distinctive (Beer 31a, b, c, Metcalf 45, Salfi 37). Actually, the present author, while investigating the possible use of the method, found that whereas intact cuticle either wet or dry gave strong fluorescence, carefully purified chitins gave only extremely faint fluorescence. Also certain membranes completely negative for chitin tests (e.g., honeybee tracheae) are equally fluorescent. It seems reasonable to suggest, therefore, that the major portion of the fluorescence is due to the protein rather than the chitin portion of cuticle. Perhaps this could be related to a greater absorption in the 2800–3000 Å region by arthropodin.

Amusing to a biologist is the fact that a patent has been granted for using fluorescence to separate shell fragments from lobster and crab meat prior to packaging for sale. The chopped-up meat ready for packaging is run on an endless belt through a dark room under a strong ultraviolet lamp. An attendant spots and removes pieces of cuticle which stand out because of the strong fluorescence (Gibson 37).

BIREFRINGENCE

The optical properties of calcareous skeletons have already been treated in the section on inorganic constituents (p. 103). The birefringence of chitinous tendons was first noted by Biedermann in 1902 and has since been repeatedly observed. The most extensive review is in Frey-Wyssling's treatise (38). The optic axis is the chitin micelle axis. The amplitude of birefringence[3] varies considerably depending both on composition and on orientation (Fig. 24). The amplitude is rather low in the general cuticle, where the micelles are arranged more or less randomly in a plane parallel to the surface (Browning 42, Pryor 40b), is considerably higher in setae when the micelles are reasonably parallel to the axis of the seta (Castle 36, Lees & Picken 45, Picken 49), and is highest in muscle tendons, where the stress has produced a very high degree of orientation (Clark & Smith 36). In all cases the amplitude of birefringence is said to be greatly increased by removal of the nonchitinous components, but it is not certain

[3] The use of birefringence in biology is largely for determination of the direction and degree of orientation of anisotropic molecules. Isotropy may indicate either truly isotropic material or a statistical isotropy due to random orientation of anisotropic particles. The actual optical constants involved are of secondary interest. A number of simplified presentations of the technique and its application are available (Richards 44a, W. J. Schmidt 28) as well as technical treatises (Ambronn & Frey 26).

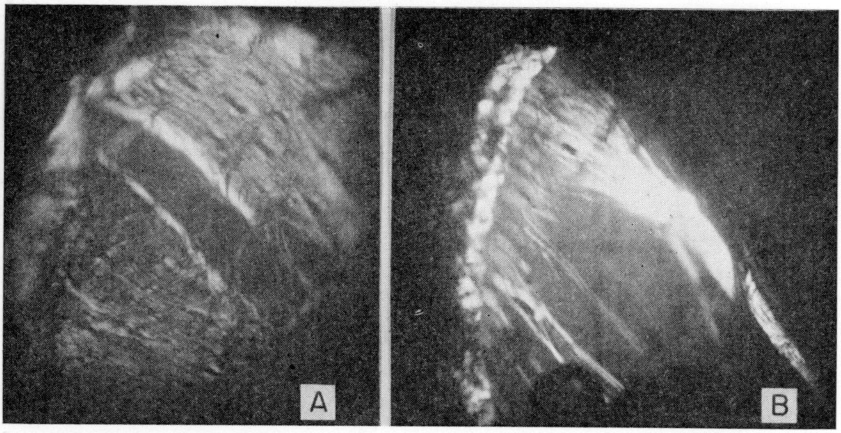

Figure 24. The birefringence of purified chitin from the leg of a tarantula. (Original.)

A. Portion of leg cuticle showing nearly parallel fibers (10–20 μ in diameter) separated by less strongly birefringent (= less well oriented) material. Note how the fibers separate and pass around the setal sockets.

B. Rim at end of leg joint with attached tendon. The rim is the nearly vertical light band on the left; the tendon is the very bright band extending diagonally to the right. The use of a full-wave compensator shows that the micelles in the tendon extend at a right angle to those in the rim to which the tendon attaches.

which is the correct explanation of this increase (see page 84). It is generally agreed that arthropod chitin possesses a fairly strong positive form birefringence, that is, a birefringence due to the shape of the molecule or micelle, and a weak negative intrinsic birefringence (Fig. 25), but efforts to assess these two components have been fraught with technical difficulties due to oriented imbibition (Castle 36, Diehl & van Iterson 35, Möhring 26, Frey-Wyssling 38, Picken 49, W. J. Schmidt 28, 34b, 36a). As to be expected, the birefringence is altered by nitration and by acetylation (W. J. Schmidt 34a, 39c). Neither cuticle nor chitin is pleochroitic, but they can be made so by appropriate staining (W. J. Schmidt 29, 36b, 37a). Many illustrations of birefringent structures, both calcified and noncalcified, can be found in the papers and books by W. J. Schmidt and Frey-Wyssling.

Since birefringence is used primarily for demonstration of molecular orientations, the data are better treated under appropriate portions of the anatomical section. In passing, we might mention here that birefringence is also shown by silk fibers (Chamot & Mason 44, Frey-Wyssling 38, Ohara 33a, b), by various wing scales of butterflies and moths, in which the orientation depends on the type of scale

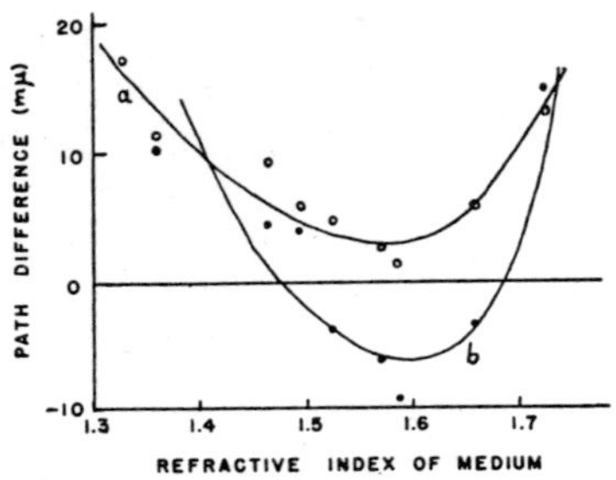

Figure 25. Birefringence curves given by chitin purified from the lateral marginal scales on the wings of *Ephestia Kühniella.* Minima in such curves give the refractive index. (a) Scales treated with 10% KOH at 90°–100° C. for about 18 hours. (b) Scales treated with Diaphanol for 14 days. The curves are drawn for convenience only, and the wide scattering of points shows how subjective the values are. Note that the curve dips below the zero line (i.e., exhibits negative intrinsic birefringence when the stronger positive form birefringence is masked) after treatment with Diaphanol, but not after treatment with alkali. (After Picken.)

being studied (Gentil 41, Picken 49, W. J. Schmidt 42a, b, Tshirvinsky 26), as a mosaic in chitinous laminae in the cocoons of a beetle, *Donacia* (Picken *et al.* 47), as concentric circles of isotropic and anisotropic material (reminiscent of Liesegang rings) (Biedermann 03), in the egg shell and its cement in lice (W. J. Schmidt 39a), in a special type of cross-fiber arrangement in the tracheae of insects (Fig. 54) (Richards & Korda 48, 50), and in only alternate laminae in the cuticle of ticks (P. Schulze 32). The report of isotropic chitin in *Limulus* presumably represents a statistical isotropy (Lafon 43a, Waterman 50), but the different optics for chitin from *Ascaris* egg shells is difficult to rationalize (W. J. Schmidt 36b).

OPTICAL ROTATION

The only paper dealing with specific rotatory power of chitin is an old one covering six species of arthropods (crustacea, arachnids, and insects) (J. C. Irvine 09). It records a specific rotation for an HCl solution at 20° C. to the D line of sodium light of —14.1°, in contrast to a value of +56.0° for glucosamine HCl. The method is said to be sensitive for chitin detection with as little as 100 mg. (with micro methods these rotational data could now be obtained with only a few mg.). Values for soluble and dispersed silk fibroin in aqueous media are —53.1° and —58.9° (Coleman & Howitt 47).

ISOELECTRIC POINTS

Differing isoelectric points are one of the factors involved in differential staining with certain dye mixtures. Approximate determinations using staining methods (Loeb 22) have been made on a few crustacea, insects, and arachnids (Table 11). The only use to which these data have been put so far is to support suggestions for the homologizing of subdivisions of crustacean cuticles with subdivisions of insectan cuticles (Dennell 46). What relationship the isoelectric points may bear to the isoionic points is not known.

SORPTION

In view of the common use of starch and cellulose in chromatographic adsorption columns, it is not surprising that direct demonstration of sorption has been obtained with chitin and cuticle (Richards & Cutkomp 46). Purified chitin from lobster shells was found to sorb an average of 17 mg./g. with a range of 11–25 mg./g. from 0.05% suspensions of DDT, and the amount sorbed was proportional to both time and concentration (Lord 48). After grinding in a mechanical mortar the same material sorbed 44–51 mg./g. However general the sorption by chitin may be, a considerable specificity is shown by these DDT data; thus, while DDT is readily adsorbed by activated charcoal, essentially negative results were obtained with tests on the sorption of DDT by asbestos, snail shells, coral, sea urchin spines, sheep wool, erythrocytes, chunks of muscle, and two different types of cellulose. It was therefore suggested that the phenomenon involves a chemisorption related to the acetylamine side groups. Various DDT analogues are also sorbed by chitin, but no systematic series of tests with other groups of chemicals is available.

The increased intensity of the 44 Å X-ray diffraction spots produced from the 33 Å spots on wetting dried cuticles shows that the water has enhanced the regularity of the crystal lattice and so must be fitting into special positions (Fraenkel & Rudall 47), but the nature of the attraction and bonding is not known.

It might be worth mentioning that alkali is readily washed from chitosan, but is much more strongly bound to chitin and can be removed only incompletely by exhaustive washing (Richards unpubl.). Also, glucosamine and acetylglucosamine are both adsorded on and can be separated on chromatographic adsorption columns (Freudenberg *et al.* 42, Hough *et al.* 48).

There is indirect evidence for sorption in the anomalies encountered in obtaining imbibition curves for form birefringence (Fig. 25) and perhaps in some of the data on pleochroism (Castle 36, Diehl & van Iterson 35, Frey-Wyssling 38, W. J. Schmidt 29, 36a, 37a). It has been suggested that cinnamic aldehyde, benzaldehyde, and aniline show oriented adsorption on the colloidal chitin framework. A more direct demonstration of sorption is shown by the change in the refractive index of solutions containing KI plus HgI_2 following immersion of chitin in the solution. Calculating from the change in refractive index, it is reported that chitin can adsorb approximately 30 mg. equivalents from solution (Diehl & van Iterson 35). The data from pleochroism[4] suggest that in some cases it is the sorbed dye which is crystalline and pleochroitic but that in other cases the pleochroitic effect is really due to the chitin (W. J. Schmidt 29, 37a). It certainly seems that these optical phenomena are most readily explained by some form of sorption, even though the data are essentially qualitative. Similar anomalies are shown by silk and cellulose (Frey-Wyssling 38).

At the present time it does not seem profitable to speculate on whether or not sorption plays a significant role in the development of arthropod cuticles. Also it is difficult to determine in such a heterogeneous complex when one is dealing with sorption and when with very weak chemical bonds. It does seem evident, however, that the inner layer of wax molecules is bound to the underlying protein in the epicuticle by forces considerably stronger than those of adsorption (Beament 48a, b). Sorptions are almost certainly involved in the various imbibition phenomena which will be discussed in other sections. Sorption has been demonstrated with the insecticide DDT and together with a postulated surface migration of the adsorbed molecules (Volmer 32, 38) has been made the basis of a hypothesis concerning the differential toxicity of this insecticide (Fan *et al.* 48, Richards & Cutkomp 46). But preliminary data do not indicate the same type of story with other insecticides. Accumulations that might involve sorption have been recorded from studies on nicotine, pyridine, and piperidine applied as gaseous insecticides (Glover & Richardson 36). Sorption methods have been used for the calculation of available internal surfaces in some materials (Schofield 47), but the technique has not been applied to cuticles as yet. Quite likely further study will show that sorption phenomena play a more important role in cuticular phenomena than is realized at present.

IMBIBITION AND SWELLING

It is well known that cuticle shrinks on drying and swells on rewetting, but no systematic study has been made of what chemicals cause swelling and what ones do not. Several methods of study are

[4] The property of appearing differently colored depending on the crystal axis along which the material is viewed.

available, with direct micrometer measurements being of greatest general applicability. Differences in wet and dry weight can be used, but are likely to contain significant errors unless correction is made for water held in relatively large spaces such as the pore canals and gland ducts. Those cuticles which show strong interference colors can be studied by interferometry for the one plane that is involved in production of these colors. And finally, X-ray diffraction studies, and to a much lesser degree birefringence analyses, are used for determining the nature of the swelling.

Of most biological interest is the demonstration that swelling is not equal in all planes, but is much greater in the direction perpendicular to the surface of the cuticle than in either of the surface directions (Table 13) (Fraenkel & Rudall 47). Combining these data with the

TABLE 13. SWELLING OF AIR-DRIED CUTICLE ON REWETTING WITH WATER
(After Fraenkel & Rudall 47.)

Species and Type	Plane of Surface %	Perpendicular to Surface %
Sarcophaga, white pupa	7.4	56
Sarcophaga, hard puparium	1.7	31
Locusta, abdomen	2.1	31
Dixippus, dorsal thorax	1.0	40
Dixippus, ventral abdomen	1.4	49

X-ray evidence for the orientation of micelles in the plane of the surface, it follows that there is a rotational orientation of the chains or micelles such that the swelling is largely limited to one direction. Since X-ray diffraction studies also show that the side chains of the molecule are oriented perpendicular to the surface, it follows that the swelling due to water is in the same direction as these side chains. This orientation is less perfect in softer cuticle, and it seems highly probable, therefore, that the greater swelling and shrinking in the plane of the surface in softer cuticles are to be related to this difference.

A few quantitative percentage values are given by Fraenkel and Rudall (Table 13), and these are in general agreement with unpublished values obtained in the author's laboratory for cuticles of *Limulus*, scorpions, cockroaches, and mosquito larvae. It would seem, therefore, that this general picture is likely to be widely applicable to noncalcified cuticles. Comparable measurements are not available for calcified cuticles. The values obtained are reasonably constant for a particular species, age, and region. The values are not related to the ecological habitat occupied by the species (Eder 40, Kühnelt 39).

The values given in Table 13 were obtained from measurement of the swelling of dried cuticles on rewetting. It seems probably incorrect to assume that these also represent the amount a normal cuticle shrinks on drying, because it has been shown that blowfly cuticles contain approximately 70% water if they are dissected in water but only approximately 55% water if they are dissected in oil (Dennell 46). Biologically speaking, this indicates that the cuticle on a living animal is not swollen to the full equilibrium value with water. General treatments on swelling show that the amount is influenced by pH, by isoelectric point, by salts, etc. (Katz 33, Vonk 31). It may also be influenced by the past history of the membrane (Carr & Sollner 43). It seems unnecessary to point out that studies on cuticular swelling and shrinking should be carefully controlled and the conditions explicitly stated.

In some cases cuticle swells to reasonably constant values, but the value depends on the chemical being used. This is particularly well studied by interferometry with cuticles showing natural physical colors (Anderson & Richards 42b, C. W. Mason 26, 27a, b, 29). With certain chemicals the amount of swelling is constant (e.g., ethyl alcohol), but with others it is variable and may go to very high values or even lead to solution of the cuticle. Thus the vapors of NH_3 and phenol produce considerable swelling, but constant, repeatable values are not readily obtained, and acidified solutions of glycerine, certain lithium salts, especially hot, etc. may lead to solution (Alsberg & Hedblom 09, Kunike 25, von Veimarn 26–28). The nature of the swelling and layer separation produced by bromine water (Goux 44) requires further study. The swelling with water is largely intermicellar as shown by the fact that the X-ray diffraction pattern is unchanged except for the shift of the 33 Å spots to a 44 Å position (Clark & Smith 36, Fraenkel & Rudall 47, Katz & Mark 24). Like cellulose (Hermans 46), both chitin and cuticle are somewhat hygroscopic, and complete removal of the water is difficult. For instance, we have obtained significantly lower weights from material dried in a vacuum oven than from comparable pieces dried to constant weight over P_2O_5 at room temperatures. Also there is a rapid regain in humid air.

As treated in some detail elsewhere (p. 185), cuticles shrink on hardening; thus the soft larval cuticle of blowflies shortens and shrinks from 150 μ to 70 μ in thickness on changing into the hard puparium (Dennell 47a). This shrinking involves both closer packing of molecules and dehydration.

Data from dried cuticles should not be interpreted as indicating more than the amount and direction of shrinking and tightness of packing which are possible. For instance, it has been reported that sections of cockroach cuticle dried by heating in the high vacuum within an electron microscope, can, under influence of the electron bombardment, shrink somewhat more and change into what looks like a mass of soap bubbles (Richards & Anderson 42a). This has been interpreted as indicating an evolution of gas within the cuticle section; the gas, being unable to escape, produces this series of bubbles. The gas was not identified, but since few gases have diameters greater than 20 Å, it was suggested that these dried and overshrunken cuticles have no pores or very few pores of this diameter. These data still appear to be valid, but they should not be interpreted as indicating more than that an unnaturally dried cuticle can attain this extreme degree of tight packing. The data should not be used in connection with problems on penetration of natural cuticles (Wigglesworth 45).

WETTABILITY

The question of the wetting of cuticle and the subsequent spreading of material on it is of immense importance in insect control. Accordingly it is rather surprising to find that while there are a large number of qualitative observational data, there is a distinct paucity of reliable quantitative figures – see the review by Hoskins (40). A large literature deals with the more complex problem of insecticidal spraying, but it is ordinarily not possible to separate the cuticle data from these complex pictures (Chapman *et al.* 43, Ebeling 39, Ginsburg 29, Hacker 25, Hoskins 33, 41, Manzelli 41, O'Kane *et al.* 30, Pearce *et al.* 42, Stellwaag 23). Quantitative evaluation usually consists of a visual measurement of one of the angles of contact (Beament 45b, Hoskins & BenAmotz 38, Stellwaag 23). In a few cases solvent action has been considered (Nitsche 33, Wigglesworth 41, 42c).

Some quantitative data on terrestrial insects are given in Figures 26 and 27, and some additional similar data are in the literature (Hoskins 40, Stellwaag 23, Wilcoxon & Hartzell 31). One might easily say that the diversity of data shown in Figure 27 is to be expected

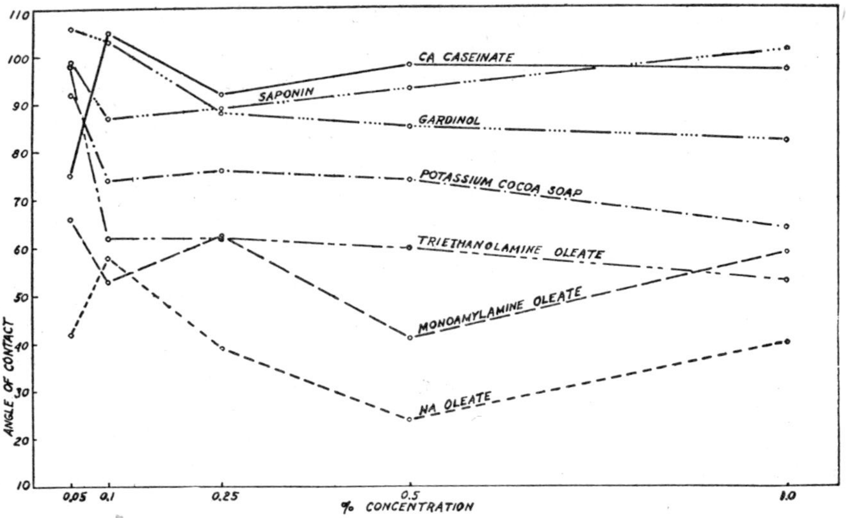

Figure 26. The contact angle given by the indicated substances on the dorsal abdominal surface of *Aphis rumicis* as a function of concentration. Note the absence of a sensible concentration effect. (After O'Kane, Glover, and Westgate.)

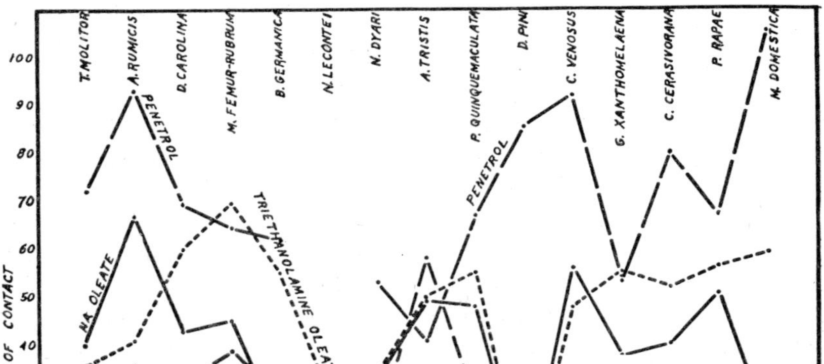

Figure 27. Graph showing the differences in wetting resulting from the application of droplets at 0.5% concentration of the four named detergents on fifteen test species of insects. No detergent gave even closely similar results on all the species used. (After O'Kane, Westgate, and Glover.) Generic names of the insects used were abbreviated. Reading from left to right they are: *Tenebrio, Aphis, Dissosteira, Melanoplus, Blatella, Neodiprion, Neodiprion, Anasa, Phlegethontius, Dilachnus, Cerastipsocus, Galerucella, Cacoecia, Pieris,* and *Musca.*

and indicates a certain amount of diversity in the nature of the outer layer on these different insects—which diversity would be considerably greater if one added values for aquatic arthropods with hydrophilic cuticles. However, the absence of any sensible concentration effect, as shown in Figure 26, is confusing and remains to be explained. See the recent paper by Pal (50).

Much as one would prefer quantitative data, some of the qualitative data are still interesting and suggestive. A vast majority of arachnids and insects have distinctly hydrophobic cuticles, whereas the crustacea tend to be hydrophilic. But *Limulus*, a number of insect larvae (Crawford 12, Pryor 40b, Thorpe 30a, b, 31, Wigglesworth 45), and some adults of insects (Brocher 10, 14, Wigglesworth 48b) are in whole or part distinctly hydrophilic. Mosquito larvae are perhaps the best-known example of a form that is in general hydrophilic but has restricted areas that are hydrophobic (Hacker 25). The general body surface of mosquito larvae is freely wetted by water and may be rewetted after the surface has been air-dried (living larvae), but after having been air-dried, it is also freely wetted by mineral oils (Richards 41). Furthermore, mosquito larvae reaching an oil-water interface usually remain in the water fraction, but with some oils (e.g., Oil of Thyme) are slowly "pulled" into the oil layer. Another example of cuticles wettable by either oil or water is shown in those cases where there is normally a movement of aqueous fluid in the tracheoles during respiration and yet these tubes can be completely filled with oil (Wigglesworth 30a). The situation is further complicated by the observation that the degree of wettability of tracheae seems to vary both with age or stage and with area (Keister 48).

It is usually assumed that the hydrofuge properties (when present) are due to waxes or other lipids. This is not necessarily true. In the bug *Aphelocheirus* the waterproofing is definitely not due to waxes but to other hydrophobic surface molecules; after wetting with the aid of a detergent, the hydrofuge property is readily restored by washing and drying (Crisp & Thorpe 48). This may well be true for some other species also.

A number of papers deal with the penetration of oil into the tracheae of insects where the situation is complicated by an uneven surface, the tubular structure, and probably the presence of pressure in front of the advancing column. It is certainly generally true that the tracheal lining is hydrophobic and lyophilic, and this property has been capitalized upon for making anatomical preparations of the tracheal system (Hagmann 40, Krogh 17). In most of these papers the oil is simply applied to a spiracle (Gäbler 39, Keister 48, F. C. Nelson 27, Wilcoxon & Hartzell 31), but this is likely to be deceptive as a number of compounds which will not penetrate through a closed spiracle will nevertheless spread once they are within the tracheal system. In the most extensive paper, over a hundred miscellaneous organic compounds were introduced directly into the tracheal system of mosquito larvae by microinjection (Richards & Weygandt 45). The results were not found to be expressible in terms of some one property, for although the benzene derivatives and cyclohexane appeared to give the best distribution a wide scattering of unrelated chemicals gave almost as good results. It seems probable that similar problems and results will be encountered with the penetration through micropyles of insect egg shells, though there will be special details (Beament 48a, b).

Unfortunately it appears to have been tacitly assumed by many workers that the surface of the cuticle is a static system not affected by the substances being used to study wetting and spreading. Perhaps this is an irrelevant criticism for papers dealing with the formulation of insecticidal sprays, but it is certainly not irrelevant for a consideration of wettability itself (Wigglesworth 41, 42c). It seems to the present author that some of the anomalies in existing data may well be occasioned by the nearly universal failure to determine this point. Despite the obvious technical difficulties involved, it seems desirable to design experiments so that one may reassess the normalcy of the cuticle surface after it has been used for a measurement.

LARGER PERIODICITIES

Gross periodicities which are many times the crystal lattice dimensions are well known in arthropod cuticles because of their relation to the production of physical colors. Periodicities have been inferred from optical studies on iridescent insects, notably in the now classical papers by C. W. Mason (26–29) and Süffert (24), and more recently have been directly examined and measured by electron microscopy (Anderson & Richards 42a, b, Kinder & Süffert 43, Kühn & An 46). A discussion of the production of physical colors will be given subsequently (Chapter 21); here only the diversity, magnitude, and conceivable methods of production of these periodicities will be considered.

Periodicities in the range of one twentieth of a micron to several microns are well known, with a sizable percentage of the cases occurring in the more restricted range of from one to several tenths of a micron (Figs. 20B, 55, 59). In fact, these spacings, which are approximately half a wave length of visible light, are so common that it may be these represent the fundamental periodicities from which longer and shorter spacings are derived by shrinking and swelling. Spacings, usually somewhat larger, are best known and most widely known in the laminae paralleling the surface of the cuticle of various arthropods (Fig. 20), and have been seen in sections in most, if not all, of the arthropod groups (p. 174). Spacings of different architecture but similar magnitude have been found in the wing scales of butterflies, moths, and mosquitoes (Fig. 59) (Anderson & Richards 42b, Kinder & Süffert 43), the microtrichia on mosquito wings and centipede antennae (Richards 44b, Richards & Korda 47), in longitudinal ridges on setae (Lees & Picken 45), in the chitinous laminae in certain beetle cocoons (Picken *et al.* 47), and doubtless in numerous other cuticular structures as yet unreported.[5] Rasping structures involved in sound production are well known, but usually of larger magnitude (Prochnow 07); for instance, the beetle *Cerambyx cerdo* has a remarkable file, composed of thousands of small parallel ridges on the cuticle surface. Similar periodicities can also be produced in silk fibrinogen pressed between glass plates (Ramsden 38). The periodicities may be found in calcified cuticles as well as in noncalcified ones (Balss 27).

Other than the existence and spacing of these periodicities, rather few facts are known. Periodicities are not limited to cuticles containing chitin (Anderson & Richards 42b, Richards 47b), and, in fact, the periodicities in cuticle sections may be lost following extraction with alkali (Richards & Anderson 42a). The electron microscope examinations show clearly that the laminae are not truly superimposed layers but periodic distribution phenomena within a continuous layer (Fig. 20B). The longitudinal striations in setae begin very close together and then become much more widely spaced as the seta grows larger (Lees & Picken 45). Spacings may be either increased or decreased by imbibition or drying (Mason 29). Clearly, the spacings are too large to be explained as monolayer phenomena (Fraenkel & Rudall 47). Particularly suggestive is the fact that the spacings may develop

[5] The periodicities involved in Liesegang ring phenomena in color patterns are considerably larger (E. Becker 37b, 38, Biedermann 03, Gebhardt 12, Huttrer 32). They are said to be due to electric potentials comparable to liquid junction potentials (Christomanos 50).

away from direct cell influence, and accordingly are not necessarily produced by the mode of deposition used by the epidermal cells.[6]

A phenomenon which seems capable of accounting for the known facts is that of Schiller planes studied by Freundlich (32). Large particles in colloidal suspension tend to become organized in horizontal planes with vertical periodicities, comparable to cuticular periodicities, probably as a result of electrostatic forces, with the particles aggregating in energy troughs produced by minima in the resultant of electrostatic repulsive and attractive forces. With flat particles, spacings up to half a micron are quite feasible. Subsequent swelling would have to be invoked to explain larger spacings, but such an increase is already known for setal ridges (Lees & Picken 45).

In some respects the idea of periodic crystallizations with competition for precursors (Becker 38, Picken 49) comes equally close to fitting the facts. Periodic crystallizations occur more rapidly and can give much larger spacings — in fact, the major difficulty is that known periodic spacings due to crystallization are much too large (macroscopic).

Reasonable as either of these two suggestions (which are not mutually exclusive) can be made to appear, neither is readily proved in such a heterogeneous system as arthropod cuticle. (See also Chapter 19.)

[6] Cases include the development of laminae in *Donacia* cocoons, which harden from a gross fluid secretion (Picken *et al.* 47), the increase in number of laminae in the exocuticle of *Sarcophaga* coincident with its thickening *after* separation from the epidermal cells (Fig. 35) (Dennell 46), and presumably the extra laminae commonly intercalated in thickened lenses (Fig. 52) (Verhoeff 26-32).

Section II

THE MICROANATOMY AND DEVELOPMENT OF THE INTEGUMENT

CHAPTER 16

The General Structure

In beginning a treatment of the general structure, or histology, of the arthropod integument (Figs. 1, 30, etc.), one is faced with the necessity of having a classification of subdivisions or subheadings and with defining the terms to be used. Definitions are by nature arbitrary, and terms tend to become indefinable by the finding of intermediates and exceptional cases, although the exceptions seem less serious in cytology and histology than in gross anatomy.

It is not difficult to argue that the cuticle is an entity rather than a complex and, accordingly, that any set of terms for subdivisions is artificial and capable of only limited application. One has only to emphasize the diversity and exceptions, and so conclude with the fact that the one common denominator is that the cuticle is a secreted layer of protein which may be modified by either the subsequent or simultaneous secretion of other components (Richards 47a, b). But such stress on the cuticle being an entity does not decrease the diversity, nor does it lessen the need for terms representing certain portions of the cuticle. At most this is a point of view which helps to bring the diversity together into one coherent picture and relegate the subdivisions and the terms to a distinctly subordinate position. Doubtless many will prefer to think of the cuticle as a complex, as though the subdivisions were discrete entities superimposed one on another and cemented together (Wigglesworth 48b). The matter is one of choice and does not particularly affect the treatment given. The material will be presented here following a coherent scheme in which the integument is viewed as an organ system which is largely a self-contained entity.

The tendency in modern cytology and histology is to use chemical definitions or to redefine older names in terms of the chemical constituents involved. This is due to the fact that such definitions have most value for cytology and histology. The tendency is well shown by the terms which have been proposed for various subdivisions of

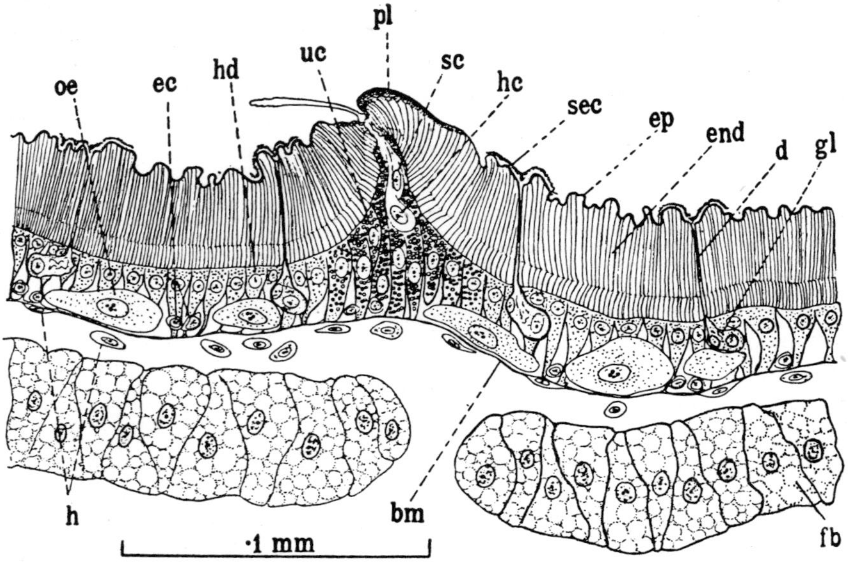

Figure 28. Semidiagrammatic longitudinal section of the tergites of a fourth instar nymph of *Rhodnius prolixus*. *bm* = basement membrane; *d* = duct of dermal gland; *ec* = "embryonic cells"; *end* = endocuticle; *ep* = epicuticle; *fb* = fat body (adipose tissue); *gl* = dermal gland; *h* = haematocytes or blood cells; *hc* = trichogen or hair-forming cell; *hd* = epidermal cells; *oe* = oenocytes; *pl* = plaque bearing a bristle; *sc* = tormogen or socket-forming cell; *sec* = secretion of dermal gland (see under tectocuticle); *uc* = urate cells. (After Wigglesworth.)

the epicuticle in recent years – these being chemical names when there is some indication of the chemical nature of the particular subdivision.

The term cuticle is to be defined as the material secreted onto or deposited on the outer surface of the epidermal cells and solidifying there to form the exoskeleton. An attempt to redefine cuticle in chemical terms would need to lay stress on the one class of chemical compounds which is found in almost all of the subdivisions, namely, protein (Richards 47b). Arthropod cuticle would then be defined or distinguished as a proteinaceous layer secreted onto the outer surface of the epidermal cells, modified in various ways by the addition of lipids, tanning agents, sometimes calcareous deposits, and almost always containing the polysaccharide chitin in its inner portion. Alternatively, one may define arthropod cuticle as a double set of layers both of which are essentially conjugated proteins: the outer set being basically composed of lipoproteins (plus lipids and tanning agents), the inner set usually composed of glycoproteins or mucopolysaccharides (plus tanning agents and sometimes calcareous deposits) (Haworth 46, Picken 49, Wigglesworth 48b). These two definitions are essentially similar, but the second method of expression has the advantage of emphasizing that the major cuticular components seem to be formed and secreted as already conjugated proteins. No one portion of either of these definitions will suffice to distinguish the cuticle of arthropods from exoskeletons of other animal groups, but the total histological and chemical picture is distinctive of the phylum.

A generalized scheme of the classification of subdivisions that will be recognized in subsequent pages is indicated by the following diagram:

- integument
  - cuticle
    - epicuticle (nonchitinous)
      - a
        - tectocuticle ("cement layer")
        - lipid epicuticle ("wax layer")
        - protein epicuticle
          - polyphenol layer
          - cuticulin layer
      - b
        - lipoprotein
        - basal protein
    - procuticle (chitin-protein)
      - a (noncalcified)
        - exocuticle (sclerotized)
        - endocuticle
      - b (noncalcified)
        - exocuticle? (hard but not sclerotized)
        - endocuticle
      - c (calcified)
        - exocuticle (sclerotized and calcified)
        - endocuticle
          - calcified
          - uncalcified
      - d (all above)
        - primary (pre-exuvial)
        - secondary (post exuvial)
  - epidermis
    - typical or ordinary cells
    - tegumental and dermal glands (including peristigmatic glands)
    - specialized cells
      - sense organs (including setae)
      - scales
      - glands not associated with cuticle production
      - miscellaneous
    - occasional cells
      - oenocytes
      - blood cells
  - basement membrane

Ever since the now classical early paper by Wigglesworth (33) it has been recognized that the most important subdivision of the cuticle is into an inner part containing chitin and an outer part without chitin. Of course, to a certain extent this division is arbitrary, but it gives the best classification when considering the entire phylum or even an entire class. The outer portion, or, if you wish, set of layers, is negative to chitin tests [1] and is called the epicuticle. For the inner portion of the cuticle, commonly accounting for considerably more than 95% of the total thickness and containing both chitin and protein, the term procuticle is here proposed.[2] The simplest terminology to cover those cases where chitin appears to be absent is to say that such cuticles consist solely of epicuticle.

The epicuticle, seemingly in general, is composed of at least two fundamentally different layers, which Dennell (46) has appropriately termed the protein epicuticle and lipid epicuticle. The terms "protein" and "lipid" are not intended to imply chemical purity, but only the predominant composition of the portions concerned. Considering the processes involved in the formation of these portions (p. 165), it is not surprising that further subdivisions can be satisfactorily defined in certain cases. In a few cases (certain beetles, the bug *Rhodnius*) another material of uncertain chemical composition is poured out from glands onto the outer surface of the epicuticle. This may harden over the outer surface as a more or less complete layer and may have considerable significance for the wettability of the cuticle. The term tectocuticle is proposed for it.[3]

[1] But see the discussion of negative chitin tests, p. 34.

[2] The most common current usage is to use the term endocuticle in a dual sense, that is, both for the original transparent chitin-protein portion of the cuticle and for that portion of this original which remains in a soft, apparently unmodified form. The dual usage is made particularly confusing by the fact that the term is used both histologically and anatomically. Such a dual usage of a single term in one structure is inconsistent with embryological terminology in general. A new term is needed to circumvent the confusion. It seems to the present author that less confusion will result by retaining the term endocuticle for the soft portion of the chitin-protein layer in fully differentiated cuticle, and proposing a new term for the original undifferentiated material. Accordingly the term procuticle is proposed for the embryologically original (parent) chitin-protein fraction.

[3] Such secretions, poured onto the fully formed surface of the epicuticle, and drying and hardening there, have been referred to by various names. Kühnelt (28c) called the layer an "accessory layer," Brocher (14) referred to it as simply an "inert grey secretion," and Wigglesworth (47b) termed it in *Rhodnius* the "cement layer." The first is ambiguous, the second a description rather than a term, and the third is inappropriate because not in keeping with usage of the

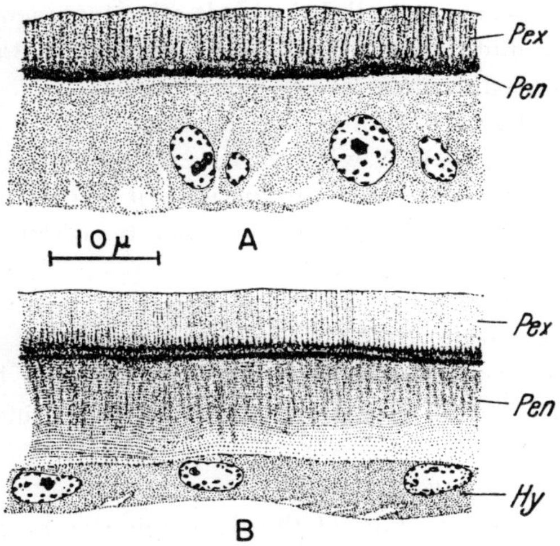

Figure 29. Sections of the integument of the pupa of a moth, *Ephestia Kühniella.* (After Kühn and Piepho.) *Hy* = epidermis; *Pen* = endocuticle; *Pex* = exocuticle.

A. During hardening and pigment formation.

B. After the completion of hardening and pigmentation.

The procuticle may remain seemingly unchanged in soft transparent cuticle and soft areas (intersegmental membranes), in which case the fully formed cuticle is said to consist of epicuticle and endocuticle (Fig. 30C). Or the outer portion of the procuticle may become hardened and darkened by sclerotization, giving an outer dark exocuticle and an inner transparent endocuticle (Figs. 28, 30E). In calcified cuticles, at least of decapod crustacea, the exocuticle and outer portion of the endocuticle become calcified. For some types of study it is desirable to distinguish between primary and secondary cuticles, that is, the portions of the cuticle secreted before molting and those secreted after molting. The division between primary and secondary cuticles may correspond to the differentiation into exocuticle and endocuticle (spiders, Browning 42), but usually the line of division between primary and secondary cuticles lies in the endocuticle.

The cuticle is secreted by an underlying layer of epidermal cells, which may be either flat, cuboidal, or columnar. In addition, there

word "cement" in histology. Accordingly the term tectocuticle, meaning covering layer, is here proposed for any material poured onto the outer surface of the formed epicuticle and hardening there as a reasonably permanent component.

are in many species unicellular glands, the tegumental and dermal glands, with minute ducts extending through the cuticle, their secretion concerned with cuticle production (Figs. 39–43). In some groups oenocytes and blood cells may also be found among the typical epidermal cells (Fig. 28). A wide variety of specialized cells not concerned primarily with the production of cuticle—sense organs, glands, etc.—are also found, but will not be discussed in detail in this book.

Beneath the epidermal cells, and more or less separating them from the body cavity, there is usually to be seen a thin membrane of uncertain origin and structure. This is called the basement membrane. When detectable, it serves to delimit the integument (Figs. 30B, 31, 44).

MISCELLANEOUS GENERALITIES

A cuticle over the surface of the developing embryo appears fairly early in development (Johannsen & Butt 41); for instance, in the house fly it appears about the time that the segmented appendages begin to differentiate (Weismann 1863). From then on a cuticle is always present on the exterior surface and usually on internal surfaces of epidermal origin, a new cuticle being formed under the old one prior to molting. In the case of invaginated imaginal discs (*Anlagen*) the cuticle may extend across the opening of the invagination in the larva rather than covering the entire invaginated surface (Mercer 00). There are no known cases of externally exposed epidermal cells without a cuticular covering. The scales on lepidopterous wings may be perforated with numerous holes (Anderson & Richards 42b, Kinder & Süffert 43, Kühn & An 46), but by this stage the scale-forming cells have degenerated. Even the microscopic ducts of unicellular glands are lined with a very thin cuticle (p. 213).

The total thickness of cuticle shows great variation not only between different species and groups but even in different areas on a single specimen. Considering the entire phylum, the range of variation in thickness is to at least several thousand times the thinnest cuticles known (compare C and D of Fig. 30). The general body covering (= exoskeleton) is extremely thin in *Peripatus* (Fig. 31), the tardigrades, and certain aquatic dipterous larvae. It is actually thinnest over chemoreceptors and in tracheoles, where in its hydrated form on the living animal it may still be a rather small fraction of a micron in thickness. When dried, and presumably considerably shrunken, the electron microscope shows that some of these membranes may be

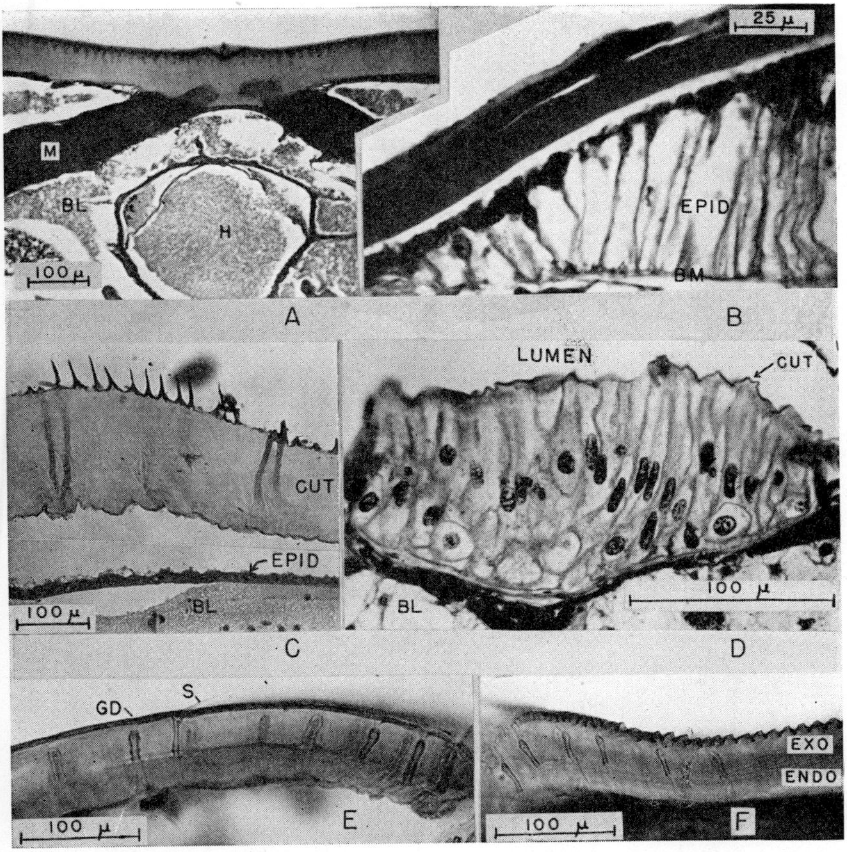

Figure 30. Photomicrographs of some representative integuments. (Original.) BL = blood; BM = basement membrane; CUT = cuticle; ENDO = endocuticle; EPID = epidermis; EXO = exocuticle; GD = gland duct; H = heart; LUMEN = lumen of hind-gut; M = muscle; S = seta.

A. Cross section through mid-dorsal line of a larva of a moth, *Heterocampa manteo.* Note arborescent tips of pore canals, thin epidermis, and partial section through muscle attachments.

B. Longitudinal section of a wing bud of a larva of a dragonfly, *Anax junius*, the epidermis having slightly separated from the cuticle during preparation of the slide. Note the attenuated cells extending down to the basement membrane, and the wide intercellular spaces.

C. Section through the thick, soft integument of a larva of a butterfly, *Papilio philenor*, the epidermis and cuticle having separated during preparation of the slide. Note the relative thicknesses of epidermis and cuticle, and the large ducts of dermal glands extending vertically through the cuticle.

D. Section of a "rectal gland" of an adult cockroach, *Blatella germanica.* Note the tall, columnar cells with an extremely thin overlying cuticle.

E–F. Sections through the integument of an adult tick, *Ixodes* sp. Note the conspicuous gland and setal ducts, smooth versus sculptured surface, and differentiation of exocuticle and endocuticle (unstained preparations).

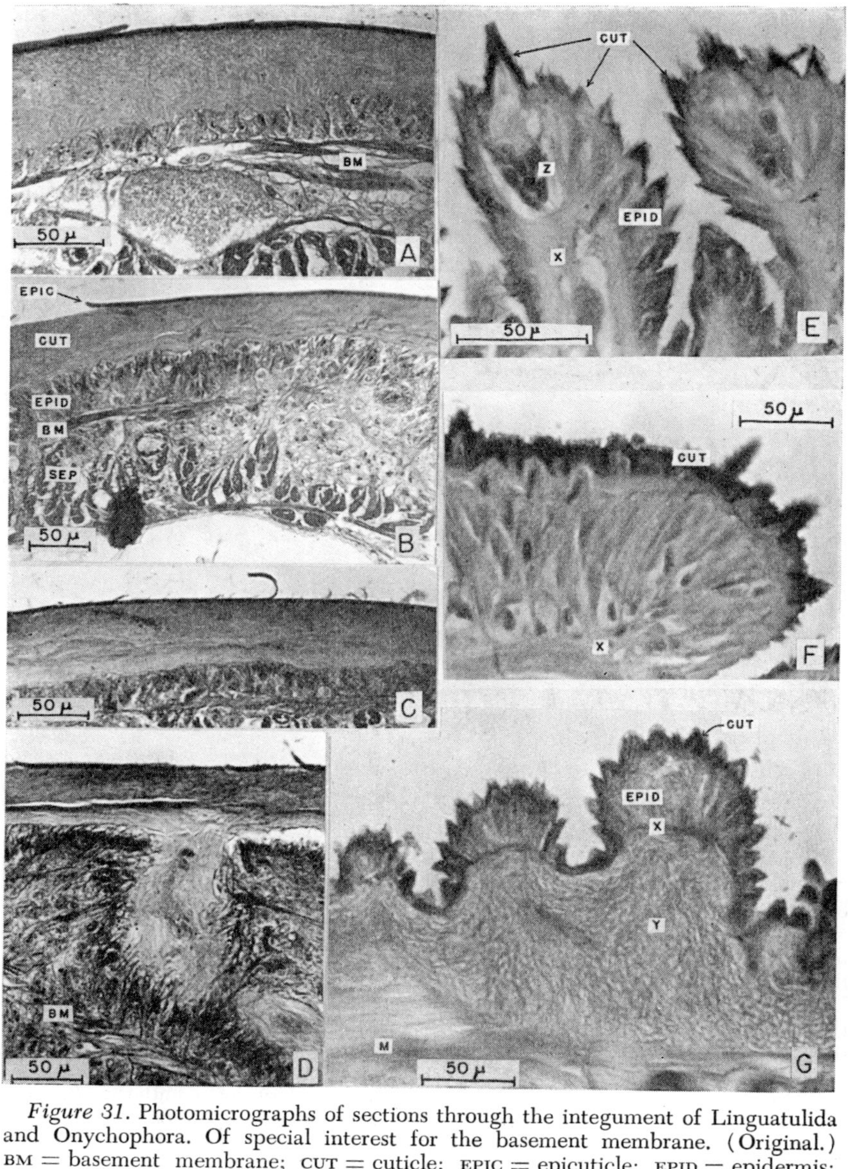

Figure 31. Photomicrographs of sections through the integument of Linguatulida and Onychophora. Of special interest for the basement membrane. (Original.) BM = basement membrane; CUT = cuticle; EPIC = epicuticle; EPID = epidermis; M = muscle; SEP = subepidermal tissues; X = presumably the basement membrane or its equivalent; Y = fibrous layer, perhaps part of basement membrane; Z = cluster of nuclei at tip of a papilla.

A. Adult of *Kiricephalus* sp. Note the open fibrous structure of the basement membrane with the fibers seemingly continuous with fibers extending between the epidermal cells and into the cuticle.

less than 0.01 micron thick (Fig. 56). The thin membranes over mosquito larvae, certain chemoreceptors, etc. may still have both epicuticle and procuticle components (Fig. 55H) (Richards & Anderson 42a, Richards unpubl.). The thickest cuticles are found in decapod crustacea and *Limulus.* The fresh cuticle of a large specimen of *Limulus* may be several millimeters in thickness and nearly a millimeter even after drying (Lafon 43a).

Considering the phylum as a whole, there seems to be little relationship between the thickness of the cuticle and the thickness of the cells that secrete it (Adam 12, Kimus 1898), although, in general, larger species with thicker cuticles also have a thicker epidermis (Willers & Durken 16). One needs to be careful, however, in making comparisons between cuticle and cell thicknesses because *both* the cuticle and the cell layer may change at different stages of the molting cycle. In the higher Diptera the epidermal cells retain approximately the same thickness throughout the molting cycle (Dennell 46, Hoop 33), but in most arthropods the cell layer increases considerably in thickness during cuticle deposition (Browning 42, Chatin 1895b, Dreyling 06, Helfer & Schlottke 35, Hoop 33, Lübben 07, A. E. Needham 46, Tower 06a, Willers & Dürken 16).

In larvae the cuticle commonly thickens during the instar at a more or less steady rate. For instance, the larval cuticle of *Bombyx* increases from 10 μ to 40 μ (Kuwana 33), of *Culex* from 0.75 μ to 2 μ (Richards & Anderson 42a), of *Sarcophaga* from 10 μ to 240 μ (Dennell 46), and of *Ixodes* from 26 μ to 103 μ (Ruser 33). At least as a rule, the cuticle of older instar larvae is thicker than that of younger instars (Klinger 36). The cuticle may also continue to thick-

---

B. Another section of same showing distinct epicuticle at torn spot, and a basement membrane which is relatively sharply defined on the left but becomes indistinguishably dispersed toward the right.

C. Another section of same for frayed epicuticle and relatively distinct basement membrane.

D. Another section of same showing apophysis (inward prolongation of cuticle) with highly fibrous epidermis and a rather broad basement membrane, which seems to be continuous with fibers both through the epidermis and into subepidermal tissues.

E. Section of papillae from the anterior end of an adult of *Peripatoides novaezealandicae.* Note especially the large cells and the vague tissue (X), which seems to represent the basement membrane.

F. Section through a leg-base of *Peripatoides* showing columnar cells which taper to end in the tissue (X).

G. Typical cross section of the general body wall of *Peripatoides.* Note the thick fibrous layer (Y), which is not readily separated from the overlying presumed basement membrane (X) or the underlying muscles.

en during adult life (Millot & Fontaine 38, Szalay 26). However, the cuticle of the adult is not necessarily thicker than that of the larva and may actually be considerably thinner (Kühnelt 28c, Wigglesworth 33). On a single specimen the variation in thickness from one region to another is not limited to such obviously different parts as gill coverings and carapace, but may be found in similarly sclerotized areas. For instance, in the adult of the beetle *Tenebrio* the abdominal tergites are only 4 μ thick while the sternites are 36 μ thick (Wigglesworth 48d). However, there is not a large amount of variation in thickness between comparable areas of different specimens taken at the same developmental stage (Richards & Fan 49).

It seems self-evident to anyone who has ever examined a section of cuticle and is willing to consider it an entity that the cuticle is an asymmetrical membrane. Recently (Hurst 41) it has been recorded that this obvious asymmetry has profound effects upon the functioning of the integument, as will be discussed later (p. 304).

Several authors have attempted to classify the cuticle structure, especially its hardness and color, according to the ecological habitats of the particular insects (Carpenter & Kalmus 41, Kalmus 41, Koidsumi 34, Kühnelt 39, Eder 40). The situation is so complex that these attempts have been no more than partially satisfactory, doubtless to some extent because chemical differentiation does not necessarily include gross changes in color and hardness. Even so, certain correlations can be made if one is willing to admit their having only partial validity. Of utmost ecological importance is the development of the lipid epicuticle, which has permitted various arthropods to migrate from moist environments and colonize even the driest terrestrial ones (p. 299).

One report has been found stating that the cuticle of the overwintering larvae of certain moths differs from that of summer forms which do not overwinter (Burgeff 21). In view of the profound differences often found between overwintering and nonoverwintering insects, commonly involving the production of a special generation, it is not surprising that this is true. Differences have also been reported during diapause (Semichon 39). Presumably the differences are merely by-products of the physiological condition of the individuals rather than a means of affording protection from the cold.

The arthropod integument, like integument in general, is capable of healing minor wounds and even regenerating a new cuticle with or without the replacement of the anatomical structure removed (Rich-

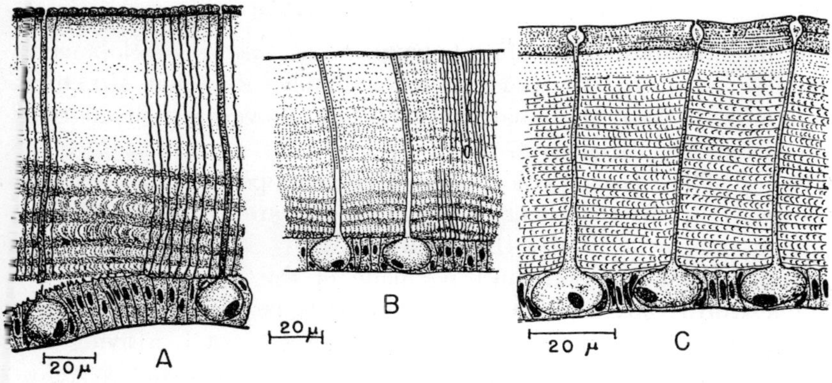

Figure 32. Sections of the integument of representative Diplopoda. (Redrawn after Silvestri.)

A. *Pachyiulus communis,* showing both pore canals and gland ducts, and, where the epidermis has separated, the processes thought to extend into these.

B. *Rhinocricus nodulipes,* showing more distinct laminations.

C. *Glomeris connexa,* showing dilated tips on the gland ducts.

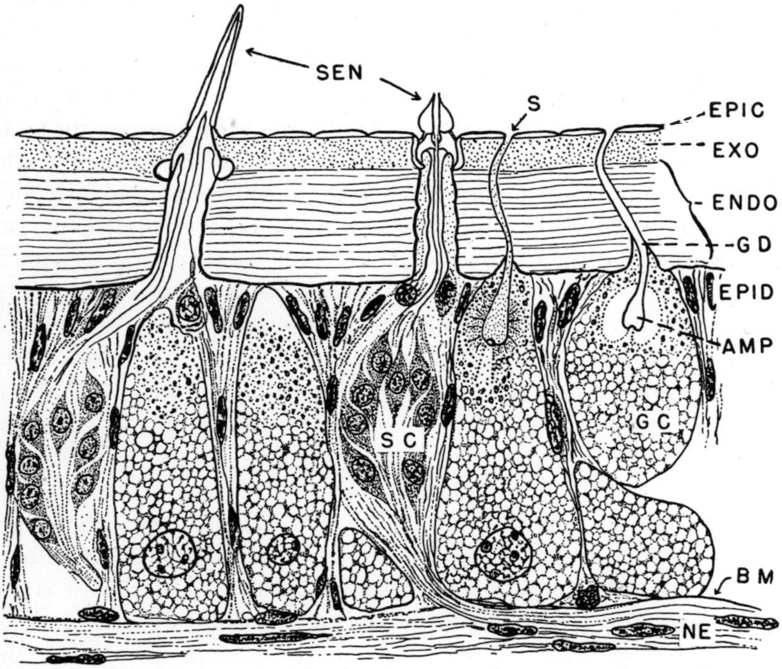

Figure 33. Section through the antenna of a centipede, *Scolopendra morsitans,* showing laminar cuticle and various types of glands and sense organs. (Redrawn after Fuhrmann.) AMP = ampulla at base of gland duct; BM = basement membrane; ENDO = endocuticle; EPIC = epicuticle; EPID = epidermal cell layer; EXO = exocuticle; G C = gland cell; G D = gland duct; NE = nerve; S = secretion; S C = sense cell; SEN = sensilla.

ards 37, Wigglesworth 37). In numerous cases developmental anomalies lead to the production of highly abnormal structures (teratology); these abnormal structures are, however, covered by a normal cuticle (Richards 37).

The development of color pattern in arthropod cuticles will be omitted from this treatment. Various reviews are available (Bodenstein 36, Caspari 41, Kühn 41, Richards 37).

Finally, some mention must be made of the recent proposal by Wigglesworth (48a, b) that the insect cuticle be viewed as a "living system." No one would question that the integument is a living system, even capable of considerable independent action, but Wigglesworth now goes further and proposes that the cuticle itself be considered "living." This view is based on the fact that cell processes extend into it, that injury to it modifies the activity of underlying cells and leads to repair, that there is a precise timing of events in its development, that it influences vital activities such as permeability, etc. There is, however, no evidence that it shows the properties of self-duplication, that it is itself sensory, that it has any part in the precise timing of its development, or that it is itself capable of repair except in the sense that a broken oil film on water can re-form. In fact no distinctions have been made between the cuticle and the properties of nonliving models except those which are patently due to the living epidermal cells. This is particularly well shown by isolated cuticles which act like nonmetabolizing, inert, physico-chemical systems (H. J. A. Koch 36, Richards & Fan 49, Ricks & Hoskins 48). But the question is largely philosophical; it is a matter of defining the terms "life" and "living." Certainly many, if not most, biologists, the present author included, will not accept the postulation that the cuticle is a living system, even though everyone will admit that the integument is.

EXCEPTIONS

It might not be amiss to chronicle the fact that exceptions are recorded for almost all the major generalities. Perhaps such a list may serve as a reminder that all points need verification and that it is not safe to assume a newly investigated species will be the same as previously investigated species simply because some points are the same.

An epicuticle is said to be lacking in some spiders (Browning 42) and in certain areas on ticks (Ruser 33). The report for spiders is discredited by Miss Sewell (unpubl.), who finds a thin epicuticle positive to tests for both proteins and lipids. The report that an epicuticle is lacking on certain iridescent wasps (Frey 36) needs reinvestigation, but the report that an epicuticle is absent along the ecdysial line of locusts seems valid (Duarte 39), as also does the recent report of no epicuticle on coackroach pulvilli (Sarkaria & Patton 49). For component fractions of the epicuticle: lipid layers are said to be absent in a few insects and spiders (Browning 42, Crawford 12, Pryor 40b, Thorpe 30b, 31, Wigglesworth 45) and, at least as far as free lipid is concerned, are probably absent from crustacea (Dennell 47b); too much uncertainty exists about the tectocuticle to warrant listing exceptions (see p. 170).

An exocuticle is absent from many species; in fact, by definition it is lacking from all nonsclerotized areas and species. Similarly, when the entire cuticle is sclerotized, an endocuticle would be said to be lacking, but examples of this are rare (Börner 04, Browning 42). The entire procuticle could be said to be absent from those areas or species which are negative to chitin tests (Marcus 28, Richards 47a, b, Richards & Korda 48, 50).[4] But it is not safe to assume that any membrane lacks some component simply because it appears to be very thin, for anal papillae, gill coverings, and chemoreceptor sense organs may have both epicuticle and procuticle (Richards unpubl.).

Pore canals (Fig. 34) are usually, but not invariably, present.[5] They are said to be generally absent from thin-skinned larvae (Eder 40), and electron micrographs show this is unquestionably true for mosquito larvae (Richards & Anderson 42a, Richards & Korda 48). They are also recorded as absent in spiders (Browning 42) and seem to be absent in the presumptive endocuticle of blowfly larvae (Dennell 46) (p. 182).

Dermal glands are recorded as absent in a number of dipterous larvae (unless one classes peristigmatic glands as homologues) (Dennell 46, Richards & Anderson 42a), and are scarce or lacking on the head capsule of many species (Hoop 33) (p. 207).

Molting has been said to be lacking in *Peripatus* (Tower 06a, but see Holliday 42) and larvae of the fly *Dacus* (Brites 30), but the reports are not convincing. Except for embryonic organs there are no authentic records of a cuticle's being absent.

[4] Presumably this would be contested by Picken (49), who, having been unable to show chitin present in young moth scales, nevertheless concludes the scale is made of chitin-protein.

[5] Discounting the fact that they are commonly not visible in histological sections and listing only cases where they are positively stated to be absent.

As far as is known, the cuticle of the body surface is always formed by an underlying layer of epidermal cells, but no cells are recognizable in the fully formed pulvillus of *Musca, Apis, Oncopeltus*, and *Melanoplus* (Hayes & Liu 47, Sarkaria & Patton 49, Schatz 50, Slifer 50). The development of the pulvillus has yet to be studied in this connection.

CHAPTER 17

Historical and Taxonomic Résumé

HISTORICAL

An extensive historical review giving credit to the hundreds of authors who have published on the structure of arthropod cuticle would be prohibitively voluminous, but some mention of significant workers is desirable. To some extent, the value or at least diversity of application of the work of various authors may be judged from the number of references in the Author Index, but this favors recent authors.

In the same paper in which he recorded the discovery of the chemical chitin, Odier in 1823 recognized the presence of protein and a covering layer which we now call the epicuticle. Adequate preliminary descriptions of the histology of cuticle and integument were given in the middle of the nineteenth century by Valentin, Leydig, C. Schmidt, Kölliker, Haeckel, and W. C. Williamson, with the classical work of Haeckel in 1857 recognizing much of the basic and grosser structure we now know and describing arthropod epidermis as "chitinogenous" epithelium. The latter half of the nineteenth century saw principally an extension of these fundamental points to other representatives of the phylum, with the names of Braun, Bütschli, Herrick, Huet, Montgomery, Pantel, Pautel, and Vitzou being outstanding. Several bitter controversies arose during this period on subjects which no longer excite us, namely, on whether the cuticle is actually secreted by epidermal cells or the distal portion of the cells is transformed into cuticle, and on the nature of the development of muscle insertions. The first quarter of the twentieth century saw the publication of many more papers, but rather little in the way of significant advances. For this period we might mention the names of Biedermann, Bonnet, Downey, Herold, N. Holmgren, Kapzov, Nordenskiöld, Novikoff, Pearson, Pérez, Plotnikow, Snethlage, Tower, and Willers and Dürken. Biedermann's (14a) monographic treatment was the outstanding product of this period.

What might be called the modern phase of study on arthropod cuticle began with the work of Kühnelt in 1928. It was placed on a firm footing by Wigglesworth in 1933. Among current (or at least recent) workers the name of Wigglesworth is most outstanding for the histology and development of insect cuticle. Other authors who have made significant contributions to the field include Beament, Browning, Dennell, Drach, Fraenkel, Hurst, Kästner, Langner, Lees, Pryor, Richards, Rudall, Ruser, Schlottke, Yalvac, Yonge, and Zschorn.

Numerous reviews have been published on the chemistry and structure of arthropod cuticle, beginning with those by Straus-Durckheim in 1828 and Burmeister in 1832. The treatments given even today in all but a few of the general zoology and general entomology textbooks are woefully inadequate and not worth citing here. Rather good reviews, to be sure, of various vintages, are given in appropriate sections of Bronn's *Klassen und Ordnungen des Tierreichs* and Kukenthal and Krumbach's *Handbuch der Zoologie*; also by Berlese (09), Kapzov (11), Biedermann (14a), Deegener (28), Kühnelt (28c), Weber (33), Hoskins and Craig (35), Snodgrass (35), Drach (39), and Wigglesworth (39, 48b). See also Day (48).

TAXONOMIC

A listing of some of the descriptive papers by taxonomic groups, with emphasis on coverage rather than on outstanding papers, has a certain usefulness. With few exceptions only papers published since 1900 will be given. Figure references are to the present book.

General: Biedermann 14a, Bronn –, Deegener 28, Kukenthal & Krumbach 26–30, Richards & Korda 48, 50, Snethlage 05, Snodgrass 35, H. Weber 33, Wigglesworth 39, 48b, Willers & Dürken 16, Zschorn 37
Onychophora: Bouvier 02, DuBoscq 20 (Fig. 31E–G)
Tardigrada: Bauman 21, 30, Marcus 28, 29, Plate 1888
Chilopoda: Attems 26, DuBoscq 1899, Fuhrmann 21 (Fig. 33)
Diplopoda: Attems 26, Effenberger 09, Fuhrmann 21, Langner 37, Rossi 02, 03, Silvestri 03, Verhoeff 26–32 (Fig. 32)
Linguatulida (Pentastomida): von Haffner 24a, b (Fig. 31A–D)
Arachnida
  Xiphosura: Lafon 43a, Patten 1893, Versluys & Demoll 22
  Trilobita: D. R. Rome 36
  Scorpiones: Pavlowsky 27, Werner 35
  Pedipalpi: Börner 04, Werner 35
  Araneae: Browning 42, Kästner 29, Millot 26a, b, Osterloh 22, Schimkewitsch 1884, Schlottke 38a (Fig. 24)
  Solifugae: Roewer 34

Pycnogonida (Pantopoda): Helfer & Schlottke 35
Opiliones: Kästner 33
Acari
Ticks: Bonnet 07, Christophers 06, Dinnik & Zumpt 49, Falke 31, Frick 36, Lees 46, 47, Nordenskiöld 08, Ruser 33, P. Schulze 32, Yalvac 39 (Fig. 30E–F)
Mites: Lundblad 30, U. Schmidt 35, Steding 24, Thor 02
Crustacea
Gills: Bernecker 09, Kimus 1898, Fiedler 08, Chen 33
Eyes: Debaisieux 44
Branchiopoda: Novikoff 05
Cladocera: Fiedler 08 (Fig. 51)
Ostracoda: Schreiber 22
Copepoda: Claus 1875b, 1881
Cirripedia: Cannon 47, Prenant 25, H. J. Thomas 44
Cumacea: Schuch 15
Isopoda: Herold 13, Patanè 36a, b, Radu 30b (Fig. 17)
Decapoda: Balss 27, Bernecker 09, Dennell 47b, Downey 12, Drach 37a, b, 39, B. Farkas 14, 27, Herrick 1896, 11, Jackson 13, Janisch 23, J. Pearson 08, Verne 21, W. C. Williamson 1860, Yonge 24, 32 (Fig. 42)
Pauropoda: Attems 26, Silvestri 02, Verhoeff 34
Symphyla: Attems 26, Verhoeff 33
Insecta
Collembola: Boelitz 33
Odonata: H. J. A. Koch 36, Sadones 1896, K. Schulze 34 (Figs. 30B, 47B)
Blattariae: H. Ito 24, Petrunkewitsch 1899, Richards & Anderson 42a (Figs. 20B, 30D, 34, 50, 54)
Mantodea: H. Ito 24, Schleip 10
Isoptera: Ahrens 30
Orthoptera: Chauvin 41, A. C. Davis 27a, Duarte 39, H. Ito 24 (Figs. 47A, 55E, 56F)
Phasmida: H. Ito 24, de Sinety 01
Mallophaga: J. E. Webb 47
Hemiptera: Poisson 24, 25, Wigglesworth 33, 40a, 42a, c, 47b, 48b (Figs. 28, 39, 56E)
Coleoptera: Biedermann 03, Casper 13, 24, Deegener 04, Kapzov 11, Korschelt 23, Kremer 18, 20, Kühnelt 28c, Lazarenko 28, Poyarkoff 10, Reuter 37, P. Schulze 13b, 15, Stegemann 29b, Tower 06a, b, Wigglesworth 48d, Zschorn 37 (Figs. 37, 47D, 49, 55A–D, 56C–D)
Strepsiptera: Cooper 38
Neuroptera: Matheson 12, Plotnikow 04 (Fig. 44)
Mecoptera: Grell 38
Hymenoptera: Adam 12, Dreher 36, Frey 36, Jacobs 24, Janet 07, 09, Plotnikow 04, Snodgrass 25, Tiegs 22 (Figs. 46, 55H)
Diptera: Assmuth 13, Dennell 46, 47a, Fraenkel & Rudall 40, 47, Gouin 46, N. Holmgren 07, Hoop 33, Kühnelt 28c, Miall & Hammond 00,

G. W. Müller 25, Pantel 1898, Pérez 10, Richards & Anderson 42a, Thompson 29, Vaney 02 (Figs. 20A, 35, 43, 55G, 56A–B)

Trichoptera: Henseval 1896, Martynow 01

Lepidoptera: Barth 45, von Buddenbrock 29, Klinger 36, Kühn 39, Kühn & Piepho 38, Kühnelt 28c, Montgomery 00, Schürfeld 35, Stossberg 38, Way 48, Zschorn 37 (Figs. 29, 30A, C, 36, 40, 41, 45, 47C, 55F, 58, 59)

CHAPTER 18

The Epicuticle, or Nonchitinous Cuticle

That the outer surface of the cuticle was covered by a material distinct from that of the matrix was recognized by Odier (1823), Straus-Durckheim (1828), Burmeister (1832), and many subsequent authors. Numerous terms have been used to designate the outer layer or layers; in many cases the precise synonymizing of these with current terminology is uncertain.[1] A long list of papers document the generality that almost, if not quite, all arthropods have such an outer, nonchitinous layer. Citing only a partial list of references, epicuticles are recorded for Chilopoda (Fuhrmann 21), Diplopoda (Fuhrmann 21, Langner 37, Silvestri 03), various Arachnida, including spiders, ticks, mites, scorpions, and *Limulus* (Kaston 35, Lees 47, Lafon 43a, Lundblad 30, Pavlowsky 27, Ruser 33, Sewell unpubl., Yalvac 39), various crustacea, ranging from the lowest to the highest classes (Balss 27, Dennell 47b, Haeckel 1857, Herold 13, Thomas 44, Vitzou 1881, W. C. Williamson 1860, Yonge 24, 32), Linguatulida (Fig. 31 B–C) (von Haffner 24b), and the various groups of insects (Burmeister 1832, Bütschli 1898, Kapzov 11, Kühnelt 28a, c, Plotnikow 04, Straus-Durckheim 1828), including Orthoptera (Fig. 34) (Duarte 39, Richards & Anderson 42a), Odonata (K. Schulze 34), Hemiptera (Wigglesworth 47b), Homoptera (H. Weber 34), Coleoptera (Hass 14, 16a, b, Wigglesworth 48d), Hymenoptera (Fig. 55H) (Frey 36, Richards unpubl.), Mallophaga (J. E. Webb 47), Lepidoptera (Kuwana 40, Way 48), and Diptera (Fig. 35) (Dennell 45, 46, Lowne 1893–95, Richards & Anderson 42a). They are to be expected also in other orders. The Tardigrada are said to lack chitin in their cuticles, and accordingly could be said to have only an epicuticle (Marcus 27,

[1] Old terms now seldom or never used include epidermis, sclerotized epidermis, outer layer, *Grenzhautchen, Grenzlamelle, Grenzsaum, Deckschicht, Dornenschicht, plasmatische* layer, *Tectostracum, Sekretrelief, Sekretschicht,* mediocuticle, epiostracum, achromatic chitin, pellicle, cuticule, cuticle, and perhaps ectostracum of some authors. Most of the papers dealing with crustacea, other than the most recent ones, use the term cuticle.

28); this is recorded to be differentiated into an outer and inner layer (Bauman 21). A number of papers deal with layers secreted onto the outer surface of the fully formed cuticle in certain beetles, perhaps the tectocuticle of the present treatment, but the situation needs a reinvestigation which considers current concepts of epicuticular structure (Blunck 10, 12b, Brocher 27, Casper 13, Kremer 20, Kühnelt 28c, Plateau 1876, P. Schulze 13a, b, 15, Sprung 32, Stegemann 29a, b). [See also the recent survey by Cloudsley-Thompson (50).]

Significant studies on the components of the epicuticle and their development are extremely difficult to make because of the thinness of the whole complex,[2] but rapid strides have been made in the past decade. We should be careful, however, not to draw sweeping or unreserved conclusions at the present time because the evidence is still scant. The epicuticle had been considered a single layer until Richards and Anderson (42a) separated the nonchitinous cuticle of the cockroach into two chemically distinct layers in 1942. That this should be possible is a logical outcome of Pryor's hypothesis (40b) on the mode of formation of the epicuticle. For not only can the subsequent demonstration of protein and lipid layers in the epicuticle be considered an outcome of this hypothesis, but the recorded differentiations within the protein epicuticle can also be considered special amplifications from it. Quite recently, Wigglesworth (47b, 48d) has demonstrated an additional, previously unsuspected, outermost layer which he has called the "cement layer," but which is here renamed the tectocuticle (see footnote, p. 148).

How many of these so-called layers should really be recognized as distinct layers seems a matter of definition or preference, at least at present. To what degree they are formed separately, how distinct they remain, and to what degree they can be homologized throughout the phylum or even throughout the class Insecta, are questions which must await further study. A tentative scheme of classification is given here to provide a framework for presenting the available data and discussing its discrepancies. It may well require early revision. The data will be treated first under the heading of species studied more precisely, and then under sublayer headings.

[2] Few estimates of thickness are available. Perhaps the commonest value will be of the order of magnitude of a micron, but the range is from a few hundred Ångstrom units (*Culex* larva, Richards & Anderson 42a) to several microns (*Eomenacanthus*, J. E. Webb 47; *Periplaneta*, Richards & Anderson 42a), to extreme values of 4 μ in *Sarcophaga* larvae (Dennell 46), 5 μ in decapod crustacea (Dennell 47b), and 15–20 μ in *Limulus* (Lafon 43a).

The layers of the epicuticle, unlike those of the procuticle, are secreted in the reverse sequence from what one might expect from their position in the fully formed cuticle: the innermost layer is secreted first, the outermost last.

In the bug *Rhodnius,* Wigglesworth (47b) has shown that there are what can be classed as four distinct sublayers (giving the terms in sequence from inside to outside): cuticulin, polyphenol, wax, and tectocuticle. In development the cuticulin layer appears first as a thin membrane over the surface of the epidermal cells. No internal differentiation can be seen in it with the compound light microscope. At this stage it gives a positive Millon's reaction, indicating the presence of proteins, and stains with Black Sudan B [3] and with osmic acid, indicating the presence of some lipoidal material; on heating with HNO_3 plus K chlorate, oily droplets are liberated, which is thought to indicate the presence of a bound lipid. The evidence then suggests a conjugated protein of the lipoprotein group. The evidence does not give any indication of the type of lipid or the type of protein concerned. Because the oenocytes (p. 218) show cyclic changes correlated with molting, reach their maximum size and appear to be discharging secretion immediately before the cuticulin layer is deposited, then appear to become inactive, Wigglesworth suggests that they produce the material for the cuticulin layer. This material is then somehow transported through the epidermal cells to its site of deposition.

Wigglesworth thinks that the pore canals, containing processes from the epidermal cells (p. 177), penetrate the cuticulin layer. Shortly after the formation of this layer, minute droplets appear on its outer surface at points thought to correspond to the tips of pore canal filaments. These enlarge, run together, and form a more or less continuous layer of semifluid material which gives an intense argentaffin reaction (p. 71), indicating the presence of polyphenols which, he presumes, are associated with protein (Figs. 13, 14). Some of these serve subsequently to tan the underlying cuticulin layer. Shortly before molting, a wax layer representing the lipid epicuticle begins to appear, at first discontinuously, over the surface of the

[3] Black Sudan B is a rather recently developed fat stain that is superior, especially in visibility, to the older Sudans (Lison 36). It is used in the same manner as red Sudans, and in the United States can be obtained from the National Aniline and Chemical Company. It should be remembered that since lipids are found in several subdivisions of the epicuticle, lipid stains (Sudans, OsO_4, and mitochondrial stains) cannot be used for identification of specific subdivisions.

polyphenol layer. Wigglesworth suggests that the wax is also secreted through the pore canals from the general epidermal cells (presumably a solubilizer or emulsifier would be required to facilitate this transport). Shortly after molting, a fluid is poured out from the dermal glands (p. 207) and spreads over the surface of the wax layer to form the tectocuticle. In *Rhodnius* the tectocuticle is said to be produced from the mixing of secretions from two different types of dermal glands (analogous to ootheca, p. 279), one of which secretes a protein solution, the other a complex lipoprotein-polyphenol mixture (Wigglesworth 48d), if we so interpret the fact that after boiling in chloroform it may stain with Black Sudan B and give droplets which show an argentaffin reaction.[4]

A similar study with similar general results has also been performed on the beetle *Tenebrio* (Wigglesworth 48d), and apparently a like study is under way on larvae of the moth *Diataraxia* (Way 48). In these two species the tectocuticle is reported to be produced by a single type of dermal gland which gives a secretion agreeing in qualitative tests with the lipoprotein-polyphenol type gland of *Rhodnius.*

In the mallophagan *Eomenacanthus,* there are certain areas where the epicuticle appears to change abruptly from a thickness of about 1 μ to a thickness of 2–4 μ (J. E. Webb 47). On the basis of general appearance in sections stained with haematoxylin, it is said that these sections show distinct tectocuticle, lipid epicuticle, polyphenol layer, cuticulin layer, and another very thin innermost layer the nature and significance of which is unknown. Of considerable interest is the fact that the photographs show the pore canals clearly penetrating to but not through the outermost of these epicuticular sublayers.

There is also a recent paper which reports that the epicuticle of various ticks (*Ixodes, Dermacentor, Hyalomma,* and *Ornithodorus*) is essentially similar to that in *Rhodnius* (Lees 47). The paper does give tests indicating the presence of lipoprotein, polyphenol, wax, and a solid tectocuticle in *Ornithodorus,* but only a soft greasy one for the Ixodid ticks. Of considerable interest is the fact that the growth of

[4] This conclusion is based on the grave assumption that an entire cuticle can be boiled in chloroform without there being any other effect than the dissolving of certain of the lipids. It does not consider the possibility of the migration of components under the influence of the heating and chemical treatment – the ever present danger in all studies on histochemical localization of components. We know conclusively that treatment with boiling chloroform does alter at least some cuticular membranes (p. 295); accordingly, while the above interpretation may be quite correct, it should not be unreservedly accepted on the evidence presented.

wax deposits over abrasions is influenced by humidity – perhaps suggesting that the wax is originally secreted in an aqueous medium. Polyphenols are demonstrated beneath the outer surface, but it appears to be only assumed that they form a layer in a position corresponding to that in *Rhodnius*. Consideration of the assumptions, peculiar statements, and partial tests presented in this paper leaves the present reviewer with an inconclusive feeling and a fear that we may be led astray if workers set out to reconcile the situation in different groups with some one picture.

The other insects in which a multiple epicuticle has been recorded were described prior to Wigglesworth's description given above, and should be re-examined in the light of it. Even so, certain points of difference are based on data that still seem entirely valid. In larvae of the fly *Sarcophaga* two constituent layers were recognized by Dennell (46). Neither of these is penetrated by ducts of the pore canals, which in this group are relatively gigantic and readily seen with a light microscope (Fig. 35). The pore canals do not enter the epicuticle at all. Further, the inner epicuticle, while positive for protein tests, was completely negative to tests for lipids. The very thin outer epicuticle, here called the lipoprotein layer, perhaps corresponds in position to the polyphenol layer, but is positive not only for the argentaffin and xanthoproteic tests (indicating polyphenols and proteins) but also strongly positive for lipids. It seems to have no parallel in Wigglesworth's scheme. The evidence is clearly contrary to the view that this layer is formed in the manner in which the polyphenol layer is said to be laid down in *Tenebrio* and *Rhodnius*. Dennell found no evidence of a wax layer, but he was not specifically looking for one. However, if a tectocuticle is not absent, it would have to be formed in a manner different from that in the bug and beetle because dermal glands are absent. (Wiesmann (38) described what appears to be the same situation in puparia of the fly *Rhagoletis*, but labels the protein epicuticle as "exocuticle.")

In a cockroach, *Periplaneta* (Richards & Anderson 42a), the now inadequate old preliminary data show only that the epicuticle can be separated by prolonged warming in concentrated HNO_3 into an extremely thin outer layer and a thicker (2 μ) inner layer, neither of which is penetrated by pore canals in the fully formed cuticle (Fig. 34).[5] Since examination was made with an electron microscope, using

[5] Both freshly emerged and fully hardened individuals were examined. If pore canals penetrate into the epicuticle, they must become filled before molting and filled only in the epicuticle.

both thin sections and isolated sheets, interpretation is not questionable, as it is when minute pore canals are studied with the light microscope. These two layers showed different degrees of resistance to the action of mineral acids and to the destructive effects of electron bombardment, but their chemical composition was not determined. Following Pryor's hypothesis, it was suggested that the thicker inner layer represented a sheet of tanned protein [6] and the thin outer layer a sheet differentiated on the surface of this by the addition of lipids which become bound to the surface protein. It does not seem desirable at the present time to homologize these two layers with the inner two recorded for *Tenebrio* and *Rhodnius*. Quite likely the well-known grease layer, which might be homologous with the lipid epicuticle, was lost in the course of preparation of the specimens used for electron microscopy. Conceivably the grease layer might be covered by a tectocuticle, although such a covering would have a hazardous existence on the surface of a mobile layer of grease which is sufficiently free to spread over water droplets (Ramsay 35). An up-to-date investigation of epicuticles where the solid wax layer is replaced by a mobile grease layer is needed (Dusham 18).[7]

In the larva of a mosquito, *Culex*, only a single epicuticular sheet was recognized in the electron microscope studies (Richards & Anderson 42a). But considering the limitations of the method employed and the implications of subsequent work with other insects, the case should be listed for reinvestigation rather than as an exception.

In the crustacea, the epicuticle is clearly double (Dennell 47b), but the homology with insectan sublayers is not clear. The inner layer (about 5 μ thick) is positive to histochemical tests for proteins, lipids, and polyphenols; it also appears to be traversed by pore canals. As such it agrees well with the cuticulin layer in *Tenebrio* and *Rhodnius* except for the permeation with polyphenols. The very thin outer layer gives positive tests for lipids, polyphenols, and presumably proteins, but differs from the insectan tectocuticle in giving these reactions without previous destructive chemical action. The situation is further complicated by uncertainty concerning the function of the tegumental glands, which may or may not have a function comparable to

[6] This thick inner layer was termed mediocuticle, leaving the term epicuticle for the very thin outer layer. This terminology was never adopted and may profitably be discarded.

[7] Since the above was written, a beginning has been made in the paper by Kramer and Wigglesworth (50), *q. v.*

that of the dermal glands of insects (p. 214) (Dennell 47b, Drach 39, Yonge 32). Only Drach (39) says the epicuticle can become calcified. Tentatively the crustacean epicuticle is classified herein, along with that of the larvae of *Sarcophaga*, as being a two-layered epicuticle; to a certain extent these layers are different from those recorded for *Rhodnius*, etc.

Briefly summarizing under the heading of layers rather than species: the cuticulin layer described for *Rhodnius, Tenebrio,* and *Diataraxia,* and stated but not demonstrated to be the same in the louse and various species of ticks, may possibly come to be recognized as general for the first-formed sublayer of the epicuticle; but if so, it would have to be recognized that the layer is in some cases penetrated by pore canals, in others not, and in some cases permeated with polyphenols, whereas in others the polyphenols form a separate sublayer. One point does appear to be irrefutable, namely, that the pore canals may penetrate the inner portions of the epicuticle in some species, stop at the epicuticle-procuticle boundary in other species, and be entirely lacking from the entire cuticle of yet other species (p. 182).[8] It seems preferable for the present to retain the name cuticulin layer for those cases where a basal lipoprotein layer is overlain by a more or less distinct layer of polyphenol.

The polyphenol layer, to be called a layer, should be demonstrated as a layer. To be sure, in some cases this has been done. However, with polyphenol constituents known to be present in other sublayers, it does not seem adequate to demonstrate the presence of polyphenols under abrasions and assume they occur in a distinct layer. Incidentally, this layer (rather than the tectocuticle) is the one that seems to me to present cement-like properties in that it is the connecting and probably the cementing material which holds the wax layer to the underlying cuticulin layer.

The lipid epicuticle, when known to be present, is usually a wax layer about 0.2–0.3 μ thick, but ranges from about 0.1–0.4 μ for waxes, with the grease layer on cockroaches being about 0.6 μ. Permeability data necessitate the assumption that the innermost layers of wax molecules are highly oriented and closely packed (Chapter 29), and

[8] Considering the nature of the methods used and the clarity of the thousands of electron micrographs prepared by Richards and his colleagues, it is inconceivable that any ducts of cytological rather than intermolecular dimensions occur in thin cuticles such as those of mosquito larvae or those forming tracheal linings, unless they are destroyed by electron bombardment. But they are not destroyed in the procuticle of cockroaches and honeybees and so presumably would not be in other procuticles.

therefore in some manner bound chemically to the underlying polyphenol layer. Presumably the term lipid epicuticle also covers the grease on the surface of the cuticle of cockroaches, locusts, and ixodid ticks, but on these further investigation is needed.

Overlying the wax layer of *Rhodnius* and *Tenebrio* is an exceedingly thin layer, here termed the tectocuticle. It is said to be produced by the dermal glands (Figs. 39–41), and accordingly could be said to include the secreted layers which have long been known to occur on the surface of certain beetles (Blunck 10, 12b, Brocher 27, Casper 13, Plateau 1876, P. Schulze 13a, b, 15, Stegemann 29a, b) and the lipid secreted by larval Odonata (K. Schulze 34) and aquatic Hemiptera (Poisson 24). In terms of development from a special gland with minute ducts, it might include the waxy layers secreted by various insects (but not by all insects producing wax), for instance, the Aleurodids (Weber 34). In this sense it might also be said to include the secretion from peristigmatic glands (Fig. 43), found in various insects and described in detail for numerous dipterous larvae where the secretion appears to "oil" the spiracular opening (Keilin 44).[9] If the term is used in this manner it would also have to include the greasy material secreted by Ixodid ticks, even though this does not form a layer which will protect the underlying waxes from extraction with chloroform (Lees 47). Whether the tectocuticle is defined as a protective covering over the wax layer or as a solidified outer layer derived from the product of dermal glands makes considerable difference in application of the term. Definitions including both points—that is, defining the tectocuticle as a protective coating secreted by the dermal glands—would be more restrictive and call for the development of additional terms for the secretions which do not protect underlying wax. The question of homology between insectan dermal glands and crustacean tegumental glands, and accordingly of a possible homologizing of the insect tectocuticle with an outer coating on the crustacea, does not seem capable of satisfactory settlement with available data.

The second classification tentatively listed, basal protein and lipoprotein subdivisions, may be only a special case of the preceding classification (or vice versa) in which the polyphenol layer is both dispersed by and modifies the underlying layers. In the insects *Sarcophaga* and *Periplaneta* the differences may conceivably be occasioned

[9] Perhaps the lipophobic nature of the larval cuticle of the petroleum fly, *Psilota*, may be due to a strongly hydrophilic tectocuticle, but it may also be due to the absence of lipid and surface lipophilic groups (Crawford 12).

by the failure of the pore canal filaments to extend into the epicuticle. This would not be true for the crustacea (Dennell 47b, Herold 13), but it could scarcely be called surprising if they were difficult to homologize in all details with insects. Much the same may be said of the lipoprotein layer, at least as it is seen in *Sarcophaga*. Whether or not the outer layer of Crustacea would be more appropriately compared with this lipoprotein layer than with the insectan tectocuticle is an open question, as already mentioned.

Very thin cuticles also have an epicuticle in all cases that have been appropriately examined: a number of thin-skinned larvae (Eder 40, Richards & Anderson 42a, Richards & Korda 48), the linings of tracheae (Fig. 55H) (Richards & Korda 48), and the extremely thin cuticles over chemoreceptors (Richards unpubl.). Certain of these may be said by definition to have only an epicuticle since no chitin is detectable (tracheae of many species, tardigrades, etc.). These very thin cuticles have no dermal glands and no pore canals, as shown conclusively by electron micrographs. Nevertheless, there is both indirect evidence from changes in wettability (Keister 48) and direct evidence from electron micrography (Richards & Korda 48) that these may be at least double if not multiple membranes. From ultraviolet photomicrographs of sections of the plastron of the bug *Aphelocheirus* it is reported that the epicuticle of this species is laminar (with the layers about 0.04 μ thick) (Thorpe & Crisp 47).

Very little is known about the ultrastructure of the epicuticle and its various subdivisions other than that permeability data seem to necessitate the assumption that the innermost layers of wax molecules are highly oriented and closely packed. Some inferences can be made from wettability data at different stages in development, but the presence of contaminants which affect the spreadability of components complicates interpretation. The epicuticle of cockroach tracheae shows a faint birefringence after isolation when examined in surface view (Richards unpubl.),[10] and light reflected from the surface of beetles may be circularly polarized (Gaubert 24), but further study is required before interpretation especially since the electron microscope studies have failed to reveal any fibrous structure.

[10] The birefringence is extremely faint and requires the use of delicate compensators capable of detecting phase retardations of only a few millimicrons or even a fraction of one. In fact, the birefringence is so faint that compensation effects are required to convince the observer that birefringence is present. Actually, calling any cuticular structure isotropic (Pryor 40b) has little significance unless accompanied by statement of thickness, orientation, and minimum phase retardation necessary for detection in the instrument being used.

While there are a number of cases where the entire cuticle is epicuticle, there are few reports of an epicuticle's being absent. The most conspicuous example is the spider *Tegeneria,* in which it is reported that there is no nonchitinous layer and also that there are no lipids or waxes (Browning 42). But Miss Sewell (unpubl.) finds a thin epicuticle in both *Tegenaria* and *Ciniflo*; this is positive to tests for proteins and lipids and seems to correspond roughly with the cuticulin layer of Wigglesworth. Thin surface layers have also been recorded in other genera of spiders, but not studied chemically (Kaston 35). It is said that a locust lacks an epicuticle along the ecdysial line, that is, along the thin line where the cuticle splits at the time of molting (Duarte 39). A peculiar situation requiring reinvestigation exists in the Chrysidids (Hymenoptera), where noniridescent species are said to possess a "typical" epicuticle, whereas iridescent species are said to lack an epicuticle and possess instead an outer layer which is neither chitinous nor soluble in alkali (Frey 36). Perhaps the latter may prove to be a tectocuticle.

In conclusion on the subject of the arthropod epicuticle, it should be remembered that the study of its internal structure and chemistry is so recent that many of the points in any treatment written now are to be viewed as tentative at best. Those points which seem valid at the present time still need amplification. It should also be remembered that the chemical terms applied to various sublayers are only the terms of gross chemical groups and are accordingly the most preliminary of determinations. That specificities exist is clearly indicated by the different melting points of waxes, differences in the ease of chemical destruction, etc., but whether these may be due to the presence of different lipids, different proteins, etc. or to different linkages, or both, is unknown. Much more serious work is needed; the field is not one which will profit from superficial study.

CHAPTER 19

The Procuticle, or Chitinous Cuticle

THE NONCALCIFIED PROCUTICLE

Noncalcified cuticle is found on all species of arthropods; when calcification occurs, it is limited to certain areas and to certain sublayers. Hundreds of anatomical and histological papers include descriptions and illustrations of the integument. These serve to document only the statement that gross histological appearance is similar throughout the phylum. Few of these papers contain significant analytical data.

From unknown precursors the cuticle components become polymerized as a solid structure with a fairly high water content (Table 10). In some cases it is definitely known that the precursors are secreted from the epidermal cells in fluid form and undergo this polymerization away from immediate contact with the secreting cells. When the soft cuticle is very thin, it may show no differentiation visible to the light microscope, but when it is more than a few microns thick, there are two types of differentiation, namely, the laminae and pore canals (Figs. 34–35), which have been recorded from such a wide range of forms that they are both probably general.[1] Staining with various dyes has not revealed additional differentiation, although subdivisions of the cuticle may be contrastingly colored by the use of techniques such as Mallory's triple stain, picro-indigo carmine, or safranin plus light green.

We have thus far spoken of the cuticle as being a secretion product, and shall continue to do so, but actually this has been at times past a hotly debated point and still cannot be called settled. The question is whether the cuticular material is secreted in fluid form and hardened outside the cells, or whether it is segregated into the

[1] Since neither of these is distinctly colored or becomes contrastingly differentiated by routine histological staining, they become indistinct or even impossible to detect when mounted in media of approximately the same refractive index. Failure to detect either one in routinely prepared histological sections is without significance.

peripheral portion of the cells, which then become the cuticle, with or without a new plasma membrane being formed between the cuticular materials and the cytoplasm of the recognizable epidermal cell.[2] The question could only be settled by locating positively the plasma membrane at all stages of development or by demonstrating the absence of a plasma membrane between the cuticle and the cytoplasm; this would seem an impossibility. Since this type of question no longer appears of fundamental importance or even great interest to biologists, it does not seem worth while to chronicle the long list of authors who have favored secretion or segregation or a combination of the two. Some references are given by Wigglesworth (48b).

It is definitely known that cuticular materials can be secreted in fluid form (Dennell 46, Picken *et al.* 47). It is not positively known that cells or cell processes can become cuticularized by the segregation of components, though the filling of pore canals, development of setae, retention of lines representing cell boundaries, and other points are cited as evidence. Elaborate processes such as are found, for instance, on the spiracular discs of ticks and on the book lungs and so-called tracheae of spiders could be most readily visualized as due to the cuticularization of cell processes (Falke 31, Kästner 29, Nordenskiöld 11). However, similar-appearing processes in the spiracular chamber of a dipterous larva (*Phormia*) have recently been found to be formed intracytoplasmically and then to have the cytoplasm withdrawn from around them; the microscopic appearances suggest intracytoplasmic segregation (Clausen & Richards unpubl.). If any of the microscopically visible cytoplasmic granules could be positively identified as formed cuticular material ("chitinosomes," Janet 07, "macromolecules," Clark 34), the cuticularization of cell parts would be the most feasible method for imagining their incorporation into the cuticle. Since no fundamental differences are involved, it seems best simply to bear in mind that both secretion and segregation probably occur, and otherwise to consider the question "dead" (Wigglesworth 48b).

LAMINAE

In cross sections all except the thinnest of arthropod cuticles show a laminar structure. As usually seen, this is visible as a set of alternating light and dark bands, which are made less distinct or even invisible by immersion in media of approximately the same refractive

[2] It has recently been suggested that Teorell diffusion potentials offer a possible mechanism for such cytoplasmic segregation (Costello 45).

index. These laminae are definitely realities; they are as distinctly sublayers of the cuticle as the main sublayers which have been given names, except for the fact that they are chemically similar to one another. In thickness they range from 0.2 μ (Richards & Anderson 42a) to 10 μ (Lafon 43a). They can be separated and peeled off from one another, especially if the cuticle is first caused to swell considerably. A photograph of a cross section of the cuticle of a tick has been published showing that alternate laminae are respectively isotropic and anisotropic (P. Schulze 32), but this may be an illusion due to the angle of this particular section; in general, cuticle sections are birefringent in cross section (Frey-Wyssling 38, Langner 37, W. J. Schmidt 34b). Examination with an electron microscope shows that in the cockroach the laminae are alternating layers of denser and less dense cuticular material (Figs. 20B, 34) (Richards & Anderson 42a). Their usual visibility under the microscope is due to a difference in refractive index, sometimes accentuated by the tendency to separate in somewhat torn sections (Fig. 20A). Incidentally, they have also been seen in sections of fossil cuticle (D. R. Rome 36).

The laminae do not represent separate layers which are cemented together; at least the dark bands contain chitin, and the material between them also contains chitin. Several authors have suggested that the laminae are delaminated as entities from the surface of the epidermal cells (Ahrens 30, Drach 39, Janet 07, Verne 21, Zschorn 37), but this has never been truly demonstrated[3] and cannot be true in certain cases. The formation of laminae in the cocoons of *Donacia* is unequivocal evidence of laminar formation away from cells (Picken *et al.* 47), but some may consider this not typical for cuticle in general. Unequivocal evidence for the cuticle itself comes from those cases where laminae clearly develop between pre-existing laminae at a distance from the epidermal cells and separated from them by the intervening layers of cuticle. For instance, the prospective exocuticle of *Sarcophaga* thickens and develops many new laminae which maintain the proper space relationships after separation of this layer from the epidermal cells by the prospective endocuticle (Fig. 35) (Dennell 46). An even clearer picture is given by lenses of ommatidia in certain species. As a general rule it seems the thickened lenses have the same number of laminae as adjacent cuticle but that these are considerably swollen (Fig. 52); however,

[3] Janet postulated that they were layers of particles, which he called "chitinosomes," which were produced by the epidermal cells at intervals and separated by the material secreted between these intervals.

in some species the spacing of laminae is kept approximately constant by the intercalation of new partial laminae in the thickened areas (Verhoeff 26–32).

Laminae are found only in the procuticle, but are commonly said not to remain visible in one or another sublayer of the fully formed cuticle. The laminae may (*Periplaneta*, Richards & Anderson 42a) or may not (*Sarcophaga*, Dennell 46) disappear after treatment with hot alkali solutions. They are patently much too thick to be monolayers of cuticular components (Fraenkel & Rudall 47). They may shrink considerably in thickness after formation (and this appears to be the general explanation of their commonly becoming thicker as one approaches the epidermal cells), but they may also increase greatly in thickness, as is shown most graphically in the lenses of eyes. They may be of somewhat different thicknesses in different species and even in procuticle subdivisions of different prospective significance (Dennell 46). And most assuredly they are not peculiar to chitinous cuticles.[4]

The birefringence of laminae requires additional study. This becomes particularly evident when one compares laminae with the Balken, which will be discussed later (p. 192). It would be not at all surprising to find micelle orientation in successive laminae at a large angle to one another, as are Balken layers.

The greater density and greater strength of the dark laminae and the one report on their birefringence all suggest that they represent layers of more tightly packed molecules. Disappearance of the laminae in *Periplaneta* after treatment with hot alkali solutions led to giving preference to the suggestion (Richards & Anderson 42a) that the dark laminae represented layers of chitin and protein separated by layers with lesser amounts of protein. Retention of the laminar appearance in *Sarcophaga* (Dennell 46) after alkali treatment shifts the preference to the second alternative; namely, that the combined chitin-protein micelles are actually more tightly packed in the denser laminae than in the less dense ones. We can presume that differences in the strength of lateral bonds between chains would account not only for differences in the strength of different cuticles but also for the amount of redistribution the chitin micelles undergo following alkali purification.

[4] Laminar external membranes are well known in plants, and in the fungi they may be composed of either chitin or cellulose (Oort & Roelofson 32); laminated cuticles are also found in the Annelida where chitin is said to be lacking (Borodin 29, Reed & Rudall 48), etc.

The suggestion that the laminae are present to provide for flexibility and for stretching by sliding over one another (Ahrens 30) is gratuitous and undocumented, and seems to the present author unnecessary and probably untrue.

As has already been pointed out, the currently available data could be rationalized in terms of origin from Schiller plane phenomena or perhaps periodic crystallizations (p. 142). But Schiller plane phenomena cannot fully account for cuticular laminae without the addition of some other process occurring subsequently, because Schiller planes have natural spacings less than a micron thick whereas cuticular laminae may be several microns in thickness (up to 10 μ). Visualization of an origin similar to that of Schiller planes would require, then, that there be subsequent swelling and, unless density is to decrease greatly, addition of molecules to the already formed layers. Visualization of origin by periodic crystallization phenomena (such as Liesegang ring formation) would require some explanation, such as difficulty of precursor diffusion, to account for the smallness of the spacings. No significant data are available. Schiller planes and periodic competitive crystallization are mentioned here only as suggestions for a problem in differentiation otherwise without tenable hypothesis.

THE PORE CANALS

The pore canals are minute ducts extending through the procuticle and sometimes into the epicuticle (Figs. 28, 32, 34, 35). They are so minute that they are seen with difficulty and then only imperfectly. They are commonly so small that they cannot be resolved as ducts by a light microscope and are seen only as linear diffraction patterns with inadequate resolution. It is only in cases where they are exceptionally large (blowfly larvae, some crustacea, etc.) or where an electron microscope has been used (cockroach, honeybee) that their structure can be adequately determined.[5] Presumably they are always

[5] How to define the term pore canal and what to accept as proof of the presence of pore canals is made uncertain by Kramer and Wigglesworth's acceptance (50) of filaments of stain as proof of the presence of pore canals in the epicuticle of cockroaches. Electron micrographs (Richards & Anderson 42a) of sections of the same species showed canals terminating several microns from the surface, and isolated sheets of epicuticle showed no holes. The reviewer is led to ask for documentation of the assumption that droplets on the surface or filaments of stain in the epicuticle demonstrate *the presence of pore canals*. It is not inconceivable that the chitin-protein matrix of the endocuticle may retain the canal of the pore canal better than the epicuticle does during the manipulations required by electron microscopy, but it is also not inconceivable that the indirect data from staining may create illusions. Certainly, these two sets of data must be reconciled or one of the techniques discredited.

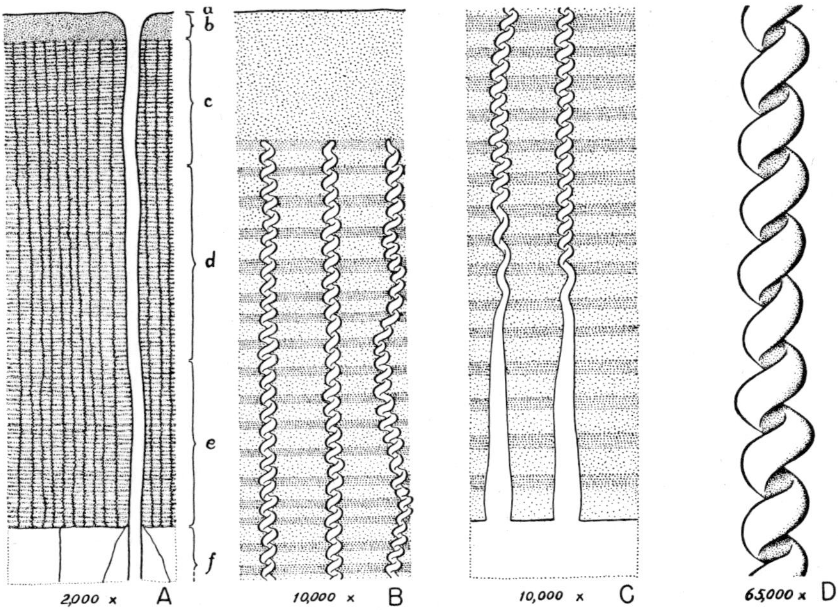

Figure 34. Section of the pronotum of a cockroach, *Periplaneta americana,* as reconstructed from electron micrographs (such as Fig. 20B). Exocuticle and endocuticle appear similar in electron micrographs. (After Richards and Anderson.) *a* = lipid epicuticle; *b* = protein epicuticle; *c* = exocuticle; *d–e* = endocuticle; *f* = position of epidermal cells.

A. Drawing at low magnification contrasting size of gland duct and pore canals.

B. Enlarged drawing of outer portion of preceding showing the double epicuticle, laminar structure of the procuticle, and helical pore canals.

C. Similar enlarged drawing of the inner portion showing the enlarged and straightened pore canals.

D. A single pore canal, greatly enlarged.

formed around filar projections from the epidermal cells; that is, the procuticle is deposited as a continuous sheet which, since it has these filaments projecting through it, solidifies with minute canals representing these processes. Considering the size of the canals, it is not surprising that there are only a few cases where admittedly inconclusive evidence supports this hypothesis (Dennell 43, 46, Scheuring 12, Tower 06, Wigglesworth 48d, Verne 21), but there are some data, and no one has advanced a tenable alternative suggestion for their development.

The pore canals, first recorded by Valentin in 1837, are usually seen only as vague or faint lines, but in cases where they are sufficiently large for adequate resolution are, somewhat surprisingly, found to be rather regular helices. Such cases are known in mites (S. Thor 02), some crustacea (Balss 27, Drach 39), and blowfly larvae (Fig. 35) (Dennell 43, 46). In some cases, focusing a microscope up and down on a surface-view preparation results in the appearance of the canals rotating; this presumably indicates a helical course (Hass 16a, Kapzov 11, Plotnikow 04, Vitzou 81, Wigglesworth 33). The more minute canals of adult cockroaches and bees have been shown to be helical by electron microscopy (Fig. 34) (Richards & Anderson 42a, Richards unpubl.), and it seems probable that the same is true for adults of the beetle *Tenebrio* (Wigglesworth 48d).

The origin of such helices is an intriguing question. Dennell (46) points out that fly larvae are subjected to a certain amount of internal pressure, and suggests that this places the developing procuticle under enough compression to throw the filaments into a helical form. Helical pore canals are now known in an assortment of widely different arthropods, and one would expect their origin to be similar throughout the phylum. Dennell only assumes that the blood pressure of fly larvae is sufficient to compress the developing cuticle; such turgidity (even if it is adequate) is not present in the cockroach. Another source of pressure seems more plausible and more generally applicable: if we assume that the cuticle framework in regions with helical pore canals first solidifies and then contracts in thickness either because of partial dehydration or of molecular packing, the filaments would be thrown into a helix as a result of this contraction.[6] Commonly (e.g., in the cockroach) laminae are thicker at the inner edge of the procuticle (where the pore canals are straight) than more superficially (Fig. 34), but the question, of course, is whether they are squeezed together or contract.[7] In Figure 34 the helices are all drawn as though turning in a clockwise direction. One would expect that some would be clockwise, some counterclockwise, but this remains to be demonstrated.

When the cuticle is stretched, one would expect the pore canals to increase in size, but their minuteness makes it difficult to be sure whether it is the canal or the helix which is becoming broader (Wigglesworth 42c). However, when the cuticle increases in thickness by

[6] Actually solidification prior to contraction is not necessary. All that is necessary is that the cuticle framework contract without a corresponding contraction of the pore canal.

[7] In *Sarcophaga* the laminae appear to remain constant in thickness within the limits to which they were resolved, but in this species the obvious intercalation of new laminae is a warning against using the laminae as landmarks.

intussusception in blowfly larvae, the helical pore canals clearly become stretched to almost straight (Fig. 35) (Dennell 46).

In quite a variety of groups the pore canals are arborescent near their outer ends (Dennell 46, Kühn & Piepho 38, Lees 46, Müller 27 Nordenskiöld 08, Plotnikow 04, Schatz 50). Presumably the corresponding cytoplasmic filaments either show a similar branching or initially are more numerous and soon become drawn together into a smaller number of ducts (Figs. 30A, 45). A similar spacing in sections at various levels suggests that little or no branching occurs for pore canals of the cockroach pronotum (Richards & Anderson 42a).

The older literature contains a certain amount of discussion as to whether the pore canals are really canals, rods, or canals that become filled with rods. We now know that they are originally canals, and that they may either remain canals or become filled with rods of cuticular material. Electron micrographs of cockroach cuticle sections show conclusively that the canals remain canals in this species. Chitosan staining and splitting of the cuticle showing rods projecting from the split surface in *Sarcophaga* larvae demonstrate conclusively that in this species the cellular filaments are replaced by cuticle; also that the cuticle of the canals is not intimately fused with the general cuticle matrix (Dennell 43, 46). Commonly it is said the pore canals extend only through the endocuticle (e.g., certain beetles Eder 40), but poor visibility makes it difficult to be sure. Which of these is the more usual situation remains to be determined. Rods said to arise from filled pore canals or from the cuticularization of cytoplasmic fibrils have been recorded from various crustacea and insects (Biedermann 03, Braun 1875, Hass 16a, N. Holmgren 02b, Plotnikow 04, Wigglesworth 48d). The rods may either contain demonstrable chitin (Dennell 46, Way 48) or be negative for chitin tests (Wigglesworth 48d). In cases where the canal does not become filled with cuticular material, it is usually assumed that the cytoplasmic filaments persist (Hass 16a, Langner 37, Leydig 1864, Poisson 24, Tower 06a, Verne 21, Wigglesworth 33).[8] The evidence for this is inconclusive; perhaps the cellular filaments may be withdrawn or may degenerate without the canal's becoming filled with a cuticular rod. It does seem certain that they would not be filled with air because ready re-wettability

[8] When fresh cuticle sections are allowed to dry in air the pore canals may suddenly become more distinct (Braun 1875, Hass 16a, Huxley 1880, Richards & Anderson 42a, Tullberg 1882, Wigglesworth 33), indicating the entrance of a film or core of air. This evidence does not, however, permit deduction concerning the contents of the pore canals (Dennell 47b).

shows that the lining remains hydrophilic, and accordingly capillary attraction would result in their filling with fluid if the filaments were withdrawn (Richards & Anderson 42a).

Since the pore canals represent cellular filaments, it is not surprising that in cases where boundaries between epidermal cells are clear, pore canals are absent from these intercellular regions (Dennell 47b).

There are only two cases where the size and number of pore canals have been recorded. In *Sarcophaga* larvae (Dennell 46) the pore canals have a diameter of about 1.0 μ and in the helical region a pitch of about 2.5 μ (Fig. 35). There are from 50 to 70 canals arising from each epidermal cell, and these give a density of approximately 15,000 per sq. mm. of surface. These figures are widely different from figures obtained from the pronotum of cockroaches (Richards & Anderson 42a), where the pore canals have an average diameter of 0.15 μ (range of 0.10 μ to 0.20 μ) and are coiled into a helix with an outside diameter of 0.25 μ and a pitch of 0.25 μ (Fig. 34). Being smaller and closer together, they have a density of approximately 1,200,000 per sq. mm.[9] In the cockroach the epidermal cells vary more in size than those of *Sarcophaga*, and the pore canals, maintaining approximately the same density irrespective of cell size, vary considerably in terms of number per epidermal cell (a range of 25 to 500 was suggested). The electron microscope has such good resolution that a number of additional calculations were possible with the cockroach. The length of the helical pore canals was found to be approximately 80 μ, that is, almost exactly twice the thickness of the cuticle, and a single pore canal has an approximate volume of 1.7 cu. μ. The pore canals account for 5–6% of the total volume of the pronotum. At the epicuticle-procuticle interface they account for approximately 2% of the surface area. At the inner margin of the endocuticle the pore canals straighten out and become considerably broader. The number 2,500,000,000 was estimated as minimal for the total number of pore canals on a single cockroach.

All the recent ideas concerning the function of pore canals and their included protoplasmic filaments are concerned with the produc-

[9] It is interesting to note that this is some 3 to 4 times the density of cilia on *Paramecium*. Incidentally, rods presumably representing pore canals in the elytra of *Euphoria* are uniformly but unsystematically arranged, with a density somewhat more than 1,000,000/sq. mm. (Mason 27b); and microtrichia, which probably represent pore canals, occur with a density of 2,000,000/sq. mm. on the plastron of the bug *Aphelocheirus* (Thorpe & Crisp 47).

tion of the cuticle.[10] The oldest of these acceptable suggestions is that the material which forms the procuticle is secreted around these filar processes (Leydig 1864), but while this may be true, it is not a necessary method of secretion of procuticle, as shown by thin membranes which lack pore canals (Richards & Anderson 42a) and by *Sarcophaga* larvae, which secrete an inner procuticle that is devoid of pore canals (Dennell 46). Other suggestions that may be additional rather than alternative are that the pore canals transport one or more of the components of the epicuticle through the already partly formed procuticle (Dennell 46, Wigglesworth 47b), that they transport to the epicuticle the oxidizing enzyme used in sclerotization (Wigglesworth 39), that they transport material for the repair of abraded cuticle (Wigglesworth 48b), and that they transport the phenolic substrate and protein for sclerotization (Kühn & Piepho 38, Pryor 40b). The evidence is strong that they do transport through the already partly formed procuticle some of the components that go into the development of the epicuticle. [The function of pore canals in egg shells of grasshoppers has not been determined (Matthée 48, Slifer 49a).] It seems to the present author doubtful that pore canals have a single specific function; very likely they are a characteristic feature of chitinogenous tissue and transport peripherally various components for cuticle production.

Pore canals are widely but not universally found in arthropod cuticles. They are recorded for Chilopodo (Fuhrmann 21), Diplopoda (Fuhrmann 21, Langner 37, Silvestri 03), Linguatulida (von Haffner 24b), *Limulus* (Lafon 43a), scorpions (Scheuring 12), mites (Steding 24, S. Thor 02), ticks (Frick 36, Lees 46, Nordenskiöld 08, Ruser 33, Yalvac 39), various groups of Crustacea, including Isopoda, Amphipoda, Ostracoda, and Decapoda (Balss 27, Braun 1875, Bronn's, Dennell 47b, Drach 39, Haeckel 1857, Hass 16a, Herold 13, Huxley 1880, Leydig 1855, 64, 78, Tullberg 1882, Valentin 1837, Verne 21, Vitzou 1881), and insects in general (Berlese 09, Eder 40, N. Holmgren 02a, b, Kühnelt 28c, Plotnikow 04), the most useful references being in Odonata (Sadones 1896), Orthoptera (Hass 16a), Blattariae (Richards & Anderson 42a), Mallophaga (J. E. Webb 47), Hemiptera (Poisson 24, Wigglesworth 33, 47b), Coleoptera (Biedermann 03,

[10] Old ideas which have only historic significance include the suggestion that these loosen the old cuticle at the time of molting (Braun 1875), that they serve to anchor the cuticle to the underlying cells (Sadones 1896), and that they represent cilia or structures homologous with cilia which have become embedded in a solid matrix (N. Holmgren 02b, Verne 21).

Bütschli 1894, Casper 13, 24, Hsu 38, Kapzov 11, Leydig 1855, Tower 06a, Wigglesworth 48d), Hymenoptera (Hsu 38, Richards unpubl.), Diptera (Dennell 43, 46, N. Holmgren 02a), and Lepidoptera (Kühn & Piepho 38, Montgomery 00).

Pore canals are absent from many very thin cuticles (Eder 40). Electron microscope examination shows pore canals absent from the thin body cuticle of mosquito larvae at all stages of development, from the tracheal walls of all arthropods, from the wing membranes of mosquitoes and blowflies, from the lining of the crop (= fore-gut) of cockroaches and blowflies, from the membrane over rectal papillae of mosquito larvae, and from various setae and sense organs (Richards & Anderson 42a, Richards & Korda 47, 48, 50, Richards unpubl.). We have to conclude that pore canals are not *necessary* constituents of cuticle, for they are absent not only from thin cuticles but also from the thick (70 μ) inner procuticle of *Sarcophaga* larvae (Dennell 46).

CHAPTER 20

Differentiation of the Procuticle

In some cases (soft transparent membrane) the procuticle undergoes little or no detectable change after its formation (Fig. 30c). This does not necessarily mean it cannot be changed. For instance, in the moth *Ephestia* one can obtain a partial pupation with omission of the molting fluid; the soft larval cuticle is not shed: more material is added to it and the whole changed into a heavily scerotized pupal skin, albeit of abnormal appearance (Fig. 36) (Kühn 39). In general it seems to be true that the soft procuticle is capable of being sclerotized, and that it becomes sclerotized in those species and areas where the appropriate chemicals are added. The dipterous puparium is especially favorable for studying this process and will be treated in some detail.

In sclerotized areas (sclerites) it is usually only the outer portion of the procuticle that becomes hardened and darkened (Figs. 1, 35). The reactions may be so slight as to be seen only with difficulty (Fig. 30F) (differential staining many help, Levereault 34) or so intense that a dark brown or black area of considerable rigidity results (Fig. 44). This altered outer portion (irrespective of the percentage of procuticle involved) is termed the exocuticle. The seemingly unaltered transparent inner portion, plus subsequent material added to it, is termed the endocuticle.[1]

[1] The exocuticle has also been called *Aussenlage, Pigmentschicht, Lackschicht, Emailschicht,* coreum, areolated layer, chitin, and even epidermis (the last is actually the oldest name, having been used by Straus-Durckheim in 1828 as well as by numerous later authors). Seemingly this is the ectostracum of arachnids, and the *Alveolarsaum* and *Stäbchenschicht* of beetle elytra. One group refers to the material forming this differentiation as *Inkrusten.* The exocuticle has also been called the primary cuticula (Tower 06a, b), the term being used differently from current usage.

The endocuticle has also been called *Innenlage, Hauptlage,* endostracum, hypostracum, uncalcified coreum, rete mucosum, chitin, secondary cuticula, and dermis (the last being used with epidermis for exocuticle and with hypodermis for what we call epidermis).

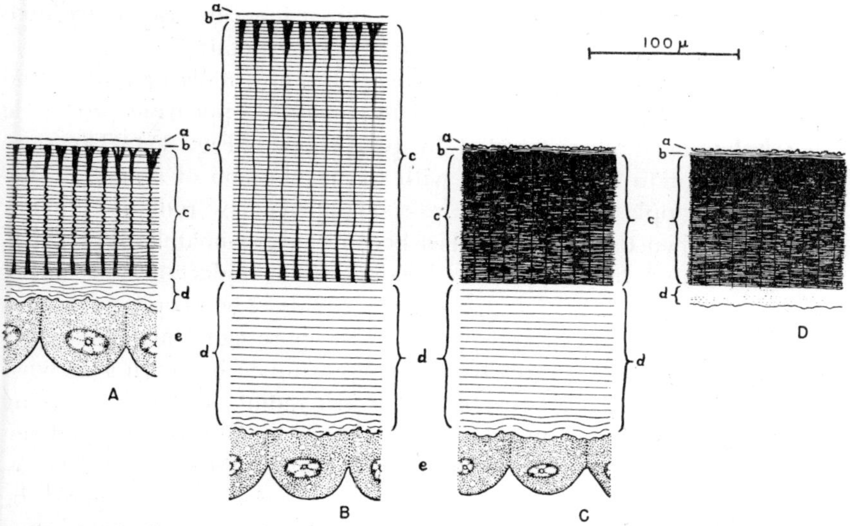

Figure 35. Changes undergone by the larval integument of a blowfly, *Sarcophaga falculata,* during the formation of the puparium. (Redrawn after Dennell.) a = lipid or outer epicuticle; b = protein or inner epicuticle; c = outer procuticle (prospective exocuticle); d = inner procuticle (prospective endocuticle); e = epidermal cells.

A. Larval cuticle at about two days after hatching. Note the arborescent pore canals, which are helical in their central part.

B. The same after the larva has become fully mature. Note that both inner and outer portions of the procuticle have thickened greatly, the pore canals have become stretched to almost straight, and the inner procuticle has no pore canals.

C. The same immediately prior to separation of the puparium from the epidermis. Note that the darkening and hardening, with concurrent shrinkage, is limited to the protein epicuticle and outer procuticle, the latter thereby becoming exocuticle.

D. The same in an old puparium. The epidermal cells have separated from the cuticle, and the endocuticle has shrunk by evaporation of water.

THE PUPARIUM OF DIPTERA

Little precise information is available on differentiation of the procuticle except for the development of the puparium studied by Fraenkel and Rudall (40, 47) and by Dennell (46, 47a). The puparium is a specialized structure, and while perhaps not completely typical for arthropod cuticles in general, none the less affords an ideal situation for studying the processes involved in sclerotization. In the higher Diptera, the skin of the last larval instar is not shed; it becomes loosened from the underlying epidermis and transforms into a hard covering around the outside of the pupa. We have, then, a situation where the soft larval procuticle and its properties can be studied; and, later, at a finite developmental stage, the transformation of this same soft cuticle into hard sclerotized puparium can also be studied. The story may profitably be reviewed in some detail.

In the last larval instar of *Sarcophaga* the epicuticle or part of the epicuticle is secreted first, followed by a typical appearing procuticle that is laminar and penetrated by pore canals (Fig. 35). The pore canals appear to be concerned with the production of epicuticle because the cytoplasmic contents are soon replaced by rods of cuticular material. When the procuticle has become approximately 40 μ thick, the pore canal filaments have become fully replaced, and subsequently secreted procuticle lacks these canals. The secretion of procuticle subsequent to disappearance of the pore canal filaments gives an inner endocuticle of grossly similar appearance but with somewhat wider laminae, a more variable isoelectric point, a strong reducing power, and a different prospective significance. A surprising and important point is that while the inner procuticle increases in thickness, the outer procuticle also increases in thickness. Material must be added to both simultaneously, and since the prospective potency of the two layers is different (p. 188), the different properties of the two layers are not due simply to chemical differences in material secreted by the epidermal cells at different times. The outer procuticle increases from a thickness of 40 μ to 140 μ. Since chemical analyses show that the several major components maintain the same percentage relationships, this is an irrefutable case of cuticular material being secreted in fluid form, diffusing through the underlying prospective endocuticle, and becoming deposited in the prospective exocuticle to form an integral portion thereof (growth by intussusception). The inner procuticle increases to become approximately 80 μ thick. Although the underlying epidermal cells show clear cell boundaries, no comparable lines are recognizable in the cuticle. The secretion of cuticular material proceeds at an approximately constant rate, and with growth of the larva increases both in thickness and surface area. The increase in surface area is something over 200% in the longitudinal axis (the distance across the arborescent tips of the pore canals increases by a similar percentage).[2] The cuticular laminae maintain approximately the same thickness and therefore must have material added to them as well as new laminae intercalated between them.

The localization of certain chemical components is different for the different layers. The oxidizing enzyme which will produce the final

[2] This does not necessarily mean that the molecular framework is so stretched. More material is added to the cuticle at this time (as shown by weight) and almost certainly some of this is incorporated in the plane of the surface.

tanning agent is located in the epicuticle, and can be demonstrated by its ability to oxidize the leuco form of methylene blue. The outer portion of the procuticle (the part with pore canals) has free tyrosine and tryptophane, and stains with methylene blue but will neither oxidize nor reduce it. The inner portion of the procuticle (the part lacking pore canals) shows none of these chemicals, but has some component which is an active reducing agent capable of changing methylene blue to the leucobase.[3]

Tests with the Nadi reagent show that the oxidizing enzyme is absent from the cuticle of young larvae at a time when the epidermal cells contain many Nadi positive granules. Since the pore canals become filled with cuticular rods prior to deposition of the oxidase in the epicuticle, the enzyme must pass through the procuticle by diffusion and become deposited in the epicuticle as a result of some concentration phenomenon.

At the time of puparium formation three separate things happen:[4] (1) the larva contracts and the cuticle becomes loosened in this contracted condition; (2) substrate for the tanning reaction diffuses in from the blood and becomes oxidized or further oxidized by the oxidase located in the epicuticle; (3) the tanning process occurs by production of an o-quinone in the epicuticle which diffuses inward through the outer procuticle, transforming it into an exocuticle. When both the protein epicuticle and the exocuticle become tanned, it is extremely difficult to distinguish between them.

Normal puparium formation requires that the larva first become contracted and the cuticle partially dehydrated. Comparison of volume and weight figures shows that dehydration alone is not adequate to account for all of the shrinkage; approximately one third of the shrinkage must be due to closer packing of the molecular chains (Fraenkel & Rudall 40, 47). If the tanning process is brought about without this previous contraction, similar coloration and some hardening are produced, but the puparium does not develop its normal rigid and brittle nature.

The eventual substrate from which the tanning agent is produced is tyrosine. Some free tyrosine is already present in the outer pro-

[3] A reducing agent (assumed to be glucose) was found in cuticle many years ago, but its significance was not realized (Mirande 05a, b). Differences in stainability of parts of the puparium are also recorded by Wiesmann (38). See also Kühnelt (49).

[4] These are in addition to the destruction of the glucose dehydrogenase of blood by the puparium-forming hormone (E. Becker 41, Dennell 49a).

cuticle (Dennell 47a, Trim 41b), but this is insufficient. More tyrosine or partial oxidation products thereof must diffuse in from the blood—which incidentally shows a decrease in tyrosine content (from 1.70% to 0.87%) concurrent with the deposition of tanning agent in the cuticle (Fraenkel & Rudall 47) but remains negative to tests for free phenols (Dennell 47a). Further evidence in favor of the derivation of cuticular components from blood tyrosine comes from the fact that the dry weight of the puparium increases by 8.8% during sclerotization, while the drop in blood tyrosine shows a maximum equivalent to 9.1% of the cuticle (Fraenkel & Rudall 47).

It is still uncertain what chemical diffuses through the cuticle for the tanning. It could hardly be the eventual tanning agent (o-quinone), because, if it were, tanning should occur from the inner layers outwardly—that is, in the reverse of the direction in which it actually does occur. On the other hand the high tyrosinase of the blood suggests that partial oxidation of the blood tyrosine occurs prior to diffusion into the cuticle. Perhaps it is "Dopa" (Fig. 12) or its deaminated derivative which diffuses into the cuticle for further oxidation (Dennell 47a). (See also Chapter 8.)

The molecular oxygen used in the oxidation of tyrosine to o-quinone is at least partly utilized in the cuticle; yet, despite its closeness to the surface, the oxygen is obtained from the tracheal system, not from air outside the body (Dennell 46, Fraenkel 35b).

The appropriate o-quinone, when formed, tans the outer procuticle to give the hard, brittle, dark exocuticle. X-ray data show that the tanning reaction involves linkages with side chains of the chitin-protein micelles (Fraenkel & Rudall 47), perhaps in the manner suggested in Figure 14. The color produced by tanning does not go directly from white to black. The original white puparium changes rather rapidly but distinctly from white to a light red brown, to a dark chestnut, and then to almost black. Quite likely the intermediate pigment structure may be different from that in the final product, but this is not yet established.

During the contraction and tanning the outer procuticle contracts approximately 50% in thickness in forming the exocuticle of the puparium. The inner procuticle, which forms the endocuticle of the puparium, also contracts a similar amount and later continues to become thinner, presumably owing to evaporation of water. Consideration of both normal development and the sclerotization of isolated cuticles in substrate solutions show that it is only the outer layer of the procuticle which is capable of forming an exocuticle. In embryological terminology: the outer portion of the procuticle has the potency for forming exocuticle, the inner portion of the procuticle does not.

Summarizing the events occurring in the sclerotization of the puparium (Fig. 35): (1) the larval cuticle contracts, becomes partly dehydrated, and the molecular chains become more highly oriented and tightly packed (Fraenkel & Rudall 47); (2) an oxidase, probably produced by certain blood cells (oenocytoids), passes from the epidermal cells through the procuticle to become deposited in the epicuticle (Dennell 47a); (3) tyrosine or a partial oxidation product thereof in the blood passes through the epidermal cells and procuticle to the epicuticle at the time of pupation; (4) at the epicuticle this substrate is oxidized through an o-dihydroxyphenol to the corresponding o-quinone, which tans the epicuticle and diffuses inward, tanning the outer portion of the procuticle to form an exocuticle; and (5) the presumptive endocuticle must differ chemically from the presumptive exocuticle, for it is immune to this chemical tanning process.

Similar events occur in the closely related genus *Calliphora*, but in this genus the epicuticle is thicker and becomes prematurely tanned in correlation with an earlier positive argentaffin reaction and a stronger Nadi reaction in the late larval stages. One would like to know how similar the processes are in the puparium of *Rhagoletis cerasi*, where a peculiar type of calcification has been reported (Wiesmann 38), but this will require reinvestigation.

THE EXOCUTICLE IN OTHER ARTHROPODS

Rather little is known about events taking place during the sclerotization process in other arthropods other than what can be deduced from similar superficial appearance and from comparison with the preceding description for puparia. Sclerotization is quite general, although perhaps not entirely universal; even transparent forms such as the fairy shrimp have the tips of the mandibles tanned (Dennell 47b).[5] It is thought that the series of chemical events occurring during sclerotization is similar throughout the phylum, but more general documentation of this assumption is desirable. The sclerites may be either thicker than the intersegmental membrane (40 μ versus 10 μ in *Tenebrio*, Wigglesworth 48d) or thinner than it (30 μ versus 50 μ in *Rhodnius*, Wigglesworth 33). The pigmentation (= sclero-

[5] Incidentally, the chaetae of earthworms seem to be similarly sclerotized (Dennell 49b).

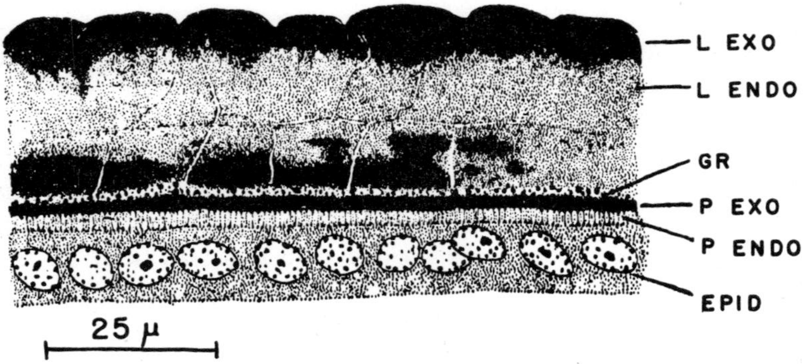

Figure 36. Section of a "pupation spot" on a ligatured larva of a moth, *Ephestia Kühniella.* Note that the inner portion of the larval endocuticle becomes sclerotized as well as a thin atypical pupal cuticle formed beneath *and continuous with* the larval cuticle. (After Kühn and Piepho.) EPID = epidermis; GR = pigment granules; L ENDO = larval endocuticle; L EXO = larval exocuticle; P ENDO = pupal endocuticle; P EXO = pupal exocuticle.

tization) almost always begins at the peripheral surface and is most intense there (Fig. 35), but in the pupa of the moth *Ephestia* is drawn as most intense at the inner surface of the exocuticle (Fig. 29) (Kühn & Piepho 38). Experiments involving the endocrine system can result in abnormal sclerotization as shown in Figure 36.

One of the most interesting conclusions to emerge from a consideration of the development of exocuticles in general is that procuticles which appear similar under the microscope may none the less have chemical differences which confer different potencies upon them. This is conclusively demonstrated by the puparium, where the inner part of the procuticle is incapable of becoming sclerotized. In general, hard exocuticle is separated from the underlying epidermal cells by a soft endocuticle (Fig. 35). Several possible explanations could be suggested, notably that the inner part is incapable of sclerotization or that the sclerotization process begins at the outer part of the procuticle and is limited in its inward extension either by quantity of substrate or by time so that the inner parts do not become sclerotized. Although satisfactory documentation is not available, one could suggest that the cases where part but not all of the procuticle present at the time of molting becomes sclerotized are limited primarily by deficiency in quantity of substrate for the tanning process (Wigglesworth 33), whereas cases in which the entire procuticle present at the time of molting becomes sclerotized occur when an adequate amount of tanning agent is available (Browning 42). The portion of the soft endocuticle which is secreted subsequent to molting seems most probably never to be exposed to the action of tanning agents; data are not available for saying whether or not it is generally capable of being tanned.

If we divide the procuticle into primary and secondary layers, that is, into portions secreted before and after molting respectively, it follows that the definitive endocuticle of the fully formed integument may consist solely of secondary cuticle (Browning 42) or may include the secondary cuticle and an inner fraction of the primary cuticle (Wigglesworth 33). In the special case of the fly puparium a secondary cuticle is not demarcated, but Dennell (46, 47a) says that the division of procuticle into outer and inner layers is not synonymous with one into primary and secondary layers.

The formation of a puparium is preceded by contraction produced by muscle action. This results in a closer packing (Pantel 1898) and better orientation of the molecular chains preceding sclerotization. Similar perfection of orientation and packing occurs in other cuticles, but it is not clear how this is brought about. In the puparium the oxidase and its substrate have an over-all distribution, and accordingly a completely sclerotized cuticle is produced. In arthropods in general the sclerotization is limited to certain regions called sclerites, which are separated from other similar areas by membrane. A number of authors have shown with a variety of species that this localization of sclerotization is due to the local production or transport into the cuticle of the substrate used to form the tanning agent; the oxidase is distributed generally over the cuticle surface (Danneel 43, Dennell 47a, Gortner 11b, Graubard 33, Henke 24, H. Onslow 16, Schlottke 38b, Tower 06a, b), though it is present in the cuticle only during the general time period when it acts (Dennell 47a, Schlottke 38b). Sclerotization, then, is controlled by the underlying epidermal cells which pass substrate out to the cuticle only in certain predetermined areas (Wigglesworth 40a, b). The nature of the differentiation which leads certain cells to pass the substrate on but others not to, is a part of the general problem of pattern formation which will not be treated (it might be added that the subject is little understood).

Sclerotization requires atmospheric oxygen and is inhibited if access to oxygen is prevented (Dewitz 02c, 16, Gortner 11a). However, both the onset and the duration of the sclerotization process vary considerably in different species. Thus silkworm larvae finish the sclerotization of the exocuticle within a few hours after molting (Kuwana 33), whereas carabid beetles show no darkening at all within this time and require about 18 hours to complete the process (Sprung 32). Darkening may, however, occur postmortem, as one might expect for such an enzymic process (Schmalfuss and Barthmeyer 30).

In some cases sclerotization seems to occur around the arborescent ends of pore canals (Figs. 30A, 45) (Kühn & Piepho 38), and in more extreme cases to give rise to wedge-shaped microsclerites which form a somewhat hardened but still flexible membrane (Escherich 1897, Hass 16a, Kühnelt 28c, von Lengerken 21, Plotnikow 04).

A number of authors have noted that the exocuticle and even the procuticle may show birefringence, indicating a recognizable degree of parallel orientation of micelles (Browning 42, Lafon 43a, Pryor 40b). The property has been used in work on setae (p. 276) and tracheae (p. 257), but not in serious studies on the general exoskeleton. Its use with the exocuticle would be difficult because of the complications arising from absorption of part of the light.

The hardening that occurs without either darkening or calcification (*Dixippus*, Fraenkel & Rudall 47) needs critical study. The fact that it occurs is mentioned elsewhere (pp. 76 and 116) and repeated here only to emphasize that sclerotization seems to be the common but not exclusive method of hardening noncalcified cuticles.

BALKEN

Kühnelt (28c) has already suggested that Balken or Balkenlagen, first described by H. Meyer in 1842, are only quantitatively different from laminae. Certainly the most commonly cited cases (Biedermann 03, Kapzov 11) are extreme ones, but critical work, especially on micelle orientations in laminae, is needed before accepting this suggestion. Birefringence rather than ordinary microscopy is the method to use. If Kühnelt's suggestion is correct, one would define Balken not merely as recognizable fiber tracts in the endocuticle (Langner 37) but as the aggregation of micelles within laminae to form microscopically visible fibers. Most of the references to Balken are in studies on the cuticle of beetles (Beauregard 1885, Berlese 09, Stegemann 29b), but similar fibrous aggregations are found in diplopods (Langner 37), tarantulas (Fig. 24A), and some crustacea (Haeckel 1864).

In some cases the Balken are said to form a definitely crossed fiber structure in which the micelle axes in one layer are at a rather constant angle (45°, 60°, or 90°) to those in the next layer (Biedermann

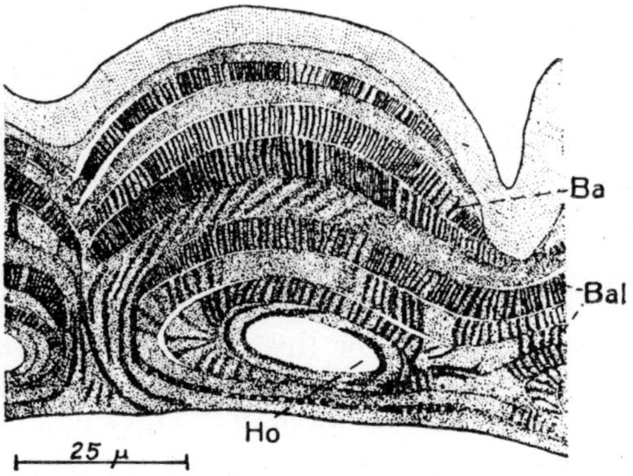

Figure 37. Section of the elytron of a beetle, *Calandra granaria,* treated with KOH and stained with azan. (After Reuter.) *Ba* = azan-stained band on Balken; *Bal* = Balken; *Ho* = lumen of elytron.

03, Frey-Wyssling 38, Haeckel 1864, Kühnelt 28c, P. Schulze 13a);[6] in other cases such a regular crossed fiber effect is said to be absent (Reuter 37). In a number of cases a relationship between micelle axes and cell arrangement has been pointed out (Casper 13, Kapzov 11, Langner 37, Wigglesworth 48d). However, it does not seem likely that cells could impose their orientation in this manner, especially when the Balken are formed while widely separated from the cells by other endocuticle, as they are in the beetle *Calandra* (Fig. 37) (Reuter 37). Mechanical forces acting subsequent to secretion seem more plausible (see papers by Castle, 37–42, also the review by Picken 40).

An unexplained point is the report that the Balken of *Calandra* give a banded staining with Azan, as shown in Figure 37 (Reuter 37).

Three highly suggestive points have been recorded on the development of Balken. P. Schulze (13a) records that they develop as parallel thickenings on the endocuticular laminae. Biedermann (02, 03) records that the Balken appear to be bundles of minute fibers rather than large single fibers (as the taenidia of cockroach tracheae have been shown to be, Richards & Korda 48). Reuter (37) records that in *Calandra* there are no Balken in the procuticle and that they develop in the *peripheral* part of the differentiating endocuticle, being at all

[6] A clear crossed-fiber pattern with the fibers 60 Å broad and 200 Å apart was found in the wing scales (negative to chitin tests) of *Morpho* butterflies (Anderson & Richards 42b), but this is a quite different order of magnitude.

times separated from the epidermal cells by a regular laminated endocuticle. It seems certain that the Balken are tightly packed fibrous structures (Biedermann 03, Gonell 26, Kunike 25). As post-secretion aggregations, perhaps brought about by mechanical stresses, they could be readily rationalized as extremely specialized laminae. But the necessary critical confirmatory data are yet to be obtained.

In a number of cases it is known that micelle orientations are in the directions of maximal strength; it is difficult for the present author to conceive of a mechanism for this development without including stresses as a major factor. Thus at leg joints the micelles in the thickened ring are oriented circumferentially, while those in the attached tendons are at a right angle to this (Fig. 24B), and tendonal attachments in general show orientations at a right angle to those in the cuticle (p. 241); orientations approaching 90° are also found in tracheal walls (p. 256). A considerable part of the necessary mathematical (Castle 37a) and technical procedure (Lees & Picken 45) is now available for a thorough analysis of the role and development of micelle orientations in arthropod cuticle, including deductions as to the stress forces necessarily involved. We need a biologist with the interest and time to undertake the job.

PRISMS

In a few cases it has been recorded that the cuticle shows a surface sculpturing which represents the margins of the underlying epidermal cells (Fuhrmann 21, Guth 19, Kölliker 1857, Viallanes 1882), but this is not generally true and, with what we now know of the mode of development of the epicuticle, should not be expected. More interesting is the fact that in some but not in other crustacea it is recorded that lines representing the cell boundaries can be seen through the entire thick procuticle (Dennell 47b, Drach 39, Vitzou 1881). This has been used to support the claim that the cuticle arises by the transformation of cells, but is not proof, since secretion followed by extremely rapid polymerization could give the same result.

Highly specialized prisms are found in the cuticle of certain beetles and give rise to the prismatic colors found (W. J. Schmidt 37b). But it does not seem to have been determined whether these prisms do or do not correspond to underlying epidermal cells.

CALCIFIED CUTICLES

There is little to be said about calcified cuticles other than what has already been presented in the chemical section (p. 100). Summarizing with reference to the topic of this chapter, calcified cuticles possess an epicuticle and the calcification is limited to the procuticle. Certainly the first part (primary cuticle) of the procuticle is secreted as a chitin-protein matrix which becomes more or less strongly sclerotized prior to calcification just as insect cuticles do (Dennell 47b, Drach 39, Novikoff 05, Langner 37). It is reported that in the inner regions deposition of chitin and protein may be concurrent with calcification (Drach 37a, b, c, Drach and Lafon 42). Generally this results in the production of three recognizable layers in the procuticle: a calcified exocuticle, a thick calcified outer portion of the endocuticle, and a moderately thick uncalcified inner portion of endocuticle (Balss 27). The combined calcified layers have sometimes been called the "calcified coreum" (W. C. Williamson 1860).

Individuals with calcified cuticles are commonly preceded by more immature forms which lack calcification. Also there is likely to be considerable difference in time of calcification between different regions of the body; thus the mandibles, chelipeds, and gastric teeth may be calcified prior to the general exoskeleton (L. W. Williams 07b).

In diplopods, the recent paper by Cloudsley-Thompson (50b) records that the sclerotized exocuticle is uncalcified and that calcification is limited to the outer portion of the endocuticle.

CHAPTER 21

Physical Colors

Space will not permit detailed treatment of the diverse optical phenomena involved in physical colors. A simplified treatment of interference, the most important source of physical colors in arthropods, will be given. Of the many papers on physical colors in insects, the ones by Malloch (11), H. Onslow (20, 21), Rayleigh (23, 30), Süffert (24), and C. W. Mason (26–29) are outstanding and should be consulted for details. The series of papers by Gentil (33–46), Kühn (39–46), and Catala (49) give good examples of how much is to be found in the way of minor anatomical variations in different groups. Some of the most important conclusions concerning the structure of iridescent butterfly scales have recently been confirmed by electron microscope examination (Anderson & Richards 42b, Gentil 42, Kinder & Süffert 43, Kühn 46, Kühn & An 46), but only the paper by Anderson and Richards gives parallel optical analyses justifying the conclusions reached (Fig. 59). Almost all the work on physical colors has dealt with insects, but the phenomena are clearly not limited to these: interference colors have been definitely recorded for several groups of crustacea (Haeckel 1864, W. J. Schmidt 26), physical colors are also reported to be present in ticks (Frick 36) and they doubtless occur in numerous other arthropods. For references to the extensive literature, the reviews by Biedermann (14b), Süffert (24), and Prochnow (27) should be consulted. In the present treatment only those points which are of interest for a general interpretation of cuticle structure will be given.

Structural colors include the following:[1]

1. Structural white, due to the scattering, reflection, and refraction of light from particles too small to be resolved by the eye, yet large in comparison to the wave length of light. The substances concerned

[1] Gentil (36c) records a case where physical color is said to be due to dense concentration of points giving diffraction rings. Also, W. J. Schmidt (37b) describes what he called a special type of prismatic color in beetles.

are usually transparent but can be colored. Many if not most insect whites are of this type.

2. Tyndall blue, due to the scattering of light by particles which have dimensions comparable to the wave length of light. The shorter wave lengths of light are scattered, the longer wave lengths transmitted; therefore the scattered or reflected light is blue, the transmitted light yellow to red. The phenomenon is uncommon in insects, yet is well shown by certain species of dragonflies.

3. Physical colors due to diffraction gratings, which are series of parallel lines spaced by somewhat more than the length of a wave of light. The best diffraction gratings have lines 1–2 μ apart. Series of parallel lines of this spacing are not uncommon in insects, but the colors they produce are seldom seen and are only rarely a major component of the general color of the insect. Outstanding exceptions are beetles of the genus *Serica* (Anderson & Richards 42a, Gentil 46, C. W. Mason 27b).

4. Colors produced by interference between reflections from superimposed thin planes. This is the common cause of physical color in arthropods and will be treated below.

5. Combinations of either two or more of the above or of one or more of the above with a true pigment.

In contrast to pigment colors, physical colors are distinguished by the fact that the color is changed or destroyed by pressure, distortion, swelling, shrinking, and immersion in media of the same refractive index; that it is unaffected by bleaching unless this causes one of the above; that all components of the light are found in either the reflected, scattered, or transmitted components; and that the phenomena are duplicated from known models. In practice immersion and swelling are the easiest first tests.

For recognizing interference from thin planes, Mason (27a) lists twelve points, including specularity, high intensity, comparison to models, relationship to Newton's series of colors, especially the predictable changes upon swelling and shrinking, complimentariness of transmitted and reflected colors, etc. A brief elementary treatment is given by Catala (49).

Interference effects due to superimposed planes are most simply and easily seen in thin wing membranes, but are found in a wide variety of arthropod structures. A simplified presentation of the phenomena is given graphically in Figure 38. In A of this figure, a ray of light passing downward impinges upon reflecting surfaces *1, 2, 3,* and

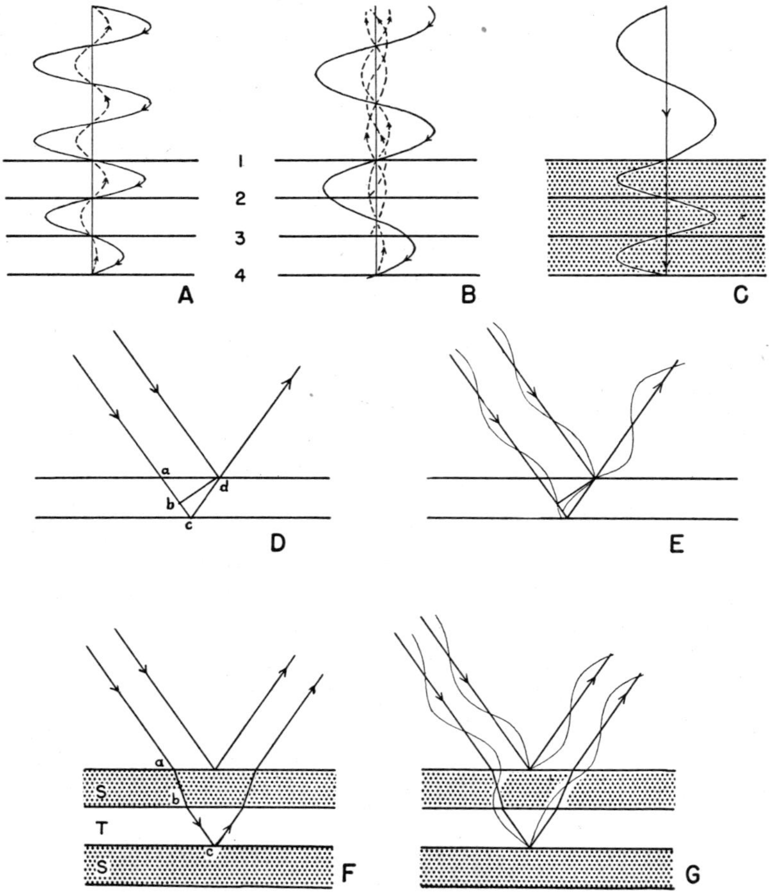

Figure 38. Diagrammatic representation of the phenomena involved in interference effects which produce physical colors in insects. For explanation see text.

4. At each of these interfaces a certain percentage of the light is transmitted, a certain percentage reflected; for an air-glass interface and an angle of 90° some 5% to 6% of the incident light is reflected and the remainder transmitted, and probably the percentages are not greatly different from this for arthropod cuticle. Some of all the wave lengths (colors) are reflected. Those waves whose length is twice the distance between reflecting planes join with rays reflected from other reflecting surfaces to reinforce one another — that is, to intensify that particular color. The reflected waves of other lengths do not fall into the same path and are said to interfere destructively with one another – that is, to decrease or vanish in intensity. This is diagrammed graphically in A and B, Figure 38. The intensity of a light beam is diagrammed by the height of the sinusoidal waves; from plane *4* a wave is reflected back which at plane *3* joins with the wave reflected there to form one of twice the height of that from *4* to 3, and this at plane *2* joins with the wave there to form one three times this height, which at plane *1* joins another to become four times the amplitude ($= 16 \times$ the intensity) reflected at plane *4*. In the case of waves of other lengths the reflected rays do not join one another harmoniously, but as shown in Figure 38B form a series of curves on both sides of the center line, the components on one side partly or completely cancelling those on the other side. In the special case where the ray reflected from plane *2* reaches plane *1* exactly half a wave length out of phase with the ray reflected from plane *1*, complete cancellation results. Complete cancellation can also result from the summation of partial cancellations produced by reflections of a large series of planes (this is the situation actually shown in Figure 38B). Clearly, from A and B, Figure 38, the larger the number of superimposed reflecting surfaces, the greater the intensity and the purity of the reinforced reflected wave lengths (color).

At angles other than 90° shorter wave lengths are intensified, as shown in D and E, Figure 38. This is contrary to the impression one is likely to obtain on first inspection, but can readily be shown mathematically. The initial misimpression is due to the fact that one is inclined to compare the length of line *a c d* in Figure 38D with twice the length of a perpendicular line between these planes. It is the line *b c d* which should be compared with twice the normal distance between these planes. A visual clarification of this is given in Figure 38E, where the parallel incident rays are drawn as sinusoidal curves.

The simplified treatment shown in A, B, D, and E, Figure 38, is adequate for a preliminary analysis of physical colors. One can even use standard equations to calculate expected intensities, or from the intensity obtained calculate the probable number of reflecting planes (Anderson & Richards 42b). Mason (27a) did this with the brilliant blue scales of *Morpho* butterflies and estimated that there were from 5 to 10 reflecting laminae. Subsequent electron microscope studies (Anderson & Richards 42b) showed an average of 12 laminae (Fig. 59), but these studies also showed that the number capable of reflecting blue light did lie between 5 and 10. However, to use interference phenomena for analysis of general cuticle structure, closer approximations are needed. Fortunately the advent of the electron microscope makes precise measurement of the actual spacings possible.

A and B of Figure 38 assume that there is only one effective refractive index (that is, that the thickness of the reflecting layer is negligible). This is an abstraction as far as cuticle studies are concerned. We are faced either with the situation shown in Figure 38C, where the wave length of the light changes owing to the refractive index of the material, or with the more complex situation shown in F and G, where the optical plane is really a double layer with material of two different refractive indices. Indeed, it is not certain that C exists in cuticle at all; we may always be dealing with F and G. And unfortunately one cannot calculate the thicknesses of such a double layer from interferometry alone unless either both refractive indices or both thicknesses are known (see Equation 5 and Figure 12 of Anderson & Richards 42b). In some butterfly scales the two layers are cuticle and air; in other scales and in cuticle in general the two layers are both cuticular. Mason (27b) suggests refractive indices of 1.59 and 1.50–1.52 for the cuticular layers in a beetle, but these figures are certainly in need of verification, and even if verified might not be applicable to cuticle in general.

The situation diagrammed in F and G, Figure 38, plus the fact that the sublayers S and *T* do not necessarily have the same ratio in successive superimposed planes, does add to an understanding of the optical properties of cuticle because the oversimplified diagrams used for A and D will not account for either the observable extinction angles or the lack of monochromaticity in the reflected light (Anderson & Richards 42b).[2]

A probable relationship between the superimposed planes producing interference effects and cuticular laminae (p. 174) is obvious and commonly assumed. Yet documentation other than electron microscope demonstration of laminae of requisite thickness in cockroach cuticle (Richards & Anderson 42a) is lacking because the requisite spacings are at the limit of the resolving powers of a light microscope. Since laminae are detected with a light microscope in noniridescent species, and not in iridescent species, it is commonly assumed that they are present in both, but in the one case resolvable and too thick for interference effects, in the other case unresolvable but shown by

[2] The impression that the scales of *Morpho* are a pure blue is an illusion due to the insensitivity of the human eye. Blue does predominate, but a long range of other wave lengths are present in decreasing percentage.

interference effects. Direct demonstration of the correctness of this assumption is desirable.[3]

If laminae capable of producing interference effects are rather generally distributed among arthropods, one may ask why iridescence is not more common. There are two ready suggestions, both probably correct but for different situations: namely, that the laminae are usually too thick in soft transparent cuticle and that they are usually masked or covered by pigment in hard cuticles where the laminae are thinner. Certainly the coloring involved in strong sclerotization of the epicuticle and exocuticle would preclude (by absorption) any visible iridescence irrespective of the thickness of the laminae. It is only when dark pigment is scant, absent, or beneath the laminae that iridescence can be obtained. This immediately raises the question of what is the correct story for iridescent beetles, especially those with underlying layers of melanin. Are the important laminae located in the epicuticle, as Frey (36) would suggest, or does the exocuticle not extend to the peripheral part of the procuticle? It is tempting to predict the answer, but saner to point out that iridescent beetles need modern analysis. Much information is contained in Mason's papers, but the layers to which he refers need anatomical identification in modern terminology.

In closing, it might not be amiss to mention that swelling and shrinking of interference planes are not limited to isolated cuticles. Tortoise beetles alter their hue during life and lose their iridescent colors on death (C. W. Mason 29). Iridescent flies of the family Calliphoridae emerge without their iridescence and develop this in the course of a few hours, the sequence of color changes indicating that the cuticle swells (Janet 09); desiccating leads to a reverse change (green to blue), suggesting shrinkage of laminae (Lafon 43b). The iridescence of chrysidid wasps is affected by humidity of the environment (Frey 36). Also iridescence may be present in some specimens of butterflies (*Colias*) and not in other specimens of the same species (Hovanitz 45). And finally, similar superimposed planes may be simply too closely spaced to reinforce visible light, and similar spacings may be found in structures anatomically unfitted to reflect significant amounts of light (Anderson & Richards 42b, Richards 44b).

[3] Strong but still partial evidence comes from puparia, where laminae can be seen in the noniridescent prospective endocuticle of late larvae and interference colors can be obtained from the inner surface of old puparia (Pryor 40b). Most authors, e.g., W. J. Schmidt (1941a, b, 1942a, b), simply assume the existence of whatever planes and spaces will most readily account for the observed optical effects.

CHAPTER 22

The Epidermis

THE GENERAL EPIDERMIS

One could hardly overemphasize the importance of the general epidermal cells (Lees 48, Wigglesworth 37, 40a). As the living components of the integument, they secrete the cuticle, probably even manufacturing part of its constituents, secrete the fluid which digests the old cuticle, absorb the digestion products of the old cuticle, repair wounds, and become differentiated in such a way that they control the development of pattern. Also some of the epidermal cells differentiate into various forms of sense organs and glands for many diverse purposes. There are many papers treating the general histology of the epidermis, and a few of these include some histochemical tests. Unfortunately there is a distinct paucity of competent cytological papers.[1]

A rather surprising development of recent years is that the epidermal system is somehow coordinated, as shown by the fact that local injury leading to repair or regeneration causes cessation of other activities (hygroscopic water uptake, molting) over all or only the abraded portion of the integument (Lees 46, Wigglesworth 45). However, regeneration (Richards 37) or recovery from the effects of toxic oils (Gäbler 39) may extend over several instars.

The epidermis consists typically of a single layer of cells (C. Schmidt 1845a, b), interspersed here and there with specialized cells of various types (Figs. 28, 35, 45, etc.), including "undifferentiated embryonic cells," and interrupted by muscle attachments (p. 241) and tracheoles which penetrate through the basement membrane (Wigglesworth

[1] The epidermis is commonly but not prevalently called hypodermis (Haeckel 1857) in entomological textbooks (usually without the corresponding terms dermis and epidermis originally used). It has also been referred to as corium, subcutaneous cell layer, skin epithelium, arthrodermis, dermal cells, and chitinogenous epithelium. The last name, coined by Haeckel in 1857, has been used more as an apt description distinguishing arthropod epidermis from the epidermis of other animals than as a name for the layer of cells.

33). The unilaminar arrangement seems due to a power, not understood, of the cells to spread into a single layer. Evidence for this is obtained both from the migration of cells in wound healing (Wigglesworth 37) and from the investment of implanted foreign bodies by epidermal cells (Danini 28). Particularly suggestive is the fact that masses rather than strings of epidermal cells grow to implanted celloidin particles but then spread out as a single layer across the surface of the celloidin. This power of migration is greatly reduced or lost in the adult stage, as are also the powers of undergoing mitosis and secreting cuticle (Zschorn 37).

Obviously if the cell number increased indefinitely, a unilaminar arrangement could not be maintained. Since the arrangement is general, it is not surprising that the presence of mitoses in the epidermis of growing animals can be correlated either with cell size or crowding (Wigglesworth 37). When such cells are caused to spread (by production of a wound over which they can migrate) mitoses occur. Some exceptions, perhaps produced by crowding, have been recorded (Cooper 38, Downey 12, Falke 31, van Rees 1889), and it is easy enough to find places in sections where it is difficult to imagine the epidermis being unilaminar.

The epidermal cells may have distinct boundaries (Brenner 15–16, Dennell 46, Kühnelt 28c), in which case in surface view they commonly are of hexagonal shape. But frequently cell boundaries cannot be distinguished between the nuclei; that is, the tissue appears to be a syncytium (Browning 42, Downey 12, Duboscq 20, H. J. A. Koch 36, Kühn & Piepho 38, Montgomery 00, Nicholls 31b). Whether such tissue is truly syncytial or whether the cell boundaries are not revealed by the methods used (Willers & Dürken 16) is another old question which seems of little interest today.[2] In *Ephestia* it is said that the epidermis is syncytial, yet later in development each nucleus is accompanied by a separate "tail" to the basement membrane (Fig. 40) (Kühn & Piepho 38). Syncytial epithelia are also usually unilaminar or equivalent thereto as shown by the fact that the nuclei are all in one plane.

When cell boundaries are distinct, cross sections through the epidermis show the cells in this view to be usually placoid, cuboid, columnar, or conical, with the pointed end at the basement mem-

[2] Dr. C. M. Williams tells me (in correspondence) that phase-contrast microscopy reveals the epidermis as a syncytium with a rich supply of intracellular bridges. The units can be caused to swell or shrink osmotically to produce the various types of figures seen in histological illustrations.

brane (Kühn & Piepho 38, Wigglesworth 33, Yalvac 39). In dipterous larvae the large nuclei may cause the cells to swell centrally and accordingly to project into the body cavity like a hanging drop (Dennell 46, Maill & Hammond 00, Thompson 29). Cells which appear placoid, cuboid, or columnar may all three be present at one time in one organ (Adam 12, Novikoff 05, S. Thor 02), or the shape may change in relation to a change in cell volume correlated with the molting cycle (p. 226). In either case, the surface area of the cells in the plane of the cuticle may be similar, and the shapes due to thickness of the epithelial layer.

The size of epidermal cells, by which is usually meant the area or dimensions in the plane of the surface of the cuticle, varies greatly throughout the phylum. It even differs considerably in different areas on a single individual (e.g., *Periplaneta*) or in different areas in a single organ. The size, like body size, may be considerably influenced by temperature and nutrition; for instance, in *Drosophila melanogaster* males reared at 28° C. have an average surface area for the wing epithelial cells of 123 μ^2 whereas males reared at 18° C. have an average area of 143 μ^2 (corresponding figures for the females are 142 μ^2 and 158 μ^2) (Alpatov 30). In *Drosophila* genic differences may result in changes in cell size without a change in the number of cells (Zarapkin 34). At least commonly the epidermal cells are larger in larvae than in adults of the same species; for instance, in larvae of the fly *Calliphora* the larval cells are approximately ten times as large as those of the adult (Pérez 10).

By far the most interesting work on cell size is that by Trager (35, 37) and C. A. Berger (38). Trager used three species: in a fly, *Lucilia*, the entire larval growth could be accounted for by increase in cell size, no mitoses occurring. The epidermal cells increased from 10.4 $\mu \times 4.6$ μ to 74.2 $\mu \times 13.0$ μ, with corresponding change in nuclear diameter from 4.1 μ to 18.5 μ. In larvae of a mosquito, *Aedes aegypti*, the general epidermal cells increased from 5.4 μ to 8.5 μ and then decreased to 5.6 μ, with an increase in number due to cell division, but some of the more specialized epidermal cells grew only by increase in size. In larvae of the silkworm, *Bombyx mori*, almost all of the cells increased by division, but the epidermal cells also increased in size from 2.9 μ to 8.7 μ. Trager points out that those tissues destined to be histolyzed and replaced at metamorphosis grow only by increase in cell size, but that the converse has exceptions. Berger (38) found similar size changes in the mosquito *Culex pipiens* (nuclear diameters changing from 3–4 μ to 10–17 μ and then being reduced) and correlated them with the phenomenon of somatic polyploidy. In this species the diploid number of chromosomes is six, but with increasing cell and nuclear size the number doubles repeatedly; counts of 12, 24, 48, and 96 are found in the hind-gut epithelium. At the end of larval life most of the nuclei contain 48 or 96 chromosomes. Early in pupal life cell divisions occur without chromosome division to give rise to smaller adult cells with 6 or 12 chromosomes. It has been suggested that this temporary polyploidy permits the gradual accumulation of chromosomal material, which is then available for rapid metamorphosis.

Granules, sometimes referred to as mitochondria or pigment granules, are recorded from a wide variety of forms and seem to be generally present. They are most common in the distal parts of the cells (Kühnelt 28c).[3] To cite an assortment of cases, they are recorded from the epidermal cells of spiders (Browning 42, Millot 26a, b, Schlottke 38a), ticks (Yalvac 39), *Limulus* (Patten 1893), Tardigrada (Plate 1888), Isopoda (Radu 30a, b), Diplopoda (Attems 26), Ephemerida (Purser 15), Odonata (H. J. A. Koch 36, Oguma 13, Purser 15), Mantida (Schleip 10), Orthoptera (Broussy 33, Chauvin 41, Hollande 43), Hemiptera (Wigglesworth 33), Coleoptera (Tower 06b), Diptera (de Boissezon 30b, Dennell 46), Trichoptera (Purser 15), and Lepidoptera (Paillot & Noël 26).

Granules may be correlated with feeding and so perhaps related to nutritional reserves (Helfer & Schlottke 35, Petrunkewitsch 1899, Wigglesworth 42b). In a number of cases they have been called urate granules, which presumably represent excretory products of the epidermal cells (Lesperon 37, Manunta 42a, Poisson 25, Wigglesworth 33). In a few cases they have been more positively identified as glycogen or fat (Keeble & Gamble 04, Paillot 39, Pardi 39, Wigglesworth 42b). In a number of diverse insects epidermal granules are positive to the histochemical test for ascorbic acid (Day 49a), but the significance of this compound in insects is unknown. In a single case they have been shown to give a positive reaction with Nadi reagent, and accordingly related to the production or storage of the oxidase[4] involved in sclerotization (Dennell 47a). In the cricket *Anacridium*

[3] Recent experience in cytology warns against unreserved acceptance of the distribution of cytoplasmic granules from routine sections. Proof that no displacement occurred during fixation is necessary.

[4] In recent years cytochemists have recognized that cellular oxidases seem always located in mitochondria.

the granules were called melanin precursors because positive to the azo, chromaffin, argentaffin, and ferric chloride tests (Broussy 33).

Commonly the granules are more or less linearly arranged in a direction perpendicular to the cuticle (de Boissezon 30b, Oguma 13, Yalvac 39), or there may appear to be definite fibrils in the cytoplasm in this direction (Attems 26, Downey 12, Kimus 1898, Kühnelt 28c). Perhaps the most extreme cases are found in the fibrous connections between the two sides of gills and wings (p. 244), where tension could be involved. All of these points are evidence for cellular polarity (Chambers 40), but the origin of cellular polarity is not understood.

Vacuoles are commonly shown in drawings. When the appropriate techniques have been used, mitochondria and golgi bodies have been demonstrated (Hollande 43, W. S. Hsu 48, Radu 30b). Alkaline phosphatases are mostly absent from the epidermis of the exoskeleton but are found in some epidermal cells of the fore-gut and hind-gut (Day 49b).

The nuclei have seldom been studied. They are usually round or oval (Lesperon 37, Montgomery 00), and are located in the basal portion of the cells (Brenner 15–16, Kühnelt 28c, Schlottke 38a), but may occasionally be irregularly placed or even in the distal portion (Browning 42, Deegener 04, Dreher 36, Duarte 39, Wigglesworth 48d). Old data, prior to development of the Feulgen staining technique, show that epidermal nuclei may contain nucleoli that stain similarly to chromosomes (chromatin nucleoli), or ones that stain differently from chromosomes (true nucleoli or plasmasomes), or both (Montgomery 00). In dipterous larvae the chromosomes may show faint bandings which are smaller and less distinct than in cells of the salivary glands, etc. (C. A. Berger 38, Tänzer 21).

It is generally agreed that ciliated epithelium is absent from arthropods, provided one excludes the Onychophora from the phylum (A. C. Davis 27b, Zilch 36). But there are cytoplasmic filaments in the pore canals (p. 178) (Dennell 43, 46, Hollande 43, Kühn & Piepho 38, Müller 27, Ruser 33, Wigglesworth 48b, Yalvac 39) and in some cases more specialized cellular processes (Falke 31, Nordenskiöld 11, Sulc 11).

Several oddities have been recorded which seem improbable but should not be dismissed until the cytology of epidermal cells is better understood. In termite queens, where the abdominal cuticle becomes tremendously enlarged in the adult, it is said that degenerating nuclei can be found in the endocuticle and that there are intracellular apodemes projecting into the epidermal cells (Ahrens 30). In the crayfish intracellular canals have been described in distal portions of the cell (Cantacuzene & Damboviceanu 32).

SPECIALIZED GLANDS ASSOCIATED WITH DEVELOPMENT OF THE CUTICLE

All of the epidermal cells are glandular in that they participate in the production of the cuticle, but there are in addition certain larger cells which develop from epidermal cells and seem to be specialized for producing some particular secretions. Such glands were noted as long ago as 1853 in isopod crustacea by Lereboullet and in 1859 for insects by Leydig. A relation to the production of the epicuticle was suggested for crustacea by Yonge (32) and for insects by P. Schulze (13b), K. Schulze (34), and finally convincingly by Wigglesworth (47b). They are said to be absent in a few groups in the phylum but have been recorded from such a wide variety of arthropods that they must be considered general irrespective of whether or not they are subdivided into groups on the basis of functions subserved by the secretion. In the Crustacea they are usually called tegumental glands; in the Insecta they are most commonly called dermal glands; it seems preferable to retain these different names for Crustacea and Insecta until more is known.[5]

Such glands have been recorded in Chilopoda (Fuhrmann 21) and several species of Diplopoda (Figs. 32–33) (Fuhrmann 21, Silvestri 03). In the Arachnida they have been recorded in Pedipalpi (Börner 04), Pycnogonida (Helfer & Schlottke 35), Araneae (Schlottke 38a), and Acarina (Fig. 30E) (Bonnet 07, Lees 46, 47, Nordenskiöld 08); in the Crustacea, in Branchiopoda (Zograf 19), Cladocera (Claus 1875a), Ostracoda (Yonge 32), Copepoda (Claus 1881, Nettovich 00), Cirripedia (P. Krüger 23, H. J. Thomas 44), Mysidacea (Yonge 32), Isopoda (Collinge 21, Herold 13, Huet 1883, Ide 1891, M. Weber 1881), Amphipoda (Yonge 32), Cumacea (Schuch 15), Phoronimidae (Claus 1879), Stomatopoda (Yonge 32), and Decapoda (Fig. 42) (E. J. Allen 1892, Balss 27, Dennell 47b, Drach 39, B. Farkas 27, Issel 10, Janisch 23, Vitzou 1881, Wallengren 01, Yonge 24, 32); and

[5] In the Crustacea they have also been called integumental glands, shell glands, cutaneous glands, and cement glands. In the Insecta they are also known as Verson's glands, exuvial glands, and molting glands. Commonly they are referred to more noncommittally as hypodermal glands, epidermal glands, cuticular glands, or simply as glands.

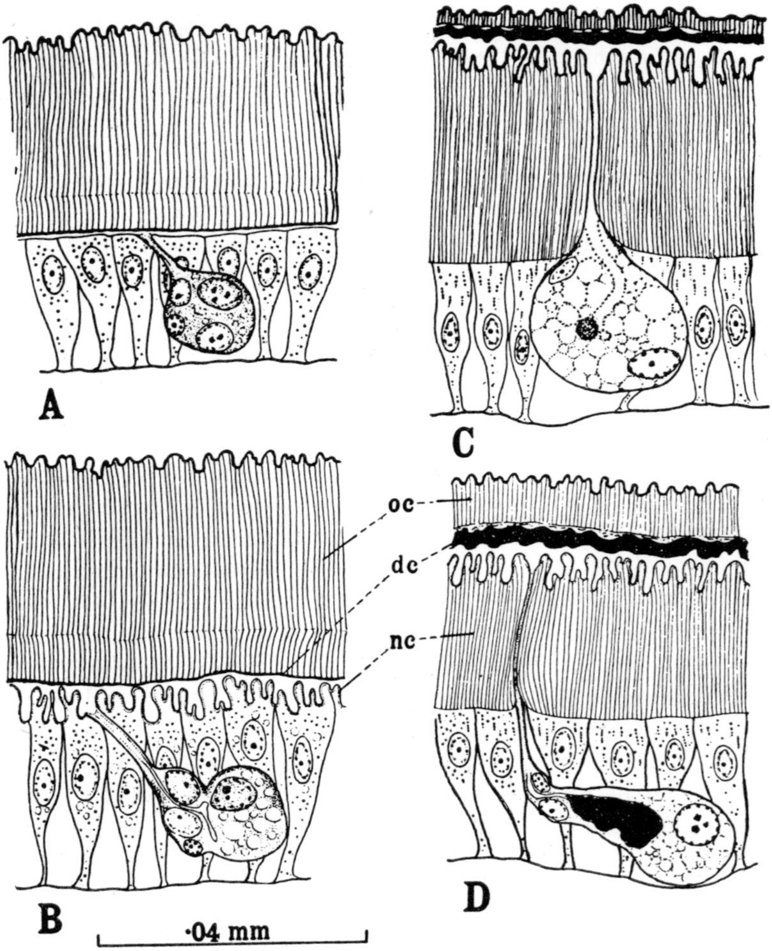

Figure 39. Changes in the dermal glands during molting in a bug, *Rhodnius prolixus.* (After Wigglesworth.) *dc* = presumably digested material; *nc* = new cuticle; *oc* = old cuticle.

A. 8 days after feeding (which is the stimulus initiating the molt); new dermal gland forming as old cuticle is loosened from the epidermal cells.

B. 11 days after feeding; dermal gland enlarging, new epicuticle being formed, and old endocuticle beginning to be digested.

C. 14 days after feeding; dermal gland much enlarged, old cuticle ready to be shed, new cuticle almost fully formed.

D. 13 days after feeding; similar to preceding, but dermal gland filled with secretion.

in the Insecta, in Collembola (Philiptschenko 06), Odonata (K. Schulze 34), Blattariae (Richards & Anderson 42a), Mantida (Hoop 33), Orthoptera (Duarte 39, Hass 16a), Hemiptera (Fig. 39) (Poisson 24, Wigglesworth 33), Homoptera (W. S. Marshall 29–30), Coleoptera (Blunck 23, Casper 13, Hoop 33, Kremer 25, Leydig 1859, Plotnikow 04, Poyarkoff 10, Roth 43, Schulze 13b, Stegemann 29b, Tower 06a, Wigglesworth 48d, Woods 29), Neuroptera (Plotnikow 04), Mecoptera (Grell 38), Hymenoptera (Bordas 08c, Hoop 33, Plotnikow 04), in some genera of Diptera[6] but not in others (except for peristigmatic glands, p. 215), Trichoptera (Martynow 01), and in Lepidoptera (Figs. 40–41) (Buddenbrock 29, Hufnagel 18, Ikeda 11, Krafft 14, Kühn & Piepho 38, Lesperon 37, Paillot 39, Plotnikow 04, P. Schulze 12, Schürfeld 35, Verson 02, 11, Wachter 30, Way 48).

It is said that some insects have unicellular dermal glands which appear to be enlarged epidermal cells *in situ* and have no duct cell (Hoop 33, Philiptschenko 06). But typically, integumental and dermal glands consist of recognizable gland and duct cells (Figs. 40–42). Excellent figures for crustacea are given by Balss (27), Collinge (21), Drach (39), and B. Farkas (27), for arachnids by Bonnet (07), and for insects by Kremer (25), Kühn and Piepho (38), Lesperon (37), W. S. Marshall (29–30), and Wigglesworth (33). In general these glands are similar in arising from epidermal cells, accumulating a secretion in vacuoles which grow and coalesce, and having the secretion poured out through an intracellular duct extending through the cuticle. Details vary tremendously.

In the Isopoda, Herold (13) has diagrammed the situation found in various genera and arranged them in a sequence, from unicellular glands without detectable duct, through unicellular glands with unicellular ducts, to bicellular glands which share a bicellular duct, to the extreme form with a binuclear unicellular gland which has a binuclear duct. This sequence is a thoroughly logical one, although it cannot be proved that development occurred in this manner. In the crustacean *Argulus* integumental glands may be single with a single duct, or double and triple with a shared branched duct (Nettovich

[6] Said to be present in *Limnophora* (Hoop 33), *Mycetophila* (N. Holmgren 07), and perhaps *Phalacrocera* (Bengtsson 1899). Said to be absent in *Calliphora* (Hoop 33), *Sarcophaga* (Dennell 46), *Dacus* (Brites 30), *Culex* (Richards & Anderson 42a), and *Aedes* (Richards & Korda 48). Also no ducts were noted in the crop linings of *Musca* and *Lucilia* examined by electron microscopy, but no specific search was made for them (and incidentally those recorded for *Limnophora* are said to lack ducts) (Richards & Korda 48).

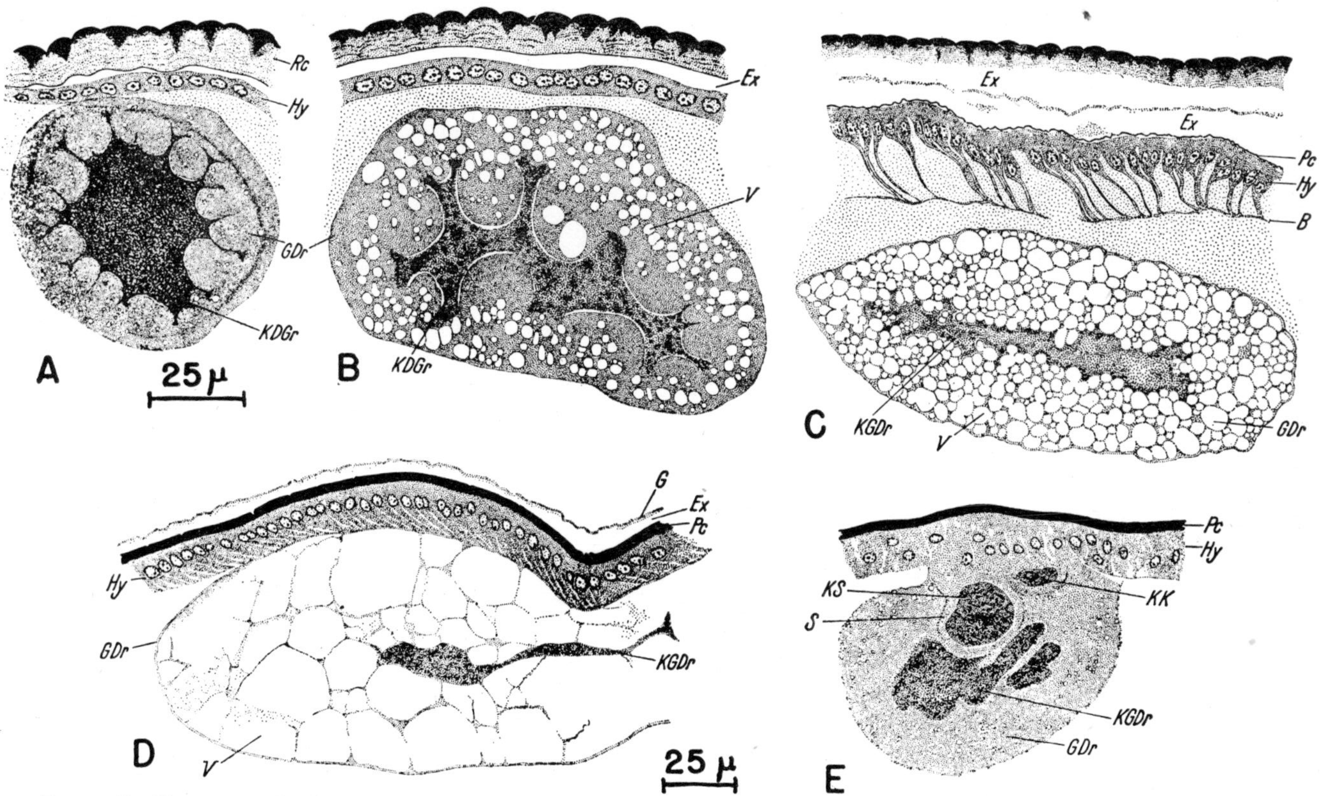

Figure 40. Changes in the dermal glands at the pupal molt in a moth, *Ephestia Kühniella.* (After Kühn and Piepho.) A–B at first magnification indicated; C–E at second. *B* = basement membrane; *Ex* = exuvial space between old and new cuticles; *G* = presumably granular layer arising from digestion of larval cuticle; *GDr* = dermal gland cell; *Hy* = epidermis; *KK* = nucleus of duct cell; *KGDr* (*KDGr*) = nucleus of dermal gland cell; *KS* = nucleus of intermediate cell; *Pc* = pupal cuticle; *Rc* = larval cuticle; S = intermediate cell; *V* = vacuole.

A–B. Successive stages in the late larva when the larval cuticle is being separated prior to formation of the pupal cuticle.

C. Early stage in formation of the pupal cuticle. D–E. Successive stages during formation of the pupal cuticle.

00). In insects the cell number is said to vary from one to four, with three perhaps the commonest number recorded. In *Rhodnius,* where there are four cells, Wigglesworth (33) says one of these forms the secretory cell, one the intracellular duct, one the duct through the epidermis, and the fourth perhaps a capsule for the other three (Fig. 39). In many Crustacea and Arachnida more cells or more nuclei in a syncytium are involved (Bonnet 07, B. Farkas 27, Helfer & Schlottke 35). In insects the dermal glands may form a globular mass in the basal portion of the epidermis (Wigglesworth 33), or an enlarged subspherical or oval mass which bulges into the body cavity but is still surrounded by the basement membrane (Woods 29), but in Crustacea the tegumental glands (Fig. 42) are commonly highly lobate cells at the end of rather long ducts extending into the body cavity (Collinge 21) or are in clusters up to 80 μ (*Homarus*) or even 500 μ (*Astacus*) in diameter (Yonge 32).

Some insects have the dermal glands segmentally arranged, but in other insects and in arachnids and crustacea they are more numerous in certain areas than in others (Balss 27, Duarte 39, Hoop 33, Lees 46, Tower 06a, Yonge 32). For instance, in ticks there are approximately 400/sq. mm. on the scutum, but 1000/sq. mm. on the alloscutum. They seem to be particularly common in hard sclerotized areas, for instance, under the pronotum of beetles and other areas that get much wear, but may be completely absent from the head capsule (Hoop 33). In fact, their distribution in decapod crustacea has been used to argue both for and against their secretion forming an important part of the epicuticle. In only a few cases have they been recorded in connection with insect tracheae, and then usually are reported near the spiracles (Lübben 07, Martynow 01, Sakurai 28). Dermal glands are commonly absent in adult insects but not in adult crustacea; this can be correlated with the fact that the adult insect normally does not molt again, whereas the adult crustacean can. They are at least usually absent in larvae of Diptera. An odd report is that they are present in the pupa of honeybees but not in the larva or adult (Schnelle 23).

The secretory cells of dermal glands may be rather small – that is, only a few times as large as the regular epidermal cells – or they may be truly giant cells, reaching up to 200–300 μ in diameter, with nuclei 70–200 μ broad (Kruger 23). The nuclei are usually round or oval, but in the giant secretory cells of Lepidoptera may be highly and irregularly lobate (Figs. 40–41) (Kühn & Piepho 38, Lesperon 37).

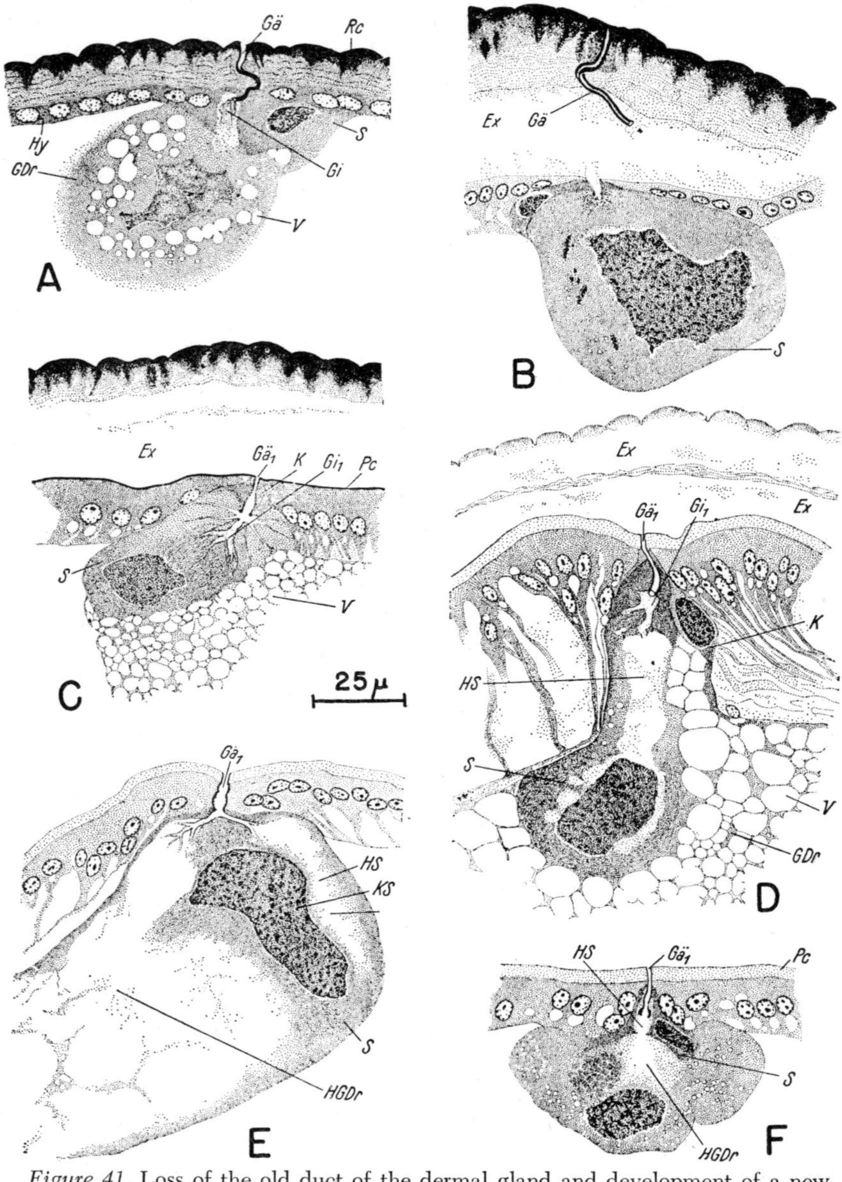

Figure 41. Loss of the old duct of the dermal gland and development of a new duct at the pupal molt in a moth, *Ephestia Kühniella*. Successive stages similar to those in Figure 39. (After Kühn and Piepho.) *Ex* = exuvial space; *Gä* = duct through larval cuticle; $Gä_1$ = new duct formed in pupal cuticle; *Gi* = loosened inner end of duct belonging to larval cuticle; Gi_1 = inner end of duct in pupa; *GDr* = dermal gland cell; *HGDr* = secretion in gland cell; *HS* = secretion reservoir; *Hy* = epidermis; *K* = duct-forming cell; *KS* = nucleus of intermediate cell; *Pc* = pupal cuticle; *Rc* = larval cuticle; S = intermediate cell; *V* = vacuole.

The ducts are from relatively small cells, and often their presence is indicated only by very small nuclei. These ducts appear to extend into the secretory cells, may cross cell boundaries in multicellular glands, and may branch either intercellularly or intracellularly (Collinge 21, Farkas 27, Woods 29). The ducts are lined with an exceedingly fine cuticle, which in insects appears to be continuous with the epicuticle, at least as far as one can judge from observation with a light microscope (Plotnikow 04, Wigglesworth 33), but in ticks the duct is said to have no epicuticular lining (Lees 46). That the duct does have a discrete lining has been revealed by electron micrographs of cuticle sections of cockroaches showing the duct lining shrunken away from the cuticle proper (Richards & Anderson 42a) and by the shed skins of beetles with the duct lining hanging from the inner surface (Poyarkoff 10). In one beetle, *Tribolium,* the duct lining is said to give a positive chitosan test (Roth 43). In a few cases the duct may have a swelling forming (presumably) a reservoir part way through the cuticle (McIndoo 16, Silvestri 03).

The majority of cases show histological evidence of a secretory phase correlated with the molting cycle, with the glands being replaced after each molt in some of them (Wigglesworth 33, Yonge 32) but not in others (Woods 29). Such has been reported in crustacea, arachnids, and insects. In insects most past authors have thought that these glands produce the molting fluid (p. 228) (Plotnikow 04, P. Schulze 12, Tower 06a, Verson 02, 11), but as von Buddenbrock (29) first pointed out, the secretion is not discharged until considerably later than the appearance of the molting fluid. This serious discrepancy has been ignored by most entomologists until quite recently (Hoop 33). By careful study of what is happening at the precise moment when the dermal glands discharge their secretions, Wigglesworth concluded that the dermal gland product forms the tectocuticle, that is, the outermost layer of the epicuticle which may be formed shortly before or shortly after molting (Way 48, Wigglesworth 47b, 48b). In ticks the dermal glands are recorded as producing a solid tectocuticle or a mobile grease (Lees 47), and presumably the mobile grease of cockroaches is produced by dermal glands.

However, it should not be forgotten that on the basis of histological appearance there are several reports of more than one type of dermal glands occurring on a single arthropod (B. Farkas 27, Issel 10, Wigglesworth 33). In *Rhodnius* it has recently been suggested that the tectocuticle is formed by a mixture of secretions from two

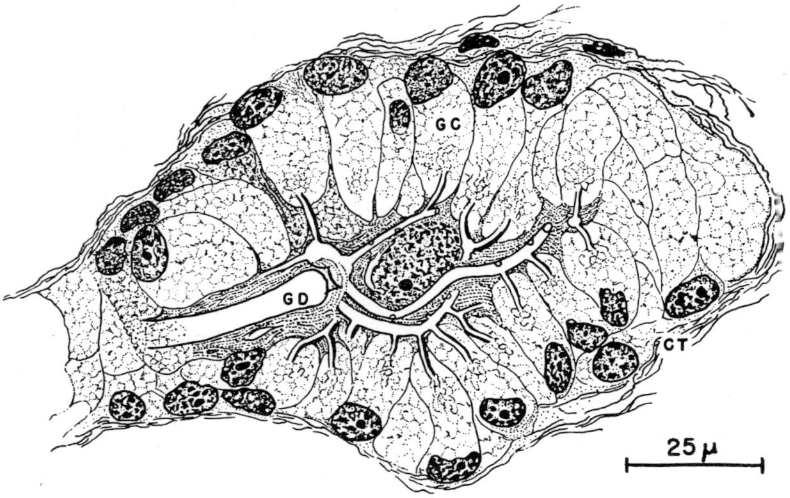

Figure 42. Longitudinal section through a multicellular tegumental gland of a crayfish, *Astacus fluviatilis.* Note the intracellular ducts joining into larger ducts. (Redrawn after Farkas.) CT = connective tissue sheath (basement membrane?); GC = tegumental gland cell; GD = common duct of gland.

gland types, whereas usually the tectocuticle comes from only one type (Wigglesworth 48d). Also, in ticks these glands are said to show two secretory phases, only one of which is correlated with molting (Lees 47). Perhaps the dermal glands have more than a single function.

The significance of the tegumental glands of crustacea is far from clear—see discussions by Yonge (32), Malaczynska-Suchcitz (36), Drach (39), and Dennell (47b). In some illustrations they are shown with the duct opening onto the outer surface of the cuticle, whereas in others the duct is shown as stopping at the inner surface of the epicuticle. It seems probable that the secretion does function in the formation of some part of the epicuticle, at least in decapod crustacea. These glands are especially common in the lining of the fore- and hind-guts (Balss 27). While it seems highly probable that the tegumental glands function in formation of the crustacean epicuticle, they or other histologically similar glands certainly have additional miscellaneous functions. In females their activity is correlated with egg laying, and they appear to supply the cement for attaching eggs to the pleopods (Braun 1877, Cano 1891, Lloyd & Yonge 40). Similar secretion is even said to form the outer layer of crustacean eggs (Yonge 35, 38b). In other cases similar glands supply cement for at-

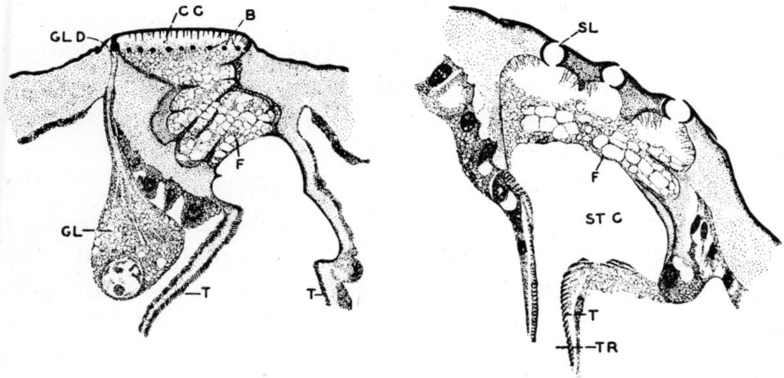

Figure 43. Longitudinal sections through the posterior spiracular apparatus of the larva of a trypetid fly showing the associated peristigmatic gland with its duct, and the peculiar "felt chamber" which seemingly acts as an air filter. (After Butt.) B = bars across inner opening within spiracular chamber; CC = cylindrical chamber within spiracle; F = felt material or reticulum; GL = gland cell; GL D = duct of gland cell; SL = spiracular slit; ST C = inner chamber within spiracle; T = taenidia of trachea; TR = lumen of trachea.

taching statoliths (Lang & Yonge 35), for the attachment of barnacles to their substrate (H. J. Thomas 44), and even for cementing together tubes in which to live (Nebeski 1880). They may be innervated (Haeckel 1864).

One set of glands which the author feels should be classed as dermal glands has been omitted up to this point, namely, the peristigmatic glands found associated with the spiracles in all dipterous larvae (Fig. 43) (Bates 34, Batelli 1879, Butt 37, Dinulesco 32, Dolley & Farris 29, Keilin 13, 44, Keilin & Tate 43, Keilin, Tate & Vincent 35, Leydig 1859, Pantel 01, Phillips 39, Wahl 1899). These are usually single, large cells which may reach a diameter of 200 μ, may extend far into the body cavity with corresponding long stalk and duct, may occur in multicellular groups, and empty via intracellular ducts which may be either single or highly branched. The secretion stains with Sudan dyes and reduces osmic acid (Dolley & Farris 29, Keilin, Tate & Vincent 35), and has accordingly been suggested to be a fatty material with the function of making the spiracles hydrophobic (Pantel 01, Wahl 1899). For details, the beautifully illustrated review by Keilin (44) should be consulted. These glands have many structural similarities to the dermal glands of other insects; their secretion supplies an important property to a certain local portion of the cuticle. They would seem to differ primarily in that their product, being not permanent, requires the constant rather than cyclic activities of the gland cells. But if the mobile grease layers of cockroaches and ticks are considered part of the epicuticle, there seems to be no good reason for not classing the secretions of dipterous larvae in the same category.[7]

EXTRACELLULAR COMPONENTS

Granules which stain with nuclear dyes are often found among the epidermal cells. They have been called "chromatin droplets" (Hufnagel 18, Poisson 24, Poyarkoff 10, Strasburger 35, Vaney 02), and do indeed give a positive Feulgen reaction (Wigglesworth 42a). They may be more numerous after the replacements involved in metamorphosis than after ordinary molting (Matheson 12). From correlations with the known degeneration of certain cells during the molting cycle, Wigglesworth concludes that they represent a stage in the dissolution of nuclei from dermal glands and oenocytes.

No other intercellular components are known, but we may expect them to be found when appropriate methods of study are applied. In other groups of animals the so-called hyaline layer between cells has great effect upon tissue organization and by the constraint it applies is said to affect cellular polarity (Chambers 40, Kopac 40).

[7] There are several other cases where similar dermal glands produce secretions which are either volatile, not permanent, or do not form a portion of the cuticle directly. What placement is given these at the present seems immaterial. Examples include the secretion which keeps beetles of the genus *Epilachna* moist (McIndoo 16), and the waxy filaments of various Homoptera and Isopoda (Brenner 15-16, Collinge 21, Huet 1883, Marshall 29, Misra 39). Perhaps the sticky secretions which cause debris to adhere to certain insect larvae are of similar origin.

CHAPTER 23

The Oenocytes, Blood Cells, and Basement Membrane

THE OENOCYTES

Oenocytes are known only in insects, where they were first adequately described by von Wielowiejski in 1886. While they are generally conceded to be an important organ of intermediary metabolism, their probable relation to molting and cuticle production is more suspected than known. Papers on oenocytes in general or including reviews of the literature are the ones by Albro (30), Gee (11), Glaser (12), Hollande (13, 14), Koller (29), Lesperon (37), Paillot (20), Verson (00), Verson and Bisson (1891), W. M. Wheeler (1892), Wigglesworth (39), and Willers and Dürken (16). Orders of insects covered include Orthoptera (Chauvin 37, Minchin 1888, Mingazzini 1889), Phasmida (de Sinety 01), Hemiptera (Poisson 24, Wigglesworth 33), Homoptera (Toth 37), Coleoptera (Albro 30, Hoop 33, Korschelt 23, Kremer 18, 20, 25, Kreuscher 22, Murray & Tiegs 35, Pardi 39, Roth 42, W. M. Wheeler 1892), Hymenoptera (Eastham 29, Janet 07, Karawaiew 1898, Koschevnikov 00, Pardi 38, Pérez 01a, b, Rössig 04, Schnelle 23, Vejdovsky 25, Weissenberg 07), Diptera (Buser 48, Day 43, Hosselet 25, Pantel 1898, Pérez 10, Thorpe 30a, Viallanes 1882, Vogt 48, von Wielowiejski 1886, Zavrel 35), and Lepidoptera (Boese 36, von Buddenbrock 29, Hufnagel 18, Paillot 39, Stendell 11, 12, Verson 1890, 00, Verson & Bisson 1891, Vickery 15, W. M. Wheeler 1892, Yokoyama 36). In the general papers cited above they are described in Collembola, Odonata, Ephemerida, Blattariae, Isoptera, Plecoptera, Corrondentia, Thysanoptera, and Trichoptera; probably they are to be found in all orders except possibly the Thysanura (W. M. Wheeler 1892).

Oenocytes originate from epidermal cells, commonly from segmental groups of cells arranged around the spiracles. They may remain in the epidermis occupying positions between the bases of epidermal cells and the basement membrane (Ephemerida, Odonata, Plecoptera, Isoptera, Hemiptera, Collembola, Blattariae, Phasmida, and some Coleoptera); or they may remain attached to the epidermis but project into the body cavity (Corrodentia, Thysanoptera, and some Coleoptera); or they may break through the basement membrane and become completely separated from the epidermis to form conspicuous clusters of cells (Lepidoptera, some Coleoptera, and some Diptera); or they may become dispersed and embedded in the so-called fat bodies (some Coleoptera, Homoptera, Hymenoptera and some Diptera). They first become visible in the embryo at a time when the cuticle is being formed, and thereafter are present, although usually undergoing periodic replacement.

Oenocytes tend to be large cells (Fig. 28). They may have a diameter of only 15–25 μ (Hosselet 25), but commonly exceed 100 μ, diameters of 150 μ (Rössig 04) and 176 μ (Koschevnikov 00) having been recorded. For relative size an extreme case is that of a cynipid larva, where the oenocytes grow from 50 μ to 150 μ, which is from slightly over 10% to over 20% of the total body length (Rössig 04). In *Tenebrio* the cells average 131 μ, but some reach 170 μ, and the clusters 1600 μ (Roth 42). In mosquito larvae there are said to be two types: small (15–25 μ) oenocytes generally distributed, and large (50–60 μ) ones segmentally arranged; it is only the larger ones which show an activity cycle correlated with molting (Hosselet 25). In honeybee larvae they are 80 μ in the worker, 100 μ in the drone, and 110 μ in the queen (Schnelle 23).

Oenocytes may arise continuously (Poisson 24), or a new generation may develop at each molt (Wigglesworth 33), or two generations, one larval and one adult, may occur in insect groups which have a pupal stage (Kremer 25, Kreuscher 22, Schnelle 23, Stendell 12). It was noted long ago that the oenocytes can undergo cyclic changes, thought to represent secretory cycles correlated with the molting cycle. Such cycles have been recorded for the moths *Bombyx*, *Ephestia*, and *Hypomoneuta*, for the beetles *Dytiscus* and *Galerucella*, for the bugs *Notonecta* and *Rhodnius*, for a Caddis-fly *Platyphylax*, for *Culex* mosquitoes and the fly *Calliphora*, for the ants *Lasius* and *Formica*, for Cynipid wasps, and for the honeybee.[1] Of particular interest in suggesting that the correlation does have real

[1] Lesperon (37) says that she could not find evidence for such a cycle in *Bombyx*, Caddis-flies, or the beetle *Hydrophilus*, but the above reports by a dozen reliable workers indicate she was in error.

significance, is the observation that nonmolting strains of silkworms have oenocytes but that these show no cyclic changes, although certain phenomena normally associated with molting are undergone (Yokoyama 36). But oenocytes are present and apparently in full activity in the adult also (Kreuscher 22, Poisson 24, W. M. Wheeler 1892, Wigglesworth 33); accordingly their function can hardly be limited to molting.

In the so-called resting condition the oenocytes at least usually have a homogeneous eosinophilic cytoplasm with a large rounded nucleus. The microscopically visible appearances suggesting activity include the cells developing pseudopodia, the nucleus becoming highly branched, and vacuoles appearing in the cytoplasm. In the cytoplasm, glycogen granules (Hollande 14, Poisson 24, Pardi 38, 39), fat droplets, and pigments can sometimes be recognized. The oenocytes of *Pieris* larvae are reported to give a positive histochemical test for alkaline phosphatase, whereas those of *Blatella, Locusta, Tenebrio,* and *Lucilia* are negative (Day 49b). In the living condition the cells are usually amber colored, but may be brown, yellow, red, green, or colorless. In adult honeybees they are first amber and then become greenish with age (Schnelle 23). Chromolipids have been suggested (Chauvin 37). None of the above substances, however, gives any clue to the functioning of the cells. As a result of enzyme tests, Glaser (12) suggested that the oenocytes produce an oxidase which is used in intermediary metabolism. More recently Wigglesworth (33), on a basis of correlating the seeming secretory activity with the molting cycle, suggests that some component of the cuticle is produced, and further, on a basis of timing and stainability, that this may be the material he calls cuticulin (Wigglesworth 47b, 48b). A somewhat similar suggestion based on even less evidence was made by Willers and Dürken (16). Clearly some other function must be subserved in the adult; Wigglesworth suggests production of material for egg shells, but the presence of smaller oenocytes in the male would imply additional functions. The hypertrophy of oenocytes in parasitized caterpillars and the presence of microsporidia in them have been recorded (Boese 36), as have also hypertrophy and phagocytosis of bacterial symbionts in aphids (Toth 37); but these are of uncertain significance.

BLOOD CELLS

In a few cases blood cells have been identified peripheral to the basement membrane and among the epidermal cells. Examples include a spider (Browning 42), crayfish (Danini 28), and insects (Wigglesworth 33). Presumably these penetrate through holes in the basement membrane by chance. Whether the blood cells are there purely by chance or for some purpose such as phagocytosis is unknown.

THE BASEMENT MEMBRANE

The basement membrane is most aptly described as a limiting membrane of uncertain structure and origin which separates the epidermal cells from the body cavity.[2] The structure was first described by Haeckel in 1857 for crustacea, where a basal layer of connective tissue is more distinct than in insects (Balss 27). But it has been pointed out that in crustacea fibers are visible throughout the epidermis, and it is questionable whether they form a sufficiently well-defined subepidermal layer to warrant the term basement membrane (Downey 12). Certainly in the crayfish, the linguatulid *Kiricephalus* (Figs. 31 A–D), scorpions, spiders, and *Limulus* (Downey 12, Lankaster 1884, 85, Schlottke 34, Versluys & Demoll 22) the fibers do ramify between epidermal cells, form only an imperfect basal membrane, and are continuous with internal connective tissue which in the arachnid entasternite has a histological structure reminiscent of vertebrate cartilage. In insects the basement membrane seems to be a more discrete structure than in other arthropods. It is most clearly seen in cases where the epidermal cells are conical and separated at their inner ends (Fig. 30B) (Kühn & Piepho 38, W. F. Mercer 00, Strasburger 35, Wigglesworth 33). In developing wings the basement membranes of the two sides may come together to form the so-called middle membrane of the wing, which is either transitory (W. S. Marshall 15) or permanent (W. F. Mercer 00). In such developing wings the two basement membranes, after fusing, may break through in certain areas, leaving the peculiar picture of epidermal cells from two sides of the wing being connected by long tails across the entire intervening space (Fig. 49) (Mercer 00, Schlüter 33). The middle membrane of the wing is distinctly birefringent (Picken 49), indicating an oriented fibrous structure; quite likely the same will be found true for the basement membrane in other areas.

In many insects the basement membrane forms a continuous homogeneous sheet, or at least no internal structures or holes can be re-

[2] Alternative names which are seldom used include *membrana propria, membrana tunica, tunica propria, Grundmembran, Grenzlamelle,* and subhypodermal cell layer. Other terms, which have been used more descriptively than as names, are internal cuticle and middle membrane of the wing.

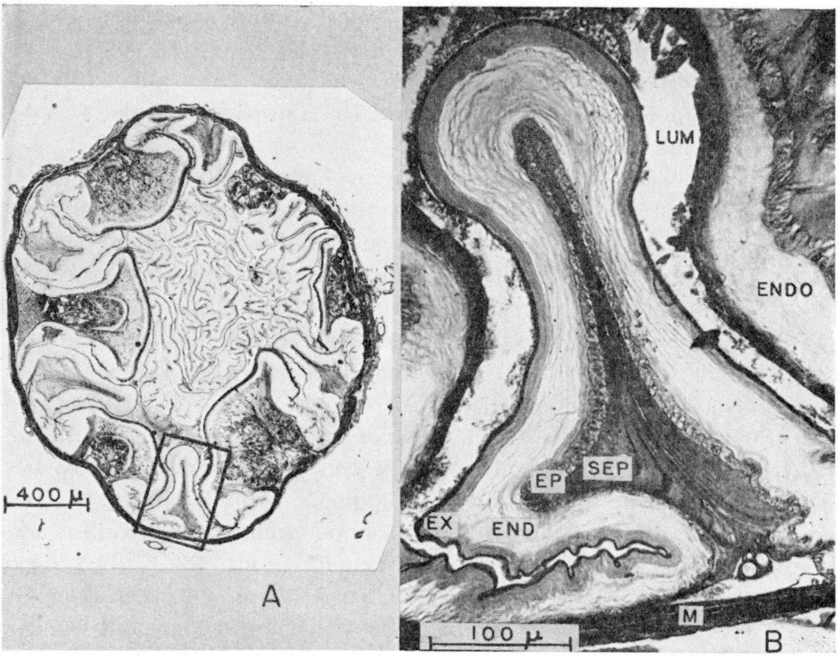

Figure 44. Photomicrographs of a cross section through the proventriculus of a larva of a neuropteran, *Corydalus cornutus.* (Original.) END (ENDO) = endocuticle; EP = epidermis; EX = exocuticle; LUM = lumen of gut; M = muscle; SEP = subepidermal material.

A. Entire section showing the typical "teeth" projecting into the lumen.

B. An enlarged view of the rectangle marked in Figure A. Note the presence of typical epicuticle, exocuticle, endocuticle, and epidermis, and especially the laminate appearance of the subepidermal material, which seems to be a greatly swollen basement membrane.

solved in it with the light microscope (Wigglesworth 33, Woods 29). At the point of muscle attachment the basement membrane becomes continuous with and indistinguishable from its sarcolemma (Duboscq 1899, Ochsé 46, Pérez 10, Woods 29). It may also be attached to other organs by delicate strands (Kreuscher 22), or have other structures of integumental origin attaching to or through it (so-called tracheae of spiders, Lamy 01; chordotonal organs, Friedrich 29, Slifer 35). Comparing these data from insects with data from arachnids and crustacea, one is inclined to take the view that the basement membrane in all arthropods is subcutaneous connective tissue which in insects and perhaps certain other cases seems quite distinct because of the paucity of internal connective tissue. Even in insects there are some regions where subepidermal material may become thick enough to show laminar differentiation – e.g., within the heavy ridges in the fore-gut of *Corydalus* larvae (Fig. 44) (Matheson 12) – and white or yellow fibers and sheaths – e.g., around the spiracular regulatory apparatus of adult Diptera (Hassan 44).

Various possible embryological origins have been suggested, but the question is extremely difficult to settle. The basement membrane may represent a true connective tissue applied to the epidermis (Balss 27, Downey 12, Sukatschoff 1899) or, as has been suggested, arise from blood cells (Lazarenko 25, 28) or more specifically from the stellate cells, which are either a part of the membrane or closely applied to it (Graber 74, A. G. Mayer 1896, Novikoff 05, Wigglesworth 33) or in the abnormal case of wound healing seem to originate from epidermal cells which degenerate (Wigglesworth 37).[3]

Whether or not this membrane is a continuous sheet, it may be repeatedly penetrated in normal development. This is shown by the penetration of newly developed muscles and tracheoles as well as by the passage of oenocytes into the body cavity (Figs. 40C, 45E).

In a few cases authors have recorded that a basement membrane is absent (N. Holmgren 07, Lowne 1893–95) (and I dare say many entomologists have never seen one in their sections!). But it is doubtful whether a layer of cells could maintain itself in such a situation without some form of limiting internal membrane (Kopac 40, 43).

[3] Dr. C. M. Williams tells me (in correspondence) that the basement membrane in Cecropia pupae is strikingly revealed by phase-contrast microscopy. He says he has watched it form from blood cells during repair of surgical injuries, the epithelial cells then growing out across it. He has come to consider the connective tissue constituents of insects to be both conspicuous and important. Hollande (20) thinks a similar membrane forms the cysts around parasites.

CHAPTER 24

Molting

The preceding chapters in this section have been concerned with the development of component layers of the integument as well as with the structure of the fully formed exoskeleton. The loosening and shedding of the old cuticle, the sequence of stages involved in the development of the new cuticle, factors which affect molting, and certain miscellaneous additional points not covered in preceding chapters remain to be treated. The molting process, or at least initiation of the molting process, is under hormonal control. In keeping with a general hormonal stimulus, one usually finds complete synchronization of the stages throughout the integument of the animal, including the cuticles on internal surfaces such as apodemes, fore-gut and hind-gut, tracheae, etc. (Deegener 04, Hinton 47, Keilin 44, Kühn and Piepho 38, Murlin 02). Implanted pieces of integument likewise molt synchronously (e.g., Piepho 38a, b). In one embryological paper it is said that molting processes in the moth *Ephestia* begin in the thorax and spread anteriorly and posteriorly therefrom (Köhler 32); this might be correlated with the presence of the prothoracic gland (endocrine) in the thorax (C. M. Williams 49) as might be inferred from the fact that implanted brains can show local control over adjacent integument (Kühn 39). In general, however, events are synchronous throughout the animal with only minor local deviations.

In decapod crustacea and certain other groups molting may continue throughout life, but in most spiders, ticks, and insects no further molts occur after the adult stage is attained. But extra molts can be induced in adult insects (up to four extra molts in *Dixippus*) by proper manipulation of the endocrine system; concurrently there is a renewal in the power of regeneration (Pflugfelder 39, Wigglesworth 40b). But reference to "suppressed molts" in adult *Drosophila* seems fanciful (Crozier *et al.* 36); at least it is undocumented.

The onset of the molting process is marked either by increase in the volume of the epidermal cells, the appearance of numerous mitoses in

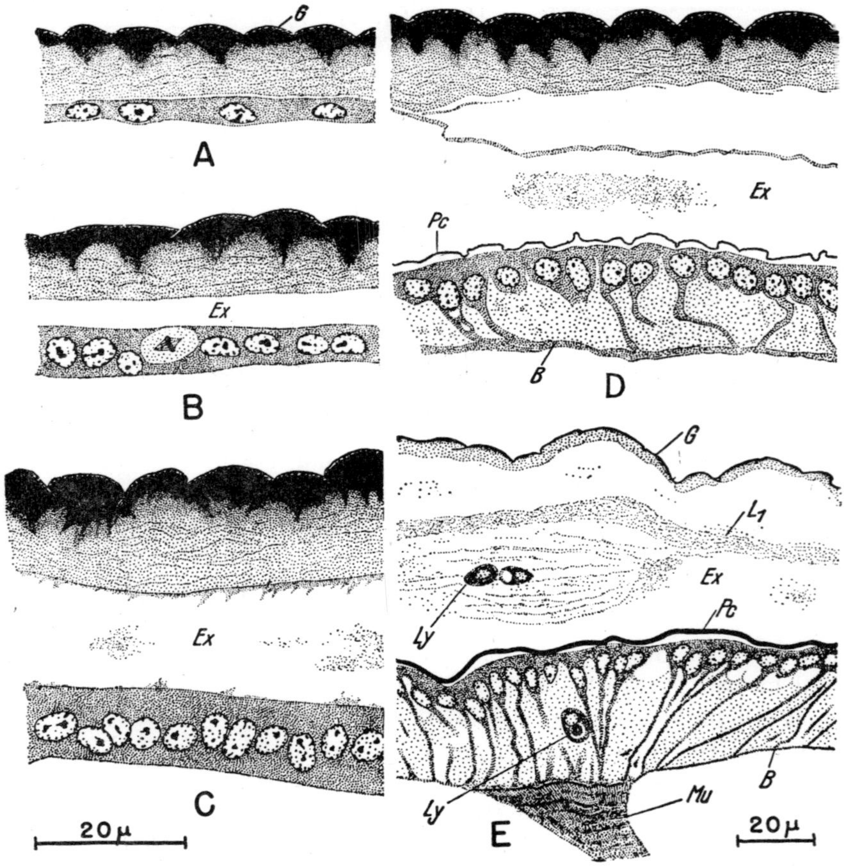

Figure 45. The series of changes from the cuticle of the last larval instar to that of the pupa in a moth, *Ephestia Kühniella.* (After Kühn and Piepho.) *B* = basement membrane; *Ex* = exuvial space; *G* = epicuticle; L_1 = remnants of the endocuticular laminae; *Ly* = lymphocytes (blood cells); *Mu* = muscle; *Pc* = pupal cuticle.

A. Fully formed larval cuticle on growing larva.

B. Early stage of molt with old cuticle loosened and mitoses beginning in the epidermis.

C. Slightly later stage with increased epidermal cell number and thickened epidermis.

D. Beginning of formation of pupal cuticle under larval cuticle.

E. Slightly later stage in formation of pupal cuticle under the nearly digested larval cuticle; note the lymphocytes both in the epidermis and in the exuvial space.

the epidermis, or visible loosening of the cuticle from the epidermal cells (Duarte 39, Kühn & Piepho 38, Paillot 39, Wigglesworth 33). In the higher Diptera, where no mitoses occur (Trager 35) and there is little change in cell thickness, loosening of the cuticle is the first detectable sign (Dennell 46, Hoop 33). In most reports the onset of mitoses is given as the first step, but this may be due to the greater certainty with which mitoses can be determined in routine histological preparations. These initial stages are followed by secretion of the molting fluid, which usually digests most of the old endocuticle, and by the deposition of at least part of the epicuticle, which is in turn followed by a continuing secretion of procuticle (Fig. 45). Subsequently the new cuticle completes its development, the old cuticle splits and is shed, the new cuticle expands and hardens, and thereby the new exoskeleton is formed. Material for more procuticle is secreted either for a while or continuously until the next molt.

The development of an arthropod is sometimes divided into molt and intermolt periods or into exuvial and cuticular phases (Hinton 47). Blunck (23) has even gone further and proposed that the molt period be divided into prophase, mesophase, and anaphase, the terms referring respectively to preparation for a molt, the acutal shedding of the old skin, and the subsequent hardening and other changes in the new skin. In some cases a "resting" phase is reasonably distinct in the sense that cuticular material is secreted for a rather definite period and then secretion appears to cease until the next molt (Browning 42). In other cases the secretion of cuticular material does not cease abruptly and may even continue throughout the instar (Dennell 46, Kühn & Piepho 38, Kuwana 33).

The intermolt phase is not necessarily large in comparison to the molting phase—at least on the basis of perpetuation of scars it is said that the new cuticle of *Daphnia* begins to be laid down when the instar is only 60% over (Anderson & Brown 30). Also one wonders how distinct the molt and intermolt phases may be in such cases as the early growth stages of shrimp, which may molt normally twelve times in 15–20 days (J. C. Pearson 39). Several authors, notably Drach (36b), have been led to question the distinctness of molt and intermolt phases, especially because of the implication that growth all occurs in the molting phase. Some similarity to the old question of whether or not metamorphosis is limited to the pupal stage in holometabolous insects (a view no longer supported by physiologists or embryologists) is apparent. Probably the division into molt phase and intermolt phase is not truly distinct in all cases, and certainly it is not similar in all cases, but the terms still have some use.

Several other subdivisions of the molt phase or of the entire cycle have been proposed; thus Drach (36b, 39) recognizes five major subdivisions for the entire cycle in crustacea, several of which can be further subdivided (he even refers to the shedding of the old cuticle as representing only a brief interruption in the molting cycle). Verhoeff (37) recognizes four stages in the molt phase of centipedes, and Kühn (39) lists six stages for a moth, the last of which could be said to include the intermolt phase. How many substages are to be recognized is a matter of choice or convenience. It does appear clear that the intermolt phase shows great differences in different species, is probably not a truly "resting" phase (Lees 48), and the epidermal cells are not equal at all intermolt periods (Drach 36b, Verhoeff 39). Chronological seriation of events may be difficult and even arbitrary (Drach 39).

Certain cells such as those of the dermal glands and oenocytes may differentiate anew at each molt either from "undifferentiated cells" or from what appear to be normal epidermal cells (Duarte 39, Wigglesworth 33). In such cases the old set of cells degenerates after the new cuticle is deposited, as described in the previous chapter. In other cases these cells simply show cyclic activity correlated with the molting cycle. There may be changes in internal organs, but except for the blood picture (Deevey 41, Yeager 45) these are related more to development than to molting cycle and will not be treated here.

The epidermal cells, as already mentioned, may increase significantly in volume (usually measured only as thickness of the epidermal layer). Thus in the crustacea the cells of *Asellus* and *Homarus* increase by approximately 2 times (Needham 46, Yonge 32); those of a spider 2.5 times (Browning 42); those of pycnogonids 3–4 times (Helfer & Schlottke 35); those of the beetle *Tenebrio* 2–4 times (Hoop 33, Wigglesworth 48d, Willers & Dürken 16). To cite a few more cases, comparable changes are recorded in the crayfish *Astacus* (Cantacuzene and Damboviceanu 32), in the collembolan *Tomocerus* (Willers & Dürken 16), in the dragonfly *Agrion* (Willers & Dürken 16), in the walking stick *Dixippus* (Willers & Dürken 16), in the bug *Rhodnius* (Wigglesworth 33), in the beetles *Leptinotarsa* (Tower 06a) and *Dytiscus* (Hoop 33), in the caterpillars of *Ephestia* (Kühn & Piepho 38), *Pieris* (Willers & Dürken 16), and *Vanessa* (Willers & Dürken 16), and in the sawfly *Nematus* (Hoop 33). The epidermal cells of tracheae (Lübben 07) and of the gut (Deegener 04) likewise thicken considerably. When the epidermal layer thickens, the nuclei may become relatively closer to the cuticle (Yalvac 39).

There is, however, little or no change in thickness of the epidermis of the flies *Sarcophaga* (Dennell 46) and *Calliphora* (Hoop 33).

Great changes are readily seen in developing wings, but here the picture is complicated by the simultaneous development of an organ and its expansion (Köhler 32, Marshall 15, W. F. Mercer 00, Powell 05, Schlüter 33, Stossberg 38).

The increase in volume of arthropod epidermal cells during secretion seems to be a rather general property, not a phenomenon restricted to formation of a new cuticle. For instance, the wax glands of adult honeybees undergo similar size changes during secreting and nonsecreting phases (Fig. 46) (Dreyling 06).[1] The same may well be true for many other epidermal glands since these show tall, columnar cells during secretion, but one needs cyclic phenomena to be sure. The volume of the epidermal cell layer should be determined rather than just its thickness, of course, because in some cases organs that become distended, actually showing a decrease in cell thickness, may nevertheless show similar volume increases (for instance, the vagina of *Drosophila* during the insemination reaction, H. T. Y. Lee 50).

Usually there is an increase in cell number by mitosis (Duarte 39, Köhler 32, Kühn 39, Trager 37, Wigglesworth 33, 40b, 48d, Willers & Dürken 16, Yalvac 39). However, in the crustacean *Asellus* (Needham 46) and the higher flies *Lucilia* and *Sarcophaga* (Dennell 46, Trager 37) no mitoses occur; growth in these is due to increase in cell size.

An invariable and truly essential step is the loosening of the old cuticle from the underlying epidermal cells. It is uncertain whether this initial loosening is due to a mere retraction of the cells (Willers & Dürken 16) or represents the beginning of the digestion of the endocuticle that usually takes place (Deegener 04). Clearly there is little if any digestion of the old cuticle in the formation of fly puparia (Dennell 47a), but in most if not all arthropods a fluid is secreted which dissolves a part of the old cuticle. The amount of the old cuticle that is dissolved varies considerably. In the formation of fly puparia there is no evident dissolution; in spiders only a little of the endocuticle is dissolved (Browning 42, Schlottke 38a); in sclerotized

[1] Also the follicular epithelium of grasshopper ovaries during deposition of yolk and chorion (Slifer 37).

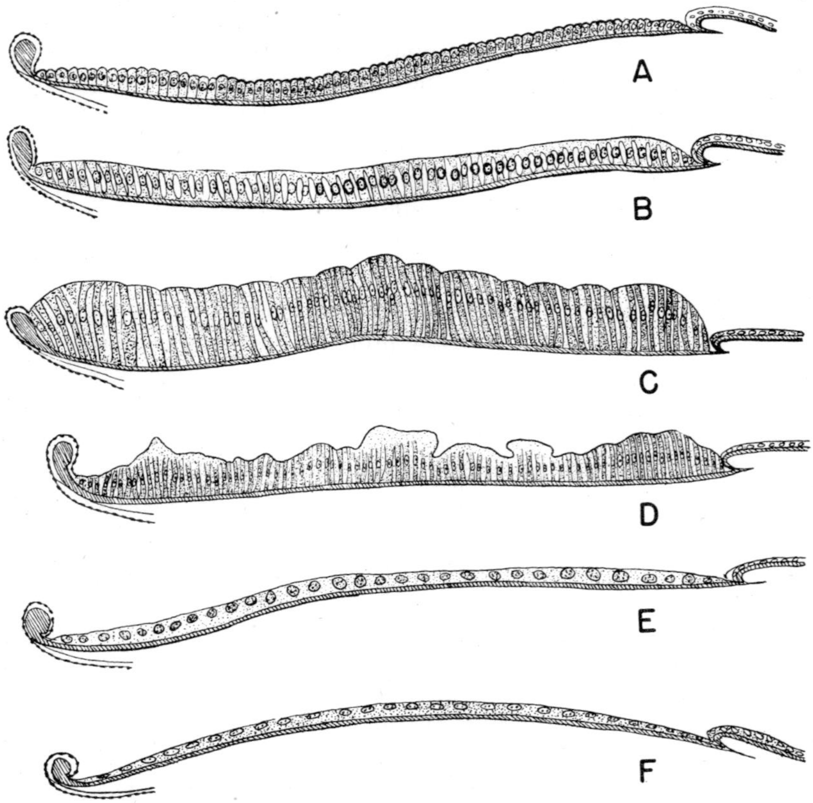

Figure 46. Sections through the wax gland of a honeybee, *Apis mellifica,* at successive stages during the secretion period. Sequence shows stages from early development when the gland cells are still similar to general epidermal cells (A), to the height of secretory activity (C), followed by regression (D), with a return to a cell layer similar to the general epidermis (F). (Redrawn by Miss Anna Stryke after Dreyling.)

cuticles most of the endocuticle may be dissolved (Fig. 45) (Wigglesworth 33, Yalvac 39); and in soft cuticles all of the procuticle may be dissolved leaving only the epicuticle (Aronssohn 10).

For a good many years it was thought that the dermal glands produced the molting fluid (and they were commonly called molting or exuvial glands), but this view has been discredited (p. 213). Since no special glands are known, the molting fluid must be secreted by the general epidermal cells (Blunck 23, von Buddenbrock 29, 31, Hoop 33, Poisson 24, Poyarkoff 10, Wigglesworth 48d, Zavrel 35). This fluid is usually present as a rather thin film and is resorbed prior to ecdysis, as shown by the fact that an emerging terrestrial arthropod is dry. Also the amount of material resorbed may be considerably greater than the amount of molting fluid present at any one moment; various percentages up to 80–90% of the dry weight of the old cuticle may be resorbed (Bergmann 38, Browning 42, Duarte 39, Evans 38a, b, Kiyomizu –, Kuwana 33, Lafon 43c, 48, Wigglesworth 33). From this it follows that at least in cases where a sizable percentage is resorbed, there must be some circulation in the sense that molting fluid is being secreted and the digestion products resorbed simultaneously for some time. Resorption from the exuvial fluid can be shown dramatically by injecting into the exuvial fluid amino acids labeled with radioactive carbon and finding the radioactivity incorporated into body proteins within 24 hours (Passonneau and Williams). Balance sheet determinations point to the re-use of resorbed cuticular components during formation of the new cuticle (Lafon 43c). The resorption of cuticular materials has been definitely recorded for spiders (Browning 42, Schlottke 38a), ticks (Ruser 33, Yalvac 39), crabs (Lafon 48, Maloeuf 40), and several orders of insects (Duarte 39, Lafon 43c, Shafer 23, Wachter 30, Wigglesworth 33).[2] In a few cases cuticular material is digested and resorbed in the adult independently of molting (ticks, Ruser 33; flies, Laing 35). As Wigglesworth points out, these facts contradict the suggestion that ecdysis is a kind of excretory phenomenon (Bounoure 19). However, the amount resorbed varies greatly in different species; values ranging from a few per cent to 90% are given.

Although it has been known for a long time, very little information is available on the nature of the molting fluid. Malpighi described the molting fluid in 1669, Gonin demonstrated it histologically in 1894, Tower pointed out in 1906 that it must contain enzymes, and Blunck in 1923 first reported that it must come from the general epidermal cells. In the beetle *Dytiscus* the molting fluid is yellowish, is neutral to litmus, and stains with Orange G but not with Delafield's haematoxylin (Blunck 23); in *Rhodnius* it is also near neutrality (Wigglesworth 33); in histological sections the space it had occupied may be full of particles, but it is not certain whether these are normally present or produced by the fixation process (Hoop 33); in the lobster the molting fluid contains nuclei (without positively dis-

[2] At this time dyes (neutral red, indigo carmine) injected between the old and new cuticle can be absorbed into the blood – a visual demonstration of the power (Wigglesworth 33).

tinguishable cytoplasm), but evidence for the participation of these in digestion of the endocuticle seems to be presumptive (Yonge 32). Likely the molting fluid in calcified species is acidic rather than neutral, but this appears not to have been demonstrated.

A study, still in progress, on the exuvial fluid of the pupae of the Cecropia moth has shown that this fluid first appears as an aqueous protein gel (95.8% water), with a pH of 7.35, no cell components, and with tyrosinase as the only detectable enzyme (Passonneau and Williams). After 8 days it becomes fluid, and the pH rises to 7.42–7.55. Proteinase and chitinase become detectable on the 14th day, and the first evident dissolution of the old endocuticle begins on the 16th day and is completed by the 19th day (at 25° C.). There is continued secretion and resorption of the fluid; the authors view this as a dynamic state involving both active secretion and active absorption (rather than passive diffusion). Perhaps specific areas (in the abdomen?) are primarily concerned with resorption.

The steps in production of a new cuticle have already been given in preceding chapters. One question does remain, namely, why is the new cuticle not digested by the molting fluid? The answer is not known. But we do know that the molting fluid digests only the soft endocuticle, the epicuticle appearing to be unaffected. There will be no occasion for surprise, then, in the fact that the new epicuticle is formed while the molting fluid is present. Very suggestive also is the recent report that chitinase and proteinase enzymes are to be found in the exuvial fluid of Cecropia moth pupae only for a short period during the latter part of the time when this fluid is present; sclerotization and pigmentation of the new cuticle have then already begun (Passonneau and Williams). In general, the bulk of the procuticle is produced rather late, after the peak of the molting fluid activity. Possible protection of the procuticle by the epicuticle seems inadequate as an explanation, especially if it should be found that digestive enzymes are generally not present at first. Why the newly formed or forming procuticle is not digested by enzymes that must pass out through it to reach the exuvial space remains to be explained.

The number of molts is normally a constant and rather small one in pterygote insects, normally lying within the range 4–12.[3] In

[3] Determination of molting and of the number of molts is often made from exuviae. In some species this method is complicated by the insect's routinely eating its exuvium. It is reported that the application of spots of certain inks (such as Higgins Eternal Black Ink) will deter cockroaches from eating their exuviae and so permit the use of this method (Philip & Fournier 46).

other groups, e.g., Crustacea and Symphyla, the number may be large and not constant, partly because the adult continues to molt at intervals. In the symphylan *Scutigerella* the larva may molt more than fifty times before attaining the adult stage, and continue to molt occasionally as an adult (Michelbacher 38). Probably even larger numbers than this occur in certain crustacea; for instance, it is well known that giant lobsters weighing thirty or more pounds have been caught. Whether the number of molts is definite or indefinite, it seems generally true that the rate of molting is higher in younger individuals. An oddity is represented by the higher Diptera, where within the puparium an extra molt occurs for the abdomen but not for the head and thorax (Fraenkel 38, Snodgrass 24).

Any genetic or physiologic unbalance leading to a failure of the molting process would be expected to be lethal. Rather few examples are known. The strain called "giant larva" in *Drosophila melanogaster* and certain nonpupating hybrids are known to be due to hormonal deficiencies resulting in failure to pupate (Hadorn & Neel 38). The most interesting case is a nonmolting strain of the silkworm where the initial steps in the molting phase (mitoses) begin and yet molting does not occur (Yokoyama 36), the only histologically observable abnormality being the continued apparent inactivity of the oenocytes. As far as the data go, it would seem that the molting cycle begins in these silkworms, but is interrupted and fails to go to completion, in correlation with an inactivity of the oenocytes. The case is particularly interesting as the only authentic example of natural interruption of the molting process, and accordingly as indicating that probably the integument is not entirely autonomous and requires more than just activation by hormones.

Nutrition has several kinds of effects on cuticle development. For instance, there are several cases where it has been recorded that thickness or weight of the cuticle increases with additional feeding. In silkworm larvae the weight of the cuticle may double in two days in fed larvae but remain nearly unchanged in starved individuals (Kuwana 33). In *Rhodnius* the thickness of the cuticle developed is correlated with the size of the blood meal; it may be more than twice as thick after a large meal as after a small meal, and the thickness may be augmented by additional small meals (Wigglesworth 48b).

The results of starvation, however, are sometimes surprising, and cannot be predicted in advance for a particular species. Unless the larva is already fully mature, pupation may be delayed indefinitely

(Križenecký 14, Singh-Pruthi 25). In a number of cases starvation has been found to result in the production of additional molts; in fact, the larva may go into what is virtually a frenzy of molting and become considerably smaller in the process (Mickel & Standish 46, Titschack 26, Wodsedalek 12). In these cases (moths and beetles) molting obviously is not correlated either with growth or periodicity. Somehow, presumably hormonally, the molting cycle is initiated repeatedly even though there is no need for growth, and even though energy must be expended in the superfluous process.

In the blood-sucking bugs (*Cimex*, Kemper 31; *Rhodnius*, Wigglesworth 33) and ticks (*Ornithodorus*, Cunliffe 21) molting requires initiation by the taking of a blood meal in excess of a certain minimal volume. At least in *Rhodnius* the distension produced is what activates the endocrine system, which in turn initiates the molting cycle. For most arthropods, the nature of the stimulus for molting and the nature of the control of the number of molts are totally unknown. Recently a mechanism has been suggested in which the hormone is viewed as acting on a dehydrogenase system in the blood, with resulting lowering of the redox potential and release of tyrosinase activity (Dennell 47a, 49, Krishnan 50), but this suggestion seems incomplete and does not cover the question of why the hormone is released at particular times.

A tremendous literature deals with the effects of temperature on insect growth, but there is almost no literature on the influence of temperature on the various steps within the molting phase or the amount of cuticle produced. Zschorn (37) reared *Tenebrio* at six different temperatures and recorded a linear relationship between temperature and time for the molting process, but a more exhaustive study is needed. In the shrimp *Crangon* there is said to be a definite temperature relationship when day and night temperatures are different (molt in daytime, but light not a controlling factor) (W. N. Hess 41).

It would seem that factors influencing molting might be most readily studied in species that undergo a large and variable number of molts. Accordingly, it is interesting that the rate of molting in symphylans is reported to be affected by sex, genetic factors, age, food, temperature, humidity, and mutilations (Michelbacher 38) – in short, by all factors one would automatically test.

Wound healing and regeneration are parts of the field of growth and need only to be mentioned here (Danini 28, Lazarenko 28,

Lüscher 47, Wigglesworth 37). Several reviews are available, which should be consulted for details and references (Bodenstein 36, Richards 37). Two points are of interest. First, healing shows that epidermal cells can migrate, that migration and mitoses cease when the epidermal continuity is re-established, and that the power of cellular migration is greatly decreased or lost in the adult stage (Zschorn 37). Second, an amputation or injury leading to regeneration may have either no noticeable effect on the molting cycle, may retard molting (V. E. Emmel 07, Zuelzer 07), or may actually accelerate the rate of molting (Michelbacher 38).

The act of shedding the old cuticle involves aspects of behavior such as hiding or attaching the old cuticle to some substrate to facilitate escape. Omitting these behavior patterns, there are four points of interest in the mechanics of shedding the old skin: the nature of pressures involved, the nature of weak lines along which the old cuticle splits, the composition of the shed skin (commonly called exuvium), and the exceptional cases where the cuticle is not shed.

A considerable number of papers report that relatively large volumes of air or water are swallowed to increase the volume of the emerging arthropod (de Bellesne 1877, Brocher 19, Causard 1898, Drach 36a, 39, Duarte 39, Eidmann 24a, b, c, Knab 09, 11, Kunkel d'Herculais 1890, 94).[4] That the distension of the gut is really significant and not merely incidental is indicated by the unsatisfactory emergence of individuals in which the distension of the gut was experimentally hindered (Eidmann 24a, b, c). That pressure transmitted by the blood is important in the eversion and distention of imaginal discs such as wings is suggested by the fact that punctures permitting the escape of blood result in imperfect inflation (Köhler 32). However, the increase in volume does not necessarily involve any large change in blood pressure; a change in true blood pressure may or may not be measurable (Homann 49, Shafer 23).[5] Incidentally, the swallowing of considerable quantities of water may give the seemingly anomalous result of a considerable increase in weight at the time of shedding the old skin (Shafer 23).

It has been known for a long time that the old cuticle does not

[4] Perhaps commonly setae act as "ecdysial hairs" to assist in emergence by deterring slipping back into the old skin during pulsating movements (Escherich 1897).

[5] Browning (42) postulates that water is absorbed from the plasma by certain blood cells and so results in distention of the body of spiders at molting. Such a mechanism calls for documentation, which is not given.

simply split at random but splits along certain predetermined lines which are commonly visible throughout development. These ecdysial lines have been shown by histological examination of locusts (Duarte 39) to be lines along which sclerotization did not take place — as one would have guessed from their lack of color. With dissolution of the endocuticle by the molting fluid, these lines become extremely weak and break easily. The position of the lines is highly variable in different groups of arthropods — see the reviews by Henricksen (31) and Snodgrass (47). The shed skin, or exuvium, consists of the epicuticle and exocuticle plus commonly some fraction of the endocuticle, as already mentioned. Ordinarily it includes all the external features of the arthropod (sclerites, setae, etc.). In some groups it may be shed in two or more pieces instead of as a unit; for instance, in the isopod crustacea the cuticle is shed from the posterior half of the body several days before that on the anterior half (Cummings 07, Herold 13, A. E. Needham 46, Nicholls 31a, Numanoi 34a, Tait 16, Verhoeff 40). The exuvium has attached to its inner surface at least a major portion of the cuticular lining of the gut, tracheae, and even apophyses.

The exuvium, or shed skin, of course, consists of that portion of the cuticle which is not digested and resorbed. Its composition seems to vary from being essentially only the epicuticle (bee larva, Aronssohn 10) to being almost the entire cuticle (spider, Browning 42). If the puparium is called an exuvium, it too would represent almost if not all of the cuticle. The exuvium definitely shows the gross structure intact, but it remains to be determined whether or not some components are removed and whether or not there are ultramicroscopic changes.[6]

When a new cuticle is formed the old cuticle is almost but not quite always shed. Now and then at molting a tracheal intima may break and leave a portion of the tube behind when the remainder is pulled out (Richards & Anderson 42b). Of more interest are the few cases where the loosened cuticle is normally not shed. Outstanding among these cases is the puparium of higher Diptera, where in certain areas four cuticles may be found one inside the other, the outer three of these being shed at the same time when the adult emerges (Fraenkel 38). The extent to which the tracheal lining is removed at molting is amazing, but it would seem that there would have to be

[6] Rosedale (46) makes the bare statement that the exuvia of locusts have a fat content of 70%, with an iodine value of 195.

some limit to the extent of ramifications that could be pulled out in this manner. Accordingly it is very interesting to see that Keister (48) has recorded that in larvae of the fly *Sciara* only a portion of the tracheal system renews its lining at the time of molting. The innermost parts (which would offer the most resistance to being removed) are never loosened from the tracheal cells; the parts closer to the spiracles are loosened from the cells and are shed. A local production and extremely little spreading of molting fluid seem indicated—unless perhaps these tracheal linings are loosened without any molting fluid being involved. This is in essence only a partial molt for the tracheal system. Yet the new cuticle of the parts that do shed their lining becomes indistinguishably fused with the unshed old cuticle at the point of junction and is recognizable only by an abrupt change in diameter of the tube. Similar abrupt changes in diameter have been observed in electron micrographs of tracheae from a variety of arthropods (Richards & Korda 50); perhaps the phenomenon is rather general.

The determination of form and changes in form of the newly emerged arthropod involves a consideration of the body as a whole. For instance, Bytinski-Salz (36) considers this to be a complex problem involving elasticity of tissue, blood pressure, external factors (especially humidity), chemical action of the molting fluid, a true form tendency of the developing integumental organs, inductive influences from other parts of the body, hormones, the constraining action of the previous cuticle, stretching and compressing from other parts of the body, as well as the sclerotization process which follows molting. We are not yet ready to analyze such a complex situation.

A beginning, but only a beginning, has been made in analyzing the influence of muscular contractions on molting and the subsequent development of form. There is some evidence that muscular contractions do give pressures which assist in ecdysis (Köhler 32, van Schreven 38). It has also been shown that muscular contractions, particularly tonicity, influence the formation of apodemes (Maloeuf 35a) and of cuticular spines (Thompson 29).

A wide variety of miscellaneous odd phenomena have been recorded. For instance, the sexual cycle of certain intestinal Protozoa is correlated with the molting cycle of their hosts (Cleveland 47); tardigrades defecate only at the time of molting (Marcus 35); in decapod crustacea, females carrying eggs or embryos do not molt (W. N. Hess 41, Scudamore 48), and molting is inhibited by parasitization with bopyrids and slowed by captivity (Nouvel 33a, b). In certain copepod crustacea the male is said to hold the female with his grasping antennae until she molts (and may even seem to assist in removing the exuvium); immediately after she molts he moves around and deposits a spermatophore (L. W. Williams 07a). In tardigrades and tyroglyphid mites cysts are formed within an exuvium, but the cyst is smaller than the shed skin and the exuvium does not undergo changes comparable to those of dipterous puparia (Marcus 35, Michael 01, J. Murray 07). And finally small pieces of epidermis implanted into the body cavity of other individuals may round up into balls which molt synchronously with the host and give rise (since the cuticle cannot be shed) to successive laminae of cuticule, which have been called "chitin pearls" (Pflugfelder 35). Similar appearing concentric balls of cuticle are produced normally in the Palmén organ of Ephemerida (a distended trachea from which the cuticle is shed but cannot be withdrawn) (Gross 03, Hsu 33).

Too late for integration into this volume a short note has been published reporting a novel type of molting in certain Acarina (Jones 50). Tyroglyphid and Oribatid mites molt by processes similar to those of insects; but in Trombiculid mites, amazingly, the epidermis separates into outer and inner layers. The outer layer of epidermis comes to lie between the old and new cuticles; it is thought to be associated with dissolution of the old endocuticle. The inner layer of epidermis secretes the new cuticle. No molting glands were found.

CHAPTER 25

Muscle Attachments, Tendons, and Apophyses

The mode of attachment of muscles to arthropod cuticle was a hotly argued question near the end of the nineteenth and beginning of the twentieth centuries. Casual examination of a section of a soft cuticle through a muscle attachment is sufficient to show that the longitudinal fibrils in the muscle (myofibrillae) are continuous with fibrils extending through the epidermal cell layer and into the procuticle (tonofibrillae or tonomitomes). The argument involved whether the tonofibrillae represent the end of the muscle itself or a tendonal attachment formed by the epidermal cell layer, and whether the tonofibrillae passed through epidermal cells or between the cells. In a sense the argument involves whether the muscles terminate at the basement membrane or extend into the cuticle. The question is discussed in practically all the old general works on arthropod anatomy and histology, and is comprehensively treated in the exhaustive review by Snethlage (05). Surely no one would argue against the view that tonofibrillae serve to strengthen attachment of muscles to cuticle; that is, that tonofibrillae are stronger anchorages than if muscles were attached to undifferentiated epidermal cells. But, with diverse arthropods having been examined, some prefer to interpret their sections as indicating that tonofibrillae pass through the epidermal cells (Boelitz 33, B. Farkas 14, von Haffner 24a, Humperdinck 24, Novikoff 05, Riley 08, Schreiber 22), usually then viewing the tonofibrillae as formed by cytoplasm of the epidermal cells (Downey 12, Duboscq 1899, Lowne 1893–95, Munscheid 33, Pérez 10, Yalvac 39). Others interpret their sections as showing that the tonofibrillae pass between cells (Barth 45, Janisch 23, Kühnelt 28c, de Sinety 01, Stamm 09, 10), and sometimes go further to interpret this as meaning that the ends of the muscle fibrils themselves become cuticularized (Chatin 1895a, Lécaillon 07a, b, Tower 06a). Other authors, especially those who examined a range of arthropod species, point out that similar preparations made from species of different groups appear to show attachment either to the basement membrane or to the epidermal cells, or to extend through or between the epidermal cells to attach on or in the cuticle (N. Holmgren 07, Pérez 10, Silvestri 03, Snethlage 05, Törne 11, Wege 09).

Certainly the superficial histological appearances may be quite diverse (Fig. 47). There are some points of general agreement and general applicability. The sheet around the outside of the muscle fibers (sarcolemma) is continuous with the basement membrane of the integument (Duboscq 1899, Ochsé 46, Pérez 10, Woods 29). The muscle fibrils are cross striated, but the fibrils seen in epidermal cells and in the cuticle show no cross striations (Duboscq 1899, Kühnelt 28c, Munscheid 33, Pérez 10); in fact, no differentiation within the tonofibrillae has yet been demonstrated. When epidermal cells are very large, fibrils clearly penetrate through them (Boelitz 33, von Haffner 24a). The tonofibrillae may extend not only through the epidermal cells but also through the procuticle (Fig. 47C) (Lécaillon 06, 07a, b, Lowne 1893–95, Ruser 33, Schreiber 22). In microscopical appearance the tonofibrillae are quite similar to cuticular fibrils present at the attachment points of chordotonal organs (Eggers 28, Slifer 35); clearly, then, fibrils of this appearance are not necessarily attached to muscles. In sections of sclerites the tonofibrillae may seem to stop at the boundary of the exocuticle, but this appears to be due to their being hidden by the color and loss of differential staining involved in the sclerotization process. As far as we know muscles do not become attached to a previously developed cuticle. New muscle attachments appear to be always formed at the time when the cuticle is being laid down; the attachment involves the formation of new tonofibrillae in the epidermis and cuticle (Munscheid 33). The tonofibrillae begin as parallel lines but diverge somewhat in successively formed layers of the cuticle so that they typically come to have the shape of a triangular trapezoid (Fig. 47C) (Thompson 29). Presumably the increasing size of the bundle of tonofibrillae is due to corresponding growth in cross sectional dimensions of the muscle. Incidentally, Poyarkoff (14) uses the fact that muscles become attached only to a developing cuticle to rationalize the interpolation of a pupal stage in higher pterygote insects. In essence, Poyarkoff's hypothesis states that interpolation of an extra preimaginal stadium permits the development of a special adult musculature subsequent to the reor-

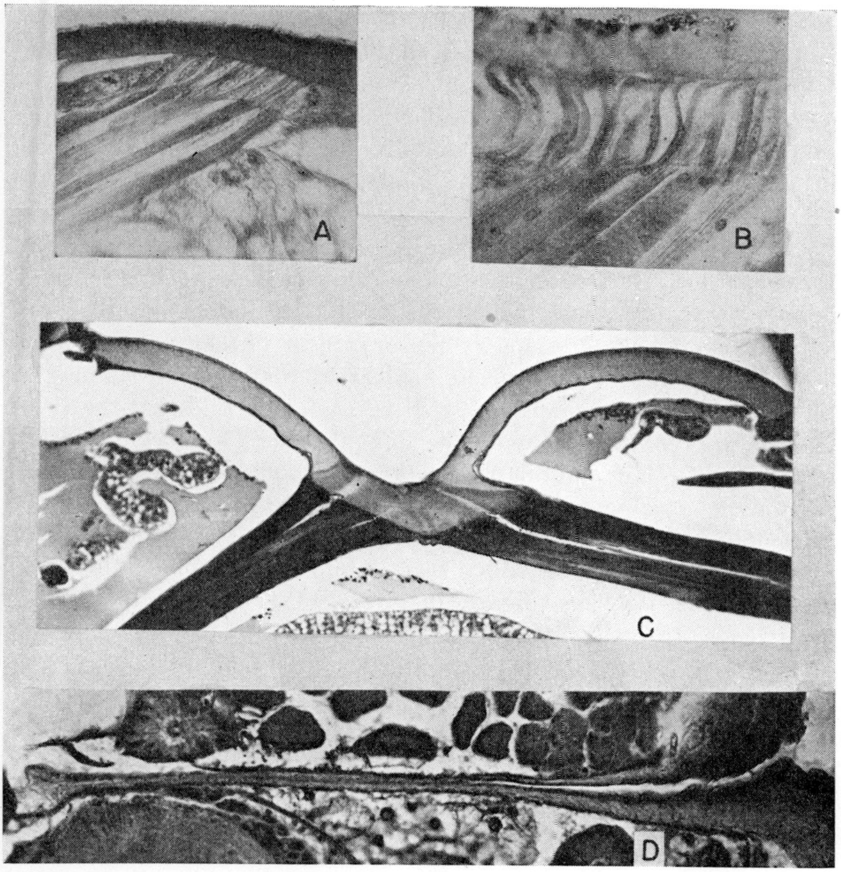

Figure 47. Photomicrographs of muscle attachments and of a small apodeme. (Original.)

A. Integument of a young grasshopper with the muscle fibrils seemingly passing through the cytoplasm of the epidermal cells to attach on the inner surface of the cuticle. (Photo by Wm. A. Riley.)

B. Integument of a dragonfly larva with muscles attaching to the basement membrane and faintly continued through the epidermis. (Photo by Wm. A. Riley.)

C. Integument of the larva of a moth, *Heterocampa manteo,* with the muscles continued through the cuticle as deeply staining groups of tonofibrillae.

D. The hard integument of an adult beetle with a small apodeme which shows the lumen due to formation by invagination; further inward (to left) the sides come together as a single line.

ganization of gross body structure — in other words, that an extra molt is required if body wall and muscular system are to be sequential rather than simultaneous in development.[1]

Both myofibrillae and tonofibrillae stain like the surrounding material; that is, the fibrils are acidophilic in muscle and in procuticle, but are basophilic in epidermal cells (Duboscq 1899, Pérez 10). With differential staining methods the color contrast may be striking and the tonofibrillae change color abruptly at the cell-cuticle interface. According to Ruser (33) the tonofibrillae of ticks give a positive iodine-zinc chloride test, which she accepts as indicating they are chitin or contain it. Presumably the degree of development of tonofibrillae varies in different species; at least the intensity of staining in the cuticle varies (Thompson 29). It is commonly said that the myofibrillae are continuous with the tonofibrillae (Korschelt 38a, b, Schreiber 22), but careful observation of good preparations shows that muscle attachments in both crayfish and dragonfly larvae are not continuous but that the tonofibrillae split and interlace with ends of myofibrillae (Downey 12, Riley 08). A similar lack of continuity is implied by the published figures of several other workers (Keilin 17, Munscheid 33, Yalvac 39).

The important functional points are that the tonofibrillae provide a strong attachment between muscle and cuticle, show no evidence of contractility, and are formed only during deposition of the cuticle. The question of whether the tonofibrillae originate from muscle or

[1] Poyarkoff's hypothesis seems a sound rationalization, but recently Hinton (48) has elaborated on this and even gone so far as to postulate that the pupa is a necessary "mold with the sole function of permitting the formation of a few muscles." In support of this he says that skeletal muscles have to develop in a straight line between fixed points whose distance apart must be the same as in the adult. This gratuitous assumption is refuted by the Odonata, where the adult and larval musculatures are different, the shape of the thorax and its actual dimensions change greatly at the last molt, and the adult muscles both extend and enlarge (Maloeuf 35b). It is true that as far as we know muscles can become attached to arthropod cuticle only when that cuticle is being formed. And considering the inverted and invaginated imaginal discs, it does not seem possible to visualize the development of appropriately inserted muscles in an adult housefly or blowfly without two molts: one to move the organs to their proper adult locus, the other to complete development, including attaching the subsequently developed muscles. But the dragonflies refute the idea that a "mold" is necessary. In fact the dragonflies go further and give evidence in favor of the idea that a pupal stage is not "necessary," but only the particular solution adopted by higher pterygote insects. Once the solution of introducing a pupal stage was adopted, extreme displacements such as seen in the larvae of higher Diptera became feasible. (Whether the pupal stage is to be called a first imaginal instar — as seems logical — is not within the province of the present book.)

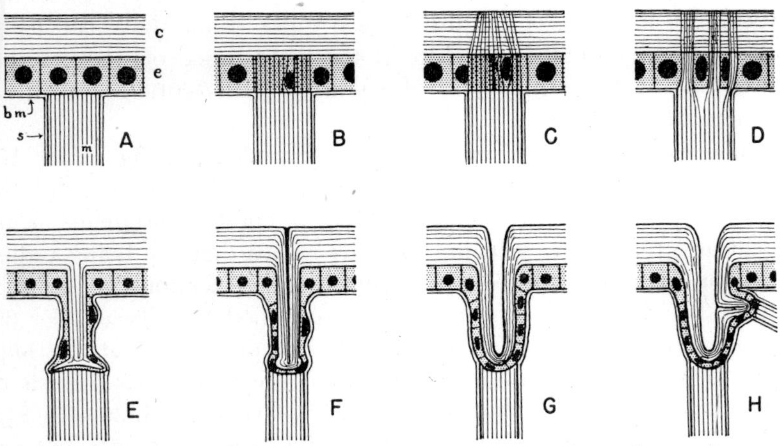

Figure 48. Series of diagrams of the various types of muscle attachment. Note the continuity of the basement membrane of the epidermis (*bm*) and the sarcolemma (*s*) of the muscle.

epidermis is not an issue of current interest. One is reminded of the difficulties involved in interpreting the structure and development of the basement membrane. It seems likely that these questions of origin or homology will be settled only as a by-product of significant work on the connective tissue elements of arthropods.

When one considers a variety of arthropods, it seems that tonofibrillae grade over into tendons, and tendons intergrade to apophyses and apodemes (Fig. 48). In this seemingly continuous series three divisions might be recognized: (1) the common situation in which the muscle extends to the basement membrane of the integument and is continued by tonofibrillae, (2) the rather uncommonly recorded situation in which the muscle fiber stops short of the basement membrane and is continued by a solid mass of connective tissue that looks like a mass of tonofibrillae plus nuclei pulled, so to speak, out of the cuticle (Barth 45, Keilin 17, Yalvac 39), and (3) the common situation in which an integumental process or invagination forms apophyses (solid) or apodemes (hollow). Most of the so-called tendons of arthropod muscles are apophyses, or apodemes which may collapse so that the hollow core is not visible (Baur 1860, Janet 1897, Korschelt 38a, Woodworth 08). All of these may combine to form elaborate endoskeletons (Edwards 1851, Giesbrecht 21), but show their origin clearly by being shed with the exuvium (Packard 1883). In some cases the apophyses may become finely branched where they attach to a muscle (Baur 1860), and in such cases one may be able to recognize all three of the histological types given above. In a few cases there are — or at least there is the appearance of — lateral tendons extending from the center of a muscle to the cuticle (Barth 45, de Sinety 01).

As one would expect from the origin of apodemes (Fig. 47D), the laminae of the general exoskeleton are continuous with those of the apodeme (Janet 07). The apodemes are thought to originate as invaginations, that is, by growing inwards rather than by being pulled in by muscle action. However, the extension of tendons, at least, is correlated with muscle contracture and sustained tonicity (Lever 30, Maloeuf 35a, Maulik 29). It certainly seems probable that the high degree of micelle orientation in muscle tendons shown by analysis of birefringence is brought about by tension (Clark & Smith 36). In Fig. 24B both the muscle tendon and the condyl to which it attaches appear highly birefringent. Insertion of a full-wave compensator into the instrument makes one of them appear bright blue, while the other is bright yellow. Both show sharp extinction. From this it follows that the micelles in the tendon are parallel to the long axis of the muscle and at a right angle to those of the ridge on which they attach. Stresses can hardly explain all details of the development of elaborate apodemes, but they must have a considerable and significant influence on the development of these.

CHAPTER 26

Wings, Gills, Epidermal Glands, Etc.

WINGS AND ELYTRA

In terms of development insect wings are simply evaginated sacks of integument which become flattened and the two sides closely appressed to one another, as was shown by Semper in 1857 (Figs. 49–50). Wings possess some special features which are not (or not so well) shown by the integument in general; only these special features will be treated here. For the general structure and development of wings numerous papers are available; consult the larger reference sources (Snodgrass 35, Weber 33) or the special papers which are available for Neuroptera (Sundermeier 40), Diptera (Pérez 10), Hymenoptera (Schlüter 33), Coleoptera (Reuter 37, Tower 03a), and Lepidoptera (Henke 46, Köhler 32, W. F. Mercer 00, Stossberg 38).

When the wing is developing, the epithelium forms a layer of normal thickness and may even consist of tall, columnar cells (Fig. 30B). Later the cell layers become very thin (Fig. 50), or in certain areas the cells may die, leaving the two closely appressed cuticles seemingly cemented together (Fig. 37).

The basement membranes of the two epithelia come together in certain areas and more or less fuse to give rise to a conspicuous but incomplete layer called the middle membrane of the wing (Fig. 30B) (W. S. Marshall 15). This middle membrane is anatomically important in determining the course of blood channels and thereby the subsequent venation of the wing. Of more interest here is the fact that having fused, it may apparently degenerate or break, leaving the epidermal cells of the two wing surfaces connected by long tails (Marshall 15, Schlüter 33). Such cellular connections between the two sides of flattened evaginations of the integument are not limited to insect wings. Similar cellular connections are seen in the book lungs of arachnids (Börner 04), in the telson of crustacea (Issel 10),

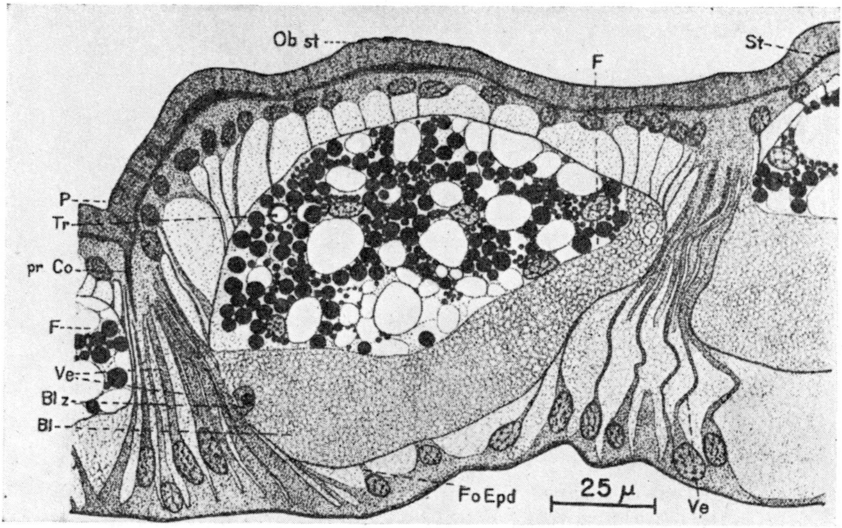

Figure 49. Cross section of the developing fore wing (elytron) of a beetle, *Calandra granaria,* at an early stage, when the organization as an evagination of the general body wall is still apparent. Note that connections between the two epithelial layers involve interruption of the basement membrane and extension of the "tails" of epidermal cells from one side to the other. (After Reuter.) *Bl* = blood; *Bl z* = blood cell; *F* = adipose or fat tissue; *Fo Epd* = process of epidermal cell; *Ob st* = upper or dorsal surface of wing; *P* = developing pit on surface; *pr Co* = cuticular connection between two wing surfaces in early stage of development; *St* = pore canals; *Tr* = trachea; *Ve* = processes of epidermal cells which connect the two surfaces of the wing.

in thin lateral extensions of the shell of various crustacea (Novikoff 05, Patanè 36, Zwack 05), and in gills (Bernecker 09, Leydig 1878). In some of these cases the cellular connections become quite fibrous and resemble connective tissue. As such they seem to intergrade over to the cuticularized pillars or columns which connect the two surfaces of beetle elytra (Reuter 37, P. Schulze 13a, Sprung 32, Stegemann 29b). As one would expect, the micelles are oriented at 90° to the two surfaces on the wing (Mason 27b).

Wings are also of interest because their thinness in certain species makes them readily available for electron microscopy (Driesch & Müller 35, Richards & Korda 48). Two significant points have come from such examination. Small spots ($<0.1\ \mu$) probably represent minute thickenings in the endocuticle, perhaps comparable to similar-appearing thickenings in the tracheae of many insects (p. 258). Of greater interest is the fact that the wing membranes of mosquitoes

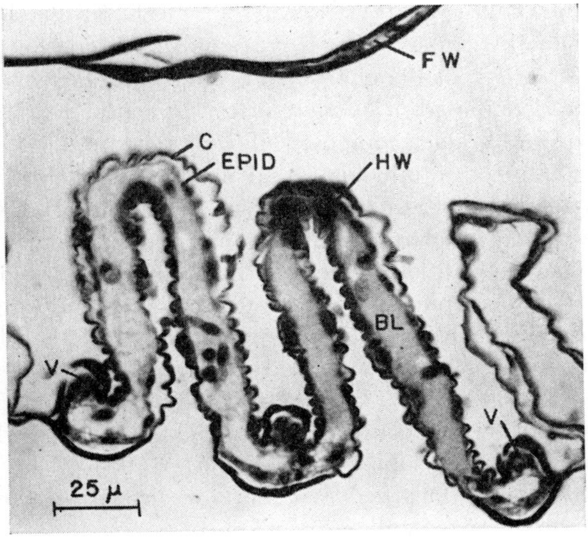

Figure 50. Cross sections of the fore and hind wings of a cockroach, *Blatella germanica.* The fore wing (FW) has the cell layers reduced but not obliterated; the hind wing (HW) has both layers of epidermis evident and separated by a blood-filled space. (Original.) BL = blood; C = cuticle; EPID = epidermis; V = vein.

purified for chitin show no detectable fibrillar structure (micelles) such as can be seen in chitin sheets purified from most other sources (Richards & Korda 48). The implication is that cross linkages between chitin chains are not the same in wing membranes as in other types of cuticle (p. 23).

Wings are useful in studying cell size in relation to organ size (p. 204), and it might be worth noting that reduction in wing size may be due either to fewer or to smaller cells (but the data come from different orders) (Alpatov 30, Henke 46, Zarapkin 30). Wings are also useful in certain studies on physical colors (C. W. Mason 27a); presumably the drying causes the normal cuticular laminae to shrink to dimensions required for the production of such colors (p. 197).

The fore wings of beetles become hard protective coverings called elytra (Figs. 37, 49). They may retain an active blood circulation and even contain adipose tissue and oenocytes in addition to the epidermal cells (Kremer 18, 20). Workers on elytra have developed a special terminology which, as Kühnelt (28c) points out, tends to obscure the similarity to normal arthropod cuticle (Bernard-Deschamps

1845, Hass 14, Hoffbauer 1892, Kremer 18, 20, E. Krüger 1898, Reuter 37, Sprung 32, Stegemann 29a, b, P. Schulze 13a, b, 15). These authors treat a section of the elytron as a single structure and recognize a dorsal layer composed of *Sekretschicht*, *Pigmentschicht*, and *Hauptlage*, and a ventral layer composed of *Hauptlage* and *Dornenschicht*. Translating into the terminology used in the present book, the thick dorsal integument of the elytron consists of a conspicuous tectocuticle, an exocuticle (probably including unrecognized epicuticle), and an underlying endocuticle, whereas the thinner ventral integument has only a thinner endocuticle (presumably plus unrecognized epicuticle) bearing microtrichia. The upper surface of the elytron may show a tuberculate pattern, and the term "cyrtome" has been applied to the tubercles (Schulze 13b). Points of interest on general cuticle structure are that wings can become so thick and hardened that they can show extensive development of Balken (p. 192) (Reuter 37), and can have the connections between the two surfaces of the wing developed as cuticularized pillars or columns.

GILLS AND LUNGS

Rather little of interest to an understanding of arthropod cuticle in general is to be derived from the papers on gill and lung structure. It may be said that gills and lungs have a thin, presumably permeable, cuticle (Dürken 23, Kimus 1898), but that there is considerable variation in cuticle thickness between species (D. A. Webb 40) and even on different areas of a single gill. In the thicker areas the cuticle may be distinctly laminate and show striations which may represent pore canals. On the gill lamellae of the crab *Eriocheir* the cuticle tapers from the base to become a mere "ghost-like film" over 80% of the gill surface (D. A. Webb 40).

The epidermal cell layer is always distinct and may be moderately thick, ranging, for instance, in insect larvae from 6 μ to 10 μ (H. J. A. Koch 36, Perfiljev 26). In crustacea the cells may be placoid, cuboid, or columnar, with or without recognizable cell boundaries, and with or without fibrillae perpendicular to the surface (Bock 25, Chen 33, Kimus 1898, D. A. Webb 40). The major interest in gills and lungs centers in the question of whether the epidermal cells take an active part in the penetration of gases. Unfortunately no postive data are available. Granules have been recorded in the gill cells of larval Odonata, Ephemerida, and Trichoptera (and even named *spadicin*) (Purser 15), and H. J. A. Koch (36) has recorded that those in the

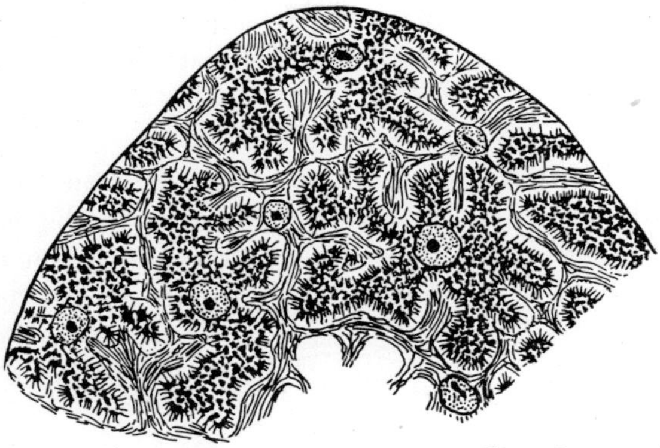

Figure 51. Surface view of the gill epidermis of *Daphnia magna* showing the two types of interlaced cells. (Redrawn after Fiedler.)

tracheal gills of dragonfly larvae are capable of being oxidized and reduced, but it remains to be demonstrated whether or not the granules take any part in the transfer of gas across the membrane. There is good evidence, however, that the cells are active in osmoregulation and ion accumulation (p. 291).

Bizarre epidermal cells of uncertain significance are found on the gills of the cladoceran *Daphnia* (Fiedler 08). Two types of cells are intermingled in this epithelium (Fig. 51). The most numerous type is a very large, highly lobate cell with a relatively small, round nucleus, the cytoplasm packed with unidentified dark bodies (large granules), and the peripheral margin of the cell highly fibrillar, with the fibrils normal to the surface and usually ending on the unidentified cytoplasmic bodies. Separating or joining together these peculiar lobate cells are smaller cells which fit into the indentations of the lobate cells; these cells have the cytoplasm filled with what on surface view looks like many fibrils but what in sections is seen to be platelets perpendicular to the surface of the gill and extending all the way from the cuticle to the basement membrane. The significance of these cytological specializations is unknown.

Commonly the epithelia or cuticles of the two surfaces of gills and lungs are joined by cellular or fibrous connections (Bernecker 09, Börner 04, Chen 33, Kimus 1898, Leydig 1878, Maloeuf 40, Versluys & Demoll 22, D. A. Webb 40). In the arachnid lung cuticular processes project from the surface and hold the leaflets apart (Berteaux 1889, Börner 04). These are said to originate from pseudopodia-like projections from the epidermal cells, which branch, may anastamose, and subsequently become solidly cuticularized (Kästner 29, Purcell 09, Schlottke 38a).

MISCELLANEOUS ORGANS

The tympanal membrane, developed in connection with the large thoracic chordotonal organ in certain families of moths, is of interest in being an extremely thin membrane with a dual origin (Eggers 19, 28). A tracheal air sac enlarges and becomes pressed against the

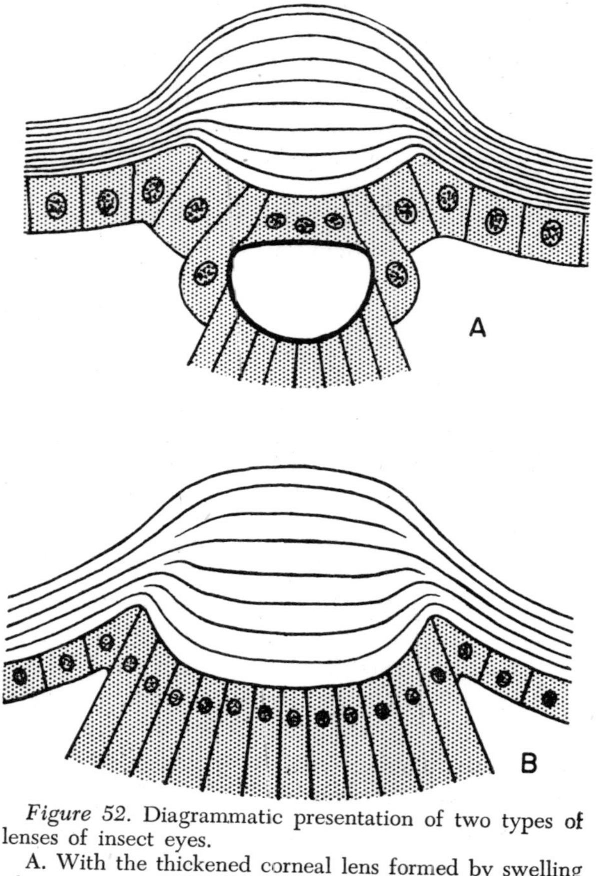

Figure 52. Diagrammatic presentation of two types of lenses of insect eyes.

A. With the thickened corneal lens formed by swelling of the normal cuticular laminae (based on larva of *Myrmeleon*). (Redrawn from Schröder after Hesse.)

B. With the thickened corneal lens formed partly by swelling of laminae, partly by intercalation of new partial laminae (based on lateral ocellus of *Cicada*). (Redrawn from Schröder after Link.)

integument in this region; both stretch and become extremely thin, the contiguous epidermal layers of integument and air sac seemingly degenerate, and sections of the fully formed membrane look like a single thin line under the light microscope. The processes involved remind one of the formation of wing membranes in species in which the cells degenerate, and they accordingly indicate that the phenomena are not restricted to wing development.

The lenses of arthropod eyes (ommatidia) are usually symmetrical swellings in the procuticle. They may be single convex, double convex, or slightly concavo-convex (Balss 27, Debaisieux 44, Dethier 42, 43, Eltringham 33, Verhoeff 26–32). The nature of their development can only be surmised, but as already mentioned in Chapter 19, it is both interesting and suggestive that the lenses may contain the same number of laminae as the contiguous parts of the cuticle, yet have the laminae greatly swollen, or may maintain approximately the same spacing of laminae and develop new intercalated ones (Verhoeff 26–32), or may develop intercalated laminae and have them swell (Fig. 52).

A number of other organs could be mentioned, but little of general interest on integumental structure is known about them. Thus the rectal glands (Fig. 30D), thought to reabsorb water from the fecal material, are formed of tall, columnar cells with an extremely thin overlying cuticle. Of unknown significance is the recent report that alkaline phosphatase is present in the rectal glands of *Lucilia* but completely absent from those of *Blatella* (Day 49b). The rectal or anal papillae, commonly mistermed anal gills, have cells of moderate to large size and are covered with a thin, homogeneous cuticle (Branch 22, Jaworowsky 1885, Miall & Hammond 00, Wigglesworth 32a, b). The cells of anal papillae have granules staining vitally and must be covered by a cuticle of unusually high permeability (Pagast 36).

Circular adhesive discs which serve for attachment, presumably by a suction-cup mechanism, are found in a few arthropods. The parasitic crustacean *Argulus* has two suckers at the anterior end for attachment to its host; these each consist of three cuticular rings and the epithelial cells which produce them plus special circular muscles in the subcutaneous layers (Claus 1875b). In males of the beetle *Dytiscus* there are, on one pair of legs, annular suckers which serve for holding the female during copulation (Blunck 12a, Korschelt 23).

Numerous other special modifications can be found in the various reference treatises covering general entomology or the entire animal kingdom. For instance, the peculiar labella of higher Diptera have grooves called pseudotracheae supported by incomplete annular thickenings of the cuticle. A similar appearing structure is seen in the peritreme of mites (Blauvelt 45).

EPIDERMAL GLANDS

In the sense that they secrete the cuticle, all the epidermal cells are glandular; however, some of the epidermal cells or groups of epidermal cells are specialized for the production of noncuticular components. The dermal and tegumental glands which contribute to the formation of the cuticle have already been treated (p. 207), and reference has been made to silk (p. 66) and waxes (p. 94) secreted by various insects. Hundreds of other papers treat the anatomy, histology, and in some cases cytology of miscellaneous glands, but usually the information available is quite meager. The chemistry of known secretions has been reviewed by Melander and Brues (06), Fredericq (24), Hedicke (29), and Maloeuf (38). An adequate review of this literature would require a copiously illustrated set of individual descriptions – not feasible in the present book. Some of the representative and outstanding papers will be cited, particularly those which bear upon a general treatment of the integumental cells, and the reader is referred to the bibliography compiled by Day (48) for additional references.

The gross appearance of epidermal glands is diverse. They may simply form an area in the integument (Fig. 46) (Dreyling 06) and, if sufficiently large, project into the body cavity (Betten 02, Wigglesworth 48d), or they may be actually invaginated, sometimes extending a long distance within the body, as seen in silk glands, salivary glands, poison glands, etc. (comparable to Fig. 42). The cells of which they are composed may appear as a rather simple epithelium as in the coxal and poison glands of arachnids (B. H. Buxton 13, Millot 31), the "green gland" of crustacea (E. J. Allen 1893), accessory reproductive glands (H. Ito 24, Metcalfe 32), or the silk glands of embiids (Lesperon 37). Or they may be larger and look somewhat different from the ordinary epidermal cells, as, for instance, in most salivary glands (Lesperon 37, Noël & Paillot 27). In some cases they show remarkable complexity, as, for instance, in the wax glands of coccids (Pollister 37), the poison glands of centipedes (Duboscq 1894, 95, Pavlowsky 13), and the urticating hairs of certain caterpillars

(Klatt 08). There may also be a wide assortment of types on a single species (W. S. Marshall 29–30, Mou 38) or in a single group (seven types of silk glands have been recognized in spiders, Apstein 1889). In the diplopod *Hirudisona*, the mass of glandular cells is illustrated as lying between the epithelium and the cuticle (Silvestri 03); and in the organ of Géné, which produces the wax for tick eggs, the secretion collects between the cells and the overlying cuticle (Lees & Beament 48).

A few cases show secreting cells with finger-like cytoplasmic processes on the side which is the secreting surface (Schäffer 1889, Sulc 11), and in many cases the cell margins on the secreting side show striations perpendicular to the surface or to the duct (Grassé & Lesperon 34, Henseval 1896, Johansson 14, Lesperon 37, van Lidth de Jeude 1878). But it should be remembered that striated borders are found in many types of epithelia, including numerous cases in the ordinary epidermis of arthropods.

A striking feature of numerous epidermal glands is the possession of intracellular ducts, or canaliculi (von Rath 1895, Saint-Hilaire 27, Schön 11, Schreiber 22), even in some cases where there is not a thick cuticle to be penetrated (as in Fig. 43). In multicellular glands the intracellular ducts join into collecting tubes which may have sizable reservoirs (Henrici 38, 40). The membrane lining these ducts is fluorescent in mosquitoes (Metcalf 45), is soluble in KOH in bees (Jacobs 24), and, while usually smooth, may have thickenings reminiscent of the taenidia of tracheae (Debot 32, Duboscq 1894, Grandjean 37, Miall & Denny 1886, Nordenskiöld 08, Ruser 33, Tänzer 21), and may even bear microtrichia (Schäffer 1889). The intracellular canals are certainly no fixation artifact because they can be seen in the living cell (Beams & King 32, 33). In some cases it is said that the intracellular ducts are formed by special cells (Engelhardt 14), as is also said of dermal glands (p. 213).

Most of the published papers have been histological, but some good cytological works have been published: for instance, on the salivary glands of a grasshopper (Beams & King 32), the silkworm (Lesperon 37), a beetle (Lesperon 37), and a caddis fly (Lesperon 37, Wajda 31), the pharyngeal glands of honeybees (Beams & King 33), the tarsal silk glands of embiids (Lesperon 37), the metasternal glands of ants (Tulloch 36), peculiar giant gland cells in certain dipterous larvae (Davidoff 28), and the silk glands of spiders (Dumitresco 38). A large special literature deals with the larval salivary glands, primarily the chromosomes, of *Drosophila* (Ross 39), *Sciara* (Metz 35, Metz & Lawrence 37), and other Diptera. In the cytoplasm, filamentous mitochondria, crescentic, semicircular or ringlike Golgi bodies (dictyosomes), and commonly other granules and vacuoles are found. In most salivary glands the nuclei are spherical or ovoidal, but in ticks it is said that the nuclei are round when the individual is off a host (and so the glands presumably inactive), but highly lobate or branched when the tick is on a host (Bonnet 06). Such lobate or polymorphic nuclei are rather common in secreting cells (Grassé & Lesperon 34, Lesperon 37, Maziarski 11). In the case of the cement glands of barnacles, it is reported that the spherical nucleus becomes highly lobate during secretion, but only on the side of the nucleus toward the duct (Krüger 23). As apparently is common for secreting cells in general, a strong alkaline phosphatase enzyme reaction is given by the silk glands of spiders (Bradfield 46) as well as by the salivary glands of various insects (Day 49b, Doyle 47, Krugelis 46, Nakamura 40).

A sequence of cytological phases during the secretion process has been recorded in a number of cases (Dumitresco 38, Jacobs 24, Paillot & Noël 29), but the significance of the changes observed is not known. As already mentioned (p. 227), the wax gland of adult honeybees, like the general epidermis, shows a considerable increase in thickness and hence volume during the secretory phase (Fig. 46) (Dreyling 06). Only two points appear to be clear in connection with the relation between cytological changes and the production of secretion: namely, that there is no topographic relation between the distribution of mitochondria and Golgi bodies and the secretory duct, and that the secretion involves the activity of the entire cell and not just some part thereof.

CHAPTER 27

The Tracheal System

The literature on the tracheal system is very large, and it is not easy to decide how much should be covered here. It seems that the line between general insect anatomy and that portion of tracheal structure that belongs in a book on integument must necessarily be arbitrary. For purposes of this book, anatomy in the sense of homologies of tracheal branches, evolution of the branching systems, and distribution to the various organs will be omitted; aspects of more questionable relevance such as intracellular versus intercellular tracheoles will be simply indexed; and only the structure of the wall will be treated in detail.

The tracheal system (Fig. 53) was discovered by Malpighi in 1669, figured by Swammerdam in 1752 and Lyonnet in 1762, given its first good treatment by Straus-Durckheim in 1828, and put on a sound footing by Palmén in 1877. The voluminous literature has been reviewed by Wahl (1899), Babák (12a), Deegener (13), Remy (25a), M. O. Lee (29), and Wigglesworth (31a).

If the "air trees" of terrestrial isopods are included (and it is difficult to exclude them) (F. D. Becker 36, Herold 13, Reinders 33, Remy 25, Verhoeff 17a, b, 19), tracheae are found in all the major classes of arthropods. It is not possible to homologize all of these.[1] In his able review Ripper (31) recognizes ten distinct types, which would necessitate as least ten separate evolutionary origins – the similarity being due to a common property or potency to produce cuticular tubes for various purposes, including their production for internal respiratory surfaces. These are (1) Onychophora, (2) Araneida, Scorpionida, and Pedipalpia, (3) Acarina and Ricinulei, (4) Pseudoscorpionida, (5) Phalangida, (6) Solpugidae, (7) Isopoda, (8) Symphyla, (9) Diplopoda, and (10) Chilopoda and Insecta. Tracheae are not neces-

[1] Bernard (1892), on the assumption that tracheae must be derived from something present in the annelids, considers that they are serial homologues derived from setiparous sacs.

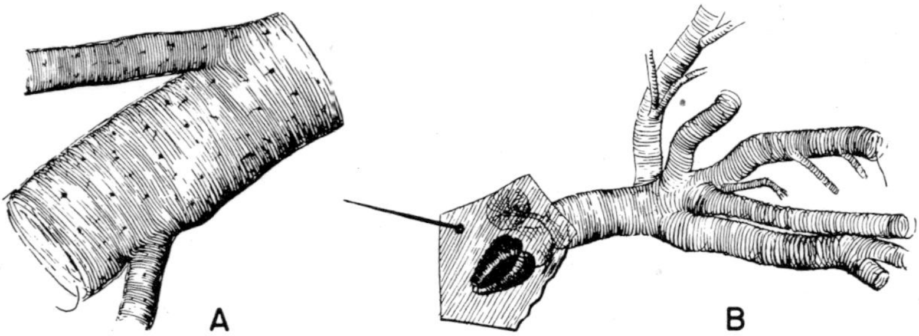

Figure 53. The gross appearance of tracheae. (Drawn by Miss Anna Stryke.)

A. Portion of the trachea of a bug, *Belostoma,* with microtrichia on the taenidia.

B. Spiracle of a beetle larva with attached tracheae and scar of former spiracle just above the now functional spiracle.

sarily present in all species of the above groups; for instance, they are absent from many mites and isopods and from a few small insects. And in insects tracheae may appear fairly early in embryonic life or not until late in larval life. When present they are sufficiently constant to afford characters of taxonomic or evolutionary significance (and are probably as constant as the blood vessels of vertebrates), but show considerable variation from one specimen to another, especially in the smaller tubes (Rühle 32).

A tracheal system is to be defined as a set of respiratory tubes derived from the integument, possessing a cuticular lining, and extending into the body cavity (Figs. 53–54). Usually they open to the outside via apertures called spiracles, usually their lining is shed with the exuvium at ecdysis, and sometimes saclike dilations called air sacs are present. In almost all cases the wall of the tube is supported by circular or helical thickenings called taenidia ("spiral thread").[2] These anatomical and histological features may be adequate for identification, but actually it is only the functional point of facilitating the

[2] While all but a few tracheae possess taenidia, these are not characteristics by which one can positively identify a trachea. Similar cuticularized tubes with thickenings for support have been commonly recorded for the ducts of salivary glands (Bonnet 06, Debot 32, Miall & Denny 1886, Nordenskiöld 08, Ruser 33, Tänzer 21) and are sometimes to be found in ducts of other glands (Duboscq 1894, Grandjean 37). On the external surface of arthropods helical or circular thickenings are well known in the pseudo-tracheae of Diptera and are likewise found in those of mites (Blauvelt 45), also in the walls of setae and microtrichia (Anderson & Richards 42a, Dethier 41, Richards & Korda 47). Outside the phylum Arthropoda helical structures are also common: for instance, in the stalks of certain Bryozoa (Rogick & Croasdale 49), the tests and flagellae of some Protozoa (H. P. Brown 45, Hadzi 38), the twist of wool fibers (Freney *et al.* 46, E. H. Mer-

transport of gases that is definitive. Accordingly, in terming any tube a trachea, it is desirable to have some evidence that the tube does function in respiration. A case in point is provided by the so-called tracheae of spiders, which, if really tracheae, are in structure unlike the tracheae of other groups. Clearly, demonstration of the presumed but questioned function of these tubes is required (Bertkow 1872, Kästner 29, Lamy 00, 01, 02, Purcell 09, 10, Richards & Korda 50).

The tracheal system may originate in the embryo as an invagination (Lehmann 26), but it commonly originates from solid cords of cells (20 μ diameter) which grow in and subsequently develop a canal through the center (Eastham 29, Lehmann 26, Palmén 1877, Weismann 1863). The tracheoles, which we could call the terminal twigs of the respiratory tree (M. O. Lee 29), often develop independently; at least in the better-studied cases they originate as cytoplasmic canals in large tracheal end cells and grow *to* the tracheae (not out from the tracheae as finer branches) (Dürken 23, Eastham 29, Keister 48, Meinert 1886, Pantel 1898, 01, Pérez 10, Weismann 1863).

An apparently unique phenomenon of integumentary structures is shown by the partial shedding of the tracheal intima. This has recently been treated in detail for larvae of the fly *Sciara* by Keister (48). The cuticle (intima) becomes loosened from the cells of the larger tracheae, not from small and more remote ones. Where the cuticle is loosened, a new one is formed and the old one withdrawn at ecdysis. The new cuticle becomes indistinguishably continuous with the unshed cuticle of smaller tubes (p. 235).

TRACHEAE

The tracheae have, in general, the typical structure of integument. A tube of epidermal cells (= ectotrachea) secretes on its inner surface a cuticle called the intima (= endotrachea). This intima is continuous with and homologous to the cuticle on the surface of the body, but has few or no gross holes such as pore canals or gland ducts. It is birefringent (Akenhurst 22, Richards & Korda 48), elastic, and said to be capable of swelling and shrinking (von Frankenberg 15, A. Koch 18). In fact, the only striking differences are in micellar organization and the common inability to detect (= absence of ?) chitin (Fig. 54).

cer & Rees 46), walls of certain cell types in many plants (Castle, etc.) (and even in α-glycoside polysaccharide molecules [Haworth 46] and in one type of crack pattern in glass tubing). Helical structure in regenerating arthropod appendages (Bordage 00) and in cracks in glass tubing (Clack & Harris 47) occurs only when stress is involved.

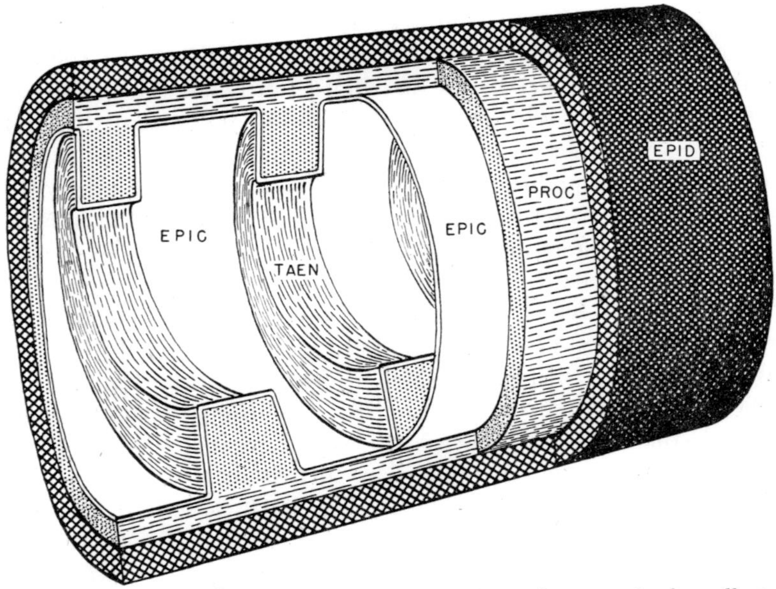

Figure 54. Semidiagrammatic reconstruction of a tracheal wall to illustrate the micelle orientations in the cuticle (based on large tracheae of a cockroach, *Periplaneta americana*). Micelles are indicated in side view as dashes or broken lines; in cross section as dots. The micelles extend along the tracheal axis in the basal sheet of the tracheal cuticle, but at an approximate right angle to this in the circumferential helical thickenings called taenidia. Note also that the epicuticle lines the lumen surface and bends out over the taenidia. (Original.) EPIC = epicuticle; EPID = epidermal cell layer; PROC = basal tube of cuticular lining (procuticle); TAEN = taenidia.

The tracheal intima is essentially an entity (Dujardin 1849) with at least the larger tracheae composed of three recognizable parts: a basic membrane and a surface membrane with the taenidia lying between the two (Burmeister 1832, Joly 1849, Lyonnet 1762, Wolf 35).[3] These three can be manually separated by teasing (Minot 76), most readily if they are first warmed with a weak alkali solution or treated with a solution of pepsin. Extensive examination by electron microscopy of representatives of almost all the tracheate groups leads to the conclusion that thickenings, presumably for support, are always to be found in tracheal walls, and that further, with the exception of the "air trees" of isopod crustacea, the questionable tracheae of spi-

[3] But it is now universally agreed that the old claims (Agassiz 1850, Blanchard 1847–49) for a "peritracheal space" in which a special circulation occurred are false.

ders, and some of the presumably tracheal tubes of symphylans, the thickenings are always organized into circular or helical thickenings called taenidia (Richards & Korda 50). The taenidium is usually regarded as helical, but circular ones were found to be common, especially in smaller tracheae and tracheoles (Fig. 56); a single trachea or tracheole may contain only helices, only circles, or both helices and circles.

The development of the tracheal intima is, then, first a question of how the lumen surface comes into being prior to deposition of the intima (this is not at all understood), and second what produces the organization of the intima components into a sheet plus taenidia. Apparently the development of taenidia is not dependent on the presence of chitin molecules because similar-appearing tracheae occur both with chitin and with no demonstrable chitin (p. 51).[4] It has been suggested that taenidia are formed around corresponding cytoplasmic ridges (Tiegs 22), but there is good evidence against this because the taenidia occur on the lumen side of a continuous basal sheet (Richards & Korda 48), may extend without interruption across several cells (Minot 76, Thompson 29), may appear suddenly, simultaneously, and completely formed along a trachea (Keister 48), and would be large enough to have been observed by some of the careful microscopists who have studied the development of tracheae. The outstanding hypothesis has been that the taenidia originate as folds which may be made solid by subsequent secretion (Dujardin 1849, Macloskie 1884, Stokes 1893), and there is one case known where the anatomy supports this hypothesis (*Musca*, p. 259), but the continuity of the basal sheet and the micelle orientations are against it as a general explanation.

Available data are consistent with the suggestion that taenidia are produced by stress forces (Richards & Korda 50).[5] This is also in harmony with current general concepts of membrane development (Picken 40). Relevant points for such an interpretation are: (1) the taenidia develop suddenly and simultaneously (Keister 48); (2) when helical they are not continuous but made up of short pieces (Merlin 01, Minot 1876); (3) they are separated from the underlying

[4] It should be remembered that the reasons for saying some tracheae lack chitin are as good as the reasons for saying the epicuticle lacks chitin.

[5] Various other suggestions for taenidial origin that have only historic interest include: that they are due to splitting brought about by drying (H. Meyer 1849), that they are cuticularized nuclear processes (Packard 1886), that they are equivalent to cuticular sculpturing or ornaments (Keilin 44), and that they represent precipitation of "periplasm" on helical "solenosomes" (Hollande 43).

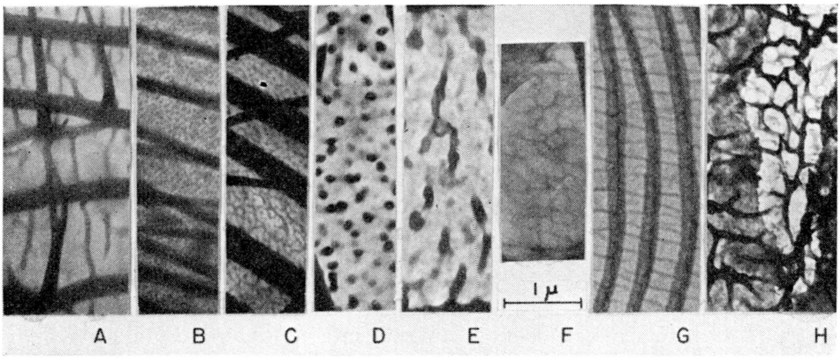

Figure 55. Representative electron micrographs of various types of tracheal walls. (After Richards and Korda.)

A–C. Small areas from three different tracheae of a beetle, *Photinus pyralis,* showing (A) microtrichiae on taenidia with only some grosser thickenings in the intertaenidial membrane, (B) minute thickenings, and (C) irregular reticulum.

D–E. More and less regular thickenings in the intertaenidial membrane of, respectively, a beetle, *Tenebrio molitor,* and a grasshopper, *Melanoplus differentialis.*

F. Reticulate intertaenidial membrane from the larva of a moth, *Malacosoma americana.*

G. Showing thickening perpendicular to the *tubular* taenidia of a small trachea in a housefly, *Musca domestica.*

H. Reticulate air-sac wall of an adult honeybee, *Apis mellifica,* in which the surface layer has been stained with osmic acid. The double nature of this cuticle is clearly shown at this point because of a small fissure in the surface layer; the reticulate thickenings are clearly in the lower layer (which, incidentally, is negative to chitin color tests).

cells by a continuous basic cuticular tube (Fig. 54); (4) the micelles extend along the longitudinal axis of the tube in the continuous basic sheet, but circumferentially in the taenidia (Fig. 54) (Richards & Korda 48); and (5) geometric analysis shows that a tube under uniform internal pressure has approximately twice as much tension circumferentially as axially (Castle 37a, Preston 48).

An analogy has been drawn with engineering data, where it is known that the strongest method of constructing a tube from fibrous components is to have the fibers extend parallel and longitudinally in the wall and to place bands of fibers around the tube at intervals (Richards & Korda 50). Correspondingly, stresses might be conceived of as producing such orientations, but we have no real knowledge of the stresses present in developing tracheae and no idea of the magnitude of force that would be required to orient molecules in a tracheal wall. It does seem reasonable, however, that the development of helices instead of rings should require only the addition of a longitudinal stress component to the postulated radial stress.

Several special cases are known. In adults of the housefly the taenidia are distinctly tubular (Fig. 55G), and accordingly these tracheae are comparable to a pipe with a corrugated wall rather than a pipe with bands around it (Richards & Korda 50). Micelle orientations have not yet been determined in fly tracheae. It is also conceivable that this type of structure might be produced by stresses, but at least the details of origin would be different. In a number of cases, particularly in beetles, microtrichia project into the lumen of the trachea (Bongardt 03, Dujardin 1849, Marcu 29–31, Richards & Korda 50, Stokes 1893). Microtrichia could hardly be accounted for by stresses, but if microtrichia arise from or around cytoplasmic filaments (p. 268), their presence is understandable. Now and then one finds a trachea where the taenidia become somewhat irregular owing to more or less complex branching or fusing (especially at places where a trachea divides), but whatever the mechanism of taenidial formation, it seems surprising that taenidia are as regular as they are.

Rationalization of the recorded exceptions to the presence of taenidia can be made but would be extremely difficult if not impossible to prove. For instance, the so-called tracheae of spiders have a complex set of surface columns which are said to arise from cellular projections (Kästner 29, Schlottke 38a); these could be viewed as interfering with taenidial formation. And the "air tree" of isopod crustacea is more like a highly lobate sac than a set of tubes; it does have thickenings, but obviously it must lack the direction necessary for orienting these (Richards & Korda 50). Also, the symphylan *Scutigerella* is very interesting in showing unoriented thickenings in some tubes but thickenings oriented into taenidia in other tubes (or other parts of the same tube); it certainly gives the impression that thickenings are of general occurrence but that they are sometimes oriented, sometimes not (if one favors a stress origin, depending on whether or not the stresses are of sufficient magnitude) (Richards & Korda 50).

As a general rule, the membrane between taenidia appears uniform when viewed with a light microscope, but some modifications have been recorded (Marcu 29–31, Wolf 35). Electron microscopy is required for the resolution of details (Fig. 55) (Richards & Anderson 42b, c, Richards & Korda 48, 50). The intertaenidial membrane is simply that portion of the continuous intima tube which is visible between taenidia. As such it includes the longitudinal fibrous elements which form this tube. It also contains patterns of thickenings which have been classified as follows:

A. Uniform within limits of resolution (electron microscope)
B. With linear thickenings
   1. Reticulum of thickenings
   2. More or less oriented thickenings
      a. Parallel to taenidia
      b. Perpendicular to taenidia
C. With small speckles due to
   1. Local thickenings in the endocuticle
   2. Evaginations presumably over minute papillae

Intermediates are common, and all three major types may be found in different tracheae of a single individual (e.g., the beetle *Photinus*), but usually there is a reasonable constancy. The types are not correlated with the presence or absence of chitin.

These types have been discussed in some detail by Richards and Korda (50). Briefly, uniform membranes could involve monolayer phenomena, especially when the membranes are extremely thin (less than 0.01 μ when dry), or there might conceivably be smaller reticula involved (beyond the resolution of an electron microscope). If uniform membranes are viewed as monolayer-type phenomena, then reticulate types are most easily viewed as due to the squeezing out of excess units, these excess units themselves becoming oriented when the necessary stress forces are operative. The lump-type, however, would seem to necessitate cellular differences, either minute papillae or (the commonest type) thickenings overlying corresponding production centers. Unfortunately this rationalization is speculative and not readily tested.

Little is known about the chemistry of tracheal walls.[6] Chitin has been recorded as present in the larger tracheae of cockroaches (*Periplaneta* and *Blatta*), moths (*Galleria*), beetles (*Dytiscus, Melontha*, and *Calandra*), mosquitoes (*Culex* and *Aedes*), blowfly larvae but not adults (*Phormia*), sawflies (*Neodiprion*), centipedes (*Lithobius* and *Scolopendra*), and millipedes (*Julus*). Negative results interpreted as indicating the absence of chitin have been obtained for tiny tracheae and tracheoles in all species and for the large tracheae of the honeybee (*Apis*), a bug (*Rhodnius*), various flies (*Musca, Sciara, Drosophila*), including the adult but not the larva of *Phormia*, and a

[6] The term trachein has been proposed (von Frankenberg 15) but without evidence that tracheal walls differ qualitatively from cuticle in general.

flea (*Xenopsylla*) (Campbell 29, Richards & Korda 50, Wester 10, van Wisselingh 1898).

Clearly at least two layers are present with the taenidia between them (Fig. 54). In the cockroach we could call these endocuticle and epicuticle (and compare the taenidia with Balken, p. 192), but two layers can also be separated in the tracheae of honeybees, which lack demonstrable chitin (Fig. 55H). Interpretation of the wettability of tracheal linings awaits satisfactory explanation (Gäbler 33, 34, 39, Krogh 17, Richards & Weygandt 45, Thorpe 30b), but is usually assumed to indicate the presence of a lipid lining.

A number of interesting modifications are known. In some cases the tracheae are oval in cross section and can be seen to dilate and collapse in living insects (Babák 12b, Dunavan 29, Krogh 20b, Portier 11, Zavrel 20), the force coming from body muscles, commonly muscles associated with the heart. Numerous insects with "closed" or partially closed tracheal systems have rudimentary spiracles with rudimentary tracheae, called funiculi, connecting with the functional tracheae; at ecdysis the rudimentary tracheae and spiracles function in withdrawing the old tracheal intima (Calvert 28, Hinton 47, Keilin 44, Keister 48, Palmén 1877). In May flies dilatations at certain points of tracheal fusion give regions ("Palmén organs") from which the intima cannot be withdrawn at ecdysis; concentric layers corresponding to the number of molts accumulate (Gross 03, Y. C. Hsu 33, Palmén 1877). Perhaps most surprising are the "inverted tracheae" which develop when some part (e.g., a nerve) grows through an air sac, becoming invested in a tracheal coat in which the layers give the illusion of being inside out (Brocher 20, Eggers 28, Janet 11). Of most interest to the topic of the present book are the so-called "tracheal funnels" which may develop when tracheae are pierced by parasites (Beard 42, Keilin 44, Thorpe 36); it seems obvious that these must supply atmospheric gases to the parasite, and perhaps their development represents an "inflammatory reaction," but little is known about them.

In several cases tracheae are associated with the endoskeleton (Kästner 33, Voges 16), and probably in all cases the tracheal system incidentally functions in helping hold the internal organs in place. Usually the tracheae ramify with gradually decreasing size, and commonly with extensive anastamoses (Alt 12), but in some cases large numbers of tubes are given off at one place (Ferrière 14, Pictet 1841, Thorpe 41, Verhoeff 26–32, Ziegler 07).

AIR SACS

The tracheal system includes relatively large bulbous dilatations called air sacs. These may function for buoyancy or in mechanical ventilation of the tracheal system (Akenhurst 22, Alt 12, Bardenfleth & Ege 16, Lowne 1893–95). Under a light microscope the air-sac walls may have a crinkled appearance. Electron microscopy has shown two general types: in the higher Diptera (*Musca, Phormia,* and *Drosophila*) the air-sac wall gives the appearance of a greatly expanded trachea with what look like widely expanded rudimentary taenidia; in the honeybee (*Apis*) irregular reticulate thickenings and folds are present without any suggestions of taenidia (Fig. 55H). An examination of the time of dilatation in relation to the time of taenidial formation might give an explanation for the two types.

TRACHEOLES

The term tracheole is used for the terminal branchings of the tracheal system. Since their discovery by Platner (1844) and Leuckart (1847) they have long been regarded as distinct from tracheae. But demonstration by electron microscopy of the presence of taenidia (too small for resolution by light microscopy) removed the one characteristic previously considered invariable (Richards & Anderson 42c, Richards & Korda 50). Tracheoles have a uniform diameter, which is usually in the range of from 0.2 μ to 0.3 μ (Buck 48, Cajal 1890, Davies 27, Effenberger 07, H. J. A. Koch 36, Morison 27, Richards & Anderson 42b, c, Richards & Korda 50), have an exceedingly thin wall (Richards & Anderson 42b), occur intracellularly [7] (I am inclined to add "of course") (Lund 11, Pantel 1898, Schäffer 1889, Thompson 20, Weismann 1863), developing on the surface of previously formed cytoplasmic canals (Dinulesco 32, Dürken 23, Eastham 29, Keister 48), and most commonly end blindly (Fig. 56C, E) although there are a number of special tissues where anastamosing networks have been recorded.[8]

[7] Incidentally, Keister (48) shows that tracheae can also develop intracellularly in *Sciara.*

[8] Tracheal fusion into networks is well known, and there would seem no occasion for surprise if tracheoles also formed networks. However, the question is not readily settled because the tubes are at the lower limit of resolution of the light microscope, and electron microscopical technique is not favorable for settling this particular question. Opposite views are held by current workers; thus Buck (48) favors the idea that anastamoses are present in light organs, whereas Richards & Korda (50) were unable to find evidence of such in the same material. Dr. M. F. Day (unpubl.) has likewise been unable to find anastamoses. Reports of networks are mainly from muscle and light organs

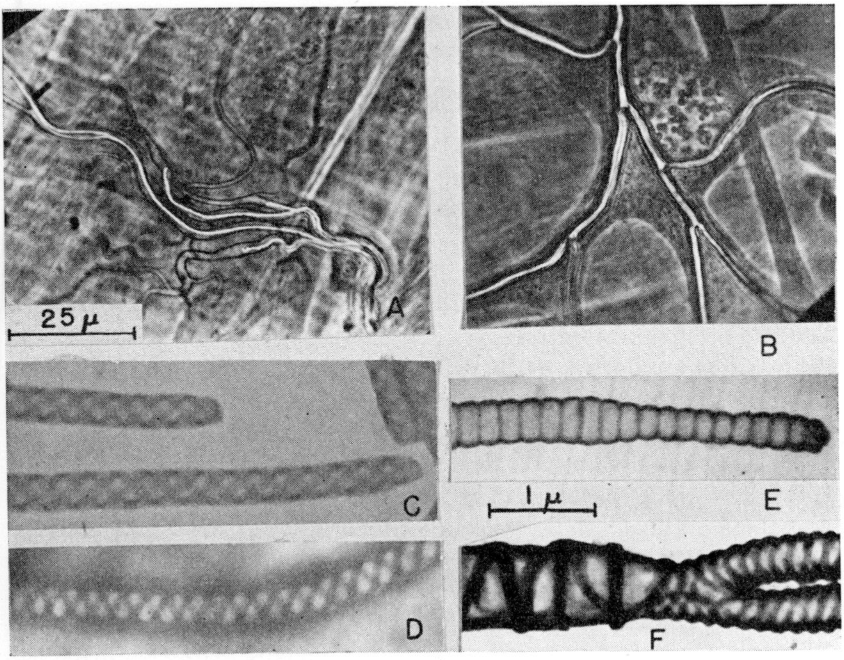

Figure 56. Photomicrographs and electron micrographs of tracheoles. (A–B, after Keister; C–F, after Richards and Korda.)

A. Air-filled 3rd instar tracheoles within fluid-filled 4th instar tracheoles in living larva of a fly, *Sciara coprophila*. Photographed with a phase contrast microscope.

B. A large stellate dorsal tracheoblast, containing air-filled tracheoles, in living larva of a fly, *Sciara coprophila*. Note the granularity of the cytoplasm and the clumped appearance of chromatin in the nucleus.

C. Electron micrograph of the isolated cuticular linings at the blind ends of tracheoles from a beetle, *Photinus pyralis*. Note helical taenidia.

D. Another preparation of same from a slightly unclean preparation, where the adjacent debris sets the tracheole off by contrast and makes the helical taenidia more distinct.

E. Blind ending of a tracheole from a bug, *Rhodnius prolixus*. Note ring taenidia.

F. Junction of small trachea and two tracheoles in a young grasshopper, *Melanoplus differentialis*.

Tracheoles have been studied most in insects (Fig. 56). In this class they have been found to develop almost always in large stellate end cells (transition cells, tracheoblasts). End cells are said to be absent in the Onychophora (Dakin 20), Collembola (Davies 27), and

(Athanasiu & Dragoiu 13, 14, Buck 48, E. Holmgren 1895, Kielich 18, Köppen 21, Lund 11, Morison 27, Townsend 04, Wahl 1899, von Wielowiejski 1882).

some beetles (Bongardt 03, Geipel 15); also tracheoles are said to arise sometimes directly from tracheae or air sacs (Morison 27). The large and typical tracheal end cells (Fig. 56B) were recognized in the middle of the nineteenth century (Leydig 1851, H. Meyer 1849, Pantel 1898, M. Schultze 1865, M. Schultze & Rudneff 1865). These tracheoblasts develop independently of the tracheae, and the tracheoles develop in the cytoplasm and subsequently make connection with the tracheae (Keister 48, W. F. Mercer 00, Pantel 01, Tiegs 22). The processes of these stellate cells (ranging from 10 μ to 80 μ, Remy 25a) commonly anastamose to form a "connective tissue layer" (Dreher 36) or "fenestrated membrane" (Poisson 26, Remy 25a, Riede 12, de Sinety 01, von Wistinghausen 1890) around the internal organs without the included tracheoles necessarily fusing. Mitochondrial granules are present (Remy 25a), and presumably these are what some early authors mistook for minute nuclei along the tracheoles (E. Holmgren 1895, Vieweger 12). Of considerable interest is the fact that these end cells show a strong reducing power for osmic acid, but it is uncertain whether this is due simply to the presence of fatty granules or to some reducing agent involved in respiratory exchanges (Buck 48, Emery 1884, Geipel 15, Lund 11, Remy 25a, M. Schultze 1865, M. Schultze & Rudneff 1865, Townsend 04, Tozzetti 1870), although Lund's (11) report that the reducing agent is thermolabile favors an enzyme.

Much of the discussion about tracheoles has involved the question of whether tracheoles or the processes containing tracheoles always end on the surface of (or between cells of) other tissues, or whether they may penetrate other cells to terminate there intracellularly. Most of the records of intracellular penetration concern muscle, but an assortment of other tissues are involved (Anglas 04, Cajal 1890, Chun 1876, Dinulesco 32, Dreher 36, Enderlein 1899, Heinemann 1872, E. Holmgren 1895, 07, Kölliker 1889, Kupffer 1873, Leydig 1885, van Lidth de Jeude 1878, Lund 11, Morison 27, Pérez 10, Poisson 26, Portier 11, Prenant 00, 11, Thulin 08, Vieweger 12, von Wielowiejski 1889, Wigglesworth 29). All authors agree tracheoles can terminate between cells, and some could find only such terminations in their material (Bongardt 03, Bruntz 08, Buck 48, Köppen 21, Remy 25a, b, Weismann 1863, 64). Dreher (36) suggested that intracellular tracheoles are only to be found in tissues which show extensive cell fusion during development, but this cannot hold for some of the seemingly authentic cases (Wigglesworth 29). The present author can see no objection to the idea that processes containing tracheoles may penetrate cells and then lose their identity, leaving only the tracheolar intima recognizable. It would seem that the problem is similar to that involved in the intracellular ducts of unicellular glands, where the duct is thought to arise from one cell, the gland from another (p. 213).

TRACHEAL EPITHELIUM

The tracheal epithelium[9] is continuous with the general epidermis and similar to it in appearance. It is usually a flat epithelium (Keister 48, Lowne 1893–95, Minot 1876, Wahl 1899) but is thicker in some groups (e.g., Lepidoptera) and may even be columnar (honeybee, Dreher 36). Phenomena associated with molting parallel those in the epidermis, with mitoses occurring mostly near the spiracles (Lübben 07, Wolf 35). The tracheal epithelium, like the general epidermis, is negative to tests for alkaline phosphatase (Day 49b). A basement membrane is recognizable in some cases (Miall & Denny 1886, Pantel 1898) and is probably always present, though it is not always identifiable (Wolf 35). Several authors have reported that the cells do not cover the entire surface of the intima (Lowne 1893–95), but one would think that they must, at least while the intima is being deposited.

Most interest in the tracheal epithelium concerns whether or not the common cytoplasmic granules[10] (brown, red, violet, or colorless) take any part in the transfer of gases (H. J. A. Koch 36, Kolbe 1893, Martynow 01, Purser 15, Remy 25a, Riede 12, Wolf 35). Summarizing: in dragonfly larvae granules are said to give a positive benzidene-peroxide reaction (Wolf 35), which is commonly listed as a good test for hemoglobin, but certainly is not specific proof (Glick 48); these granules do show spectroscopic changes on chemical oxidation and reduction, but the spectra are different from those for the tetrapyrrole nucleus (H. J. A. Koch 36); cytoplasmic granules are commoner around small tubes, are most numerous in end cells, and in many insects oxidize indigo white to indigo blue (Remy 25a); and, as already has been mentioned (p. 264), granules in the tracheal end cells commonly reduce osmic acid strongly. Convincing evidence is lacking.[11]

[9] Sometimes referred to as ectotrachea, peritoneal membrane, matrice tracheene, cellular coat, or outer cell layer.

[10] The term spadacin was suggested by Purser (15).

[11] Since the above was written, Dr. M. F. Day has informed me (in correspondence) that such granules show the same histochemical reactions as similar appearing granules in other epidermal cells.

SPIRACLES

Tracheae open to the outside through spiracles (except for a few cases of closed systems). Modifications of these openings have extensive ecological and taxonomic importance; for details, see especially the reviews by Babák (12a), Hinton (47), and Keilin (44). The area around the aperture may be modified into a spiracular plate, which in some groups becomes elaborately differentiated, and in ticks is called the cribriform plate (Falke 31, Hassan 44, Keilin 44, Mellanby 35, Adolf Müller 24). In some cases there are many minute openings into a lobate spiracular chamber (Thorpe & Crisp 47). Within the spiracle there may be a special spiracular chamber which has no taenidia but may have some form of filtering apparatus. At the inner end of the spiracular chamber is located a valve-type closing apparatus (seldom lacking, and lacking only in species restricted to moist habitats). Typical tracheal structure begins inside the valve. Profitable consideration of the development of complex spiracles does not seem possible at present, although one could say cell movements, cellular projections, and sclerotization patterns are all involved.

Two points might be listed. First, in certain dipterous larvae and some other groups there is a spongy filtering apparatus within the spiracular chamber (Butt 37, Keilin 44, J. E. Webb 46); strong supporting bars may project into this mass (Fig. 43). In a recent study it was found that these rods and bars develop intracytoplasmically and then have the cytoplasm withdrawn from around them (Clausen & Richards unpubl.). Second, the development of an elaborate spiracular plate and filter chamber may introduce complications in molting. Keilin (44) recognizes three intergrading types: those in which the spiracle functions as the ecdysial opening and those in which a new spiracular plate is formed either around the old scar or adjacent to it (Fig. 53B).

CHAPTER 28

Sculpturing, Sensillae, and Miscellaneous Structures

A number of aspects of the integument remain. These are grouped together in the present chapter for rather cursory treatment. Surface sculpturing is commonly described in taxonomic papers, especially for groups routinely examined with a compound microscope (e.g., thrips), but little is known about it. Sense organs are truly a part of the integument but, except for their cuticles, are better left for treatments on sensory physiology. Other miscellaneous structures which are not truly integumentary (egg shells, spermatophores, ootheca, lac cells, peritrophic membrane) will be mentioned only insofar as they add to material given in the preceding chapters.

SURFACE SCULPTURING

Either macroscopic or microscopic sculpturing or both can be seen on the surface of most arthropods (Figs. 30F, 39, 57) (Ljungdahl 17). Most general is a microscopic hexagonal sculpturing, in some cases known to, in other cases thought to, represent the boundaries between the underlying epidermal cells (Attems 26, Dennell 47b, Fuhrmann 21, Kühnelt 28c, Silvestri 03, Zschorn 37). In Cladocera, where no sculpturing can be seen on the normal cuticle, lines probably representing intercellular boundaries can be developed by treatment with alkali (Guth 19, Morimoto 36).

One might suspect that surface sculpturing was produced by exposure of the surface to air or by contraction of the underlying layers. Perhaps this is true in some cases, but the puparium of higher Diptera contracts without producing noticeable sculpture, and in spiders it is reported that the surface sculpturing is visible before molting, in fact from the time of formation of the surface layer (Browning 42).

Minute tubercles other than microtrichia (see below) may be produced either by local thickenings in the epicuticle (Schulze 13b, 15, Woods 29) or by thickenings in the underlying procuticle (Richards

& Anderson 42b). The origin of such minute thickenings is not known, but they may be quite definite and be species specific. In larvae of various races of silkworms tubercles range from absent to as dense as one per 25 μ^2 (Kuwana 32). In tracheae, electron micrographs show that pimples (too small for resolution by a light microscope) may be due either to thickenings in the endocuticle or to presumed short cellular protuberances (Richards & Korda 48, 50).[1]

CUTICULAR PROJECTIONS

Cuticular sculpturing grades over into projections, some of which subserve highly specialized functions. Obviously, tuberculate patterns could be treated under either heading. As a basis for treatment five classes will be recognized:

A. Microthickenings of the cuticle
B. Projections formed around cellular filaments (microtrichia) Fig. 57G–I
C. Acellular projections of multicellular origin ("spines")
   1. Localized group of columnar cells (Fig. 57C–D
   2. Folds solidly cuticularized Fig. 57E–F
   3. Intracytoplasmic strands with cytoplasm withdrawn
D. Projections involving fixed evaginations of epidermis (spines) Fig. 57A
E. Projections with unicellular sockets (scales and sensillae) Fig. 57B

Microthickenings have already been treated. Little is known about them other than that different sublayers of the cuticle may be involved. Probably these grade over into the next group (microtrichia), and it seems even more likely that the groups B through D intergrade. Clearly, combinations occur in that spines may bear both microtrichia and sensillae (Alt 12, Ulrich 24).

Microtrichia are usually defined as acellular projections from the surface of the cuticle (Fig. 57). It is difficult to imagine their formation as mere protuberances of cuticular material. Selecting examples from diverse arthropods, there are numerous cases in which cellular processes can be seen projecting into the base of microtrichia or even extending to the tip (Fig. 57G) (Alt 12, Schäffer 1889, Silvestri 03); these grade over to cases where no cytoplasmic filament can be seen with a light microscope but the microtrichia appear to be continua-

[1] Kühnelt (28c) distinguishes between "idiocuticular" structures, involving only what we now call the epicuticle, and "epicuticular" structures, which involve lower sublayers. This terminology cannot be used now, but a corresponding one using current terms can be substituted readily if occasion arises.

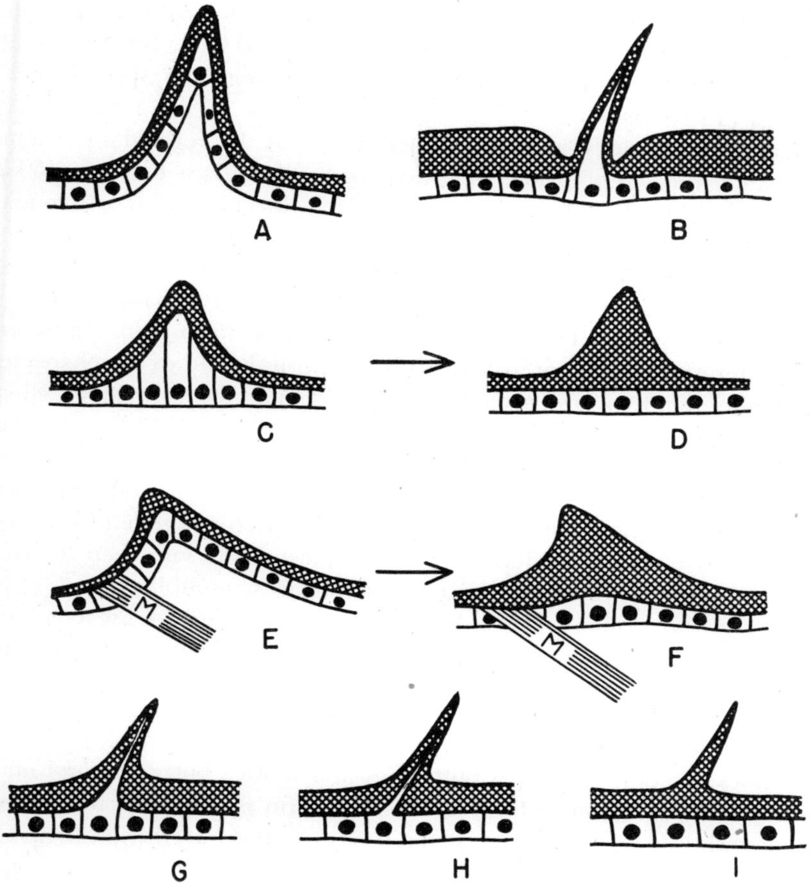

Figure 57. Diagrammatic representation of various types of cuticular protuberances. For description see text.

tions of visible pore canals in the cuticle (Fig. 57H) (G. W. Müller 27) and by electron microscopy may be shown to have a core of material readily soluble in weak alkali solutions (Richards & Korda 47); thence to cases which by electron microscopy are shown to be solid or to have only an indentation at the base (Fig. 57I) (Driesch & Müller 35, Richards & Korda 50), or by ultraviolet microscopy to have "roots" going through the epicuticle (Thorpe & Crisp 47). It seems most reasonable to assume that microtrichia are always formed around cellular processes (sometimes around pore canal filaments) but may sometimes become solidly cuticularized.

In most cases microtrichia appear as simple tapering projections even in electron micrographs (Richards & Korda 50), but they may show a helical twist (Richards & Korda 47) or regularly spaced thickenings (Richards 44b).

Larger, eventually acellular projections, may be formed in several ways. On the jumping legs of grasshoppers there is a tubercle 150 μ high and 120 μ broad on the femur, which develops from an elongation of underlying epidermal cells, and the protuberance subsequently becomes filled with cuticular material (Fig. 57C–D) (Slifer & Uvarov 38). Somewhat similar-appearing structures have been described in a wasp (Tiegs 22) and the millipede *Pachyiulus* (Silvestri 03). More commonly, or at least to be found in larvae of many species of higher Diptera, are projections that seem to be formed by muscular contractions and then to be made solid (Fig. 57E–F) (Lowne 1893–95, Pantel 1898, Richards & Fan 49, Thompson 29). These have been aptly described as "fixed distortions." Recently, solid branched projections in the spiracular chamber of a dipterous larva (*Phormia*) have been found to be formed intracytoplasmically and then to have the cytoplasm withdrawn (Clausen & Richards unpubl.).

Multicellular spines of the type shown in Figure 57A are common (Efflatoun 27), and may occur either with or without a membranous ring permitting movement at the base.

SCALES

Scales are best known in butterflies and moths, but are found on a scattering of other insects (Fig. 58); the term is also used in connection with similar-appearing structures in certain terrestrial Isopoda (Verhoeff 01a, 16). Presumably scales evolved from tactile setae, and indeed innervated scales (sensilla squamiformia), are said to occur in all groups of Lepidoptera (Vogel 11). In most cases there is no demonstrable innervation, and the scales seem to serve other functions. Scale development and structure have been studied intensively in the Lepidoptera, especially by Kühn and his students working on the phenomena of developmental physiology.

Scales develop from epidermal cells which undergo two divisions (Köhler 32, Stossberg 38). The first division gives rise to a scale mother cell and a rudimentary cell which degenerates; the subsequent division of the scale mother cell gives rise to a scale-forming cell (trichogen) and a socket-forming cell (tormogen). The scale-forming cell becomes quite large, vacuolated, and with an unusually large nucleus. A process grows out, expands and flattens, differentiates

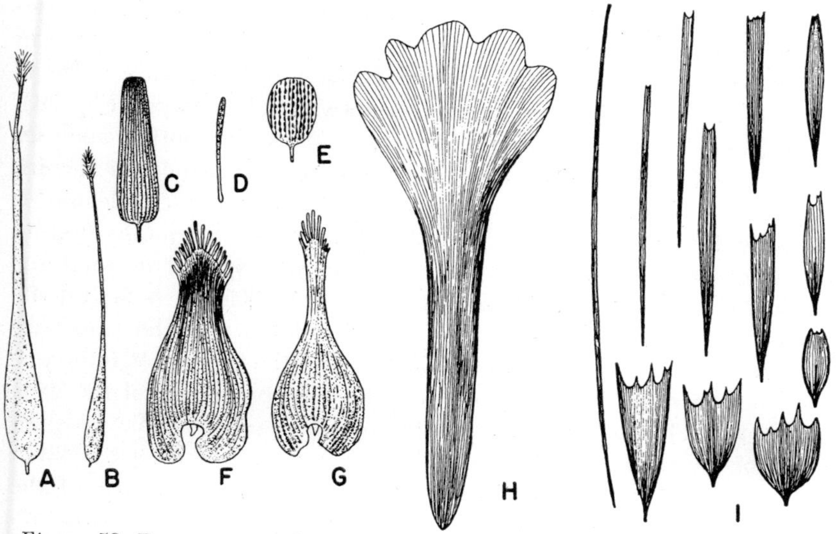

Figure 58. Representative butterfly and moth scales. (Redrawn by Miss Anna Stryke, mostly after Scudder.)
A. *Oeneis jutta*
B. *Megisto eurytus*
C. *Strymon titus*
D. *Danaus plexippus*
E. *Plebeius scudderii*
F. *Pieris oleracea*
G. *Pieris rapae*
H. *Atalopedes campestris*
I. A lasiocampid moth

with secretion of the architecturally amazing scale, and then the cell retracts and usually degenerates. Commonly there are two layers of scales, with the underlying ones of different appearance from the covering scales. In a single species it seems that gross shape, fine structure, and color are all correlated (Caspari 41, Kühn 41).

Attempts to analyze the development of scales in chemical terms (Braun 39, Häuslmayer 37, Picken 49, Reichelt 25) have not been impressive, but it can be recorded that when first formed the scales are completely soluble in alkali and that they may remain so (*Morpho, Erasmia,* etc.), but in most cases have chitin added (Richards 47b). It could be said, if one wishes, that some scales have only an epicuticle, others both epicuticle and endocuticle. This would presumably be contested by Picken (49), who having failed to demonstrate the presence of chitin in young scales of *Ephestia* by either chemical tests or birefringence, none the less manages to conclude (it seems quite gratuitously) that the young scale is composed of chitin-protein and that the chitin content increases in later development (when chitin does indeed become demonstrable).

The structure of the fully formed scale ranges from a rather simple one to one of extreme complexity. A relatively simple basal membrane, with some thickenings and holes, forms what was one side of the flattened scale and is connected by supporting pillars with an upper, incomplete membrane which bears vanes in groups (Fig. 59). It has been shown by electron microscopy and parallel optical analyses that thickenings in these vanes form the reflecting planes for the iridescent colors of the scales of *Morpho* butterflies (Anderson & Richards 42b). Similar vanes in other butterflies and moths and in mosquitoes may act similarly or be too closely spaced to reinforce visible light (L. Emmel & Jakob 48, Gentil 42, Kinder & Süffert 43, Kühn 46, Kühn & An 46). It has been postulated that the vanes are produced by elevation of the vane areas, with the pulling of intervane membrane over to become incorporated as the basal part of the vane (Kühn 46). This hypothesis seems to encounter serious difficulties because the vanes may be multiple leaflets (Anderson & Richards 42b); also, while comparable spacings may be found in other parts of the scale, this type of architecture is found only in the vanes. More recently it has been shown that the vanes can increase in spacing and have new ones intercalated during development (Picken 49); this could be compared with the phenomena seen in development of laminae in the procuticle (p. 175).

Recently Picken (49) has used birefringence to analyze scale development in the moth *Ephestia*. He finds the scales to be birefringent from the earliest recognizable stages, and accordingly (like setae, *q.v.*) to be formed as fibrillar aggregates which during growth increase in volume more rapidly than in length or surface area. The structural variations seen in different scale types are all compatible with the properties of fibrillar aggregates, and can be viewed as resulting from the orderly displacement of a fibrillar organization laid down in the scale rudiment.

The production of physical colors by scales has already been mentioned (p. 196).

The most minute anatomy ever recorded for any arthropod structure is the crossed-fiber pattern shown by electron microscopy in the vanes on scales of *Morpho* butterflies (Anderson & Richards 42b). Here, a clothlike mesh of fibers 60 Å broad and 200 Å apart was discovered (the scales shrank by approximately 20% during electron bombardment; it is not known whether the mesh shrank similarly or even uniformly). This is smaller than the spacings in collagen chains and, directly or indirectly, is almost certainly related to the molecular architecture of the vane.

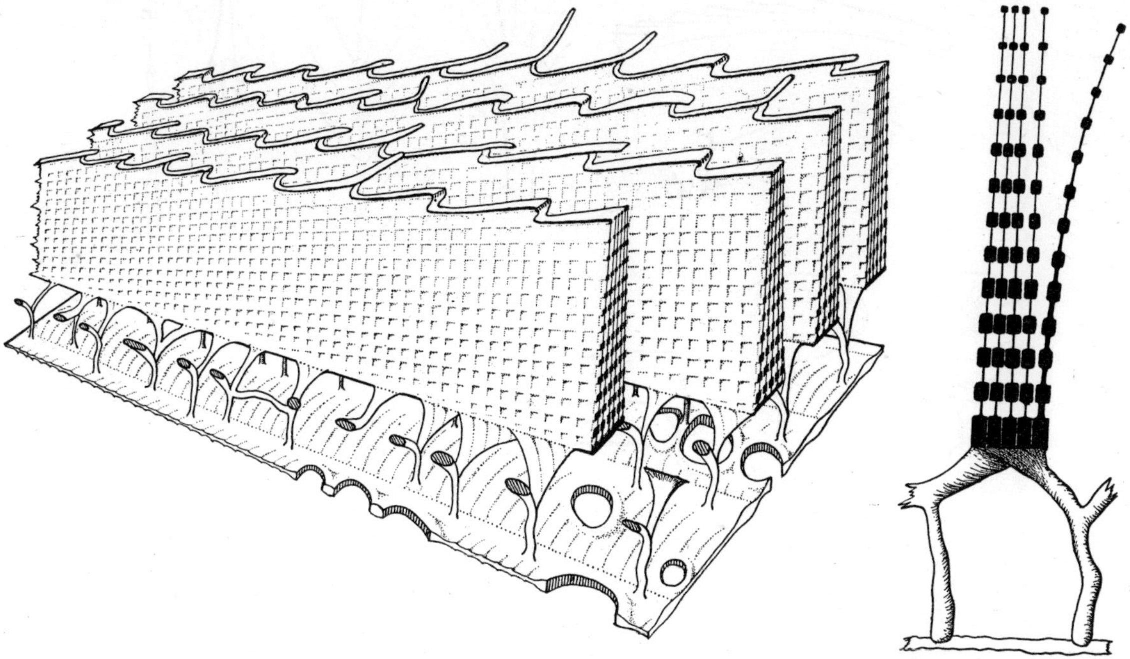

Figure 59. A schematic and idealized reconstruction of a small portion of an iridescent scale from a butterfly, *Morpho cypris*, based on electron micrographs. On the right is a diagrammatic drawing of a cross section of one rib with its vanes and supports; one vane is drawn as cut through a vertical mullion. (After Anderson and Richards.)

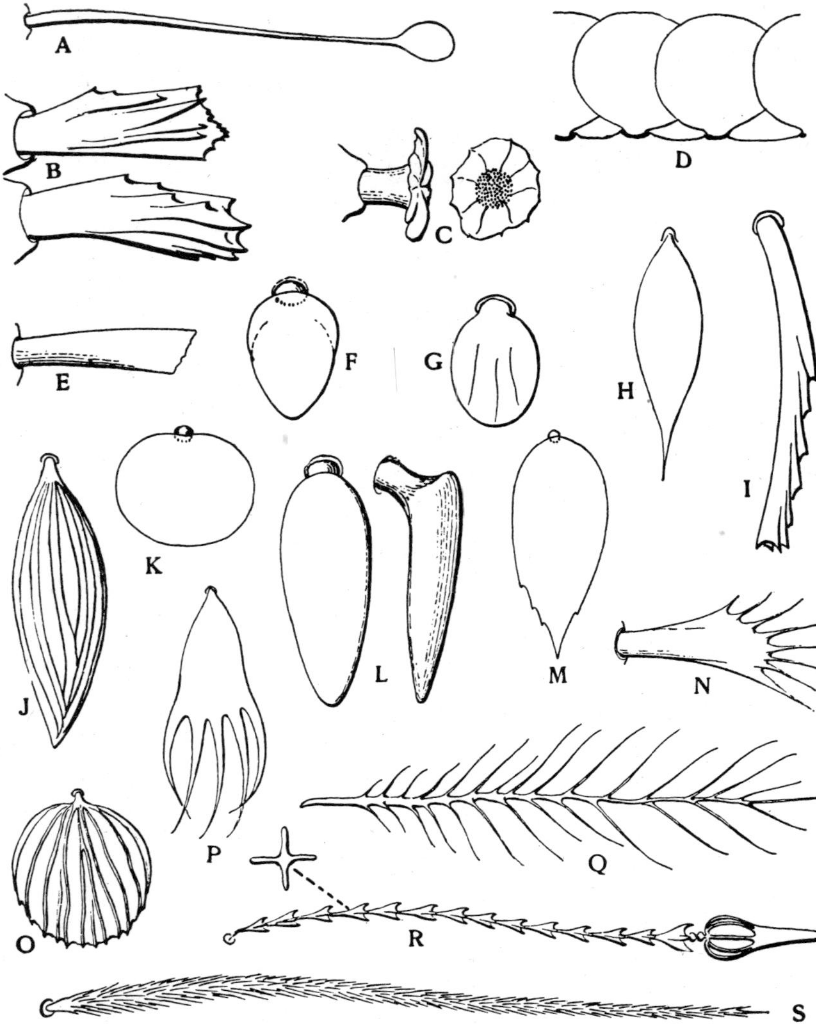

Figure 60. Some unusual types of modified setae. (After Ferris.)
A. Spatulate seta from Psyllia nymph.
B–C. Two types of setae from larva of a beetle, *Brachypsectra.*
D. Fanlike seta from a scale insect, *Paralecanium luzonicum.*
E. Blunt seta from a louse, *Hoplopleura disgrega.*
F. Flattened seta from a walrus louse, *Antarctophthirus trichechi.*
G. Flattened seta from an elephant louse, *Haematomyzus elephantis.*
H. Flattened and pointed seta from a louse, *Ctenophthirus cercomydis.*
I. Serrate seta from a bedbug, *Cimex lectularius.*
J. Flattened, ribbed seta from a beetle, *Alaus.*
K. Another fanlike seta from a louse, *Antarctophthirus trichechi.*
L. Stalked, flattened seta from the same louse.

Scales may become modified for other purposes. A considerable literature treats scent scales (which are commonly found on only the male). The scale-forming cell may either remain alive as a secreting gland cell, or a certain amount of secretion may be stored up and the cell degenerate (Barth 49, Dixey 32, Eltringham 33, Illig 03, Stobbe 12). Many types have been described, particularly by Eltringham.

SENSILLAE

Treatment of sensillae will be restricted to those few papers which give data on the cuticle over sensillae. Numerous reviews of the extensive literature are available: Demoll (17), Deegener (28), Eltringham (33), Silvestri (03), Snodgrass (26, 35), H. Weber (33), and the various chapters in Bronn (1866–1948) and in Kukenthal and Krumbach (26–30). The little information available on the integumentary nervous system is reviewed by Tonner (36).

The sensillae have been classified on the basis of gross appearance into trichoid (Figs. 1, 57B), campaniform, and placoid types (Snodgrass 26). The trichoid type has numerous subheadings for hairlike, scalelike, peglike, and sunken types. These are the forms most used for taxonomic work and illustrated in many taxonomic papers. Relatively simple forms predominate, but some are indeed both weird and wonderful. A range of insectan types has been brought together by Ferris (34), some of whose drawings are reproduced as Figure 60. Other strange types occur: long spatulate setae with unilateral projecting leaflets (Richards 38); multicellular setae with a flexible basal region in crustacean statocysts (Kinzig 18); plumose and serrated types (Laubmann 12); setae with swollen bases and helical thickenings on centipede maxillae (Richards & Korda 47); etc. More recent treatment of setae and other sensillae in arachnids is given by Gossel (35) and in crustacea by Gicklhorn and Keller (26), Haller (1880), and Rome (47), but even the better cytological papers (Hsü 38, Sihler 24) show little of interest on cuticle structure other than gross shape. In general sensillae are formed by two cells: a sensilla-forming cell (trichogen, Graber 1877) and a socket-forming cell (tormogen, Lees & Waddington 42, Schwenk 47, Wigglesworth 33), to which one or sometimes more sensory nerve cells are added. "Split"

M. Scalelike seta from a fur seal louse, *Antarctophthirus callorhini*.
N. Fimbriate seta from a scale insect, *Coccus caudatus*.
O–P. Other scalelike setae from a beetle, *Alaus*.
Q. Plumose seta from a bee of the genus *Xylocopa*.
R. The amazing "pendicle seta" from larva of dermestid beetles.
S. "Rat tail" seta from larva of dermestid beetles.

bristles in *Drosophila* are produced by an extra mitosis which results in a group of four cells, either one or two of which may develop into trichogens (Lees & Waddington 42).

The cuticle of trichoid setae consists of both epicuticle and endocuticle, as can be shown by the fact that the setae are recognizable on both epicuticles isolated with acid and endocuticles isolated with alkali. The micelles usually extend longitudinally in relation to the setal axis (Castle 36, Lees & Picken 45) but may extend in a helical path for part or all of the length (Anderson & Richards 42a, Dethier 41, Richards & Korda 47). The one significant study is that by Lees and Picken (45). Using various genetic strains of *Drosophila melanogaster,* they analyzed size, growth rates (may increase 1000 times in volume), birefringence, and strength. They showed that the longitudinal micelles are aggregated into ridges where the orientation is more nearly perfect, that there is a definite periodicity but that the ridges once formed can increase in size, that the interridge material is less well oriented, that the cuticle shows strong three-dimensional bonding after sclerotization but that on removal of other components the chitin chains separate readily, showing strong bonds only in the long axis, and that dilatations during development show distinct plastic flow with no tendency to return to normal (no noticeable elasticity). To the general entomologist it may be more interesting that Lees and Picken also record that the setae grow only at the tips, that there is a distinct correlation between shape, birefringence, and strength (the more bristle-like the stronger), that the bristle can be viewed as a hollow cylinder blown in a plastic medium by pressure of the cell process which, due to early formation of the basal wall, can extend most readily in length, and that normal bristles result only when size increase and synthesis of cuticular material are balanced.

Of general ecological interest is the fact that areas with hydrophobic setae can act as air reservoirs for aquatic, air-breathing insects (Crisp & Thorpe 48, C. Davis 42, Harpster 41, 44, Maloeuf 36, Thorpe & Crisp 47, 49).

Setae may also become modified as urticating structures. An enlarged gland cell discharges an urticating substance (in the Brown Tail Moth said to be thermolabile) into dehiscent spicules or into a seta with an open tip (Gilmer 25, Kephart 14, Klatt 08, Tyzzer 07).[2]

Virtually nothing is known about the cuticles over other forms of

[2] The effect of urticating hairs on human skin has recently been reinvestigated by Hill, Rubenstein, and Kovacs (1948, Jour. Amer. Med. Assoc., 138:737–40) and by Steele and Sawyer (1944 Jour. Maine Mel. Assoc., 35:157).

sensillae. While relatively gross holes (about 1 μ diameter) have been found in the cuticle of lepidopterous scales after the trichogen has been withdrawn or degenerated (Anderson & Richards 42b, Kühn & An 46), there is no evidence that such holes are ever found over living cells. In the author's laboratory a number of types of sensillae have been examined by electron microscopy without finding such holes except in scales (Richards unpubl.). It is commonly assumed that chemoreceptors must have thin cuticles; perhaps this is true, but at present it is only a reasonable assumption because of the great difficulty of identifying the functions of specific receptors (Dethier & Chadwick 48). Data are needed on the question of whether the cuticles over chemoreceptors differ from the general body cuticle in any important respects other than thickness.

Some sense organs which are invaginated have a cuticular covering over the entire invagination (sensilla ampullacea), but the chordotonal organs (scoloparia) are invaginated (and may form another attachment, similar to that of a muscle, at the invaginated end) and have the cuticle closed off over them (Debaisieux 38, Slifer 35, 36).

MISCELLANEOUS SIMILAR-APPEARING MEMBRANES

The following structures are not integumentary, at least not in the same sense as the general exoskeleton. They do show some similarities, and will be treated briefly (and incompletely) for points which bear on the subject matter of preceding chapters.

The peritrophic membranes. The fore-gut and hind-gut are ectodermal and lined with a cuticle continuous with and strictly homologous to that on the outer surface of arthropods (Wigglesworth 30b). The mid-gut (stomach) lacks a comparable cuticle. Sometimes its cells are directly exposed to the gut contents, but commonly in insects and at least in some other arthropods (e.g., *Daphnia,* Chatton 20), the mid-gut cells are separated from the food bolus by one or more thin membranes (Aubertot 38, von Dehn 33, Wigglesworth 30b). Two general types occur, separately or in the same species: a thin tube secreted by a ring of cells at the anterior end of the mid-gut and extending backwards (Diptera, Dermaptera), and strands or partial or complete sheets delaminated from the surface of the mid-gut cells (most other insect orders). The honeybee is the most commonly cited example of a species having both (Kusmenko 40), and sections show the outermost layer following every detail of the cell surfaces (Hering 39, Whitcomb & Wilson 29).

Much of the literature deals with embryonic origin (whether from ectoderm or endoderm) (Butt 34, Chatton 20, von Dehn 33, 36, Henson 31, Hering 39, Platania 38), but that involved question is beyond the scope of the present treatment. Only two points concerned with embryology are of interest here, namely, that since chitinous membranes can be delaminated from the mid-gut, the power of producing chitin is not (as some assume) limited to ectodermal derivatives (Brug 32, A. C. Davis 27, Henson 31, Wigglesworth 39), and it is reported that the formation of the peritrophic membrane of honeybees is different at different stages of development (Hering 39).

The peritrophic membranes contain chitin, and in fact give an intense chitosan reaction readily (von Dehn 36, Wigglesworth 29, 30b) although they may be dispersed if passed directly from concentrated alkali solutions to the surface of water. They are resistant to trypsin (Wigglesworth 29) and pepsin (Richards & Korda 48), have a fluorescence similar to that of cuticle (Salfi 37), are birefringent (Hövener 30), stain blue with Ehrlich's haematoxylin (Wigglesworth 29), and presumably contain protein also, since while positive protein tests might be due to adhering contaminants (Wigglesworth 29), treatments that would remove protein result in changes visible with an electron microscope (Richards & Korda 48). Incidentally, chitosan can be recovered from grasshopper feces, where it was presumed to come from the peritrophic membrane (A. W. A. Brown 37).

When an "annular mold" is present (Diptera, Dermaptera), the peritrophic membrane has been viewed by some authors as resulting from the molded solidification of a fluid secretion (Wigglesworth 30b), but this has been contested by others (von Dehn 33), who feel it is always delaminated from the surface of the epithelial cells, either locally or throughout the mid-gut. Be that as it may, the secretion is both continuous and rapid because the tube may be elongated with sufficient speed to form a membrane around the feces. In unfed larvae of the fly *Eristalis* a rate of 6 mm. per hour has been recorded (Aubertot 32a), and in bees and wasps as many as half a dozen membranes may be delaminated from the surface of the mid-gut cells per day (Rengel 03); in dragonfly larvae two (Aubertot 32b).

Despite the similarities between peritrophic membranes and cuticle, there are important differences, an understanding of which might aid materially in interpreting the cuticle. The peritrophic membrane is highly permeable, permitting even large protein molecules to penetrate readily[3] (de Boissezon 30a, b, Castelnuovo 34, von Dehn 33,

[3] Tests where acids and alkalis were used should be discarded; see p. 294 (Richards & Korda 48).

Montalenti 31a, b, Wigglesworth 29). In Diptera, the peritrophic membrane gives a stronger chitosan test than does the lining of the fore-gut (Wigglesworth 29); in sections viewed with a light microscope it appears very thin, yet in an electron microscope it is almost too dense for penetration (denser than the wing of a mosquito, and denser than the cuticle of mosquito larvae which has readily measurable thickness); and, finally, after extraction with either alkali or pepsin it gives a pattern in the electron microscope that, while not understood, is nevertheless different from that given by any of the various types of cuticles examined (Richards & Korda 48). Existing data do not explain the structure of the peritrophic membrane, but they do suggest that the structure is unlike that of any known cuticle.

Oothecae. It has been known for a long time that the ootheca of the cockroach is formed from the secretion of two different accessory glands associated with the female reproductive tract (Bordas 08a). This situation was used by Pryor (40a) to develop the chemical picture of sclerotization that has since been generally accepted as representing the chemical processes occurring in the cuticle (p. 188). One gland secretes a water-soluble protein which hardens around the egg mass; the other secretes an o-dihydroxyphenol which, after being oxidized to the corresponding quinone, tans the protein. Primary cross linkages are formed to give a substance Pryor terms sclerotin, which is more stable than keratin and does *not* have parallel molecular chains (shown by isotropy and by giving an X-ray powder pattern). It gives reactions closely comparable to those given by the inner or protein epicuticle after tanning. Here, then, is a noncuticular substance which is closely similar to a portion of the cuticle. No chitin is involved (Campbell 29).

Numerous other insects deposit groups of eggs inside protective coverings, e.g., phasmids, but the nature of these different-appearing coverings remains to be determined. As already mentioned (p. 214), the secretion of tegumental glands may hold some crustacean eggs together and to the pleopods.

Egg shells. The insect egg shell, or chorion, is secreted by the follicular epithelium of the ovary, and it seems advisable to follow Beament in restricting the term chorion to those shells or shell components which are so produced (46b). As such, the chorion can be said to lack chitin (or at least be negative for chitin tests; Table 2, p. 50) and be rich in protein (Table 4). Commonly the chorion is referred to as composed of "chorionin"; Beament restricts this term to the lipoproteins forming the outer portion of the egg shell. Waxes are present on the shell (Christophers 45, Ongaro 33, p. 94) but appear to be added to the chorion either by the ovum (Beament 46a) or by a special waxing organ (Lees & Beament 48). Accordingly the wax may be on either the inner (insect) or the outer (tick) surface.

In some cases the chorion appears homogeneous in cross section (Johannsen & Butt 41), but in most cases two general subdivisions, called exochorion and endochorion, can be recognized. The exochorion may be much thicker than the endochorion (*Pteronarcys*, Miller 39, or it may be much thinner (*Melanoplus*, Slifer & King 34), or both may be thick (*Rhodnius*, Beament 46b). In a louse, *Pediculus*, outer and inner birefringent layers are separated by a middle layer that is isotropic (W. J. Schmidt 39a). Surface sculpturing is common, may show good taxonomic characters (Klein-Krautheim 36), and may be partly produced by a molding effect of the secreting cells.

In *Rhodnius, Melanoplus*, and, probably, insects in general a very thin layer of wax lies immediately under the chorion (and one can recognize primary and secondary layers based on time of secretion). In the remarkable eggs of phasmids a thick layer of calcareous crystals and sphaerites lies under the chorion (p. 107). In grasshoppers the embryonic serosa secretes a cuticle underlying the egg shell (see below). And in decapod crustacea and ticks there is no chorion, as that term is used here; according to Yonge (35, 38b) the egg of various decapods leaves the ovary without any shell, gets a chitinous shell while in the oviduct (he thinks secreted by the epithelium of the oviduct), and then gets a covering over the outer surface from secretion of tegumental glands at the time of egg laying; according to Burkenroad (47) the eggs of the shrimp *Palaemonetes* are laid without any shell and then develop four membranes in the next day or two (two before and two after fertilization); according to Lees & Beament (48) the egg shell of ticks is secreted by the oocyte and then waxed by secretion from the organ of Géné (with in some cases contributions from the vaginal wall). Obviously, then, egg shells are less consistent than cuticle in arthropods, and, as will be seen from the following more detailed accounts, differ greatly in different insects.

In the bug *Rhodnius*, Beament has recorded seven layers taking part in the formation of the chorion (46a, b, 47, 48a, b). In order of secretion, and hence from inside to outside of the shell, these are: (1) a discontinuous inner polyphenol layer of large granules, (2) a 1–2 μ layer of tanned protein, (3) a discontinuous outer polyphenol layer of small granules, (4) a very thin amber layer of tanned protein impregnated with lipid, (5) an 8 μ layer of soft protein containing polyphenol and tyrosine,[4] (6) an 8 μ layer of soft lipoprotein, and (7) the sculptured surface layer of more resistant lipoprotein. The first five constitute the endochorion, the last two the exochorion. Of interest is the fact that large and small pore canals extend from processes of the follicular cells through the exochorion; also the stainability of the follicular cells is correlated with the component being secreted at that time. The shell is highly impermeable to chemicals other than corrosive agents such as formic acid, but the water impermeability is conferred by the wax layer secreted by the ovum inside the chorion. An elaborate micropylar complex is present but becomes occluded by wax, "cement," air, and water plugs.

In the grasshoppers *Melanoplus* and *Locustana*, Slifer and others have shown that the chorion has recognizable proteinaceous exochorion and endochorion subdivisions (Jahn 35b, Slifer 37), with the endochorion having the outer and inner borders darker. There is also a temporary mucilaginous coat over the outer surface when the egg is first laid. This chorion is soluble in solutions of NaOCl ("*Chlorox*") (Slifer 45), has a thin wax layer on its inner surface (Slifer 48, 49a),[5] and has a low isoelectric point (exochorion pH 2.2, endochorion pH 3.7, Jahn 35a, b). After the extraembryonic membranes are formed, the serosa secretes a seemingly typical cuticle on its surface and immediately under the chorion; effectively this increases the protection afforded by the egg shell (Cole & Jahn 37, Jahn 35a) as well as giving a shell composed of chorion underlain by wax, which is underlain by a chitin-protein cuticle.[6] The serosal cuticle consists of a thin, papillated, outer "yellow cuticle" which lacks chitin (= epicuticle) and a thick, inner, laminated "white cuticle" which contains chitin and is fibrous (= procuticle) (Jahn 35b, Matthée 48, Schutts 49, Slifer 37). The epicuticle has been called a "cuticulin layer" (Cole & Jahn 37, Jahn 36). This cuticle is penetrated by fine pore canals (Matthée 48), which may perhaps be helical (Slifer 49a). At the special water ab-

[4] Perhaps the copper found in *Lucilia* egg shells is involved in tyrosinase (Waterhouse 45).

[5] This wax is soluble in xylol, toluol, CCl_4, $CHCl_3$, and partly soluble in benzene. It is insoluble in alcohol, ether, and acetone.

[6] It is interesting that none of the animals reported to have chitin in their egg shells obtain this in the ovary. In nematodes the egg receives a proteinaceous shell in the ovary, the ovum secretes a chitinous shell within this, prior to the maturation divisions, and another proteinaceous shell inside this, subsequent to the maturation divisions (Wottge 37). In crustacea the reported chitinous shells are also secreted after the ovum leaves the ovary, but the origin of the chitin is uncertain (Yonge 35, 38b).

sorbing area (hydropile)[7] the epicuticle becomes much thicker and the pore canals become more numerous; this area is rendered water-impermeable during diapause by a secondary layer of wax (Slifer 49a). And finally, special embryonic organs called pleuropodia secrete a fluid which digests this procuticle shortly before hatching (Slifer 37).

Miscellaneous structures. Various other miscellaneous solid structures are produced by arthropods. Mention might be made of spermatophores, the envelopes secreted by accessory glands of the male reproductive system and enveloping a packet of sperm (Blunck 12c, Gerhardt 13, 14, Khalifa 49a, b). These can be classified into a number of different-appearing types (G. Gilson 1887), which may show constant differences even between rather closely related species (Petersen 07), and are completely formed by the male, since typical ones can be obtained without copulation (Weidner 34). The most elaborate and perhaps best known are those of crickets (Regen 24). In insects spermatophores are inserted into or partly into the female reproductive tract, but in crustacea they are sticky and simply applied to the appropriate region of the female (Andrews 11, 31, Burkenroad 47). Like the chorion of egg shells, spermatophores are moderately resistant to alkali solutions, but hot concentrated solutions completely disperse them.

Various Homoptera produce waxy cases in which they live. Many of these are specific; for instance, the lac insect produces an elaborate structure (Mahdihassan 38) from which both wax (p. 95) and shellac (Sen 37) can be obtained.

[7] Absorption of water also occurs in species of Hemiptera, Coleoptera, and Hymenoptera (Kerenski 30, C. G. Johnson 37).

Section III

THE PERMEABILITY OF THE CUTICLE

CHAPTER 29

General Remarks on the Permeability of the Cuticle

The field of membrane permeability is intricate. Discussions of it are, of necessity, filled with assumptions and speculative thinking. It is easy enough to read a few treatises and then become eloquent with the language of physical chemistry, but the small amount of unequivocable data on the permeability of arthropod cuticle makes this undesirable. In this section an attempt will be made only to document the statement that it is extremely difficult to obtain valid permeability data and to make profitable deductions therefrom, to state what seem to be the major particular properties that need to be taken into account, and to outline rather briefly the available data, with emphasis on their limitations.

The difficulties encountered in formulating a general definition of the term membrane need not concern us, since we are dealing with a specific case, the diversity and heterogeneity of which has been given in preceding chapters. We do need to distinguish, however, between penetration and permeability. Penetration is the actual passage of material through a barrier membrane. Permeability is a statement of the amount of penetration that would be expected under a stated set of conditions. With a homogeneous membrane the penetration is directly proportional to surface area and to partial pressure differences on the two sides of the membrane; it is inversely proportional to the thickness of the membrane, and dependent on the nature of the membrane and of the substance penetrating. For comparative purposes, with different membranes or different substances it is necessary to have comparable statements. This necessitates a statement of the amount penetrating in unit time over unit area under a unit difference in concentration; one of the common convenient expressions is the amount in moles / sq. cm. / second or minute / mole difference in concentration. Two different concepts are involved: the property of permeability, which is a characteristic of the membrane, and the driving force (usually concentration), which may be independent of the membrane. Most of the data from arthropod cuticles show only penetration under some large but more or less unknown driving force, a minority give relative values which appear to be due to the membrane rather than to the driving force, but only a very few papers present valid data for quantitative permeability values. Even these last are capable of receiving only limited interpretation in biophysical terms because of the heterogeneity of the system.

GENERAL MEMBRANE PROPERTIES

Every entomologist should read one or two of the general treatments on membrane permeability, partly to realize the complexity of the phenomena involved but even more to truly realize the difficulties of interpretation. The short reviews by Höber (36) and Teorell (49) are very readable and good. The larger reviews by Davson and Danielli (43) and by Brooks and Moldenhauer-Brooks (41) are probably known to most entomologists by title; a number of others are available. Repeated attempts have been made to deduce the structure and properties of the plasma membrane of cells from permeability data —and some advance has been made in this direction. From the well-known early theories explaining permeability in terms of partition coefficients (lipid solubility) and molecular sieve structure, hypotheses progressed through the mosaic and combination theories to the so-called paucimolecular theory, which states that the plasma membrane is a lipid layer with adsorbed monomolecular protein layers at each water interface and minor nonhomogeneities. Still inadequately accounted for is the high rate of water penetration, the penetration of certain ions, and the penetration of very large molecules. Actually, deducing structure from permeability data is a highly indirect procedure, and while it has been moderately successful with homogeneous membranes such as collodion, it is much more difficult with heterogeneous membranes. I have heard deducing membrane structure from permeability data compared to deducing the structure and properties of the Hudson River from measurement of the rate of traffic flow into New York City without even direct information as to what fraction went over the river, what fraction on the river, and what fraction in tubes under the river. The analogy is far-fetched, and certainly not to be taken seriously, but it does serve to illustrate the point that structural deductions from permeability data are indeed indirect.

The structure of monomolecular films or monolayers presents several points of interest (Mitchell 39). The evaporation of water through monomolecular films is greatly retarded only when the molecules are very tightly packed and only when the molecules contain few or no hydrophilic groups (Sebba & Briscoe 40). For instance, no resistance is offered by films of cholesterol or oleic acid, but the resistance given by a single molecular layer of stearic acid, cetyl alcohol, or n-docosanol may exceed the resistance given by a film of indicator oil 100 molecules thick. In general there is a relation to chain length, longer molecules giving greater resistance, but there appears to be no relation to whether the film is "solid" or "liquid." Most of the work with monolayers deals with highly purified chemicals, which certainly would not be found in natural membranes, and accordingly it is interesting to see that small traces of impurities may have great effects. For instance, one part of cholesterol in 1800 parts of a C_{23} acid is said to reduce the resistance to evaporation by 40% (Langmuir & Schaefer 43). In thin films (Bangham 46), and also with cuticular waxes (Beament 48b), molecules may be rather well oriented, yet more than a single layer thick.

Various natural and artificial membranes are known to imbibe certain solvents and so swell (Katz 33, Vonk 31). The swelling may be both inter- and intramicellar (Carr & Sollner 43), and it is postulated that this swelling accounts for the anomolous permeability shown by swollen membranes (Höber 36). Conversely, when a membrane becomes fairly dry, it may shrink to such an extent that it becomes virtually impermeable (G. King 44). In purified chitin, X-ray diffraction analyses show that the swelling is intermicellar (Katz & Mark 24), but the situation in normal cuticle remains to be determined. The reasonable assumption that shrinking lowers penetration has already been used to explain the decreasing rate of evaporation from certain insects in a dry atmosphere (Wigglesworth 45). Conclusive demonstration of the possibility of cuticle's shrinking so much that it becomes virtually impermeable to even small molecules is shown by the unnatural situation of a thick section of cockroach cuticle evolving gas under the influence of intense electron bombardment and becoming a mass of bubbles (Richards & Anderson 42a).

Surface active agents do not penetrate membranes more rapidly than other molecules of the same size (Höber 36), but adsorbed molecules are capable of surface migration (Volmer 32), and, if proper surfaces are available through the membrane, could readily be visualized as facilitating transport. However, the role of adsorption in permeability is not clear.

The electrical properties of membranes can be measured with relatively great precision, but interpretation is difficult and the data are often ambiguous (Carr & Sollner 43, Kurt Meyer & Bernfeld 46, Teorell 49). For natural membranes the complications introduced by the presence of impurities (Sollner *et al.* 41) and heterogeneity are particularly serious. The relative values obtained by complex impedance seem less likely subject to technical difficulties and so definitely to have biological significance (Cole & Jahn 37). The author is not prepared to discuss the electrical properties of membranes, but anyone can observe that such work should be done by or in collaboration with a competent physical chemist and that even the physical chemists are not in agreement on the interpretation of complex effects.

The rate of uptake or penetration of common ions is generally in a definite order. Thus, for salts with a common anion the penetration of cations is in the order $K > Na > Ca > Mg > Sr > Li$. For salts with a common cation, the sequence is $NO_3 > Cl > HCO_3 > HPO_4 > SO_4$. Accordingly, if it is desired to facilitate the penetration of an ionized organic acid into cells, it should be applied as the potassium salt. Correspondingly, an ionized base should be applied as the nitrate. A large literature deals with the question of whether electrolytes penetrate in the ionized or molecular form, but the problem is not readily settled (Burtt 45, Hoskins 32, Ricks & Hoskins 48). Related to this problem is the question of Donnan equilibria, that is, the unequal distribution of ions on two sides of a membrane due to the presence of a nonpenetrating ion (Davson & Danielli 43). This may be expected from cuticular membranes also, but seems not yet to have been studied. Similar unequal distribution can occur with nonelectrolytes (Deasy 46).

And, finally, two old ideas in the membrane permeability field have recently been used in connection with penetration of arthropod cuticle. The older of these is the partition coefficient or lipid solubility hypothesis proposed by Overton at the end of the nineteenth century. This hypothesis states that the ease of entry of substances into a cell is a function of their solubility in lipids. Water is an outstanding exception. The phenomenon will be treated subsequently (p. 315). The second of these hypotheses is the mosaic membrane theory first advanced by Nathansohn in 1904 as a diagrammatic method for circumventing the difficulties with lipid and sieve membrane theories by combining them and assuming that both are correct but for different, small, adjacent areas. On the cytological scale, the mosaic membrane theory is no longer held (Bayliss 15), but in the molecular range it certainly seems to apply to some of the phenomena shown by monolayers (Höber 36, Sebba & Briscoe 40). The presence of anything other than perfectly symmetrical molecules in a tightly packed monofilm would give on surface view a structure which could be called a mosaic. But it is difficult to visualize the functioning of such molecular mosaicism in multimolecular films. Nevertheless the idea has recently been invoked in papers on cuticle permeability (Hurst 43a, b, 45b, McLintock 45, J. E. Webb & Green 45), although without convincing documentation.[1]

GENERAL CUTICLE STRUCTURE IN RELATION TO PERMEABILITY

With the possible exception of places where it is exceedingly thin, the cuticle is a heterogeneous, asymmetrical membrane (Beament 45a, Hurst 41). The structural and chemical diversities have already been treated, but it seems desirable to list here briefly those which certainly affect the picture of cuticle permeability. The majority of insects possess a lipid layer which may be highly oriented and quite water resistant (Beament 45a), but in crustacea, spiders, and a few insects either no lipid is demonstrable or such as is present appears to have no effect on the penetration of water (Browning 42, Davies 28, Eder 40, Lafon 48, Theodor 36, Wigglesworth 45). Beament (48b) recognizes three types of lipids present in cuticle: (1) a fluid or solid wax layer which is highly water resistant, (2) protein layers which are impregnated with wax and show an intermediate water resistance, and (3) layers of lipoproteins which show little resistance to the passage of water. These lipid layers are always underlain by nonlipid material, and commonly are overlain by a tectocuticle of uncertain composition (p. 147). In most species a portion, frequently the greater part, is penetrated by pore canals which seem originally to contain protoplasmic filaments and may or may not be subsequently filled with cuticular material (Beament 46b, Dennell 46, Eder

[1] The mosaic membrane idea is often presented as a *diagrammatic* representation of a situation that would account for observed penetration data (analogous to the manner in which a wiring diagram represents an electrical instrument, but differing in that the diagram is only postulated). When used in this manner the mosaic diagram may be a useful visualization of data without necessarily being a correct *picture* of the ultrastructure of the membrane. It seems to the present author that some misunderstanding has arisen because ideas presented as diagrams have been mistakenly interpreted as pictures.

40, Kühnelt 39, Richards & Anderson 42a, Wigglesworth 33, 47b, 48d). One is accordingly led to wonder how much of the cuticle must be penetrated before the diffusing substance reaches the epidermal cells, and what role if any the cells may play in forming a barrier in the integument. There is some evidence that the penetration of water into gills (D. A. Webb 40) and the hygroscopic absorption of water vapor may involve functioning of the epidermal cells (Lees 46, 47). However, the cuticle is ordinarily so much less penetrable than the cells that permeability seems to be a function of the cuticle alone. Thus one may obtain the same general rate of penetration in living and dead animals (Bredenkamp 42, Maloeuf 37, Wigglesworth 45), and the rate of penetration of arsenic may be the same into living animals and through isolated cuticles (Ricks & Hoskins 48).

The thickness of the entire cuticle has no necessary relationship to water permeability, as shown by the fact that thin-cuticled species may be highly resistant to desiccation, whereas thick-cuticled species may not (Eder 40, Kühnelt 39). This is apparently due to the fact that the water-resistant layer is an extremely small fraction of the total thickness (p. 300). Accordingly it is not surprising that total cuticle thickness may have a demonstrable effect on the penetration of lipid soluble materials (Wigglesworth 42c). As one might expect, the permeability may be higher at the time of ecdysis than shortly thereafter (Anderson 46, Schumann 28, Smallman 42, Wigglesworth 45, Wigglesworth & Gillett 36). But, of more biological significance, permeability may vary greatly from one area of the body to another—with data being available for ticks, crustacea, and insects (Berger & Bethe 31, E. T. Burtt 45, J. S. Kennedy *et al.* 48, Slifer 50, Wiesmann 46). And also there is in general a reduction in permeability with age, both within a single instar and between successive instars (Fig. 61) (Crozier *et al.* 36, Klinger 36, Lennox 40, Morozov 35, Pepper & Hastings 43, Ricks & Hoskins 48, G. G. Robinson 42, Wigglesworth 42c).

Penetration through the arthropod cuticle may sometimes result in the appearance of a droplet on the side toward which diffusion is taking place. Thus an insect immersed in oil may exude droplets of water (Wigglesworth 42c); insects or insect eggs immersed in oil may show droplets appearing in the underlying cells (O'Kane & Baker 34, 35, Wigglesworth 42c), or oil may be similarly absorbed in digestion through the crop wall (Sanford 18); and mosquito larvae with their tracheae filled with essential oils may show droplets emerging into the nervous tissue from the tracheae and growing to give an appear-

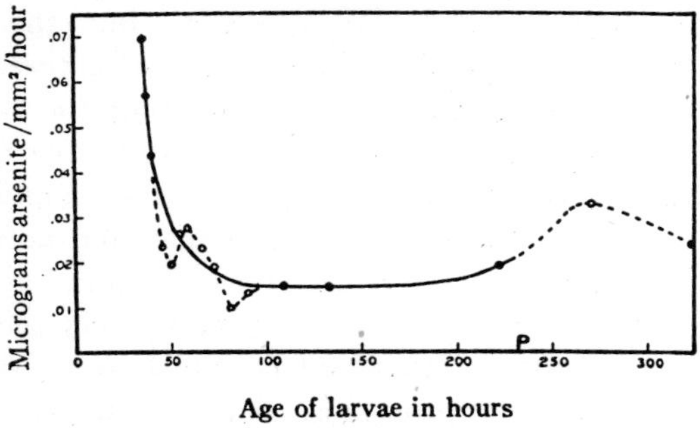

Figure 61. Effect of age of larvae upon rate of entry of arsenite in a fly, *Sarcophaga securifera.* The letter *P* indicates approximate age for pupation. (After Ricks and Hoskins.)

ance reminiscent of a bunch of grapes (Fig. 64C) (Richards & Weygandt 45). The explanation of such droplet-type penetration is not clear. The phenomenon is said to be aided by the presence of a small amount of oleic acid (Wigglesworth 42c), and it would certainly seem that interfacial molecules must be present, whether they come from the material applied or from the animal. But the phenomenon of exuding droplets seems simple in comparison to the almost fantastic, although readily verifiable, observation that if a droplet of water is placed on an insect leg at a point where a trachea comes near the surface, a corresponding droplet will appear in the lumen of the trachea; removal of the droplet from the cuticle surface by wiping or evaporation is followed by disappearance of the droplet in the trachea (Pal 47).

OSMOREGULATION AND ION REGULATION

Osmoregulation and ion regulation, including ion accumulation, are perhaps not beyond the subject of this book, but a detailed treatment of the phenomena would lead far afield into blood chemistry, excretory processes, and unequal ion distribution. The literature in osmoregulation has been reviewed by Krogh (39), and the significance of the various components in the ionic environment is discussed at length by Heilbrunn (43). It would be worth while to review this literature in detail if it led to an understanding of what is called "active absorption," but even the concept of active absorption is not universally accepted and the strongest proponents of it (Höber 40, Krogh 38, 46a, b) can offer data only for its existence without supplying a satisfactory explanation. Certainly movements against apparent concentration gradients are common, but the question is whether the membrane expends energy to move material in a direction opposite to that of free diffusion or whether the cellular membranes can be so organized as effectively to reverse the concentration gradients (Osterhout 49). One point can be made, namely, that there is no evidence that arthropod cuticle ever plays an active part (involving energy expenditure) in the transfer of material across it; cases involving apparent active transfer concern cell layers such as the gill epithelium. That salt concentration by larvae of *Culex* and *Chironomus* involves an active metabolic process is clearly indicated by its failure in nitrogenated water (Hers 42). It seems certain that "steady state" phenomena, rather than equilibrium conditions, are involved (Krogh 46a).

The work on osmoregulation and ion regulation involves primarily aquatic animals and usually is complicated by the possibility of absorption via the gut. However, there are reasons for thinking that the greater part of the exchange takes place through external surfaces, especially gills. Thus tests indicate that very little swallowing or even no detectable swallowing may occur (Maloeuf 40), that the mouth and anus may be plugged without affecting the processes (Huf 36, Nagel 34), that *Limulus* may be suspended in air with only its gills touching the water surface and yet show all the phenomena (Garrey 05), and that mosquito larvae may be left with the mouth not plugged provided the anal papillae are ligatured (Wigglesworth 32b). There is, then, evidence that some or all of the external surfaces are permeable to water and the common salts of the environment. The view that osmoregulation is secondary to ion regulation seems reasonable (Pieh 36, D. A. Webb 40). Numerous other references dealing with these phenomena in arthropods are available (Bateman 33, Bethe 28, 30, Boné & Koch 42, Drach 39, Gofferje 18, Harnisch 34, Herrmann 31, H. Koch 34, 38, H. Koch & Krogh 36, Margaria 31, Robertson 37, 39, Schlieper 29, Schumann 28).

METHODS OF STUDYING CUTICLE PERMEABILITY

Various methods have been used to obtain data on cuticle permeability, with or without the membranes receiving some experimental treatment (heat, scratching, chemical extraction). Most of the data so obtained are only grossly qualitative and demonstrate some penetration or the absence of detectable penetration. The few studies which have been more extensive or have produced significant data will be treated in subsequent chapters. The methods used may be outlined as follows:

A. Use of isolated pieces of cuticle
  1. Penetration of substances with grossly visible change
    a. Colored dyes of various molecular sizes and affinities (Alexandrov 35, MacGinitie 45, Morozov 35, Richards & Fan 49)
    b. Oil drops (Klinger 36)
    c. Acids and alkalies used with an indicator (Alexandrov 35, Morozov 35)
    d. Solutes with a biological indicator (Skvortzov 46)
    e. Formation of a precipitate (e.g., oxalate^{-} and Ca^{++}, giving Ca oxalate)
  2. Chemical determination of penetrating substance
    a. By analytical methods (Bredenkamp 42, Richards & Fan 49, Ricks & Hoskins 48)
    b. By bio-assay (Bredenkamp 42, Ivanova 37)
  3. Physical determination of penetration
    a. Osmotic effects (Abbott 26)
    b. Water loss in transpiration (Beament 45a)
    c. Fall in column of liquid (O'Kane *et al.* 40, Umbach 34)
    d. Change in any measurable physical property of the dialysate (Brightwell 38)
    e. Change in electrical properties of the system (Cole & Jahn 37, Jahn 35a, 36, Richards & Fan 49)
  4. Use of isotopes as tracers
  5. Comparison penetration in two directions (outside → inside vs. inside → outside) (Beament 45a, Hurst 41)

B. Use of intact animal
  1. Penetration of substances with grossly visible changes
    a. Colored dyes (Bond 33, Fischel 08, Gicklhorn 31, Gicklhorn & Süllman 31, Pagast 36, Richards & Weygandt 45, Slifer 49a)
    b. Oil as drops or with a dye (O'Kane & Baker 34, 35, Richards & Weygandt 45, Sanford 18)
    c. Acids or alkalies following previously absorbed indicator (Gicklhorn & Süllman 31)
    d. Solutions that lead to visible histological changes, especially "fixation" (Pagast 36)
  2. Chemical determination of penetrating substances
    a. Normal body constituents (see Ion Regulation)

b. Nonbiological compounds (Berger & Bethe 31, O'Kane & Glover 35, 36, Ricks & Hoskins 48)

3. Physical determination of penetration
   a. Osmotic effects (see Osmoregulation) (Evans 43, 44, Subklew 34)
   b. Water loss in transpiration (Beament 45a, Eder 40, Kühnelt 39, Wigglesworth 45)
   c. Measurement of electrical properties
4. Use of isotopes as tracers (Govaerts & Leclercq 46, Hansen *et al.* 44)
5. Deductions from reactions (stimulation, narcosis, death)
   a. Immersion, preferably of nonfeeding stages (see cutaneous respiration) (Apple 41, Breakey & Miller 35, Crauford-Benson 38, Hoskins 32, Hurst 40, Krogh 14, Lennox 40, Richards & Fan 49, G. G. Robinson 42, Shepard & Richardson 31, Slifer 49b, etc.)
   b. Local application (common in chemoreceptor work) (Berger & Bethe 31, Fulton & Howard 38, Hockenyos 33)

C. Use of models (Alexander *et al.* 44d, Beament 45, Hurst 41, 48)

In connection with the use of isolated cuticles, it has commonly been assumed that since the cuticle is a durable sheet, it can be treated with impunity, dried, and rewetted, and even treated with fairly strong solutions of alkali to remove lipids. There are now good reasons for saying that isolated cuticles must be handled with care, or the data obtained from them will be without biological validity (changes can be shown by X-ray diffraction and electron microscopy) (Fraenkel & Rudall 47, Richards & Korda 48). Isolated cuticles can be kept in distilled water or dilute solutions of certain salts such as KCl – especially if sterile – for some days or weeks without detectable change (Richards & Fan 49). They cannot, however, be treated with solutions of alkalies, detergents, acids, or numerous other chemicals without undergoing destructive change, despite the membranes superficially appearing normal (Richards & Korda 48).

In cases where both normal and alkali-treated membranes have been used (Alexandrov 35, Iljiskaya 46, Umbach 34, Yonge 36), presumably the values for the normal membranes are reasonably valid, but those from the alkali-treated membranes have no biological significance. And in those cases where alkaline solutions were used for cleaning the membranes before use, the data have no validity at all (Eidmann 22). It is particularly unfortunate that the extensive work of Yonge (36) is subject to so much possibility of technical error from reagents used and from the bacteria that obviously must have been present. It would not be surprising if the relative values obtained by Yonge were accurate, but it does not seem possible to place confidence in them until they have been repeated or at least partially checked using precautions we now know necessary.

The shrinkage resulting from drying is more readily reversed in the whole cuticle than in purified chitin, but it is not safe to assume that a rewetted membrane is identical in permeability terms with the same membrane before drying, because changes in micelle orientation do accompany the drying process (Fraenkel & Rudall 47). A dry organic membrane may have very different permeability values from the same membrane when wet (G. King 44, Northrup 29), and it seems obvious that penetration values for dry cuticles (Kuster 34) lack biological significance except for cases where the cuticle is dry, or nearly so, in life (see also Reckie & Aird 45, Rigden 46). Also drying can obviously give curling, as anyone can verify, and it would not be surprising if one or more of the component sublayers developed microcracks as a result. Further complications are involved when the cuticle being used possesses pore canals or other ducts, and it seems that the use of isolated cuticles should be limited to the membranes which are free from pore canals, gland ducts, and even sensillae (O'Kane *et al.* 40).

For these and other reasons it is becoming increasingly obvious that the precise conditions of any experiment should be explicitly stated. Highly precise quantitative figures are meaningless when the conditions of the specimen are unknown (Krogh 18). Even the question of the percentage of various components present in the tested solution should be stated definitely because it is well known that higher rates of penetration are obtained when solutes are tested at greater dilution and that mixed salts may give different rates from those given by pure salts. In this connection it has been reported that the presence of Ca^{++} makes lobster cuticle only half as permeable to Na^{+}, and that tests of ion permeability give different relative values for solutions of pure salts from those obtained from solutions approximating sea water (D. A. Webb 40).

It is usually assumed that treatment with hot or boiling chloroform does not alter the cuticle properties other than removing the reasonably discrete lipid epicuticle (Beament 45a, Wigglesworth 45), and this may well be true as far as can be determined from measurements of transpiration. However, more precise analysis using complex electrical impedance shows that there are effects, for if the diagram obtained after extraction with chloroform is appropriately subtracted from the diagram obtained for the normal cuticle, a new diagram is obtained which, instead of being a semicircle extending to the intersection of abscissa and ordinate, crosses both abscissa and ordinate and curves back toward the zero point (Richards unpubl.). It follows that the portion of membrane remaining after treatment with hot chloroform is not a completely unaltered fraction of the original normal cuticle. Presumably the amount of change is negligible insofar as experiments on transpiration are concerned. But one should not assume that such membranes are "unaltered."

What to say about the penetration of substances which destructively affect the cuticle composition is arbitrary. If the chemical is so corrosive that it gradually destroys all the cuticle components, any permeability value given would be nonsense. If the chemical removes most other components and leaves the chitin micelles behind, as alkaline solutions will do, a changing rate of penetration will be obtained, which will reach a constant value as one approaches purification of the chitin. This could be formulated in permeability terms for studies involving the penetration of such substances. With more specific and less destructive effects, such as treatment with chloroform, the change may be definite and values obtained have real use.

Another necessary precaution involves the question of natural abrasion (Wigglesworth 44b, 47a). What to call "normal" in a soil-inhabiting insect is again arbitrary. Originally the cuticle is formed intact, but in certain insects is promptly abraded against particles in its environment. Correspondingly, attention should be paid to the possibility of abrasion in preparing isolated cuticles for permeability studies.

Future studies on cuticle permeability involving the use of isolated cuticles must, to be acceptable, include tests demonstrating the validity of data presented. Reasons should be presented for thinking that the isolated cuticle still has reasonably similar properties to those it had when it was on the intact insect, and by repeated tests with the same membrane show that the properties have remained constant or changed only in a manner which has been taken into account in interpreting the data.

The use of intact animals is not fraught with as great difficulties in terms of invalidating changes occurring in the cuticle, but, except for transpiration, the analyses determining the amount of substance penetrating and the strength of the driving force are more difficult. It is to be hoped that persons favorably situated will make use of isotope tracers, which have the advantage of being usable both with isolated cuticles and with intact animals.

Whether one deals with isolated cuticles or intact animals, a wide range of individual variation is found even among supposedly identical individuals of one species (Richards & Fan 49). Accordingly, for quantitative work one must deal with averages from large numbers or refer to ranges or to a particular membrane. For studies on the effects of specific treatments (e.g., abrasion) the best validation is to obtain a normal value for a particular membrane, treat it, and then redetermine the value (Wigglesworth 45). The structural basis for the demonstrated range of variation remains to be determined.

In closing this discussion of the significance of work done to date on cuticle permeability, we might note that the interpretations available are of biological rather than biophysical interest. Considering the high degree of heterogeneity of arthropod cuticle, this state of affairs is likely to continue. A physical chemist who was trying to convince me that all the mysteries of collodion membranes should be solved first, concluded with the statement that "animal membranes are dirty messes"—a remark that seems especially appropriate for arthropod cuticle. But it is with these "dirty messes" that a biologist has to work, and it seems to the present author that significant advances are more likely to come from the collection of valid data than from facile comparison with simpler and relatively pure systems. Certainly such comparisons without supporting data are of little use.

CHAPTER 30

The Penetration of Water and Gases

THE ABSORPTION OF WATER

In general the permeability of hard arthropod cuticle to water is decidedly low in both terrestrial and aquatic species (Maloeuf 37, Pieh 36, Wigglesworth 32a). For the crop of cockroaches (Abbott 26) and the larval cuticle of blowflies (Richards & Fan 49) penetration is so low that osmometer experiments gave negative results. In contrast a high order of permeability to water, approximating that of the plasma membrane,[1] may be found in areas with the function of water, salt, or gas exchange (Berger & Bethe 31, von Gorka 14, Jordan & Lam 18, Laszt & Süllman 36, D. A. Webb 40, Wigglesworth 32a, b, Yonge 24). Presumably this will be true of the general cuticle for soft-bodied insects which live in moist environments and desiccate rapidly in normal air (Davies 28, Eder 40, Morrison 46, Theodor 36, Waloff 41). Incidentally the shell of most arthropod eggs is nearly impervious to water, but the shells of those species which normally absorb liquid water during development obviously must be permeable to water at this time (C. G. Johnson 37, Kerenski 30, Slifer 38) and may even have elaborate specialized structures for this purpose (Matthée 48, Slifer 38).

More interesting and perhaps even to be called surprising is the fact that a good many insects and ticks can absorb water from vapor in the air, that is, are hygroscopic. This phenomenon has been reported for several species of ticks (Lees 46, 47, 48), for *Chortophaga* (Orthoptera) (Bodine 21, Ludwig 37), for *Cimex* (Hemiptera) (Wigglesworth 31b), for *Tenebrio, Leptinotarsa,* and *Graphosoma* (Coleoptera) (Breitenbrecher 18, P. A. Buxton 30, Govaerts & Leclercq 46, Mellanby 32), for the pupae of *Agrotis* and *Ephestia* (Lepidoptera) (Kozhanchikov 34), and for the prepupae of fleas (Edney 47). Pre-

[1] An average value is 1 μ^3/μ^2/min./atm. or approximately 6 g./cm.^{2}/hr./atm. (Davson & Danielli 43). Since 1 mole equals 24.4 atmospheres of pressure, this is equivalent to *ca.* 135 μmol./mm.^{2}/hr./mole difference in concentration.

sumably this absorption is through the general body cuticle, but it has been proved only for the ticks (Lees 46–48). Apparently the phenomenon involves an "active absorption" by the epidermal cells; at least the phenomenon is not shown by dead specimens, and injuries leading to the necessity of cuticle repair upset the balance of the system. In most cases the absorption of water vapor takes place only in moist air, most often only when the air is near saturation, but in the prepupae of fleas it is said to occur at all relative humidities above 50%, although most rapidly at high humidities (Edney 47). In larvae of *Tineola* (Lepidoptera) on fasting the weight always falls, but the percentage of water rises in moist air and falls in dry air (Mellanby 34b).

The integument is probably somewhat permeable to water in all arthropods, and, if so, one should expect a certain amount of interchange between body water and atmospheric water in all species. Accordingly it is interesting to see that insects exposed to an atmosphere containing heavy water have their blood come into equilibrium with the air in a few days (Govaerts & Leclercq 46). This is true irrespective of whether the insect normally gains or loses weight in a saturated atmosphere. It is recorded that thirteen days are required for equilibration in *Tenebrio* larvae, but only five days in adult *Tenebrio, Leptinotarsa,* and *Graphosoma.*

An extensive symposium of papers covering fundamental aspects of water penetration, as well as botanical, zoological, and textile applications, was published by the Faraday Society in 1948 (Symposium 48).

TRANSPIRATION, OR THE LOSS OF WATER

Terrestrial arthropods, being small, have a relatively large surface area and must be protected from excessive evaporation or they soon become desiccated. In those insects which live exposed to a normal atmosphere, most of the water loss occurs via the tracheal system through the spiracles, and if an insect is induced to leave its spiracles open, it soon desiccates (Bergold 35, Mellanby 34–36). But if water loss through the respiratory system is prevented, the rate of weight loss, taken as an index of transpiration, is extremely low — several thousand times lower than the average rate for the plasma membrane. Measurements made on various species of ticks and insects normally lie in the range of < 1–2 mg./cm.^{2}/hr. (Lees 47, Wigglesworth 45) when an individual is exposed to a dry atmosphere within a desiccator. (See Rohwer [31] for evaporation rates from free water surfaces.)

An understanding of the nature and the chemistry of the cuticular structure responsible for this remarkable resistance to the evaporation of water from insects is the one outstanding development in the field of cuticular permeability, and the experiments leading to their elucidation by Wigglesworth and Beament seem certain to go down in entomological history as classics in this field. These developments, all within the past five years, have already been the subject of several reviews (Beament 48b, Wigglesworth 46, 48b) and are widely known; accordingly they can be treated rather briefly.

To state the case in a single sentence, the cuticular resistance to evaporation from most insects is due to the presence of a thin layer of lipid (usually wax, Table 5) near the outer surface of the cuticle, and the passage of water outwards is due to passive diffusion, for it has been demonstrated that it is immaterial whether the arthropod is alive or dead (Wigglesworth 45). The lipid layer has been estimated as usually having a thickness of 0.2–0.3 μ, that is, about thirty molecular layers thick; and the inner portion adjacent to the underlying protein epicuticle is highly oriented and must be both tightly packed and strongly bound to be relatively impermeable to water and resistant to removal by adsorptive particles (Beament 45a, 48b). A relationship between lipid layers and the restriction of transpiration is no new idea (Eder 40, Hockenyos 39, Keilin 13, Kühnelt 28a, 39, Mellanby 36, Ramsay 35, Schulz 30, H. Weber 31, Woods 29), but it was little more than a guess until the demonstration by Ramsay (35) that transpiration from cockroaches increased abruptly when the temperature was raised to the point where the lipid layer was disturbed.

The establishment of the above hypothesis rests on five main lines of evidence: (1) If the rate of evaporation from an insect or tick is measured at various temperatures, it is found to increase rather abruptly at a fairly definite point on the temperature scale (Fig. 62), and this temperature closely corresponds to the transition point or change of phase point of lipids extractable from the cuticle of the particular species (Table 6) (Beament 45a, 48b). It is somewhat lower than the actual melting point of the solid waxes, but the interpretation of insectan data is documented by similar results with known monofilms (Alex Müller 32, Stallberg *et al.* 45). In terrestrial insects this transition point or breaking point for different species lies in the range 30°–60° C. (but may be lower in aquatic forms) (Wigglesworth 45); in ticks different species occupy the range 32°–75° C. (Lees 47). (2) The extraction of lipids from the surface of the cuticle by means of chloroform, ether, or peanut oil results in elimination of

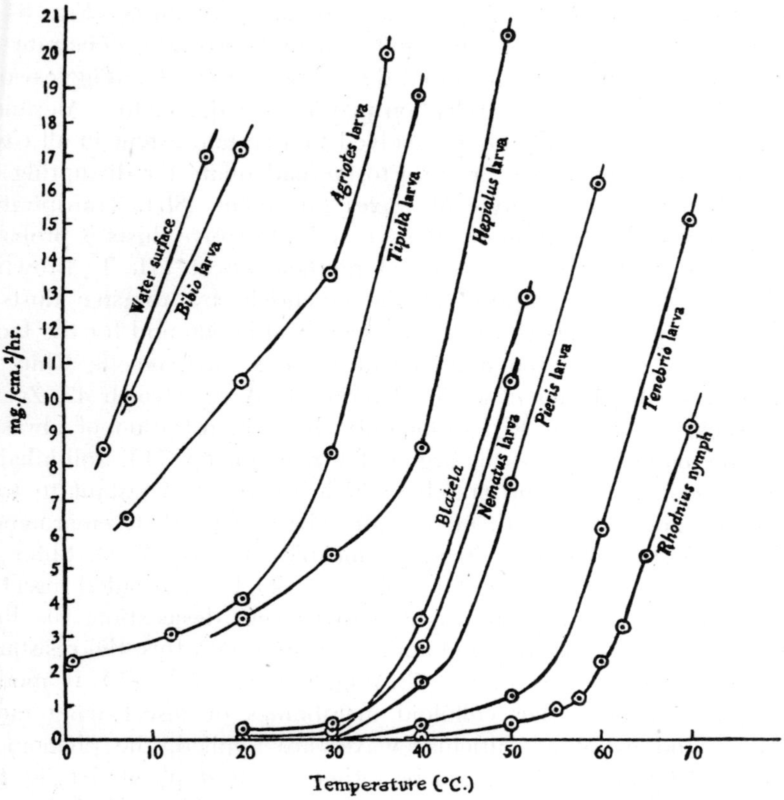

Figure 62. The rate of evaporation of water from dead insects of the genera named as a function of the temperature. Spiracles occluded. Compare Figure 63. (After Wigglesworth.)

the temperature effect and relatively free permeability at ordinary temperatures (Lees 47, Ludwig 48, Wigglesworth 42c, 45). In a few cases the vapor of chloroform is also partly effective. Likewise detergents (Wigglesworth 45) can result in a great increase in the rate of evaporation, but it should be remembered that detergents not only affect the lipids destructively but may also affect the underlying layers (Richards & Korda 48). In a number of insects found in moist or aquatic environments no lipid layer, no appreciable resistance to evaporation, and no temperature transition point can be found (Davies 28, Richards 41, Theodor 36, Wigglesworth 45).[2] (3) Scratching

[2] The situation in the petroleum fly, the larvae of which live in open oil pools (Crawford 12, Thorpe 30a, b, 31), should be reinvestigated in this connection. See also the recent paper on diplopods by Cloudsley-Thompson (50b).

of the outer surface of the cuticle with abrasive dusts (Fig. 64A), with the scratchings only sufficiently deep to partially penetrate the epicuticle, likewise leads to rapid desiccation (Lees 47, Wigglesworth 44a, 45). In some cases adsorption may be a major factor (Alexander *et al.* 44a, b) and probably is involved to a certain extent in all cases, though adsorptive forces are said to be inadequate for disrupting the most important inner layer of waxes (Beament 48b). Transpiration following the application of abrasive and adsorptive dusts is probably always enhanced by the so-called pin-hole effect (H. T. Brown & Escombe 00). The rupture of the epicuticle by abrasive dusts is thought to account both for their insecticidal action and for the facilitation they give to the entrance of poisons (Briscoe 43, Chiu 39, Kalmus 44, Kitchener *et al.* 43, Parkin 44, Wigglesworth 45, Zacker 37, Zacker & Kunike 30). Commonly the demonstration of abrasion may be made by use of the argentaffin reaction (p. 71). Soil-inhabiting insects may develop cuticles which are highly resistant to transpiration and yet have them so badly abraded by their environment that the cuticle becomes freely permeable (Evans 43, 44, Slifer 50, Subklew 34, Wigglesworth 44b, 45, 47a). (4) If an abraded insect or tick is kept in a moist atmosphere to prevent desiccation, the lipid layer is demonstrably restored and, correlated with this, the resistance to desiccation returns (Lees 47, Wigglesworth 45). (5) If models are made, using either celluloid membranes or insect wing membranes, and extracted cuticular waxes are applied, the phenomena exhibited by intact insects can be rather closely duplicated (Fig. 63) (Beament 45a). Phase transitions in monolayers also occur below the melting point (Stallberg & Stenhagen 45). An interesting (but not fundamental) datum is that if various natural and artificial waxes are tested both on cuticle and on artificial membranes, the greatest resistance to water penetration is obtained with the cuticular waxes of plants and insects deposited on insect wing membranes (Alexander *et al.* 44a, Beament 48b).

Although the above hypothesis of transpiration being restricted by a lipid layer appears soundly documented, it should not be assumed to dominate the picture in all cases. Apparently the tight packing of chitin-protein micelles involved in sclerotization (Fraenkel & Rudall 47) is not necessarily adequate to deter the movement of water seriously (see Reckie & Aird 45, Rigden 46). However, sclerotization may involve or become accompanied by the development of a considerable degree of water impermeability as strikingly shown by Lafon's (43b) report that the epicuticle and part of the exocuticle of

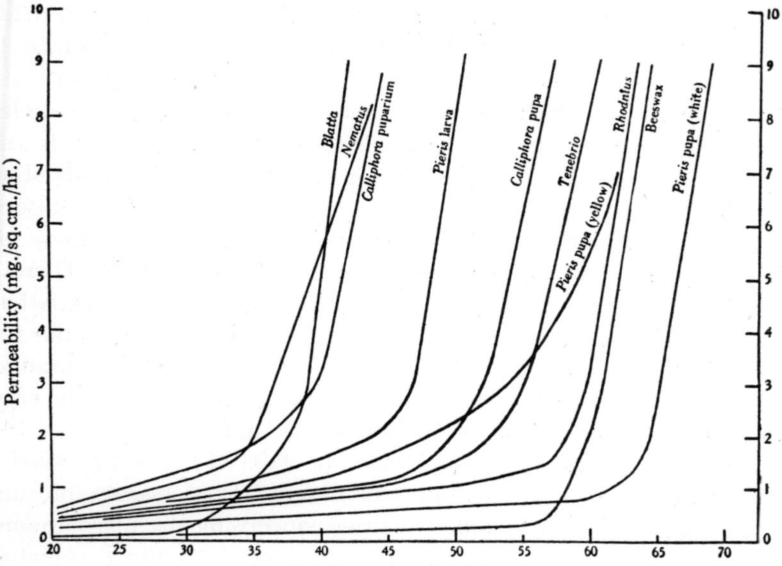

Figure 63. The rate of evaporation of water through extracted wing membranes (*Pieris*) covered with approximately 1 μ of wax from the various insects named. Compare Figure 62. (After Beament.)

certain beetles may be ground away and yet the cuticle remain hydrophobic and relatively impermeable. Perhaps this is due to shrinkage attendant on drying, as has also been suggested to account for the rapid decrease in transpiration of soil-inhabiting insects suddenly placed in a dry atmosphere (Wigglesworth 45). The larvae of *Sarcophaga* are said to be unaffected by abrasion (Dennell 45), but related genera give sharp temperature transition points (Wigglesworth 45), and deep scratching with emery cloth makes the cuticle freely permeable as determined by measurement of electrical impedance (Richards unpubl.).[3] This has led to the suggestion that in blowfly larvae a relatively thick protein layer is impregnated with wax rather than that the wax forms a more discrete surface layer (Beament 48b). The situation in spiders requires further investigation, but Dr. R. Dennell informs me (in correspondence) that Miss Sewell has unpublished data from abrasion experiments similar to Wigglesworth's data

[3] Dennell (50) has recently reported that the endocuticle of blowfly larvae is dispersed by fluids of the environment (including enzymes), whereas the epicuticle is not. From this he postulates that the primary function of the epicuticle is to protect the larva from the action of these digestive fluids. This may well be one of the functions of the epicuticle in blowfly larvae.

on terrestrial insects. Also, in *Drosophila* a correlation has been made between the darkness of mutants and the degree of resistance to desiccation, but it needs experimental verification (Kalmus 41b, c).

The nature of the control of water movement in crustacean cuticles, both aquatic and terrestrial, also needs to be studied. Abrasion is said to be without significant effect (Lafon 48); terrestrial isopods show no indication of a temperature effect of the type found in insects (Edney 49); and although lipoproteins seem to be present, these are not thought to retard evaporation in insects (Beament 48b). There is no indication as to whether specific differences are due to variations in tanning or lipoproteins. Calcification alone can hardly be the full answer because of the relatively large amount of soft membranous area. Yet "land crabs" are well known, and even the common crayfish may sometimes be found wandering on land.

As already mentioned, Hurst (43a, b, 45b, 48) has proposed a mosaic membrane theory to represent the cuticle of insects, presumably basing this on similar older theories concerning the plasma membrane of cells. As a diagrammatic presentation of certain penetration phenomena, the mosaic idea has some advantages (and can be made to account for almost anything), but it seems to the present author in need of more documentation and further development before it will be notably helpful (see p. 289).

An unexpected situation is the reported functional asymmetry of cuticles to the passage of water (Beament 45a, Hurst 41, 48). This is sometimes stated simply as water passing in the direction of epicuticle → endocuticle more rapidly than in the reverse direction. Such a simple statement is not supported by the data and is probably untrue. What the authors report is that in the complex system water-cuticle-air (or water-cuticle-alcohol), water passes through the cuticle more rapidly when the cuticle is turned one way than when it is turned the other. Several possible mechanisms have been formulated by Hurst (48): either one side of the membrane (presumably the endocuticle) may change properties on being exposed to air versus water, or the endocuticle may expose a greater surface area for evaporation (or possibly have molecular valves). The phenomenon is similar to certain problems encountered in packaging items of commerce. It will bear repeating that it is dependent on an asymmetrical *system* in which the cuticle is only one component; it is not thought to be due solely to the asymmetry of the cuticle. Presumably it will not be encountered when water is on *both* sides of the membrane. However, with fluids other than water (benzene, hexane, Hurst 48) it may be.

Hurst (41) recorded differences of 100 times for passage of water in the two directions through the cuticles of *Calliphora* larvae in a water-cuticle-air system. Beament (45a) recorded differences of 1.6, 4, and 20 times for *Rhodnius* cuticles in such systems, and more recently (Symposium 48) has said that having tested three species of insects and two species of ticks, he has come to feel that the higher values are due to poor technique and the actual difference is always less than 5 to 1.[4]

Supposedly related to cuticle asymmetry is the curious report that whereas larvae of *Calliphora* and *Tenebrio* both withstand desiccation in a dry atmosphere for a long time, the *Tenebrio* larva dries rapidly if confined in contact with a *Calliphora* larva (Hurst 41). It was postulated that this is due to the lipid of *Calliphora* being more hydrophilic than that of *Tenebrio*.

A considerable literature exists on the ecological aspects of transpiration. Clearly species which cannot resist evaporation cannot live in dry environments (Manton & Ramsay 37), and desert species may even develop hydromania and devour anything containing water (Husain & Mather 36), or actively absorb water through the integument (Colosi 33). Since the question of ecological niches is so complex, and since transpiration is only one of the factors involved, correlations are both difficult and, at least at present, of dubious value (P. A. Buxton 24, 30, 31, 32b, Eder 40, Gunn 33, Koidsumi 34, Kühnelt 39, Ludwig 45, Mellanby 34–36). The elaborate classification scheme proposed by Kalmus (41a) is subject to so many exceptions that it can be considered no more than a tentative beginning (Carpenter & Kalmus 41). No discussion of the ecological literature will be attempted here. It might be remarked that there seems to be no good correlation between transpiration and the demonstrable presence of pore canals (Kühnelt 39), and most certainly there is no correlation between total cuticle thickness and transpiration (Eder 40, Kühnelt 39, Mellanby 34a). A point of some ecological significance with ticks is the report that there is a large increase in water loss following engorgement, but the reason for this is not yet known.

PERMEABILITY TO GASES

The cuticle overlying all chemoreceptors (Dethier & Chadwick 48) and respiratory surfaces (gills, book lungs, tracheae) is, of course,

[4] Differences of 1.1 and 2 times have been recorded for rates of endosmosis versus exosmosis for the plasma membrane of living cells. See Davson and Danielli, p. 118. Differences for solutes were reported by Yonge (36), but unfortunately these data are of questionable validity (p. 295).

adequately permeable to the appropriate molecules. But more than penetrability is involved in biological responses, and true permeability values cannot be obtained unless methods are used for measuring both the driving force and the amount of movement through the membrane. It is not correct, however, to assume that aquatic or semiaquatic arthropods with tracheae or lungs cannot respire through the general cuticle, or that aquatic forms (*Limulus,* certain decapod crustacea) may not survive long periods of exposure in air (until the gills dry). The literature on cutaneous respiration has been discussed by numerous authors (Fraenkel & Herford 38, M. O. Lee 29, Maloeuf 36, Richards 41, Wigglesworth 31a) and will not be cited here in detail because it tells little other than the qualitative fact that such gaseous exchanges can take place and do take place in different amounts in different species. For instance, if survival time in aerated water is taken as an index of cutaneous respiration, then for similar-sized dipterous larvae the sequence of relative penetrability values would be *Culex pipiens* < *Aedes aegypti* = *Mochlonyx* < *Corethra,* the last named having a closed tracheal system and adequate cutaneous respiration (Fraenkel & Herford 38, A. Koch 18, 20, 21, Richards 41).

Terrestrial and semiterrestrial isopods withstand immersion to various degrees (Becker 36, Nicholls 31a, Reinders 33). Presumably this indicates that the cuticle over respiratory surfaces is adequately permeable under the conditions of the high diffusion rate of oxygen in air, but is inadequate when the driving force is reduced by the slow diffusion rate of oxygen in solution in water. In this connection, although it may seem superfluous, it may be pointed out that statements sometimes made based on the erroneous assumption that immersion of a terrestrial arthropod gives anaerobic conditions are invalid. Immersion in nontoxic mineral oils may likewise permit cutaneous respiration, and the higher solubility of oxygen in mineral oil may result in less evidence of anoxia from immersion in oil than from immersion in water, provided the cuticle is dry (Richards 41). Interposition of a water film between the insect and the oil seemingly imposes adverse diffusion potentials; at least it leads to rapid suffocation.

In terrestrial insects manometric measurements may show some gas exchange, which probably indicates cutaneous respiration, since the spiracles, mouth, and anus were plugged (*Dixippus*) (von Buddenbrock & von Rohr 22). Dried cuticles of libellulid larvae are said to permit a slow penetration of O_2 and CO_2 (Kuster 34). Probably when measurements are made it will be found that most arthropods show some diffusion of gas through the general cuticle. Obviously the egg shell and embryonic membranes must be permeable to gases, since measurable oxygen consumption occurs. Of particular interest to the present treatment is the recent report by Tuft (50) suggesting that the resistance of an egg shell (*Rhodnius*) to the penetration of oxygen is due to the chorion, rather than to the wax layer that causes the resistance to desiccation.

The complicated processes involved in filling of the tracheal system with gas, and the movement of fluid back and forth within the tracheoles of certain species, are not sufficiently understood for discussion (see Bult 39, Keilin 24, Keister & Buck 49, Wigglesworth 38). The data do show that fluid as well as gases can penetrate tracheal walls.

There is a large literature on fumigation in insect control (Sun 47), but the complications in applied studies make the data uninterpretable in terms of interest to the present discussion, except for the qualitative demonstration by Glover and Richardson (36) of the penetration of gaseous nicotine, pyridine, and piperidine.

Only three sets of quantitative data of interest here have been found. It is reported that gas within the closed tracheal system of libellulid larvae comes into equilibrium with the gas in the environment in 10–12 minutes (Wallengren 15; see also Krogh 11). Precise measurements of area and volume are necessary before these figures can be translated into permeability values. More interesting is the fact that there is definite evidence that the gaseous exchange takes place purely by passive diffusion, since it has been reported to be of the same magnitude for gas diffusing across the membranes in each direction and since the rate is dependent on the partial pressure gradient rather than the absolute gas tension (H. J. A. Koch 36). Krogh's (18) seemingly precise value for the penetration of oxygen is uninterpretable on the basis of information published.

CHAPTER 31

The Penetration of Electrolytes, Nonelectrolytes, and Insecticides

THE PENETRATION OF ELECTROLYTES

Recently two papers have been published giving quantitative permeability values for the larval cuticles of higher Diptera, the values being either obtained from living individuals or accompanied by ancillary tests to validate the determinations made (Fig. 61, Table 14). The cuticles of higher dipterous larvae are particularly suitable for this purpose because they are reasonably homogeneous and do not have setae or open gland ducts or pore canals (Fig. 20A). Also sheets of sufficient size to use in diffusion cells can readily be obtained. The data available are not sufficiently extensive to warrant detailed discussion, but it may be noted that all of the values are quite low. Although transpiration rates through the cuticle are considered low, nevertheless these values for the passage of water are much higher than the corresponding rates for any of the five solutes for which data are available.

One of these papers (Richards & Fan 49) deals primarily with the question of variability between different individuals. It was found that variations of from 3 to 4 times the lowest value were the most constancy that was obtained from membranes of supposedly identical *Phormia* larvae (since single tests involved fairly small numbers, this may be by coincidence more constant than the actual "normal" variability). Extremes of 8.7 times were obtained for KCl, 10 times for methylene blue, and 18 times for $CoCl_2$. If membranes were taken from individuals of different cultures and of only approximately the same age and history, roughly twice this amount of variation was found. Variations of 4, 6, and 11 times within single experiments were found for the penetration of arsenite into *Sarcophaga* larvae (Ricks & Hoskins 48). This amount of variability is adequate to account for the variations in biological responses such as mortality and sensory

TABLE 14. PENETRATION THROUGH THE CUTICLE OF FULLY GROWN FLY LARVAE

Membrane	Solution Tested		μmol./mm.²/hr./mole conc. diff.		Authority
			Range	Average	
Phormia regina	0.10 M KCl.....		0.004–0.061	0.033	Richards & Fan 49
	0.10 M $CoCl_2$..		0.0012–0.041	0.0123	Same as above
	0.10 M urea.....		0.003–0.0275	*ca.* 0.0136	Same as above
	0.0003 M methylene blue..............		0.0014–0.020	*ca.* 0.012	Same as above
Sarcophaga securifera	0.128–0.223 M arsenic (plus phosphate buffer)	pH 5	...	0.0008	Ricks & Hoskins 48
		pH 7	...	0.00067	
		pH 9	...	0.00037	
		pH 10	...	0.00020	
		pH 11.5	...	0.00012	
Calliphora erythrocephala	Transpiration of water.............		...	(*ca.* 0.15)[1]	Wigglesworth 45
Average cell membrane	Water		...	*ca.* 135	Davson & Danielli 43

[1] This value is for the rate of passage of water to dry air (rather than for a mole concentration difference).

reactions, but it would be a gratuitous and dubious assumption to say that variation in permeability does account for them.

At pH 5–7 arsenite is primarily in molecular form, whereas at pH 11 it is primarily ionic, but unfortunately the dissociation curve is rather closely paralleled by the solubility curve. Accordingly it is not clear which phenomenon is the cause of the different penetration rates at different pH's (Ricks & Hoskins 48).

In the work done with chemical determination of penetrating substances (Richards & Fan 49) a difference in rate of penetration of cations and anions was not detected. But the measurement of sizable concentration potentials (with KCl solutions) for *Sarcophaga* larvae shows that the permeability values for K^+ and Cl^- must be significantly different (Ricks & Hoskins 48).[1]

[1] Incidentally KCl is one of the fastest penetrating salts known in general membrane work. Perhaps the values given for KCl in Table 14 are maximal for salt penetration through these cuticles. The values may actually be higher than would be obtained from living larvae since the tests were made with pure salt solutions in the absence of Ca^{++} (D. A. Webb 40).

The relative rates for penetration of different ions is, as far as determined, in their usual order (p. 288),[2] but the ratios reported by different authors are not in good agreement and also do not agree well with classical mobilities (Jahn 35a, Subklew 34, D. A. Webb 40, Yonge 36). Naturally, the values deduced from toxicity effects (Bodine 23, Buchmann 31, Subklew 34) and ion regulation studies (Gicklhorn & Süllman 31, Gofferje 18, A. Koch 21, Nicholls 31b, Pagast 36) can be accepted only with reservations. A possible relation to the ionic balance of the solutions being used has already been mentioned. For cuticle, the subject needs further investigation because, while D. A. Webb (40) and others (Apple 41, Barnes 38) have reported much lower penetration rates for Na^+ when Ca^{++} was also present, Ricks and Hoskins (48) obtained the same magnitude of penetration rates when measuring arsenite penetration through isolated cuticles and into intact animals.

One would expect considerable differences in penetration through different types of cuticle even on a single individual, but few quantitative data are available. In crabs the general body surface and the gill surfaces have roughly the same area, but more than 95% of the penetration of iodides takes place through the gills in immersed animals (Berger & Bethe 31). Very likely this is an extreme case, and less difference is to be expected between sclerites and intersegmental membranes. In three related genera of dipterous larvae the penetration rates vary independently of cuticle thickness (Alexandrov 35).[3] Perhaps this independence is related to the presence of wax layers (Skvortzov 46); at least treatments to remove or disrupt the wax layers of grasshopper eggs result in relatively rapid penetration of aqueous solutions containing I + KI (Slifer 49b).

A few values related to the penetration of electrolytes have been determined by electrical methods (Cole & Jahn 37, Jahn 35a, 36, Richards & Fan 49, Ricks & Hoskins 48). Analysis of the actual values determined has not proceeded sufficiently far for interpretation in biophysical terms. Incomplete preliminary data on complex impedance of blowfly larval cuticles suggest that electrolyte penetration, like the transpiration of water, may be largely controlled by the epicuticle (Richards unpubl.); but further study is needed. Of some biological interest are the relative statements that "chemical chain" potentials of

[2] Except for the single case of Yonge's report that the lithium ion penetrates more rapidly than calcium (Yonge 36).

[3] Alexandrov states that these differences are due to differences in the epicuticles, but the statement is based on the effects of treatment with alkali solutions and accordingly is not based on valid evidence even if true.

grasshopper egg membranes are slightly lower than corresponding values for onion skin membranes and for the chorion of fish eggs, and that the electrical resistance increased tremendously ($>$ 500 times) after formation of the inner cuticle secreted by the serosa and the concommitant deposition of wax layers.

PENETRATION OF DYES

Numerous dyes, both vital and toxic, have been shown to diffuse through the cuticle of aquatic arthropods, but with the exception of methylene blue no quantitative data are available (Table 14) (Alexandrov 35, Bond 33, Fischel 08, Gicklhorn 31, Gicklhorn & Süllman 31, Koehring 30, 31, Pagast 36, Richards & Fan 49). In most of these cases it seems clear that at least some of the dye penetrated through the cuticle, and the use of dye molecules of different sizes (MacGinitie 45) could be employed in studies on the maximum size of molecules that may penetrate through cuticle. Neutral red has been used most frequently, but a variety of other dyes have been employed, including alizarin, congo red, Bismarck brown, toluidine blue, methylene blue, fast green, and crystal violet. Slifer (50) has recently reported that dye absorption into grasshopper tarsi is greatly facilitated by abrasion.

An extensive but specialized study dealt with the penetration of lipids and lipid soluble dyes through tracheal walls, but the technique employed did not permit expression of the data in quantitative terms (Richards & Weygandt 45). It was shown definitely that in some cases the solvent might penetrate without the dye (solute left precipitated in tracheal lumen). In another specialized study it was shown that water-soluble dyes do not detectably penetrate the shell of grasshopper eggs until the lipid layer has been disrupted by the application of xylol (Slifer 49a).

THE PENETRATION OF NONELECTROLYTES

Significant quantitative data on the penetration of nonelectrolytes are notable for their absence. Tentative figures for urea are given in Table 14. Much data from the field of contact insecticides demonstrates penetration but tells nothing about the process (p. 313). There are numerous other qualitative demonstrations of penetration: for instance, the penetration of fat through the crop wall (Abbott 26, Petrunkewitsch 1899, Sanford 18), the penetration of many lipids and lipid solvents through tracheal walls (Richards & Weygandt 45), the penetration of alcohol and fixing fluids through gills and anal papillae

(Pagast 36), and the penetration of fat droplets through the body wall (Wigglesworth 42c). Differences between species are well illustrated by narcosis from ethyl urethane (Krogh 14), which readily anesthetizes nondecapod crustacea but is not so effective against decapods, and anesthetizes larvae of *Chironomus* but not those of *Dytiscus*. Perhaps the most interesting point on the penetration of nonelectrolytes singly is that apolar paraffin oils are usually (but not always) said to penetrate better than vegetable oils (G. G. Robinson 42, Wigglesworth 42c) — this is the reverse of the relative penetration for the mammalian skin.

One extremely interesting point was discovered by Hurst (40), namely, that while blowfly larvae are resistant to immersion in both alcohol and kerosene, they are quickly killed, with loss of water and entrance of alcohol, if immersed in a mixture of these two. To use chemical terminology, feebly dissociating compounds with high dielectric constants penetrate more readily in the presence of apolar substances of low dielectric constant. The phenomen has been confirmed and extended by Wigglesworth (41, 42c), who shows that effective mixtures include ethyl alcohol + kerosene, acetone + kerosene, carbon bisulfide + ethyl alcohol, butyl alcohol + medicinal paraffin oil, pyridine + paraffin oil, pyridine + dedocyl thiocyanate, and benzene + ethyl alchohol, the last three being distinctly less effective. As with other permeability phenomena, considerable variation in rate exists between different individuals, as shown by differences of 10 times or more in the time required for inactivation within single groups of larvae (Richards & Fan 49). Inactivation and effervescence are more rapid with some species (*Calliphora*) than with others (*Phormia*), more rapid with younger larvae than older larvae, and more rapid with lighter oils than heavier oils (Hurst 40, Richards & Fan 49, Wigglesworth 41). Presumably the effect is limited to relatively impervious cuticles; at least the more permeable cuticles of gills, anal papillae, hind-guts, and tracheae are freely permeable to alcohol.

Study of the penetration of nonelectrolytes is further complicated by imbibition and destructive or solvent action. Thus it is recorded that insects immersed in mineral oil will slowly exude water droplets onto the outer surface of the cuticle (Wigglesworth 41, 42c). This has been interpreted as indicating that the oil disrupts the lipid epicuticle, and polar substances crowding into the oil-water interface literally draw water from within the insect.

THE PENETRATION OF INSECTICIDES

Most work on permeability is carried on with analysis of a single variable at any one time. Unfortunately this is not possible with much of the work on insecticide penetration. The field is so complex that it is probably correct to say that insecticide penetration defies satisfactory analysis at present. An interesting diagram showing possible relations among twenty-three independent variables is given by Sun (47). Certainly quantitative analysis of such situations is not possible now. Yet it is part of the role of physiology to explain these phenomena, however slow advances may be. If we are to understand insecticide penetration, unambiguous data are essential. But unambiguous data are very difficult to obtain, especially for mixtures, and we are far from being able to handle such complex situations in a quantitative manner. Of necessity physiological studies on this subject, like projects on insecticide development, are largely empirical, partly because the empirical method is more accurate (especially when one does not understand the phenomena being measured). Reports of an insecticide having been developed intellectually and then produced lack conviction (Lauger *et al.* 44). Interesting recent discussions are given by Hoskins (40), Lennox (40), Sun (47), Wigglesworth (48b), and A. W. A. Brown (50). (See also section on Wettability, p. 137.)

Many of the points treated in preceding sections are relevant to insecticide penetration also (Table 14). They will not be repeated in detail. Thus, in general, there is a relation to age, older larvae being more resistant than younger ones (Fig. 61) (Bredenkamp 42, Klinger 36, Ricks & Hoskins 48), but the age-mortality curves may show odd peaks indicative of complications (Sun 47). Local differentiations, sometimes related to sclerotization, commonly affect the rate of insecticide entry;[4] more favorable loci for absorption of toxins have been recorded in various arthropods (Berger & Bethe 31, Burtt 45, Griffiths & Tauber 43, Hickin 45, Hockenyos 33, J. S. Kennedy *et al.* 48, Klinger 36, Lauger *et al.* 44, Lepesme 37a, b, Moriyama 39, Potts & Vanderplank 45). As is to be expected, the greater the area involved, the more arsenic penetrates (O'Kane & Glover 35, 36). Gaseous insecticides can penetrate the cuticle and may even show accumulation in it (Glover & Richardson 36). Also there is commonly at least a gross relationship between the rate of penetration of vital dyes or insecticides and the speed of insecticide action in different species

[4] Correlations comparable to those made for transpiration (p. 300) have also been made for insecticide penetration but are not yet satisfactorily developed (Goldsmith & Harnly 46, Kalmus 42, Kalmus *et al.* 42).

(Alexandrov 35, Iljiskaya 46) and between the rate of transpiration and insecticide action (Wigglesworth 45, 48b). Those agents or treatments which facilitate transpiration also appear to facilitate the entrance of insecticides, though it remains to be shown how quantitative the relationship is.

Many of the general qualitative statements concerning the entry of insecticides through cuticle are also applicable to egg shells. Thus wax layers are present (Beament 46a, b, 47, 48a, 49, Cole & Jahn 37, Jahn 34, 35a, 36, Lees & Beament 48, Ongaro 33), and the disruption of these waxy layers with xylol makes the shell readily permeable to dyes and toxins (Slifer 49a, b). Oil can penetrate insect eggs and appear as droplets on the inner surface (O'Kane & Baker 34, 35), but recent evidence indicates this is not necessary for a toxic effect (Smith & Pearce 48) and warns against assuming that toxicity data necessarily imply penetration. Likewise certain insect eggs may absorb water (Birch & Andrewartha 42, Matthée 48, Slifer 38, 46). Transpiration through the egg shell may be much less than through the cuticle of the newly hatched larva; thus in a dry atmosphere an egg may develop satisfactorily and yet the larva promptly desiccate at hatching (Ludwig 45). Of more interest to insecticide literature is the fact that nicotine is said to penetrate into housefly eggs more readily in the presence of NaCl, less readily in the presence of $CaCl_2$ (Apple 41), and the major penetration may be through the micropyles, where complex barriers may be formed by successive regions of wax, protein, water, and even air (Beament 48a). (See also Evans 34b.)

All insecticide workers realize that certain of their toxins are relatively ineffective for external application and yet very potent when injected. Fortunately the ease of absorption into arthropods and other groups of animals is not always the same. It seems very clear that penetration phenomena give part of the answer to the selective action of DDT, but only a beginning has been made toward analyzing the reasons for this (Dresden & Krijgsman 48, Fan *et al.* 48, Richards & Cutkomp 46, Seagren *et al.* 45, Tobias *et al.* 46). There is evidence that the same may be said for pyrethrum, and quite likely the same is true for all insecticides showing highly selective action.

For further discussion of insecticide penetration it seems desirable to make a primary division into two groups: one for those compounds, mixtures, or treatments which destructively affect the cuticle composition, the other for those toxins or mixtures which penetrate cuticle without producing detectable alteration. In general, dry residual insecticides would tend to fall into the second category except when they contain an abrasive agent (likewise dusts and dust mixtures when these penetrate through the cuticle); insecticide mixtures active in an oil carrier probably tend to fall in the first category.

The penetration of insecticides which destructively affect the cuticle can be closely analogized to the phenomena recorded for transpiration (p. 300) (Wigglesworth 48b). In insect cuticles we have a heterogeneous set of barrier layers, and if one or more of these are removed by solvent action (lipids) or disrupted by detergents or interrupted by abrasions (Fig. 64A), the efficiency of the barrier is lowered and may even become negligible. Since the wax and tectocuticle layers on the extreme outside of the cuticle are the ones which present the most formidable barrier to the entry of insecticides, it is their disruption or interruption which most facilitates entry (but see recent paper by David & Gardiner 50). Any oil will probably mix more or less thoroughly with the waxes and partially disrupt them provided the oil can first penetrate the thin tectocuticle. Seemingly detergents will aid in passage through the tectocuticle as well as themselves having a certain amount of disruptive effect on the wax layers. In some cases mineral oils are said to be the more efficient insecticide carriers (G. G. Robinson 42), in other cases vegetable oils (Fulton & Howard 38, 42). Naturally, strong corrosive agents such as lime are also effective (Hockenyos 39).[5]

Insecticides which penetrate without detectably altering the normal structure of the cuticle are more comparable to general membrane permeability phenomena. But unfortunately, as was pointed out in Chapter 29, this type of permeability is far from being well or satisfactorily understood. The moving force is probably always diffusion, but even in the case of inorganic poisons such as arsenite (p. 309) it is not clear whether the penetration is predominantly controlled by solubility, electrical charges, or molecular size in relation to hypothetical pores through the cuticle.

The well-known hypothesis that the penetration of a substance into a cell is related to its partition coefficient has recently been invoked in cuticle penetration (Wigglesworth 41). A partition coefficient is a ratio between the solubility of a substance in two different immiscible media, and is usually determined between some oil such as olive oil and water. This seems at best a rather indirect statement, and "chemical potential" is a preferable and more directly intercomparable measure (Broyer 47, E. T. Burtt 45, Ferguson 39). The term

[5] Almost certainly the penetration of parasitic and saprophytic fungi is fundamentally different (Steinhaus 49).

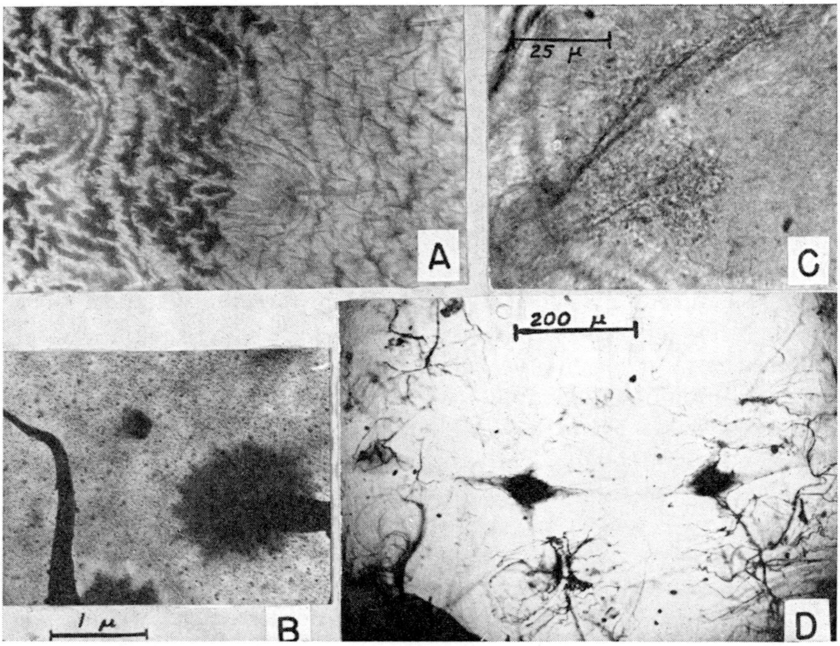

Figure 64. A. Surface view of a portion of the cuticle of a bug, ***Rhodnius prolixus***, after treatment of the outer surface with ammoniacal silver nitrate. The left half had been previously rubbed with alumina dust; the right half is normal; the alumina, having cut through the outer layers of the epicuticle, permits the reagent to contact and react with the underlying polyphenols. (After Wigglesworth.)

B. Electron micrograph of surface view of small portion of wing of a mosquito, *Aedes aegypti,* after soaking cut fragment in ammoniacal silver nitrate for 24 hours (penetration could be through cut edge and inner or outer surface of cuticle). The light browning seen under the light microscope is here resolved into many submicroscopic silver particles. Note that the particles have about the same size and density on the transparent wing membrane and on the heavier bases of the microtrichia. (Original.)

C. Low power photomicrograph of portion of whole mount of supraoesophageal ganglion of a mosquito larva showing droplet-type penetration of propylene glycol monolaurate from injected tracheae. (After Richards and Cutkomp.)

D. Low power photomicrograph of two abdominal segments of a mosquito larva whose tracheae had been filled with xylol stained with Black Sudan B. Larva opened and gut removed; stain (black) in tracheae and nerve ganglia. Stain-filled tracheae also shown branching around and through uncolored muscle, adipose tissue and epithelial tissue. A selective penetration into tissues based on chemical potentials and on the nature of tracheal distribution (see text). (After Richards.)

chemical potential can be explained as a ratio between the solubility of a solute in a solvent and the amount that is actually present in solution; this ratio then is a direct expression of the tendency the solute molecules will have to leave the solvent medium or to enter it. A most favorable chemical potential for absorption will be given by solvents which have a relatively low solubility for a toxin, not by those in which the toxin is highly soluble (E. T. Burtt 45). Classical chemical potentials are derived from fluid oils where there are no fixed particles and no sieve effect (Kurt Meyer & Sievers 36), whereas the cuticular waxes are usually solid; accordingly a wax-water value is desired (J. E. Webb & Green 45).

Three intergrading situations are found:[6] (1) the membrane itself may be lipid, (2) the membrane although not composed of lipids may still have lipophilic side groups (H. King 43), and (3) a high concentration of lipids may be present on one side of the membrane although distinct from it (Fig. 64D).

The lipid components in the outer portion of the epicuticle may actually dissolve certain insecticides, such as pyrethrum powder (Hutzel 42), or show a quantitative relationship to insecticide susceptibility which suggests this (Klinger 36, Pepper & Hastings 43). Penetration of the underlying, essentially hydrophilic procuticle presumably indicates the presence of lipophilic groups, which may be diagrammed as a mosaic of lipid columns (J. E. Webb & Green 45), although such a mosaic has not been demonstrated and may not be present. Lipid materials on one side of the membrane but distinct from the membrane should not affect the permeability value (p. 285) but can increase the amount and rate of penetration (increase the driving force); they can and do result in local accumulations (Fig. 64B) which may give the illusion of selective pharmacological action (and a general cellular toxin may appear as a selective nerve poison) (Glover & Richardson 36, Richards 41, 43, 44a, Richards & Cutkomp 45, Richards & Weygandt 45).

[6] A word of caution should be given concerning comparison of partition coefficient data for cell membranes and arthropod cuticles (Danielli 37). For cells, the entrance of nonelectrolytes (including water) is said to be limited *not by the interface* but *by the interior of the membrane* – and it is not possible at present to distinguish between the interior of the membrane and the interior of the cell. In other words, there is no proof that *the plasma membrane itself* has a limiting effect on the penetration of nonelectrolytes into cells – the effect could all be due to the nature of the cell interior (and so comparable to penetration into a solid body without a discrete surface membrane; see Kurt Meyer & Sievers 36). In contrast, the arthropod cuticle is a distinct membrane with known effects that can be demonstrated by the use of isolated cuticles.

More obscure is the peculiar story involved in the selective action of DDT, as partially analyzed by Richards and his associates (Fan *et al.* 48, Richards & Cutkomp 46). The relevant points brought out in this study are: (1) that DDT shows a strong selective action against groups of animals which have chitin in their cuticles, (2) that there is a positive temperature coefficient when the insecticide is either applied in concentrated form or injected into the animal, (3) that a negative temperature coefficient may be obtained (Lindquist *et al.* 45, 46, Potter & Gillham 46) but is only obtained when the application is external *and* when the dosage is small or the concentration at the outer surface is dilute — in other words, only when quan-

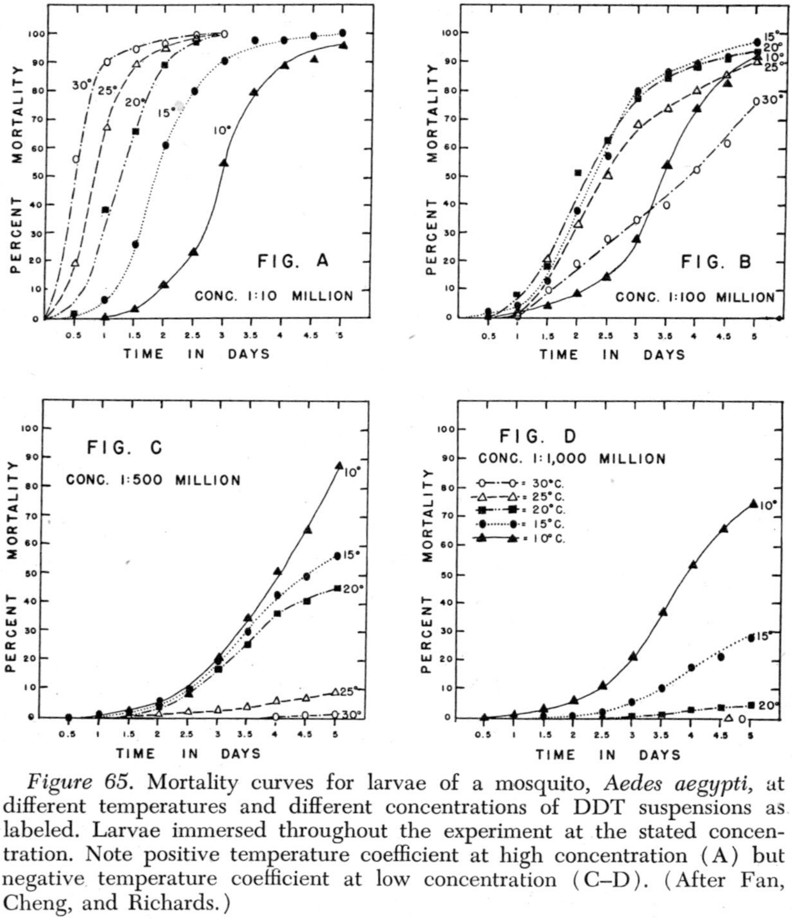

Figure 65. Mortality curves for larvae of a mosquito, *Aedes aegypti,* at different temperatures and different concentrations of DDT suspensions as labeled. Larvae immersed throughout the experiment at the stated concentration. Note positive temperature coefficient at high concentration (A) but negative temperature coefficient at low concentration (C–D). (After Fan, Cheng, and Richards.)

titative considerations show that concentration is needed (Fig. 65), and (4) that DDT is adsorbed by cuticle (Lord 48, Upholt 47). Since the negative temperature coefficient is obtained only by external application the possibility of its being an illusion due to competition between rate of toxic action and rate of decomposition or excretion is eliminated. The phenomenon must be explained in terms of the integument. Rationalizing from these facts, an hypothesis was advanced stating that at low concentrations of DDT arthropod cuticle selectively accumulates DDT from the environment by adsorption processes, has the DDT molecules move through the cuticle perhaps by surface migration (Volmer 32), and then eluted by chemical potentials at the inner surface of the cuticle. The hypothesis still seems reasonable but it is highly speculative and does not account for the known resistance of certain species of arthropods. Whatever explanation may eventually prove acceptable, the peculiar temperature-cuticle-DDT relationship certainly requires elucidation.

CONCLUDING STATEMENT ON PERMEABILITY

In closing this short treatment of cuticle permeability, it might be well to repeat that some unexpected phenomena have been encountered (the role of destructive effects, the results with polar-apolar mixtures, factors associated with the selective action of DDT, and the multiplicity of diverse barriers), and that a good analysis of one phenomenon has been made (transpiration). But most data are inadequate or invalid, and most insecticide literature is too complicated by other factors or phenomena. These examples illustrate the need for valid, unambiguous data on cuticle permeability, and serve as a warning against the naive fitting of penetration data of uncertain interpretation into the concepts presented in general treatises on membrane permeability. A precise statement of experimental conditions is necessary for evaluation and for comparison of data. Clearly the cuticle is not a system of such stability that it can be handled with impunity or exposed to a wide array of chemical agents, although under favorable circumstances it may retain reasonably normal properties for long periods. The number of papers that must be discarded or repeated shows that validation of data is of paramount importance.

BIBLIOGRAPHICAL INDEX OF AUTHORS

THE italicized numbers in parentheses at the end of each reference indicate the pages on which the reference is cited.

References marked with an asterisk (*) have not been seen in the original; commonly the abstract or citation on the basis of which the reference is here included is given in parentheses. References marked with a double asterisk (**) are known to me only by title.

Abbott, R. L. 1926. Contributions to the physiology of digestion in the australian roach, *Periplaneta australasiae* Fab. J. Exp. Zool., 44:219–235. (*293, 298, 311*)

Abderhalden, E. 1925. Beitrag zur Kenntnis der synthetischen Leistungen des tierischen Organismus. Z. physiol. Chem., 142:189–190. (*31*)

———, and L. Behrend 1909. Vergleichende Untersuchungen über die Zusammensetzung und den Aufbau verschiedener Seidenarten. Z. physiol. Chem., 59:236–238. (*67*)

Abderhalden, E., and K. Heyns 1931. Über die bei der Hydrolyse von Tussahseidenfibroin sich bildenden Abbauprodukte. Z. physiol. Chem., 202:37–48. (*12, 38, 62, 63*)

——— 1933. Nachweis vom Chitin in Flügelresten von Coleopteren des oberen Mitteleocäns. Biochem. Z., 259:320–321. (*12, 54*)

Adam, A. 1912. Bau und Mechanismus des Receptaculum seminis bei den Bienen, Wespen und Ameisen. Zool. Jahrb., Anat., 35:1–74. (*153, 161, 204*)

Agassiz, L. 1850. On the circulation of the fluids in insects. Proc. Amer. Assoc. Adv. Sci., 2:140–143. (*256*)

Ahrens, W. 1930. Über die Korpergliederung, die Haut und die Tracheenorgane der Termitenkönigin. Jena Z. Naturw., 64:449–530. (*161, 175, 177, 207*)

Akenhurst, S. C. 1922. Larva of *Chaoborus crystallinus* (*Corethra plumicornis*). J. R. Micr. Soc., pp. 341–372. (*255, 262*)

Albro, H. T. 1930. A cytological study of the changes occurring in the oenocytes of *Galerucella nymphaeae* Linn. during the larval and pupal periods of development. J. Morph. & Physiol., 50:527–567. (*217*)

Alders, N. 1927. Beitrag zur Kenntnis der Seidenlarven. Biochem. Z., 183:446–450. (*62, 64*)

Aleksandrov, V. Y., *see* Alexandrov, V. Y.

* Aleshina, V. I. 1938. Destruction of chitin by sulfate reducing bacteria, and changes of the oxidation-reduction conditions in the reduction of sulfates. Microbiol. (USSR), 7(7):850–859. (*55, 56*)

Alexander, P., and D. H. R. Barton 1943. The excretion of ethylquinone by the flour beetle. Biochem. J., 37:463–465. (*74*)

Alexander, P., J. A. Kitchener, and H. V. A. Briscoe 1944a. Inert dust insecticides. I. Mechanism of action. Ann. Appl. Biol., 31:143–149. (*94, 123, 302*)

——— 1944b. Inert dust insecticides. II. The nature of effective dusts. *Ibid.*, pp. 150–156. (*94, 123, 302*)

——— 1944c. Inert dust insecticides. III. The effect of dusts on stored products pests other than *Calandra granaria*. *Ibid.*, pp. 156–159. (*302*)

——— 1944d. The effect of waxes and inorganic powders on the transpiration of water through celluloid membranes. Trans. Faraday Soc., 40:10–19. (*294*)

* Alexandrov, V. Y. 1934. (The permeability of the chitin of some dipterous larvae and a method of investigating it.) (In Russian with German summary.) J. Biol., Moscow, 3:490–507. (*293*)

——— 1935. Permeability of chitin in some dipterous larvae and the method of its study. Acta Zool., 16:1–19. (*293, 294, 310, 311, 314*)

Allen, E. J. 1892. On the minute structure of the gills of *Palaemonetes varians*. Quart. J. Micr. Sci., 34:75–84. (*207*)

——— 1893. Nephridia and body-cavity of some decapod crustacea. *Ibid.*, pp. 403–426. (*250*)

Allen, T. H., and J. H. Bodine 1941. Enzymes in ontogenesis. 17. The importance of copper for protyrosinase. Science, 94:443–444. (*75*)

Allen, T. H., G. E. Boyd, and J. H. Bodine 1942. Enzymes in ontogenesis. 21. Unimolecular films and fractions of protyrosinase activators from grasshopper egg oil. J. Biol. Chem., 143:785–793. (*75*)

Allen, T. H., A. B. Otis, and J. H. Bodine 1942. The pH stability of protyrosinase and tyrosinase. J. Gen. Physiol., 26:151–155. (*75*)

——— 1943. Changes in properties of protyrosinase due to shaking. Arch. Biochem., 1:357–364. (*75*)

Alpatov, W. W. 1930. Phenotypical variation in body and cell size of *Drosophila melanogaster*. Biol. Bull., 58:85–103. (*204, 245*)

Alsberg, C. L., and C. A. Hedblom 1909. Soluble chitin from *Limulus polyphemus* and its peculiar osmotic behavior. J. Biol. Chem., 6:483–497. (*19, 136*)

Alt, W. 1912. Über das Respirationssystem von *Dytiscus marginalis* L. Z. wiss. Zool., 99:357–413, 414–443. (*261, 262, 268*)

Alverdes, F. 1912. Über konzentrisch geschichtete Chitinkörper bei *Branchipus grubii*. Zool. Anz., 40:317–323. (*52*)

Ambronn, H. 1890. Cellulose-Reaction bei Arthropoden und Mollusken. Mitt. Zool. Sta. Neapel, 9:475–478. (*36, 39*)

———, and A. Frey 1926. Das Polarisationsmikroskop. Akad. Verlagsgesellschaft, Leipzig. (*130*)

Aminoff, D., and W. T. J. Morgan 1948. Hexosamine components of the human blood group substances. Nature, 162:579–580. (*11, 12*)

Anderson, B. G. 1946. Comparison of immobilization time-concentration relationships for *Daphnia* in solutions of various inorganic salts. Anat. Rec., 94:370. (*290*)

———, and L. A. Brown 1930. Chitin secretion in *Daphnia magna*. Physiol. Zool., 3:485–493. (*225*)

Anderson, T. F., and A. G. Richards 1942a. Nature through the electron microscope. Sci. Monthly, 55:187–192. (*67, 140, 197, 200, 254, 276*)

——— 1942b. An electron microscope study of some structural colors in insects. J. Appl. Physics, 13:748–758. (*136, 140, 141, 150, 193, 196, 199, 200, 201, 272, 273, 277*)

Andrews, E. A. 1911. Sperm transfer in certain Decapoda. Proc. U.S. Nat. Mus., 39:419–434. (*282*)

——— 1931. Spermatophores of an Oregon crayfish. Amer. Nat., 65:277–280. (*282*)

Anglas, J. 1904. Du rôle des trachées dans la métamorphose des insectes. C. R. Soc. Biol., 56:175–176. (*264*)

Apple, J. W. 1941. The influence of sodium and calcium chlorides on toxicity of nicotine to eggs of *Musca domestica* L. J. Econ. Ent., 34:84–85. (*294, 310, 314*)

Apstein, C. 1889. Bau und Function der Spinndrüsen der Araneida. Arch. f. Naturges., 55(1):29–74. (*67, 251*)

Araki, T. 1895. Über das Chitosan. Z. physiol. Chem., 20:498–510. (*26, 27*)
Ariyama, H., and K. Takahasi 1929. Über den relativen Nährwert der Kohlenhydrate und verwandten Substanzen. Biochem. Z., 216:269–277. (*31*)
Armbrecht, W. 1919. Chitose. Biochem. Z., 95:108–123. (*28*)
Aronssohn, F. 1910. Sur la nature des enveloppes abandonées par les abeilles a l'intérieur des alvéoles de la cire. C. R. Soc. Biol., 68:1111–1113. (*51, 116, 228, 234*)
Assmuth, J. 1913. *Termitoxenia assmuthi* Wasm. Anatomisch-histologische Untersuchung. Halle Nova Acta Leop., 98:187–316. (*161*)
Astbury, W. T. 1933. Fundamentals of Fiber Structure. Oxford Univ. Press. (*6*)
——— 1943. X-rays and the stoichiometry of the proteins. Adv. in Enzymology (Interscience Publ. Co., N. Y.), 3:63–108. (*6*)
———, and F. O. Bell 1939. X-ray data on the structure of natural fibers and other bodies of high molecular weight. Tabul. Biol., 17:90–112. (*18*)
Astbury, W. T., and R. Lomax 1935. An x-ray study of the hydration and denaturation of proteins. J. Chem. Soc., p. 846–851. (*60*)
Astrup, T., I. Galsmar, and M. Volkert 1944. Polysaccharide sulfuric acid esters as anticoagulants. Acta Physiol. Skand., 8:215–216. (*29*)
Athanasiu, I., and I. Dragoiu 1913. Sur les capillaires aériens des fibres musculaires chez les insectes. C. R. Soc. Biol., 75:578–582. (*263*)
——— 1914. La structure des muscles striés des insectes et leur rapports avec les trachées aériennes. Arch. d'anat. micr., 16:345–361. (*263*)
Attems, C. G. 1926. Myriapoda, and Chilopoda. *In* Kukenthal and Krumbach, Handbuch der Zoologie, 4:1–238, 239–402. (*160, 161, 205, 206, 267*)
Aubertot, M. 1932a. Origine proventriculaire et évacuation continue de la membrane péritrophique chez les larves d'*Eristalis tenax*. C. R. Soc. Biol., 111:743–745. (*278*)
——— 1932b. Les sacs péritrophiques des larves d'*Aeschna*; leur évacuation périodique. *Ibid.*, pp. 746–748. (*278*)
——— 1933. Sur le proventricule des larves des Diptères némocères; origine du tube péritrophique et rôle des sinus valvulaires. *Ibid.*, pp. 1005–1007. (*278*)
——— 1938. Sur les membranes péritrophiques des insectes. Arch. Zool. Exp. & Gen., 79(Not. & Rev.):49–57. (*277*)
Awerinzew, S. 1907. Die Struktur und die Chemische Zusammensetzung der Gehäuse bei den Süsswasserrhizopoden. Arch. Protistenkunde, 8:95–119. (*42, 43*)
Babák, E. 1912a. Die Mechanik und Innervation der Atmung (Tracheaten). *In* Winterstein, Handbuch vergl. Physiol., vol. 1. (*253, 266*)
——— 1912b. Zur Physiologie der Atmung bei Culex. Int. Rev. Ges. Hydrobiol. Hydrogr., 5:81–90. (*261*)
Babers, F. H. 1941. Glycogen in *Prodenia eridania* with special reference to the ingestion of glucose. J. Agr. Res., 62:509–530. (*30*)
Baldwin, E. 1947. Dynamic Aspects of Biochemistry. Cambridge Univ. Press. (*6, 77*)
* Balli, A. 1934. Variazioni quantitative dei due componenti della fibra serica, sericina e fibroina, nel bozzolo di *Bombyx mori*. Atti. Soc. Nat. Mat. Modena, 65:3–15. (*67*)
* ——— 1939. L'azione del digiuno assoluto, nei bachi da seta di quinta età, sulle variazioni quantitative della fibroina e della sericina nel filo serico. Riv. Biol. Firenze, 28:37–43. (*67*)
Balss, H. 1927. Decapoda. *In* Kukenthal and Krumbach, Handbuch der Zoologie, 3(1):840–1038. (*86, 87, 101, 141, 161, 163, 179, 182, 195, 207, 209, 211, 214, 220, 222, 249*)

Bangham, D. H. 1946. Saturated adsorbed films and the structure of deeply super-cooled water. Nature, 157:733. (*287*)

* Bardenfleth, K. S., and R. Ege 1916. On the anatomy and physiology of the air sacs of the larva of *Corethra plumicornis*. Vidensk. Meddel. Dansk. Naturh. Foren Kobenhavn, 67:25–42. (*262*)

Barnes, T. C. 1938. Experiments on *Ligia* in Bermuda. 5. Further effects of salts and of heavy sea water. Biol. Bull., 74:108–116. (*310*)

Barrows, W. M. 1925. Modification and development of the arachnid palpal claw, with special reference to spiders. Ann. Ent. Soc. Amer., 18:483–516. (*66*)

Barth, R. 1945. Untersuchungen am Hautmuskelschlauch der Raupen von *Catocala*-Arten (zugleich ein Beitrag zur Frage des Insertion der Arthropodenmuskels). Zool. Jahrb., Anat., 69:405–434. (*162, 237, 241, 242*)

——— 1949. Vergleichend morphologische Studien über die Duftschuppen der Pieriden *Pieris brassicae* und *Pieris rapae* und der Satyrine *Coenonympha pamphilus*. *Ibid.*, 70:397–426. (*275*)

* de Bary 1866. Morphologie der Pilze. (Cited by Rammelberg 1931.) (*14*)

Batelli, A. 1879. Contribuzione all'anatomia ed alla fisiologia della larva dell' *Eristalis tenax*. Bull. Soc. Ent. Ital., 11:77–120. (*215*)

Bateman, J. B. 1933. Osmotic and ionic regulation in the shore crab, *Carcinus maenas*, with notes on the blood concentrations of *Gammarus locusta* and *Ligia oceanica*. J. Exp. Biol., 10:355–371. (*292*)

Bates, M. 1934. The peristigmatic gland cells of trypetid larvae (Diptera). Ann. Ent. Soc. Amer., 27:1–4. (*215*)

Bath, J. D., and J. W. Ellis 1941. Some features and implications of the near infrared absorption spectra of various proteins: gelatin, silk fibroin and zinc insulinate. J. Physical Chem., 45:204–209. (*69, 120, 129*)

Bauman, H. 1921. Beitrag zur Kenntnis der Anatomie der Tardigraden (*Macrobiotus hufelandii*). Z. wiss. Zool., 118:637–652. (*160, 164*)

——— 1930. Die Cuticula von *Macrobiotus hufelandii*. Zool. Anz., 88:72–74. (*160*)

Baur, A. 1860. Über den Bau der Chitinsehnen am Kiefer der Flusskrebse. Arch. Anat. Physiol., pp. 113–144. (*241*)

Bayliss, W. M. 1915. Principles of General Physiology. Longmans Green, London. (*289*)

Beament, J. W. L. 1945a. The cuticular lipoids of insects. J. Exp. Biol., 21:115–131. (*96–98, 289, 293–295, 300, 302–305*)

——— 1945b. An apparatus to measure contact angles. Trans. Faraday Soc., 41:45–47. (*137*)

——— 1946a. The waterproofing process in eggs of *Rhodnius prolixus* Stähl. Proc. R. Soc. London, ser. B, 133:407–418. (*98, 99, 281, 314*)

——— 1946b. The formation and structure of the chorion of the egg in an hemipteran, *Rhodnius prolixus*. Quart. J. Micr. Sci., 87:393–439. (*50, 66, 280, 281, 289, 314*)

——— 1946c. Waterproofing mechanism of an insect egg. Nature, 157:370. (*281*)

——— 1947. The formation and structure of the micropylar complex in the egg shell of *Rhodnius prolixus*. J. Exp. Biol., 23:213–233. (*281, 314*)

——— 1948a. The penetration of the insect egg-shells. I. Penetration of the chorion of *Rhodnius prolixus*. Bull. Ent. Res., 39:359–383. (*98, 134, 140, 281, 314*)

——— 1948b. The role of wax layers in the waterproofing of insect cuticle and egg-shell. Disc. Faraday Soc., no. 3, pp. 177–182. (*85, 94, 98, 134, 140, 281, 287, 289, 300, 302–304*)

——— 1949. The penetration of insect egg shells. II. The properties and permeability of sub-chorial membranes during development of *Rhodnius prolixus*. Bull. Ent. Res., 39:467–488. (*115, 314*)

Beams, H. W., and R. L. King 1932. The architecture of the parietal cells of the salivary glands of the grasshopper, with special reference to the intracellular canaliculi, Golgi bodies and mitochondria. J. Morph., 53:223–242. (*251*)

—— 1933. The intracellular canaliculi of the pharyngeal glands of the honey bee. Biol. Bull., 64:309–314. (*251*)

Beard, R. L. 1942. On the formation of the tracheal funnel in *Anasa tristis* DeG. induced by the parasite *Trichopoda pennipes* Fabr. Ann. Ent. Soc. Amer., 35:68–72. (*261*)

Beatty, R. A. 1949. The pigmentation of cavernicolous animals. 3. The carotenoid pigments of some amphipod crustacea. J. Exp. Biol., 26:125–130. (*90, 91*)

* Beauregard, H. 1885. Recherches sur les insectes vésicants. J. Anat. Physiol., 21:483–534. (*192*)

—— 1890. Les Insectes Vésicants. Alcan, Paris. (*114*)

Becker, E. 1937a. Die Farbstoffe der Insekten. Ent. Rdsch., 54:301–303, 338–340, 346–347, 368–370, 406–407, 425–428, 481–486. (*86, 91*)

—— 1937b. Die rotbraune Zeichnung der Wespennestmütter, eine durch mechanischen Reiz ausgelöste Pigmentablagerung in Liesegang'schen Ringen. Z. vergl. Physiol., 24:305–318. (*141*)

—— 1937c. Über das Pterinpigment bei Insekten und die Färbung und Zeichnung von Vespa im besonderen. Z. Morph. Ökol. Tiere, 32:672–751. (*91*)

—— 1938. Eine gut analysierbare Pigmentablagerung in Liesegang'schen Ringen bei Insekten. Forsch. u. Fortschr., Berlin, 14:9–11. (*141, 142*)

—— 1941. Über Versuche zur Anreicherung und physiologischen Charakterisierung des Wirkstoffs der Puparisierung. Biol. Zbl., 61:360–388. (*76, 187*)

Becker, F. D. 1936. Some observations on respiration in the terrestrial isopod, *Porcellio scaber* Latr. Trans. Amer. Micr. Soc., 55:442–445. (*253, 306*)

Becking, L. B., and J. C. Chamberlin 1925. A note on the refractive index of chitin. Proc. Soc. Exp. Biol. & Med., 22:256. (*120*)

** Beer, S. 1931a. Sulla fluorescenza presentata dai bozzoli e della seta sotto l'azione dei raggi ultravioletti. Boll. Lab. Zool. Bachicoltura Milano, 2:150–190. (*121, 130*)

** —— 1931b. Sulla fluorescenza presentata dalla larva del *Bombyx mori* sotto l'azione della luce di Wood. *Ibid.*, pp. 191–194. (*121, 130*)

** —— 1931c. Nuove osservazioni sulla fluorescenza presentata dalle larve del *Bombyx mori* sotto l'azione della luce di Wood. *Ibid.*, pp. 195–206. (*121, 130*)

* Beguin, M. 1874. Hist. des Insectes qui peuv. être empl. comme vésicants. Paris. (Cited by Beauregard 1890.) (*114*)

Behm, R. C., and J. M. Nelson 1944. The aerobic oxidation of phenol by means of tyrosinase. J. Amer. Chem. Soc., 66:711–714. (*75*)

Behr, G. 1930. Über Autolyse bei *Aspergillus niger*. Arch. Mikrobiol., 1:418–444. (*25*)

Bell, D. J. 1948. The structure of glycogens. Biol. Rev., 23:256–266. (*31*)

de Bellesne, J. 1877. Phénomènes qui accompagnent la metamorphose chez la Libellule déprimée. C. R. Acad. Sci., 85:448–450. (*233*)

Bendich, A., and E. Chargaff 1946. The isolation and characterization of two antigenic fractions of Proteus OX-19. J. Biol. Chem., 166:283–312. (*13*)

Benecke, W. 1905. Über *Bacillus chitinovorus*, einen Chitin zersetzenden Spaltpilz. Bot. Zeit., 63:227–242. (*54–56*)

* Bengtsson, S. 1899. Über sogennanten Herzkörper bei Insektenlarven. Bihang. K. Svenska Vet.-Akad. Handl., 25:3–23. (Cited by Holmgren 1907.) (*209*)

Benton, A. G. 1935. Chitinovorous bacteria – a preliminary survey. J. Bact., 29:20, 449–464. (*55, 56*)

Benton, J. R. 1907. The strength and elasticity of spider thread. Amer. J. Sci., ser. 4, 24:75–78. (*122*)

Berger, C. A. 1938. Multiplication and reduction of somatic chromosome groups as a regular developmental process in the mosquito, *Culex pipiens*. Carnegie Inst. Wash., Contrib. to Embryology, Publ. no. 496, pp. 210–232. (*204, 206*)

Berger, E., and A. Bethe 1931. Die Durchlässigkeit der Körperoberflächen wirbelloser Tiere für Jodionen. Pfluger's Arch. Ges. Physiol., 228:769–789. (*290, 294, 298, 310, 313*)

Bergmann, M., and C. Niemann 1938. On the structure of silk fibroin. J. Biol. Chem., 122:577–596. (*62, 64, 68, 69*)

Bergmann, M., and L. Zervas 1931. Synthesen mit Glucosamin. Ber. dtsch. Chem. Ges., 64B:975–980. (*11*)

———, H. Rinke, and H. Schleich 1934. Über Dipeptide von epimeren Glucosaminsäuren und ihr Verhalten gegen Dipeptidase. Konfiguration des d-Glucosamins. Z. physiol. Chem., 224:33–39. (*11, 28*)

Bergmann, M., L. Zervas, and E. Silberkweit 1931a. Über die Biose des Chitins. Naturwiss., 19:20. (*11, 13*)

——— 1931b. Über Chitin und Chitobiose. Ber. dtsch. Chem. Ges., 64:2436–2440. (*11, 13, 14*)

——— 1931c. Über Glucosaminsäure und ihre Desaminierung. Ber. dtsch. Chem. Ges., 64:2428–2436. (*28*)

Bergmann, W. 1938. The composition of the ether extractive from exuviae of the silkworm, *Bombyx mori*. Ann. Ent. Soc. Amer., 31:315–321. (*94–96, 229*)

Bergold, G. 1935. Die Ausbildung der Stigmen bei Coleopteren verschiedener Biotype. Z. Morph. Ökol. Tiere, 29:511–526. (*299*)

Berlese, A. 1909. Gli Insetti. Kramer, Milan. (*182, 192*)

Bernard, H. M. 1892. An endeavour to show that tracheae arose from setiparous sacs. Zool. Jahrb., Anat., 5:511–524. (*253*)

* Bernard-Deschamps 1845. Recherches microscopiques sur l'organisation des élythres des Coléoptères. Paris. (*245*)

Bernecker, A. 1909. Zur Histologie der Respirationsorgane bei Crustaceen. Zool. Jahrb., Anat., 27:583–630. (*161, 244, 247*)

Berteaux, L. 1889. Le poumon des Arachnides. La Cellule, 5:253–317. (*247*)

Berthelot, M. 1859. Sur la transformation en sucre de la chitine et de la tunicine principes immédiats contenus dans les tissus des animaux invertébrés. Ann. d. Chim. et d. Phys., ser. 3, 56:149–156. (*81*)

Bertho, A., F. Hölder, W. Meiser, and F. Hüther 1931. Zur Synthese peptidähnlicher Körper aus Aminozuckern und Aminosäuren. 1. Glucosamin als Komponente. Ann. d. Chem., 485:127–151. (*11, 28*)

Bertkow, P. 1872. Über die Respirationsorgane der Araneen. Arch. f. Naturges., 38:208–233. (*255*)

Bethe, A. 1928. Ionendurchlässigkeit der Körperoberfläche von wirbellosen Tieren des Meeres als Ursache der Giftigkeit von Seewasser abnormer Zusammensetzung. Pfluger's Arch. Ges. Physiol., 221:344–362. (*292*)

——— 1930. The permeability of the surface of marine animals. J. Gen. Physiol., 13:437–444. (*292*)

Betten, C. 1902. The larva of the caddis fly *Molanna cinerea* Hagen. J. N. Y. Ent. Soc., 10:147–154. (*250*)

Bevelander, G., and P. Benzer 1948. Calcification in marine molluscs. Biol. Bull., 94:176–183. (*105*)

Bhagvat, K., and D. Richter 1938. Animal phenolases and adrenaline. Biochem. J., 32:1397–1406. (*74, 76*)

* Bialaszewicz, K. 1937. (Variations in composition of silkworms during the final larval period.) Acta Biol. Exptl. (Warsaw), 11:20–42. (Chem. Abstr., 32:7576.) (*114*)

Biedermann, W. 1898. Beiträge zur vergleichenden Physiologie der Verdauung. Pfluger's Arch. Ges. Physiol., 72:105–162. (*77*)

——— 1901. Über den Zustand des Kalkes in Crustaceenpanzern. Biol. Zbl., 21:343–352. (*85*)

——— 1902. Über die Structur des Chitins bei Insekten und Crustaceen. Anat. Anz., 21:485–490. (*130, 159, 193*)

——— 1903. Geformte Sekrete. Z. allg. Physiol., 2:395–481. (*21, 132, 141, 159, 161, 180, 182, 192–194*)

——— 1914a. Physiologie der Stütz- und Skelettsubstanzen. *In* Winterstein, Handbuch vergl. Physiol., 3(1):319–1188. (*6, 17, 42, 159, 160*)

——— 1914b. Farbe und Zeichnung der Insekten. *Ibid.*, 3(2):1657–1994. (*86, 196*)

Bierry, H., B. Gouzon, and C. Magnan 1939. N-acétylglucosamine et sucre protéidique. C. R. Soc. Biol., 130:411–413. (*11*)

Birch, L. C., and H. G. Andrewartha 1942. The influence of moisture on the eggs of *Austroicetes cruciata* with reference to its ability to survive desiccation. Australian J. Exp. Biol. Med. Sci., 20:1–8. (*314*)

Blanchard, E. 1847. On the circulation in insects. Ann. Mag. Nat. Hist., ser. 1, 20:112–114 (also C. R. Acad. Sci., 24:870. 1847). (*256*)

——— 1848. De la circulation dans les insectes. Ann. Sci. Nat. Zool., ser. 3, 9:359–398. (*256*)

——— 1849. De l'appareil circulatoire et des organes de la respiration dans les Arachnides. *Ibid.*, ser. 3, 12:317–352. (*256*)

Blauvelt, W. E. 1945. The internal morphology of the common red spider mite (*Tetranychus telarius* Linn.). Cornell Univ. Agr. Exp. Sta., Mem. no. 270, 35 pp. (*66, 250, 254*)

Blount, B. K., A. C. Chibnall, and H. A. Mangouri 1937. The wax of white pine chermes. Biochem. J., 31:1375–1378. (*95*)

Blunck, H. 1910. Zur Kenntnis der Natur und Herkunft des "Milchigen Sekrets" am Prothorax des *Dytiscus marginalis* L. Zool. Anz., 37:112–113. (*116, 164, 170*)

——— 1912a. Beitrag zur Kenntnis der Morphologie und Physiologie der Haftscheiben von *Dytiscus marginalis* L. Z. wiss. Zool., 100:459–492. (*249*)

——— 1912b. Die Schrechdrüsen des *Dytiscus* und ihr Sekret. *Ibid.*, pp. 493–508. (*164, 170*)

——— 1912c. Das Geschlechtsleben des *Dytiscus marginalis* L. *Ibid.*, 102:169–248. (*282*)

——— 1923. Die Entwicklung des *Dytiscus marginalis* L. vom Ei bis zur Imago. *Ibid.*, 121:171–391. (*209, 225, 228, 229*)

Bobin, G., and H. Mazoué 1946. Topographie, histologie, caractères physiques et chimiques des soies d'*Aphrodite aculeata* L. (Annélide, polychaète). Bull. Soc. Zool. France, 69:125–134. (*46*)

Bock, F. 1925. Die Respirationsorgane von *Potamobius astacus* Leach. Z. wiss. Zool., 124:51–117. (*246*)

Bodenstein, D. 1936. Das Determinationsgeschehen bei Insekten mit Ausschluss der frühembryonalen Determination. Ergebn. Biol., 13:174–234. (*156, 233*)

Bodine, J. H. 1921. Factors influencing the water content and the rate of metabolism of certain Orthoptera. J. Exp. Zool., 32:137–164. (*298*)

——— 1923. A note on the toxicity of acids for mosquito larvae. Biol. Bull., 45:149–152. (*310*)

———, and T. H. Allen 1941a. Enzymes in ontogenesis (Orthoptera). 19. Protyrosinase and morphological integrity of grasshopper eggs. Biol. Bull., 81:388–391. (*75*)

——— 1941b. Enzymes in ontogenesis (Orthoptera). 20. The site of origin and the distribution of protyrosinase in the developing egg of a grasshopper. J. Exp. Zool., 88:343–351. (*75, 76*)

Bodine, J. H., and D. L. Hill 1945. Action of synthetic detergents on protyrosinase. Arch. Biochem., 7:21–32. (*75*)

Bodine, J. H., and T. N. Tahmisian 1943. The development on an enzyme (tyrosinase) in the parthenogenetic egg of the grasshopper, *Melanoplus differentialis*. Biol. Bull., 85:157–163. (*75*)

———, and D. L. Hill 1944. Effect of heat on protyrosinase. Heat activation, inhibition and injury of protyrosinase and tyrosinase. Arch. Biochem., 4:403–412. (Abstract in Anat. Rec., 89:546.) (*75*)

Boelitz, E. 1933. Beiträge zur Anatomie und Histologie der Collembolen. Zool. Jahrb., Anat., 57:375–432. (*161, 237, 238*)

Boese, G. 1936. Der Einfluss tierischen Parasiten auf den Organismus der Insekten. Z. Parasitenkunde, 8:243–284. (*52, 217, 219*)

de Boissezon, P. 1930a. Sur l'histologie et l'histophysiologie de l'intestin de *Culex pipiens* L. C. R. Soc. Biol., 103:567–568, 568–570, 1232–1233. (*278*)

——— 1930b. Contribution à l'étude de la biologie et de l'histophysiologie de *Culex pipiens* L. Arch. Zool. Exp. & Gen., 70:281–431. (*205, 206, 278*)

Bond, R. M. 1933. A contribution to the study of the natural food-cycle in aquatic environments. Bull. Bingham Ocean. Coll., Yale, 4(4): 1–89. (*293, 311*)

Boné, G., and H. J. Koch 1942. Le rôle des tubes de Malpighi et du rectum dans la régulation ionique chez les insectes. Ann. Soc. Zool. Belg., 72:73–87. (*292*)

Bongardt, J. 1903. Beiträge zur Kenntnis der Leuchtorgane einheimischer Lampyriden. Z. wiss. Zool., 75:1–45. (*259, 264*)

Bonnet, A. 1906. On the anatomy and histology of the Ixodidae. Ann. Mag. Nat. Hist., ser. 7, 17:509–511. (*252, 254*)

——— 1907. Recherches sur l'anatomie et la développement des Ixodidés. Ann. Univ. Lyon, ser. 1, 20:1–171. (*159, 161, 207, 209, 211*)

Bordage, E. 1900. On the spiral growth of appendages in course of regeneration in Arthropoda. Ann. Mag. Nat. Hist., ser. 7, 5:314–316 (also C. R. Acad. Sci., 129:455–457, 1899). (*255*)

——— 1901. Contribution à l'étude de la régénération des appendices chez les arthropodes. Ann. Soc. Ent. France, pp. 304–307. (*52*)

Bordas, L. 1908a. Rôle physiologique des glandes arborescentes annexées à l'appareil générateur des Blattes. C. R. Acad. Sci., 147:1495–1497. (*279*)

——— 1908b. Produit de sécrétion de la glande odorante des Blattes. Bull. Soc. Zool. Paris, 33:31–32. (*250*)

——— 1908c. Les glandes cutanées de quelques Vespides. *Ibid.*, pp. 59–64. (*209*)

Börner, C. 1904. Beiträge zur Morphologie der Arthropoden. 1. Ein Beitrag zur Kenntnis der Pedipalpen. Zoologica (Stuttgart). 17(42): 1–174. (*157, 160, 207, 243, 247*)

Borodin, D. N. 1929. Vergleichende Histologie der Hautorgane bei den Chloraeniden (Polychaeta). Z. Morph. Ökol. Tiere, 16:26–48. (*176*)

Bounoure, L. 1911. La sécrétion de la chitine chez les coléoptères carnivores. C. R. assoc. Fr. avanc. Sci., Paris, 40:112, 523–526. (*113*)

* ——— 1912. L'influence du régime alimentaire sur le production de la chitine chez les coléoptères. C. R. Congr. Savant. Fr., Sect. Sci., pp. 189–193. (*110*)

——— 1913. L'influence de la taille des insectes sur la production de la chitine, sécrétion de surface. C. R. Acad. Sci., 157:140–142. (*113*)

* ——— 1919. Aliments, chitine et tube digestif chez les coléoptères. Hermann, Paris. (Cited by Wigglesworth 1933.) (*229*)

Bouvier, E. L. 1902. Sur l'organisation, le développement et les affinités du *Peripatopsis blainvillei*. Zool. Jahrb., Suppl. 5, vol. 2 (3):675–730. (*160*)

Brach, H., and O. von Fürth 1912. Untersuchungen über den chemischen Aufbau des Chitins. Biochem. Z., 38:468–491. (*11, 15*)

* Braconnot, H. 1811. Recherches analytique sur la nature des champignons. Ann. Chim., 79:265–304. (*14*)

Bradfield, J. R. G. 1946. Alkaline phosphatase in invertebrate sites of protein secretion. Nature, 157:876–877. (*70, 79, 252*)

Branch, H. E. 1922. A contribution to the knowledge of the internal anatomy of Trichoptera. Ann. Ent. Soc. Amer., 15:256–275. (*249*)

von Brand, T. 1940. Further observations upon the composition of Acanthocephala. J. Parasitol., 26:301–307. (*43*)

Braun, M. 1875. Über die histologischen Vorgänge bei der Häutung von *Astacus fluviatilis*. Arb. zool.-zootom. Inst. Würzburg, 2:121–126. (*30, 159, 180, 182*)

——— 1877. Zur Kenntnis des Vorkommen der Speichel- und Kittdrüsen bei den Dekapoden. Arb. Zool. Inst. Würzburg, 3:472–479. (*214*)

Braun, W. 1939. Contributions to the study of development of the wing-pattern in Lepidoptera. Biol. Bull., 76:226–240. (*37, 271*)

Breakey, E. P., and A. C. Miller 1935. A method for comparing the ovicidal properties of contact insecticides. J. Econ. Ent., 28:353–358. (*294*)

Brecher, L. 1924. Die Puppenfärbungen der Vanessiden. Arch. mikr. anat. Entw. Mech., 102:517–548. (*126*)

——— 1938. Pigment Bildung bei Wirbellosen und Wirbeltieren. Tabul. Biol., 16:140–161. (*86*)

———, and F. Winkler 1925. Übereinstimmung positiver und negativer Dopareaktionen an Gefrier schnitten mit jenen an Extrakten. Arch. mikr. anat., 104:659–663. (*72*)

Bredenkamp, J. 1942. Zur Kenntnis der Wirkungsweise der Kontaktgifte mit besonderer Berüchsichtigung der Insektencuticula. Z. angew. Ent., 28:519–549. (*290, 293, 313*)

Breitenbrecher, J. K. 1918. The relation of water to the behavior of the potato beetle in the desert. Carnegie Inst. Wash., Publ. no. 263, pp. 341–384. (*298*)

Brenner, W. 1915–1916. Die Wachsdrüsen und die Wachsausscheidung bei *Psylla alni* L. Z. wiss. Insekt. Biol., 11:290–294; 12:6–9. (*203, 206, 216*)

Brightwell, S. T. P. 1938. A method for investigating membrane permeability. Bull. Ent. Res., 29:391–403. (*293*)

Brill, R. 1930. Zur Kenntnis des Seidenfibroins. Naturwiss., 18:622. (*67*)

* Briscoe, H. V. A. 1943. Some new properties of inorganic dusts. J. Roy. Soc. Arts, 91:593–607. (Chem. Abstr., 38:1570.) (*302*)

Brites, G. 1930. Contribution a l'étude des mues chez les diptères. La larve de la mouche de l'olive a-t-elle des mues? C. R. Soc. Biol., 105:133–134. (*157, 209*)

Brocher, F. 1910. Les phénomènes capillaires; leur importance dans la biologie aquatique. Ann. Biol. Lacustre, 4:89–138. (*139*)

——— 1914. Observations biologiques sur les Dyticides. *Ibid.*, 6:303–313. (*139, 148*)

——— 1919. Le mécanisme physiologique de la dernière mue des larves des Agrionides (transformation en imago). *Ibid.*, 9:183–200. (*233*)

——— 1920. Étude expérimentale sur le fonctionnement du vaisseau dorsal et sur la circulation du sang chez les insectes. 3. Le *Sphinx convolvuli*. Arch. Zool. Exp. & Gen., 60:1–45. (*261*)

———— 1927. Quelques mots sur les Dytiques à propos du livre du Prof. Korschelt. Ann. Biol. Lacustre, 15:85–92. (*164, 170*)

Bronn, H. G., ed. 1866–1948. Klassen und Ordnungen des Tierreichs. Leipzig. (*6, 160, 182, 275*)

Brooks, S. C., and M. Moldenhauer-Brooks 1941. The Permeability of Living Cells. Protoplasma Monographien series, vol. 19, 395 pp. Bornträger, Berlin. (*286*)

Broussy, J. 1933. Sur la nature et l'origine du pigment hypodermique d'*Anacridium aegyptium* (L.). C. R. Assoc. Anat., Nancy, 28:110–117. (*71, 72, 87, 92, 205*)

Brown, A. W. A. 1937. A note on the chitinous nature of the paritrophic membrane of *Melanoplus bivittatus* Say. J. Exp. Biol., 14:252–253. (*27, 39, 49, 278*)

——— 1950. Insect Control by Chemicals. Wiley, New York. (*313*)

Brown, F. A., Jr. 1934. The chemical nature of the pigments and the transformations responsible for color changes in *Palaemonetes*. Biol. Bull., 67:365–380. (*91*)

——— 1944. Hormones in the Crustacea: their source and activities. Quart. Rev. Biol., 19:32–46, 118–143. (*93*)

Brown, H. P. 1945. On the structure and mechanics of the protozoan flagellum. Ohio J. Sci., 45:247–301. (*254*)

Brown, H. T., and F. Escombe 1900. Static diffusion of gases and liquids in relation to the assimilation of carbon and translocation in plants. Phil. Trans. R. Soc., London, ser. B, 193:223–291. (*302*)

Browning, H. C. 1942. The integument and moult cycle of *Tegenaria atrica* (Araneae). Proc. R. Soc. London, ser. B, 131:65–86. (*48, 85, 92, 94, 109, 119, 121, 130, 149, 153, 156, 157, 160, 172, 190–192, 203, 205, 206, 220, 225, 226, 228, 229, 233, 234, 267, 289*)

Broyer, T. C. 1947. The movement of substances through a two-phased solution system. Science, 105:67–69. (*315*)

Brug, S. L. 1932. Chitinisation of parasites in mosquitoes. Bull. Ent. Res., 23:229–231. (*52, 278*)

Brunswick, H. 1921. Über die Mikrochemie der Chitosanverbindungen. Biochem. Z., 113:111–124. (*27, 28, 35*)

Bruntz, L. 1908. Sur la structure et le réseau trachéen des canaux excréteurs des reins du *Machilis maritima* Leach. C. R. Acad. Sci., 146:871–873. (*264*)

Bucherer, H. 1935. Über den mikrobiellen Chitinabbau. Zbl. Bact. Parasitenk. Infect., Abt. 2, 93:12–24. (*55*)

———, and W. Schmidt-Lange 1940. Chemische Untersuchungen am Tuberkelbazillus. Arch. Hyg. Bact., 124:298–303. (*45*)

Buchmann, W. 1931. Untersuchungen über die Bedeutung der Wasserstoffionkonzentration für die Entwicklung der Mückenlarven. Z. angew. Ent., 18:404–417. (*310*)

Buck, J. B. 1948. The anatomy and physiology of the light organ in fireflies. Ann. N. Y. Acad. Sci., 49:397–482. (*262–264*)

von Buddenbrock, W. 1929. Beitrag zur Histologie und Physiologie der Raupenhautung mit besonderer Berücksichtigung der Versonschen Drüsen. Z. Morph. Ökol. Tiere, 18:701–725. (*162, 209, 213, 217, 228*)

——— 1931. Untersuchungen über die Häutungshormone der Schmetterlingsraupen. Z. vergl. Physiol., 14:415–428. (*228*)

———, and G. von Rohr 1922. Die Atmung von *Dixippus morosus*. Z. allg. Physiol., 20:111–160. (*306*)

Bult, T. 1939. Over de Beweging der vloeistof in de Tracheolen der Insekten. Van Gorcum & Co., Assen. (Abstract in Biol. Abstr., vol. 16, 1942.) (*307*)

Burgeff, H. 1921. Beiträge zur Biologie der Gattung *Zygaena* F. (*Anthrocera* Scop.). 4. Über die Entwicklung der Zygaenenraupen. Mitt. Münch. Ent. Ges., 11:50–64. (*154*)

Burk, R. E., and O. Grummitt 1943. The Chemistry of Large Molecules. Interscience Publ. Co., New York. (*6*)

Burkenroad, M. D. 1947. Reproductive activities of decapod crustacea. Amer. Nat., 81:392–398. (*280, 282*)

Burmeister, H. 1832. Handbuch der Entomologie. G. Reimer, Berlin. (English translation 1836.) (*160, 163, 256*)

Burtt, E. D., and B. P. Uvarov 1944. Changes in wing pigmentation during the adult life of Acrididae. Proc. R. Ent. Soc. London, ser. A, 19:7–8. (*92*)

Burtt, E. T. 1945. The mode of action of sheep dips. Ann. Appl. Biol., 32:247–260. (*288, 290, 313, 315, 317*)

Buser, J. 1948. Aspect histologique des phénomènes de metamorphose chez *Piophila caseii* L. (Diptera, Cyclomorpha). Arch. Zool. Exp. & Gen., 85:109–119. (*217*)

Bütschli, O. 1874. Einiges über das Chitin. Arch. Anat. Physiol. wiss. Med., pp. 362–370. (*15*)

*——— 1894. Vorläufiger Bericht über fortgesetzte Untersuchungen an Gerinnungsschäumen, Sphärokristallen und die Struktur von Zellulose- und Chitin-Membranen. Verh. Naturf. Ges. Heidelberg, 5:230–292. (Cited in Wigglesworth 1948b.) (*15, 159, 183*)

*——— 1898. Untersuchungen über Strukturen, inbesonder über Strukturen nichtzelliger Erzeugnisse des Organismus und über ihre Beziehungen zu Strukturen, welche ausserhalb des Organismen stehen. Leipzig. (Cited in Kühnelt 1928c, Wigglesworth 1948b, etc.) (*159, 163*)

——— 1908. Untersuchungen über organische Kalkgebilde nebst Bemerkungen über organische Kieselgebilde, insbesondere über das spezifische Gewicht in Beziehung zu der Struktur, die chemische Zusammensetzung und Anderes. Abh. Ges. Wiss. Göttingen, N. F., 6:1–177. (*101*)

Butt, F. H. 1934. The origin of the peritrophic membrane in *Sciara* and the honey bee. Psyche, 41:51–56. (*278*)

——— 1937. The posterior stigmatic apparatus of trypetid larvae. Ann. Ent. Soc. Amer., 30:487–491. (*215, 266*)

Buxton, B. H. 1913. Coxal glands of the arachnids. Zool. Jahrb., Suppl., 14:231-282. (*250*)

Buxton, P. A. 1924. Heat, moisture and animal life in deserts. Proc. R. Soc. London, ser. B, 96:123–131. (*305*)

——— 1930. Evaporation from the mealworm and atmospheric humidity. *Ibid.*, 106:560–577. (*298, 305*)

——— 1931. The law governing the loss of water from an insect. Proc. Ent. Soc. London, 6:27–31. (*305*)

——— 1932a. The proportion of skeletal tissue in insects. Biochem. J., 26:829–832. (*50, 51, 110*)

——— 1932b. Terrestrial insects and the humidity of the environment. Biol. Rev., 7:275–320. (*305*)

Bytinski-Salz, H. 1936. Die Ausbildung des Chitinpanzers in der Schmetterlingspuppe. Biol. Zbl., 56:35–61. (*235*)

Cajal, S. R. 1890. Coloration par le méthode de Golgi des terminaisons des trachées et des nerfs dans les muscles des ailes des insectes. Z. wiss. Mikr., 7:332–342. (*262, 264*)

Calvert, P. P. 1928. The significance of odonate larvae for insect phylogeny. Trans. IV Int. Congr. Ent., pp. 919–925. (*261*)

Campbell, F. L. 1929. The detection and estimation of insect chitin; and the irrelation of chitinization to hardness and pigmentation of the cuticula of the american cockroach, *Periplaneta americana* L. Ann. Ent. Soc. Amer., 22:401–426. (*5, 15, 28, 32–34, 37, 39, 40, 42, 47, 49–52, 66, 81, 109, 111, 116, 261, 279*)

Cannon, H. G. 1947. On the anatomy of the pedunculate barnacle *Lithotrya*. Phil. Trans. R. Soc. London, ser. B, 233:89–136. (*161*)

* Cano, G. 1891. Morfologia dell' apparecchio sessuale femminile glandole, del cemento e fecondazione nei crostacei decapodi. Mitt. Zool. Sta. Neapel, 9:483–531. (Abstract in J. R. Micr. Soc., p. 467, 1891.) (*214*)

Cantacuzene, J., and A. Damboviceanu 1932. Modifications cytologiques qui se produisent dans le tégument de l'*Astacus fluviatilis* au moment de la mue. C. R. Soc. Biol., 109:998–1000. (*106, 207, 226*)

Carpenter, G. D. H., and H. Kalmus 1941. Physiology and ecology of cuticle color in insects. Nature, 148:693–694. (*154, 305*)

Carr, C. W., and K. Sollner 1943. The structure of the collodion membrane and its electrical behavior. 7. Water uptake and swelling of collodion membranes in water and solutions of strong inorganic electrolytes. J. Gen. Physiol., 27:77–89. (*136, 287, 288*)

* Cartier, P. 1948. Mineral constituents of calcified tissues. Bull. Soc. Chim. Biol., 30:65–81. (Chem. Abstr., 42:7852.) (*100*)

Caspari, E. 1941. The morphology and development of the wing pattern of Lepidoptera. Quart. Rev. Biol., 16:249–273. (*156, 271*)

——— 1949. Physiological action of eye color mutants in the moths *Ephestia kühniella* and *Ptychopoda seriata*. *Ibid.*, 24:185–199. (*92*)

Casper, A. 1913. Die Körperdecke und die Drüsen von *Dytiscus marginalis*, ein Beitrag zur feineren Bau der Insektenkörpers. Z. wiss. Zool., 107:387–508. (*161, 164, 170, 183, 193, 209*)

——— 1924. Körperdecke und Drüsen. *In* Korschelt, Der Gelbrand, 1923. (*161, 183*)

* Castelnuovo, G. 1934. Ricerche istologische e fisiologische sul tubo digerente di *Carausius (Dixippus) morosus*. Arch. Zool. Ital. Torino, 20:443–466. (*278*)

Castle, E. S. 1936. The double refraction of chitin. J. Gen. Physiol., 19:797–805. (*49, 84, 120–123, 130, 131, 133, 276*)

——— 1937a. Membrane tension and orientation of structure in the plant cell wall. J. Cell. Comp. Physiol., 10:113–121. (*119, 193, 194, 258*)

——— 1937b. The distribution of velocities of elongation and of twist in the growth zone of *Phycomyces* in relation to spiral growth. *Ibid.*, 9:477–489. (*193, 254*)

——— 1938a. Orientation of structure in the cell wall of *Phycomyces*. Protoplasma, 31:331–345. (*45, 53, 193*)

——— 1938b. The effect of torque on the axis of spiral growth in *Phycomyces*. J. Cell. Comp. Physiol., 11:345–358. (*193, 254*)

——— 1940. Discontinuous growth of single plant cells measured at short intervals, and the theory of intussusception. *Ibid.*, 15:285–298. (*193*)

——— 1942. Spiral growth and reversal of spiraling in *Phycomyces*, and their bearing on primary wall structure. Amer. J. Bot., 29:664–672. (*53, 193, 254*)

——— 1945. The structure of the cell walls of *Aspergillus* and the theory of cellulose particles. *Ibid.*, 32:148–151. (*24, 33, 39, 45*)

Catala, R. 1949. Contribution à l'étude des effets optiques sur les ailes des papillons. Encycl. Ent., no. 25, 78 pp. Lechevalier, Paris. (*196, 197*)

Causard, M. 1898. Sur le rôle de l'air dans la dernière mue des nymphes aquatiques. Bull. Soc. Ent. France, pp. 258–261. (*233*)

Cayeux, L. 1933. Rôle des trilobites dans la genèse des gisements de phosphate de chaux paléozoiques. C. R. Acad. Sci., 196:1179–1182. (*101*)

Chambers, R. 1940. The relation of extraneous coats to the organization and permeability of cellular membranes. Cold Spring Harbor Symp. Quant. Biol., 8:144–153. (*206, 216*)

Chamot, E. M., and C. W. Mason 1944. Handbook of Chemical Microscopy. Wiley, New York. (*67, 121, 131*)

Chapman, P. J., G. W. Pearce, and A. W. Avens 1943. Relation of composition to the efficiency of foliage or summer type petroleum fractions. J. Econ. Ent., 36:241–247. (*137*)

Chatin, J. 1892a. Sur l'origine et la formation du revêtement chitineux chez les larves des Libellules. C. R. Acad. Sci., 114:1135–1138. (*30*)

* ——— 1892b. Sur le procès général de la cuticularisation tégumentaire chez les larves des Libellules. Bull. Soc. Philomath. Paris, 4:105–106. (*30*)

——— 1895a. Observations histologiques sur les adaptations fonctionnelles de la cellule epidermique chez les insectes. C. R. Acad. Sci., 120:213–215. (*237*)

——— 1895b. La cellule épidermique des insectes, son paraplasma et son noyau. *Ibid.*, pp. 1285–1288. (*153*)

Chatton, E. 1920. Les membranes péritrophiques des Drosophiles (Diptères) et des Daphnies (Cladocères); leur genèse et leur rôle à l'égard des parasites intestinaux. Bull. Soc. Zool. France, 45:265–280. (*277–278*)

Chauvin, R. 1937. Les oenocytes du criquet pélerin (*Schistocerca gregaria* Forsh.). C. R. Soc. Biol., 126:781–782. (*217, 219*)

——— 1939a. Sur le pigment rose rejecté dans les excrements par le criquet pélerin au moment de la mue. *Ibid.*, 130:1194–1195. (*91*)

——— 1939b. Histologie du tégument chez le criquet pélerin. Bull. Histol. appl., Lyon, 16:137–148. (*89*)

——— 1941. Contribution à l'étude physiologique du criquet pélerin et du déterminisme des phénomènes grégaires. Ann. Soc. Ent. France, 110:133–272. (*161, 205*)

Chen, P. S. 1933. Zur Morphologie und Histologie der Respirationsorgane von *Grapsus grapsus* L. Jena. Z. Naturwiss., 68:31–116. (*161, 246, 247*)

* Chevreul, — 1820. *In* Saint-Hilaire, Troisième Mémoire sur l'Organisation des Insectes. (Cited by Straus-Durckheim 1828.) (*101, 114*)

Chibnall, A. C., A. L. Latner, E. F. Williams, and C. A. Ayre 1934. The constitution of coccerin. Biochem. J., 28:313–325. (*95*)

Chibnall, A. C., and S. H. Piper 1934. The metabolism of plant and insect waxes. Biochem. J., 28:2209–2219. (*99*)

———, A. Pollard, J. A. B. Smith, and E. F. Williams 1931. The wax constituents of the apple cuticle. Biochem. J., 25:2095–2110. (*95*)

Chibnall, A. C., S. H. Piper, A. Pollard, E. F. Williams, and P. N. Sahai 1934. The constitution of the primary alcohols, fatty acids and paraffins present in plant and insect waxes. Biochem. J., 28:2189–2208. (*95, 97*)

Chitwood, B. G. 1938. Further studies on nemic skeletoids and their significance in the chemical control of nemic pests. Proc. Helm. Soc. Wash., 5:68–75. (*43*)

Chiu, S. F. 1939. Toxicity studies of so-called "inert" materials with the rice weevil and the granary weevil. J. Econ. Ent., 32:810–821. (*123, 302*)

Christomanos, A. 1950. Electric potential of solutions as a cause of the formation of Liesegang rings. Nature, 165:238–239. (*141*)

* Christophers, S. R. 1906. The anatomy and histology of ticks. Sci. Mem. Officers Med. Sanit. Dept. Gov. India, no. 23, 55 pp. (*161*)

——— 1945. Structure of the *Culex* egg and egg-raft in relation to function. Trans. R. Ent. Soc. London, 95:25–34. (*280*)

* Chun, C. 1876. Über den Bau, die Entwicklung und physiologische Bedeutung der Rectaldrüsen bei den Insekten. Abh. Senkenb. Naturf. Ges. Frankfurt, 10:27–55. (*264*)

Clack, B. N., and N. L. Harris 1947. Spiral cracks in glass tubing. Nature, 159:541. (*255*)

Clark, G. L. 1934. The macromolecule and the micelle as structural units in biological materials with special reference to cellulose. Cold Spring Harbor Symp. Quant. Biol., 2:28–38. (*23, 174*)

———, and A. F. Smith 1936. X-ray diffraction studies of chitin, chitosan and derivatives. J. Physical Chem., 40:863–879. (*13–15, 17, 18, 21, 22, 25–28, 35, 49, 128, 130, 136, 242*)

Clarke, F. W., and W. C. Wheeler 1922. The inorganic constituents of marine invertebrates. U. S. Geol. Survey, Prof. paper no. 124, 62 pp. (*100–102, 104*)

Claus, C. 1875a. Die Schalendrüse der Daphnien. Z. wiss. Zool., 25:165–173. (*207*)

——— 1875b. Über die Entwicklung, Organisation und systematische Stellung der Arguliden. *Ibid.*, 217–284. (*161, 249*)

——— 1879. Der Organismus der Phronimiden. Arb. Zool. Inst. Wien, 2:59–146. (*207*)

——— 1881. Neue Beiträge zur Kenntnis der Copepoden unter besonderer Berücksichtigung der Triester Fauna. *Ibid.*, 3:313–332. (*161, 207*)

Clausen, M. B., and A. G. Richards 1951. Studies on arthropod cuticle. 6. Intracellular and extracellular formation of cuticle in the developing posterior spiracular chamber of a blowfly larva (*Phormia regina*). J. Morph., in press. (*24, 174, 266, 270*)

Cleveland, L. R. 1947. Sex produced in the protozoa of *Cryptocercus* by molting. Science, 105:16–17. (*235*)

Cloudsley-Thompson, J. L. 1950a. Epicuticle of arthropods. Nature, 165:692–693. (*85, 164*)

——— 1950b. The water relations and cuticle of *Paradesmus gracilis* (Diplopoda, Strongylosomidae). Quart. J. Micr. Sci., 91:453–464. (*101, 106, 195, 301*)

Coblentz, W. W. 1912. A physical study of the fire fly. Carnegie Inst. Wash., Publ. no. 164, 45 pp. (*120, 128*)

Cohn, E. J., and J. T. Edsall 1943. Proteins, amino acids and peptids. Reinhold, New York. (*62, 64*)

Cole, K. S., and T. L. Jahn 1937. The nature and permeability of grasshopper egg membranes. 4. The alternating current impedance over a wide frequency range. J. Cell. Comp. Physiol., 10:265–275. (*281, 288, 293, 310, 314*)

Coleman, D., and F. O. Howitt 1947. Silk proteins. Proc. R. Soc. London, ser. A, 190:145–169. (*62, 64, 68, 69, 120, 125, 132*)

Collinge, W. E. 1921. A preliminary study of the structure and function of the cutaneous glands in the terrestrial Isopoda. Ann. Mag. Nat. Hist., ser. 9, 7:212–222. (*66, 207, 209, 211, 213, 216*)

* Colosi, I. S. 1933. L'assunzione dell'acqua per via cutanea. Pubb. Staz. zool. Napoli, 13:12–38. (Cited by Wigglesworth 1948b.) (*305*)

Cooper, B. 1938. The internal anatomy of *Corioxenos antestiae* Blair (Strepsiptera). Proc. R. Ent. Soc. London, ser. A, 13:31–54. (*161, 203*)

Costello, D. P. 1945. Segregation of oöplasmic constituents. J. Elisha Mitchell Sci. Soc., 61:277–289. (*174*)

Cox, E. G., T. H. Goodwin, and A. I. Wagstaff 1935. The crystalline structure of the sugars. 2. Methylated sugars and the conformation of the pyranose ring. J. Chem. Soc., pp. 1495–1504. (*11*)

Cox, E. G., and G. A. Jeffrey 1939. Crystal structure of glucosamine hydrobromide. Nature, 143:894–895. (*11*)

Crauford-Benson, H. J. 1938. An improved method for testing liquid contact insecticides in the laboratory. Bull. Ent. Res., 29:41–56. (*294*)

Crawford, D. L. 1912. The petroleum fly in California, *Psilopa petrolei* Coq. Pomona College J. Ent., 4:687–697. (*95, 139, 157, 170, 301*)

Crisp, D. J., and W. H. Thorpe 1948. The water-protecting properties of insect hairs. Disc. Faraday Soc., no. 3, pp. 210–220. (*139, 276*)

Crozier, W. J., G. Pincus, and P. A. Zahl 1936. The resistance of Drosophila to alcohol. J. Gen. Physiol., 19:523–557. (*223, 290*)

Cummings, B. F. 1907. Notes on terrestrial isopods from north Devon. Zoologist, ser. 4, 11:465–470. (*234*)

Cunliffe, N. 1921. Some observations on the biology and structure of *Ornithodorus moubata* Murray. Parasitology, 13:327–347. (*232*)

Cutler, W. O., W. N. Haworth, and S. Peat 1937. Methylation of glucosamine. J. Chem. Soc., pp. 1979–1983. (*11*)

Cutler, W. O., and S. Peat 1939. Some derivatives of methylated glucosamine. J. Chem. Soc., pp. 274–279. (*11*)

Dakin, W. J. 1920. Fauna of Western Australia. 3. Further contributions to the study of the Onychophora: The anatomy and systematic position of the West Australian *Peripatoides*, with an account of certain histological details of general importance in the study of *Peripatus*. Proc. Zool. Soc. London, pp. 367–389. (*263*)

Dallemagne, M. J., and J. Melon 1946a. La localisation de l'apatite et du phosphate tricalcique dans l'émail dentaire. Arch. d. Biol., 57:79–98. (*100, 105*)

——— 1946b. Nouvelles recherches relatives aux propriétés optique de l'os: La birefringence de l'os mineralisé; Relations entre les fractions organiques et inorganiques de l'os. J. Wash. Acad. Sci., 36:181–195 (brief reviews in Nature, 157:453, 1946; Amer. Scientist, vol. 35, no. 1, 1947). (*100, 105*)

Damboviceanu, A. 1930. Métabolism du calcium chez *Astacus fluviatilis*. C. R. Soc. Biol., 105:913–914. (*106*)

* ——— 1932. Composition chimique et physico-chimique du liquid cavitaire chez les crustacés décapodes (Physiologie de la calcification). Arch. Roum. Path. exper. Microbiol., 5:239–309. (Cited by Robertson 1941.) (*106*)

Danielli, J. F. 1937. The activation energy of diffusion through natural and artificial membranes. Trans. Faraday Soc., 33:1139–1147. (*317*)

——— 1945. Reactions at interfaces and their significance in biology. Nature, 156:468–470. (*87, 91*)

Danini, E. S. 1928. Untersuchungen über die regenerativen Eigenschaften des Hautepithels. Z. mikr.-anat. Forsch., 12:507–536. (*203, 220, 232*)

Danneel, R. 1943. Melaninbildende Fermente bei *Drosophila melanogaster*. Biol. Zbl., 63:377–394. (*75, 76, 87, 191*)

——— 1946. Melaninbildende Fermente bei *Drosophila melanogaster*. 2. Nachweis einer Dehydrase Neuformulierung der Tyrosinase-Tyrosin Reaktion. *Ibid.*, 65:115–119. (*75*)

Darmon, S. E., and K. M. Rudall 1950. Infra-red and X-ray studies of chitin. Trans. Faraday Soc., in press. (*22, 27, 129*)

David, W. A. L., and B. O. C. Gardiner 1950. Factors influencing the action of dust insecticides. Bull. Ent. Res., 41:1–61. (*315*)

Davidoff, W. N. 1928. Über den histologischen Bau der Rochschen Organe bei der Larve von *Mycetobia pallipes* Meig. Z. mikr.-anat. Forsch., 12:219–231. (*251*)

Davies, W. M. 1927. On the tracheal system of Collembola, with special reference to that of *Sminthurus viridis*. Quart. J. Micr. Sci., 71:15–30. (*262, 263*)

——— 1928. The effects of variation in relative humidity on certain species of Collembola. J. Exp. Biol., 6:79–86. (*289, 298, 301*)

Davis, A. C. 1927a. Studies on the anatomy and histology of *Stenopelmatus fuscus* Hald. Univ. Calif. Publ. Ent., 4:159–208. (*161, 278*)

——— 1927b. Ciliated epithelium in the Insecta. Ann. Ent. Soc. Amer., 20:359–362. (*206*)

Davis, C. 1942. Oxygen economy of *Coxelmis novemnotata* (King) (Coleoptera: Dryopidae). Proc. Linn. Soc. N. S. Wales, 67:1–8. (*276*)

Davson, H., and J. F. Danielli 1943. The Permeability of Natural Membranes. Cambridge Univ. Press. (*286, 288, 298, 305*)

Day, M. F. 1943. The function of the corpus allatum in muscoid Diptera. Biol. Bull., 84:127–140. (*217*)

——— 1948. References for an outline of insect histology. Spec. Publ., Council Sci. Ind. Res. (Australia), 223 pp. (*160, 250*)

——— 1949a. The distribution of ascorbic acid in the tissues of insects. Australian J. Sci. Res., ser. B, 2:19–30. (*205*)

——— 1949b. The distribution of alkaline phosphatase in insects. *Ibid.*, pp. 31–41. (*79, 206, 219, 249, 252, 265*)

Deasy, C. L. 1946. Unequal distribution of diffusible nonelectrolytes across a membrane. Science, 104:388–389. (*288*)

Debaisieux, P. 1938. Organes scolopidiaux des pattes d'insectes. La Cellule, 47:77–202. (*277*)

——— 1944. Les yeux de crustacés: Structure, développement, réactions à l'éclairement. *Ibid.*, 50:9–122. (*52, 161, 249*)

Debot, L. 1932. L'appareil séricigène et les glandes salivaires de la larve de *Simulium*. La Cellule, 41:205–216. (*251, 254*)

Deegener, P. 1904. Die Entwicklung des Darmkanals der Insekten während der Metamorphose. Zool. Jahrb., Anat., 20:499–676. (*161, 206, 223, 227*)

——— 1913. Respirationsorgane. *In* Schröder, Handbuch der Entomologie, 1:317–382. (*253*)

——— 1928. Haut und Hautorgane. *Ibid.*, pp. 1–60. (*6, 160, 275*)

Deevey, G. B. 1941. The blood cells of the Haitian tarantula and their relation to the moulting cycle. J. Morph., 68:457–487. (*30, 226*)

von Dehn, M. 1933. Untersuchungen über die Bildung der peritrophischen Membran bei den Insekten. Z. Zellforsch. Mikr. Anat., 19:79–105. (*277–279*)

——— 1936. Zur Frage der Natur der peritrophischen Membran bei den Insekten. *Ibid.*, 25:787–791. (*278*)

Demoll, R. 1917. Die Sinnesorgane der Arthropoden. Vieweg & Sohn, Braunschweig. (*275*)

Dennell, R. 1943. Pore canals of the insect cuticle. Nature, 152:50. (*178–180, 183, 206*)

——— 1944. Hardening and darkening of the insect cuticle. *Ibid.*, 154:57–58.

——— 1945. Insect epicuticle. *Ibid.*, 155:545. (*85, 123, 163, 303*)

——— 1946. A study of an insect cuticle: The larval cuticle of *Sarcophaga falculata* Pand. (Diptera). Proc. R. Soc. London, ser. B, 133:348–373. (*36, 37, 51, 71, 94, 109, 112, 113, 121, 133, 136, 142, 148, 153, 157, 161, 163, 164, 167, 174–183, 185–189, 191, 203–206, 209, 225, 227, 289*)

——— 1947a. A study of an insect cuticle: The formation of the puparium of *Sarcophaga falculata* Pand. (Diptera). *Ibid.*, 134:79–110. (*72, 75, 76, 87, 88, 115, 119, 137, 161, 185–189, 191, 205, 227, 232*)

——— 1947b. The occurrence and significance of phenolic hardening in the newly formed cuticle of Crustacea Decapoda. *Ibid.*, pp. 485–503. (*71, 85, 101, 157, 161, 163, 164, 168, 169, 171, 180–182, 189, 194, 195, 207, 214, 267*)

——— 1949a. Weismann's ring and the control of tyrosinase activity in the larva of *Calliphora erythrocephala*. *Ibid.*, 136:94–109. (*73, 76, 89, 187, 232*)

——— 1949b. Earthworm chaetae. Nature, 164:370. (*47, 189*)

——— 1950. Epicuticle of blowfly larvae. Nature, in press. (*58, 303*)

Deschiens, R., and F. Pick 1948. Une particularité tinctoriale des oeufs d'*Ascaris megalocephala*. Bull. Soc. Path. Exot., 41:212–213. (*43*)

Dethier, V. G. 1941. The antennae of lepidopterous larvae. Bull. Mus. Comp. Zool., 87:455–507. (*254, 276*)

——— 1942. The dioptric apparatus of lateral ocelli. 1. The corneal lens. J. Cell. Comp. Physiol., 19:301–313. (*120, 249*)

—— 1943. The dioptric apparatus of lateral ocelli. 2. Visual capacity of the ocellus. *Ibid.*, 22:115–126. (*120, 249*)
——, and L. E. Chadwick 1948. Chemoreception in insects. Physiol. Rev., 28:220–254. (*277, 305*)
Dewitz, J. 1902a. Recherches expérimentales sur la métamorphose des insectes. C. R. Soc. Biol., 54:44–45. (*77*)
—— 1902b. Sur l'action des enzymes (oxydases) dans la métamorphose des insectes. *Ibid.*, pp. 45–47. (*77*)
—— 1902c. Untersuchungen über die Verwandlung der Insektenlarven. Arch. Anat. Physiol., pp. 327–340, 425–442. (*77, 191*)
—— 1916. Bedeutung der oxydierenden Fermente (Tyrosinase) für die Verwandlung der Insektenlarven. Zool Anz., 47:123–124. (*77, 191*)
—— 1921. Weitere Mitteilungen über die Entstehung der Farbe gewisser Schmetterlingkokons. Zool. Jahrb., allg. Zool., 38:365–404. (*77*)
* Diehl, J. M. 1936. (Vegetable chitin.) Chem. Weekblad, 33:36–38. (Chem. Abstr., 30:2594.) (*42, 45*)
——, and G. van Iterson 1935. Die Doppelbrechung von Chitinsehnen. Kolloid Z., 73:142–146. (*131, 133, 134*)
Dinnik, J., and F. Zumpt 1949. The integumentary sense organs of the larvae of Rhipicephalinae (Acarina). Psyche, 56:1–11. (*161*)
Dinulesco, G. 1932. Recherches sur la biologie des Gastrophiles. Anatomie, physiologie, cycle évolutif. Ann. Sci. Nat. Zool., ser. 10, 15:1–183. (*215, 262, 264*)
Dixey, F. A. 1932. On the plume scales of the Pierinae. Trans. Ent. Soc. London, pp. 57–75. (*275*)
Dolley, W. L., and E. J. Farris 1929. Unicellular glands in the larvae of *Eristalis tenax*. J. N. Y. Ent. Soc., 37:127–134. (*215*)
Dous, ——, and —— Ziegenspeck 1926. Das Chitin der Pilze. Arch. Pharm., 264:751–753. (*24, 25*)
Downey, H. 1912. The attachment of muscles to the exoskeleton in the crayfish, and the structure of the crayfish epiderm. Amer. J. Anat., 13:381–399. (*159, 161, 203, 206, 220, 222, 237, 240*)
Doyle, W. E. 1947. Some properties of phosphatases in the salivary glands of *Drosophila*. Anat. Rec., 99:633–634. (*252*)
Drach, P. 1935a. Aperçu sur les modifications subies par le squelette, avant la mue, chez les crustacés décapodes. C. R. Acad. Sci., 201:157–159. (*100*)
—— 1935b. Phénomènes de résorption dans l'endosquelette des décapodes brachyoures, au cours de la période qui précède la mue. *Ibid.*, pp. 1424–1426. (*105*)
—— 1936a. L'eau absorbée au cours de l'exuviation, donnée fondamentale pour l'étude physiologique de la mue. Definitions et déterminations quantitatives. *Ibid.*, 202:1817–1819. (*233*)
—— 1936b. Le cycle parcouru entre deux mues et ses principales étapes chez *Cancer pagurus*. *Ibid.*, 2103–2105. (*225, 226*)
—— 1937a. Généralités sur le développement des textures cristallines dans le squelette tégumentaire des décapodes brachyoura. *Ibid.*, 205:249–251. (*100, 105, 161, 195*)
—— 1937b. Morphogénèse de la mosaique cristalline externe dans le squelette tégumentaire des décapodes brachyoures. *Ibid.*, pp. 1173–1176. (*100, 105, 161, 195*)
—— 1937c. L'origine du calcaire dans le squelette tégumentaire des crustacés décapodes. *Ibid.*, pp. 1441–1443. (*100, 105, 195*)
—— 1939. Mue et cycle d'intermue chez les crustacés décapodes. Ann. Inst. Océanogr., 19:103–392. (Includes large bibliography on crustacean cuticle.)

(*30, 100, 103, 105, 160, 161, 169, 175, 179, 182, 194, 195, 207, 209, 214, 226, 233, 292*)

———, and M. Lafon 1942. Études biochimiques sur le squelette tégumentaire des décapodes brachyoures (Variations au cours du cycle d'intermue). Arch. Zool. Exp. & Gen., 82:100–118. (*49, 85, 100, 101, 105, 109, 111, 195*)

Dreher, K. 1936. Bau und Entwicklung des Atmungssystems des Honigbiene (*Apis mellifica* L.). Z. Morph. Ökol. Tiere, 31:608–672. (*161, 206, 264, 265*)

Dresden, D., and B. J. Krijgsman 1948. Experiments on the physiological action of contact insecticides. Bull. Ent. Res., 38:575–578. (*314*)

Dreyling, L. 1906. Die wachsbereitenden Organe bei den gesellig lebenden Bienen. Zool. Jahrb., Anat., 22:289–330. (*153, 227, 228, 250, 252*)

Driesch, E., and H. O. Müller 1935. Elektronenmikroskopische Aufnahmen von Chitinobjekten. Z. wiss. Mikr., 52:53–57. (*244, 269*)

Duarte, A. J. 1939. On ecdysis in the African migratory locust. Agronomia Lusitana, Lisbon, 1:22–40. (*157, 161, 163, 172, 206, 209, 211, 225–227, 229, 233, 234*)

Duboscq, O. 1894. La glande venimeuse des myriapodes chilopodes. C. R. Acad. Sci., 119:352–354. (*250, 251, 254*)

——— 1895. La glande venimeuse de la *Scolopendra*. Arch. Zool. Exp. & Gen., ser. 3, 2:575–582. (*250*)

* ——— 1896. Les glandes ventrales et la glande venimeuse de *Chaetechelyne vesuviana*. Bull. Soc. Linn. Normandy, 9:151–173. (*250*)

——— 1899. Recherches sur les Chilopoda. Arch. Zool. Exp. & Gen., ser. 3, 6:481–650. (*160, 221, 237, 238, 240*)

——— 1920. Notes sur *Opisthopatus cinctipes* Purc. 1. Sur les poils des papilles primaires et leur développement. 2. Les organes ventraux du cerveau. Arch. Zool. Exp. & Gen., 59(Not. & Rev.): 21–27. (Onychophora.) (*160, 203*)

Dudich, E. 1929. Die Kalkeinlagerungen des Crustaceenpanzers in polarisiertem Licht. Zool. Anz., 85:257–264. (*103, 104*)

** ——— 1930. Die Kalkeinlagerungen des Crustaceenpanzers in polarisiertem Licht. Arb. Ung. Biol. Forsch. Inst. Tihany, 1:224–253. (*103*)

——— 1931. Systematische und biologische Untersuchungen über die Kalkeinlagerungen des Crustaceenpanzers in polarisiertem Lichte. Zoologica (Stuttgart), 30(5/6), Heft 80, pp. 1–154. (Large bibliography.) (*101, 103–105*)

——— 1932. Die Kalkreservekörper von *Hyloniscus riparius* und das Zenker'sche Organ. Állat. Közlem Budapest, 29:1–15. (*106*)

Dujardin, F. 1849. Résumé d'un mémoire sur les trachées des animaux articulés et sur la prétendue circulation péritrachéenne. C. R. Acad. Sci., 28:674–677. (*256, 257, 259*)

* Dumazert, C., and H. Lehr 1942. Iodometric microdetermination of glucosamine. Trav. membres Soc. Chim. Biol., 24:1044–1046. (*11*)

Dumitresco, M. 1938. Les glandes séricigènes tubulaires de *Theridium tepidariorum*. Arch. Zool. Exp. & Gen., 79(Not. & Rev.): 58–68. (*251, 252*)

Dunavan, D. 1929. A study of respiration and respiratory organs of the rat-tailed maggot, *Eristalis arbustorum*. Ann. Ent. Soc. Amer., 22:731–739. (*261*)

Dupont-Raabe, M. 1949. Les chromatophores de la larve de *Corethra*. Arch. Zool. Exp. & Gen., 86(Not. & Rev.): 32–39. (*93*)

Durand, E., A. Hollander, and M. B. Houlahan 1941. Ultraviolet absorption spectrum of the abdominal wall of *Drosophila melanogaster*. J. Hered., 32:51–56. (*120, 125*)

Dürken, B. 1923. Die postembryonale Entwicklung der Tracheenkiemen und ihrer muskulatur bei *Ephemerella ignita*. Zool. Jahrb., Anat., 44:439–614. (*246, 255, 262*)

Dusham, E. H. 1918. The wax glands of the cockroach (*Blatta germanica*). J. Morph., 31:563–574. (*94, 168*)

Duspiva, F., and M. Cerny 1934. Die Bedeutung der Farbe für die Erwärmung der Käferelytren durch sichtbares Licht und Ultrarot. Z. vergl. Physiol., 21:267–274. (*127*)

* Dutt, S. 1936. Putrefactive decomposition of Bengal silk cocoon. Allahabad Univ. Stud., Sci. Sect., 12:21–26. (*57*)

Eastham, L. E. S. 1929. The post-embryonic development of *Phaenoserphus viator* Hal. (Proctotrypoidea), a parasite of the larva of *Pterostichus niger* (Carabidae), with notes on the anatomy of the larva. Parasitology, 21:1–21. (*217, 255, 262*)

Ebeling, W. 1939. The role of surface tension and contact angle in the performance of spray liquids. Hilgardia, 12:665–698. (*137*)

von Ebner, V. 1910. Über Fasern und Waben. Eine histologische Untersuchung der Haut der Gordiiden und der Knochengrundsubstanz. Sitz-ber. d. Wien Akad., Abt. 3, 119:285–326. (*43*)

Eder, R. 1940. Die kutikuläre Transpiration der Insekten und ihre Abhängigkeit vom Aufbau des Integumentes. Zool. Jahrb., allg. Zool., 60:203–240. (*94, 136, 154, 157, 171, 180, 182, 183, 289, 290, 294, 298, 300, 305*)

Edney, E. B. 1947. Laboratory studies on the bionomics of the rat fleas. 2. Water relations during the cocoon period. Bull. Ent. Res., 38:263–280. (*298, 299*)

——— 1949. Evaporation of water from woodlice. Nature, 164:321–322. (*304*)

Edwards, H. M. 1851. Observations sur le squelette tégumentaire des crustacés décapodes et sur la morphologie de ces animaux. Ann. Sci. Nat. Zool., ser. 3, 16:221–291. (*241*)

Effenberger, W. 1907. Die Tracheen bei *Polydesmus*. Zool. Anz., 31:782–786. (*262*)

——— 1909. Beiträge zur Kenntnis der Gattung *Polydesmus*. Jena Z. Naturwiss., 44:527–586. (*160*)

Efflatoun, H. C. 1927. On the morphology of some Egyptian trypaneid larvae with descriptions of some heretofore unknown forms. Bull. Soc. Ent. Egypte, pp. 17–50. (*270*)

Eggers, F. 1919. Das thoracale bitympanale Organ einer Gruppe der Lepidoptera Heterocera. Zool. Jahrb., Anat., 41:273–376. (*248*)

——— 1928. Die stiftführenden Sinnesorgane. Zool. Bausteine, 2(1):1–353. (*238, 248, 261*)

Eidmann, H. 1922. Die Durchlässigkeit des Chitins bei osmotischen Vorgängen. Biol. Zbl., 42:429–435. (*294*)

——— 1924a. Untersuchungen über Wachstum und Häutung der Insekten. Verh. dtsch. Zool. Ges., 29:124–129. (*233*)

——— 1924b. Untersuchungen über Wachstum und Häutung der Insekten. Z. Morph. Ökol. Tiere, 2:567–610. (*233*)

——— 1924c. Untersuchungen über den Mechanismus der Häutung bei den Insekten. Arch. mikr.-anat. Entw., 102:276–290. (*233*)

Einsele, W. 1937. Studies of multiple allelomorphic series in the house-mouse. 2. Methods for the quantitative estimation of melanin. J. Genet., 34:1–18. (*87*)

Eloff, G., and V. L. Bosazza 1938. Penetration of ultra-violet rays through chitin. Nature, 141:608. (*126*)

Elson, L. A., and W. T. J. Morgan 1933. A colorimetric method for the determination of glucosamine and chondrosamine. Biochem. J., 27:1824–1828. (*11*)

Eltringham, H. 1933. The Senses of Insects. Methuen, London. (*249, 275*)

Emery, C. 1884. Untersuchungen über *Luciola italica* L. Z. wiss. Zool., 40:338–355. (*264*)

Emmel, L., and A. Jakob 1948. Über den Feinbau einiger Schuppen von Culiciden. Zool. Jahrb., Anat., 69:435–442. (*272*)

Emmel, V. E. 1907. Relations between regeneration, the degree of injury, and moulting in young lobsters. Science, 25:785. (*233*)

Enderlein, G. 1899. Die Respirationsorgane der Gastriden. Sitz-ber. A. Wien Akad. Math.-Naturwiss., Abt. 1, 108:235–304. (*264*)

Engelhardt, V. 1914. Über die Hancocksche Drüse von *Oecanthus pellucens* Scop. Zool. Anz., 44:219–227. (*251*)

Escherich, K. 1897. Einiger über die Häutungshaare der Insekten nach ihrem Funktionswechsel. Biol. Zbl., 17:542–544. (*192, 233*)

Evans, A. C. 1932. Some aspects of chemical changes during insect metamorphosis. J. Exp. Biol., 9:314–321. (*65*)

——— 1934a. On the chemical changes associated with metamorphosis in a beetle (*Tenebrio molitor*). *Ibid.*, 11:397–401. (*65*)

——— 1934b. Studies on the influence of the environment on the sheep blow-fly, *Lucilia sericata* Meig. 1. The influence of temperature and humidity on the egg. Parasitology, 26:366–377. (*314*)

——— 1938a. Studies on the distribution of nitrogen in insects. 1. In the castes of the wasp, *Vespula germanica* (Fabr.). Proc. R. Ent. Soc. London, ser. A, 13:25–29. (*65, 113, 229*)

——— 1938b. Studies on the distribution of nitrogen in insects. 2. A note on the estimation and some properties of insect cuticle. *Ibid.*, pp. 107–110. (*40, 65, 81, 113, 229*)

——— 1943. Value of the pF scale of soil moisture for expressing the soil moisture relations of wireworms. Nature, 152:21–22. (*294, 302*)

——— 1944. Observations on the biology and physiology of wireworms of the genus *Agriotes*. Ann. Appl. Biol., 31:235–250. (*294, 302*)

Ewing, H. E. 1912. Notes on the molting process of our common red spider (*Tetranychus telarius* L.) (Acarina). Ent. News, 23:145–148. (*66*)

Falke, H. 1931. Beiträge zur Lebensgeschichte und zur postembryonalen Entwicklung von *Ixodes ricinus* L. Z. Morph. Ökol. Tiere, 21:567–607. (*48, 161, 174, 203, 206, 266*)

Fan, H. Y., T. H. Cheng, and A. G. Richards 1948. The temperature coefficients of DDT action in insects. Physiol. Zool., 21:48–59. (*134, 314, 318*)

Farkas, B. 1914. Beiträge zur Anatomie und Histologie des Oesophagus und der Oesophagealdrüsen des Flusskrebses. Zool. Anz., 45:139–144. (*30, 161, 237*)

——— 1927. Zur Kenntnis der Tegumentaldrüsen der Decapoden. Zool. Jahrb., Anat., 49:1–56. (*161, 207, 209, 211, 213, 214*)

Farkas, K. 1903. Zur Kenntnis des Chorionins und des Chorioningehaltes der Seidenspinnereier. Pflüger's Arch. Ges. Physiol., 98:547–550. (*66, 121*)

Farr, W. K., and S. H. Eckerson 1934a. Formation of cellulose membranes by microscopic particles of uniform size in linear arrangement. Contrib. Boyce Thompson Inst., 6:189–203. (*24*)

——— 1934b. Separation of cellulose particles in membranes of cotton fibers by treatment with hydrochloric acid. *Ibid.*, pp. 309–313. (*24*)

Farr, W. K., and W. A. Sisson 1934. X-ray diffraction patterns of cellulose particles and interpretations of cellulose diffraction data. Contrib. Boyce Thompson Inst., 6:315–321. (*24*)

Fassbinder, K. 1912. Beiträge zur Kenntnis der Süsswasserostracoden. Zool. Jahrb., Anat., 32:533–576. (*104*)

Fauré-Fremiet, E. 1912. Graisse et glycogène dans l'oeuf de l'*Ascaris megalocephala*. Bull. Soc. Zool. France, 37:233–234. (*30*)

——— 1913. Le cycle germinatif chez l'*Ascaris megalocephala*. Arch. Anat. Micr., 15:435–757. (*13, 43*)

Ferguson, J. 1939. The use of chemical potentials as indices of toxicity. Proc. R. Soc. London, ser. B, 127:387–404. (*315*)

Ferrière, C. 1914. L'organe trachéo-parenchymateux le quelques Hémiptères aquatiques. Rev. Suisse Zool., 22:121–145. (*261*)

Ferris, G. F. 1934. Setae. Can. Ent., 66:145–150. (*274, 275*)

———, and J. C. Chamberlin 1928. On the use of the word "chitinized." Ent. News, 39:212–215. (*5*)

Fiedler, P. 1908. Mitteilung über das Epithel der Kiemensächchen von *Daphnia magna*. Zool. Anz., 33:493–496. (*161, 247*)

* Fischel, A. 1908. Untersuchungen über vitale Färbung an Süsswassertieren, insbesondere bei Kladoceren. Leipzig. (Cited by Yonge 1936.) (*293, 311*)

Fischer, E. 1907. Über Spinnenseide. Z. physiol. Chem., 53:126–139. (*62, 63*)

Florkin, M., and F. Lozet 1949. Origine bactérienne de la cellulase du contenu intestinal de l'escargot. Arch. Int. Physiol., 57:201–207. (*57*)

———, and H. Sarlet 1949. Sur la digestion de la cire d'abeille par la larve de *Galleria mellonella* Linn. et sur l'utilisation de la cire par une bactérie isolée à partir du contenu intestinal de cette larve. Arch. Int. Physiol., 57:71–88. (*58*)

* Foa, C. 1912. The colloidal properties of natural silk. Z. Chem. Ind. Kolloide, 10:7–12. (Chem. Abstr., 6:1674.) (*67, 68*)

* Folpmers, T. 1921. Die Zersetzung des Chitins und des Spaltungsproduktes desselben, des Glucosamins, durch Bakterien. Chem. Weekbl., 18:249; Centralbl. Bakt., 57:97. (Cited by Hock 1941.) (*56*)

Forbes, W. T. M. 1930. What is chitine? Science, 72:397. (*5, 41*)

Ford, E. B. 1941. Studies on the chemistry of pigments in the Lepidoptera, with reference to their bearing on systematics. 1. The anthoxanthins. Proc. R. Ent. Soc. London, ser. A, 16:65–90. (*91*)

——— 1942. Studies on the chemistry of pigments in the Lepidoptera. 2. Red pigments in the genus *Delias*. *Ibid*., 17:87–92. (*92*)

——— 1944a. Studies on the chemistry of pigments in the Lepidoptera. 3. The red pigments of the Papilionidae. *Ibid*., 19:92–106. (*92*)

——— 1944b. Studies on the chemistry of pigments in the Lepidoptera. 4. The classification of the Papilionidae. *Ibid*., pp. 201–223. (*92*)

——— 1947a. A murexide test for the recognition of pterins in intact insects. *Ibid*., 22:72–76. (*92*)

——— 1947b. Studies on the chemistry of pigments in the Lepidoptera with reference to their bearing on systematics. 5. *Pseudapontia paradoxa*. *Ibid*., pp. 77–78. (*92*)

Fox, D. L. 1947. Carotenoid and indolic biochromes of animals. Ann. Rev. Biochem., 16:443–470. (*88, 90*)

Fraenkel, G. 1935a. Observations and experiments on the blowfly (*Calliphora erythrocephala*) during the first day after emergence. Proc. Zool. Soc. London, pp. 893–904. (*73*)

——— 1935b. A hormone causing pupation in the blowfly *Calliphora erythrocephala*. Proc. R. Soc. London, ser. B, 118:1–12. (*188*)

——— 1938. The number of moults in the cyclorrhaphous flies (Diptera). *Ibid*., ser. A, 13:158–160. (*231, 234*)

———, and M. Blewett. 1943. The basic food requirements of several insects. J. Exp. Biol., 20:28–34. (*31*)

Fraenkel, G., and G. V. B. Herford 1938. The respiration of insects through the skin. J. Exp. Biol., 15:266–280. (*306*)

Fraenkel, G., and K. M. Rudall. 1940. A study of the physical and chemical properties of the insect cuticle. Proc. R. Soc. London, ser. B, 129:1–35. (*5, 18, 19, 21, 36, 49, 51, 54, 59, 61, 117, 119, 161, 185, 187*)

——— 1947. The structure of insect cuticles. *Ibid*., 134:111–143. (*18, 19, 25, 39,*

40, 47–51, 59, 61, 72, 74, 76, 81–84, 87, 88, 101, 109–112, 114, 116, 121, 122, 133, 135, 136, 141, 161, 176, 185, 187–189, 192, 294, 295, 302)

Franceschini, J. 1938. I carattere del tegumento in varie razze di *Bombyx mori.* Boll. Soc. Ital. Biol. sperim., Milan, 13:221–222. (*92*)

Franke, W. 1940. Tyrosinase. *In* Nord-Weidenhagen, Handbuch der Enzymologia. (*75*)

Fränkel, S., and C. Jellinek 1927. Über *Limulus polyphemus.* Biochem. Z., 185:384–388. (*11, 25, 48*)

Fränkel, S., and A. Kelly 1901. Beiträge zur Konstitution des Chitins. Sitz-ber. Wien Akad. Math.-Nat. Kl., Abt. 2B, 110:1147–1156. (*11*)

——— 1902. Beiträge zur Konstitution des Chitins. Monatschr. f. Chem., 23:123–132. (*11, 15*)

von Frankenberg, G. 1915. Die Schwimmblasen von *Corethra.* Zool. Jahrb., all. Zool., 35:505–592. (*66, 255, 260*)

Fredericq, L. 1924. Die Sekretion von Schutz und Nutzstoffen. *In* Winterstein, Handbuch vergl. Physiol., 2:112–165. (*250*)

Freney, M. R., K. R. Deane, and J. R. Anderson 1946. Twist in wool. Nature, 157:664. (*254*)

Freudenberg, K., H. Walch, and H. Molter 1942. The separation of sugars, amino sugars and amino acids. Naturwiss., 30:87. (*11, 133*)

Freundlich, H. 1932. Kapillarchemie. Acad. Verlagsges. Leipzig. (*142*)

Frey, W. 1936. Untersuchungen über die Entstehung der Strukturfarben der Chrysididen nebst Beiträgen zur Kenntnis der Hymenopterencuticula. Z. Morph. Ökol. Tiere, 31:443–489. (*116, 157, 161, 163, 172, 201*)

Frey-Wyssling, A. 1938. Submikroskopische Morphologie des Protoplasmas und seiner Derivate. Protoplasma Monographien series, vol. 15, 317 pp. Bornträger, Berlin. (*6, 67, 123, 130, 131, 133, 134, 175, 193*)

——— 1948. Submicroscopic Morphology of Protoplasm and Its Derivatives. Elsevier, New York. (*6, 131*)

Frick, G. 1936. Das Zeichnungsmuster der Ixodiden. Versuche der Analyse einer Tierzeichnung. Z. Morph. Ökol. Tiere, 31:411–430. (*87, 92, 161, 182, 196*)

Friedrich, H. 1929. Vergleichende Untersuchungen über die tibialen Scolopalorgane einiger Orthopteren. Z. wiss. Zool., 134:84–148. (*221*)

Fuchs, R. F. 1914. Der Fareenwechsel und die chromatische Hautfunktion der Tiere. *In* Winterstein, Handbuch vergl. Physiol., 2(2):1189–1656. (*93*)

Fuhrmann, H. 1921. Beiträge zur Kenntnis der Hautsinnesorgane der Tracheaten. 1. Die antennalen Sinnesorgane der Myriopoden. Z. wiss. Zool., 119:1–49. (*155, 160, 163, 182, 194, 207, 267*)

Fulton, R. A., and N. F. Howard 1938. Effect of addition of oil on the toxicity to plant bugs of derris and other insecticides. J. Econ. Ent., 31:405–410. (*294, 315*)

——— 1942. Effect of the addition of sulfonated oil on the toxicity of cube and derris to plant bugs. J. Econ. Ent., 35:867–870. (*315*)

* von Fürth, O. 1903. Vergleichende chemische Physiologie der niederen Tiere. (*15*)

——— 1904. Physiologische und chemische Untersuchungen über melanotische Pigments. Centr. allg. Path. pathol. Anat., 15:617–646. (*86*)

——— and M. Russo. 1906. Über kristallinische Chitosanverbindungen aus Sepienschulpen. Ein Beitrag zur Kenntnis des Chitins. Beitr. Chem. Physiol. Path., 8:163–190. (*15, 27, 48, 50*)

von Fürth, O., and E. Scholl 1907. Über Nitrochitine. Beitr. Chem. Physiol. Path., 10:188–198. (*28*)

Gäbler, H. 1933. Tracheeninjektionsmethode für frisches und in Alkohol fixiertes Material. Z. wiss. Mikrosk., 50:188–194. (*261*)

——— 1934. Formveränderungen und Degeneration von Stigmen durch Olinjektion. Z. wiss. Zool., 146:135–152. (*261*)

——— 1939. Die Eindringvermögen verscheidener Flüssigkeiten in die Tracheen und seiner Folgen. Z. angew. Ent., 26:1–62. (*140, 202, 261*)

Gabreil, C. 1903. Das Hautchen am Halsschilde der Gattung *Lathridius*. Z. Ent. Breslau, pp. 17–20. (*96*)

Garrey, W. E. 1905. The osmotic pressure of sea water and of the blood of marine animals, including some observations on the permeability of animal membranes. Biol. Bull., 8:257–270. (*292*)

Gaubert, P. 1924. Sur la polarisation circulaire de la lumière réfléchie par les insectes. C. R. Acad. Sci., 179:1148–1150. (*127, 171*)

Gautrelet, J. 1902. Des formes élémentaires du phosphore chez les invertébrés. C. R. Acad. Sci., 134:186–188. (*100*)

Gebhardt, F. A. M. W. 1912. Die Hauptzüge der Pigmentverteilung im Schmetterlingsflügel im Lichte der Liesegangischen Niederschläge im Kolloiden. Verh. dtsch. Zool. Ges., 22:179–204. (*141*)

Gee, W. P. 1911. The oenocytes of *Platyphylax designatus* Walker. Biol. Bull., 21:222–234. (*217*)

Geipel, E. 1915. Beiträge zur Anatomie der Leuchtorgane tropischer Käfer. Z. wiss. Zool., 112:239–290. (*264*)

Gentil, K. 1933. Die Entstehung der Schillerfarben bei *Calliphora eximia*. Ent. Rundschau, 50:105–110. (*196*)

——— 1935a. Die Entstehung der Schillerfarben bei *Morpho sulkowskyi*. *Ibid.*, 52:41–44. (*196*)

——— 1935b. Die Entstehung der Schillerfarben bei *Urania ripheus*. *Ibid.*, pp. 112–114. (*196*)

——— 1935c. Der Bau der Schillerschuppen von *Papilio paris*. *Ibid.*, pp. 230–232. (*196*)

——— 1936a. Die Entstehung der Schillerfarben bei *Chrysopa perla*. *Ibid.*, 53:173–175. (*196*)

——— 1936b. Die Entstehung der Schillerfarben bei Ichneumoniden. *Ibid.*, pp. 361–364. (*196*)

——— 1936c. Die Entstehung der Schillerfarben bei *Opisicoetus personatus*. *Ibid.*, pp. 594–596. (*196*)

——— 1941. Beiträge zur Kenntnis schillernder Schmetterlingsschuppen auf Grund polarisationsoptischer Untersuchung. Z. Morph. Ökol. Tiere, 37:591–612. (*132, 196*)

——— 1942. Elektronenmikroskopische Untersuchung des Feinbaues schillernder Leisten von Morpho-Schuppen. *Ibid.*, 38:344–355. (*196, 272*)

——— 1946. Die Riesenschuppen des Schmetterlings *Xyleutes mineus*. Senckenbergiana, 27:63–66. (*196, 197*)

Gerhardt, U. 1913. Copulation und Spermatophoren von Grylliden und Locustiden. 1. Zool. Jahrb., Syst., 35:415–532. (*282*)

——— 1914. Copulation und Spermatophoren von Grylliden und Locustiden. 2. *Ibid.*, 37:1–64. (*282*)

Germar, B. 1936. Versuche zur Bekämpfung des Kornkäfers mit Staubmitteln. Z. angew. Ent., 22:603–630. (*123*)

Gessard, C. 1904. Sur la tyrosinase de la mouche dorée. C. R. Acad. Sci., 139:644–645. (*77*)

* Gibson, E. C. 1937. Freeing edible crustacean flesh from chitin material. U. S. Patent no. 2,080,263. (Chem. Abstr., 31:5058.) (*130*)

* Gicklhorn, J. 1925. Beobachtungen über die Kalkinkrustation der Schale der Cladoceren. Lotos Prag, 73:157–166. (*100*)

——— 1931. Elektive Vitalfärbung im Dienste der Anatomie und Physiologie der

Exkretionsorgane von Wirbellosen (Cladoceren als Beispiel). Protoplasma, 13:701–724. (*293, 311*)
———, and R. Keller 1926. Neue Methoden der elektiven Vitalfärbung zwecks organspecifischer Differenzierung bei Wirbellosen. (Über den Bau, die Innervierung und Funktion der Riechstabe von *Daphnia magna*). Z. wiss. Zool., 127:244–296. (*275*)
Gicklhorn, J., and H. Süllman 1931. Die Permeabilität der Kiemensäckchen von *Daphnia magna*. Protoplasma, 13:617–636. (*293, 310, 311*)
Giersberg, H. 1928. Über den morphologischen und physiologischen Farbwechsel der Stabheuschrecke *Dixippus* (*Carausius*) *morosus*. Z. vergl. Physiol., 7:657–695. (*93*)
Giesbrecht, W. 1921. Das Skelett von *Squilla mantis* L. Mitt. Zool. Sta. Neapel, 22:459–522. (*241*)
Giese, A. C., and P. A. Leighton 1937. Phosphorescence of cells and cell products. Science, 85:428–429. (*121*)
Gilbert, G. A., and J. V. R. Marriott 1948. Starch-iodine complexes. Trans. Faraday Soc., 44:84–93. (*35*)
Gilmer, P. M. 1925. A comparative study of the poison apparatus of certain lepidopterous larvae. Ann. Ent. Soc. Amer., 18:203–239. (*276*)
Gilson, E. 1895a. De la présence de la chitine dans la membrane cellulaire des champignons. C. R. Acad. Sci., 120:1000–1002. (*42*)
——— 1895b. Das Chitin und die Membranen der Pilzzellen. Ber. dtsch. Chem. Ges., 28:821–822. (*28*)
——— 1895c. Recherches chimiques sur la membrane cellulaire des champignons. La Cellule, 11:7–15. (*28*)
Gilson, G. 1887. Étude comparée de la spermatogénèse chez les arthropodes. La Cellule, 4:5–93. (*282*)
Ginsburg, J. M. 1929. Relation between toxicity of oil and its penetration into respiratory siphons of mosquito larvae. Proc. 16th Ann. Mtg. N. J. Mosq. Exterm. Assoc., pp. 50–63. (*137*)
Glaser, R. W. 1912. A contribution to our knowledge of the function of the oenocytes of insects. Biol. Bull., 23:213–224. (*217, 219*)
——— 1918. Anthocyanin in *Pterocomma smithiae*. Psyche, 24:30. (*91*)
Glick, D. 1948. Techniques of Histo- and Cytochemistry. Interscience, New York. (*37, 265*)
Glover, L. H., and C. H. Richardson 1936. The penetration of gaseous pyridine, piperidine and nicotine into the body of the american cockroach, *Periplaneta americana*. Iowa State Coll. J. Sci., 10:249–260. (*134, 307, 313, 317*)
* le Goffe, M. 1939. (The biology of *Lepidurus apus*, phyllopod crustacean). Bull. Soc. Sci. Bretagne, Sci. math. phys. nat., 16:35–50. (Chem. Abstr., 40:2899.) (*31*)
Gofferje, M. 1918. Die Wirkung verschiedener Salze auf Larven von *Culex pipiens* L. Mitt. Zool. Inst. Westfäl Wilhelma Univ. Münster, 1:9–11. (*292, 310*)
Goldberg, L., and B. de Meillon 1948. The nutrition of the larva of *Aedes aegypti* Linnaeus. 4. Protein and amino-acid requirements. Biochem. J., 43:379–387. (*87, 89*)
Goldschmidt, S., K. Martin, and W. Heidinger 1933a. Über das Seidenfibroin. 2. Die Einwirkung von Hypobromite auf Seide. Ann. d. Chem., 505:255–261. (*68*)
——— 1933b. Über das Seidenfibroin. 3. Die Einwirkung von Salzsäure auf Seide. *Ibid.*, pp. 262–273. (*68*)
Goldschmidt, S., and K. Straus 1930. Über das Seidenfibroin. Ann. d. Chem., 480:263–279. (*68*)

Goldsmith, E. D., and M. H. Harnly 1946. The comparative toxicity of thiourea to four mutants of *Drosophila melanogaster*. Science, 103:649–651. (*313*)

Gomori, G. 1950. Pitfalls in histochemistry. Ann. N. Y. Acad. Sci., 50:968–981. (*71, 74, 79*)

Gonell, H. W. 1926. Röntgenographische Studien an Chitin. Z. physiol. Chem., 152:18–30. (*17, 21, 194*)

* Gonin, J. 1894. Recherches sur la metamorphose des lépidoptères. De la formation des appendices imaginaux dans la chenille du *Pieris brassicae*. Bull. Soc. Vand. Sci. Nat., 30:89–138. (Cited by Tower 1902.) (*229*)

Good, P. M., and A. W. Johnson 1949. Paper chromatography of pterins. Nature, 163:31. (*92*)

Goodings, A. C., and L. H. Turl 1940. The density and swelling of silk filaments in relation to moisture content. J. Textile Inst., 31:T–69–80. (*118, 120, 121*)

Goodrich, E. S. 1896. Notes on Oligochaetes. Quart. J. Micr. Sci., 39:51–69. (*44*)

Goodwin, T. W. 1949. Carotenoid distribution in solitary and gregarious phases of the African migratory locust and the desert locust. Biochem. J., 45:472–479. (*90, 91*)

———, and S. Shrisukh 1948. The carotenoids of the locust integument. Nature, 161:525–526. (*90, 91*)

——— 1949. The carotenoids of the integument of two locust species (*Locusta migratoria migratorioides* R. & F. and *Schistocerca gregaria* Forsk.). Biochem. J., 45:263–268. (*90, 91*)

von Gorka, A. 1914. Experimentelle und morphologische Beiträge zur Physiologie der Malpighi'schen Gefässe der Käfer. Zool. Jahrb., Anat., 34:233–238. (*298*)

Gortner, R. A. 1911a. Studies on melanin. 2. The pigmentation of the adult periodical cicada (*Tibicien septemdecim* L.). J. Biol. Chem., 10:89–94. (*74, 191*)

——— 1911b. Studies on melanin. 4. The origin of the pigment and the color pattern in the elytra of the Colorado potato beetle (*Leptinotarsa decemlineata* Say). Amer. Nat., 45:743–755. (*76, 88, 191*)

Gossel, P. 1935. Beiträge zur Kenntnis der Hautsinnesorgane und Hautdrüsen der Cheliceraten und der Augen der Ixodiden. Z. Morph. Ökol. Tiere, 30:177–205. (*275*)

Gouin, F. 1946. Recherches morphologiques sur le mesentéron et le proctodeum des larves de Chironomides. Arch. Zool. Exp. & Gen., 84:335–374. (*161*)

Goux, L. 1944. Note sur la constitution du tégument chez la larve d'une Aleurode. C. R. Soc. Biol., 138:627–628. (*136*)

Govaerts, J., and J. Leclercq 1946. Water exchange between insects and air moisture. Nature, 157:483. (Also in C. R. Soc. Biol., 140:1028, 1946, and in Bull. Soc. Chim. Biol., 29:33–34, 1947.) (*294, 298, 299*)

Graber, V. 1874. Über eine Art fibrillären Bindegewebes der Insektenhaut und seine lokale Bedeutung als Tracheensuspensorium. Arch. Mikr. Anat., 10:124–144. (*222*)

* ——— 1877. Die Insekten. München. (Cited by Wigglesworth, 1948b.) (*275*)

* Grana, A., and C. Oehninger 1944. Constitución química y propriedades biológicas de la membrana hidática. Arch. Urug. Med. Cir. & Esp., 24:231–236. (*43*)

Grandjean, F. 1937. *Otodectes cynotis* (Hering) et les prétendues trachées des Acaridiae. Bull. Soc. Zool. France, 62:280–290. (*251, 254*)

Grassé, P., and L. Lesperon 1934. Quelques données nouvelles sur la sécrétion de la soie chez le Bombyx du mûrier (*Sericaria mori* L.). Arch. Zool. Exp. & Gen., 76(Not. & Rev.):90–101. (*251, 252*)

Grassmann, W., L. Zechmeister, R. Bender, and G. Tóth 1934. Über die Chitin-Spaltung durch Emulsin-Präparate. 3. Über enzymatische Spaltung von Polysacchariden. Ber. dtsch. Chem. Ges., 67B:1–5. (*14, 38, 77*)

Graubard, M. A. 1933. Tyrosinase in mutants of *Drosophila melanogaster*. J. Genet., 27:199–218. (*76, 88, 191*)

Grayson, J. M., and O. E. Tauber 1943. Carotin – the principal pigment responsible for variations in colouration in the adult grasshopper, *Melanoplus bivittatus*. Iowa State Coll. J. Sci., 17:191–196. (*91*)

Grell, K. G. 1938. Der Darmtraktus von *Panorpa communis* und seine Anhänge bei Larve und Imago. Zool. Jahrb., Anat., 64:1–86. (*161, 209*)

Griffiths, A. B. 1892. La Pupine, nouvelle substance animale. C. R. Acad. Sci., 115:320–321 (also Bull. Acad. R. Belg., ser. 3, 24:592, 1892). (*14*)

Griffiths, J. T., Jr., and O. E. Tauber 1943. Evaluation of sodium fluoride as a stomach poison and as a contact insecticide against the roach *Periplaneta americana* L. J. Econ. Ent., 36:536–540. (*313*)

Gross, J. 1903. Über das Palménsche Organ der Ephemeriden. Zool. Jahrb., Anat., 19:91–106. (*236, 261*)

Gunn, D. L. 1933. The temperature and humidity relations of the cockroach (*Blatta orientalis*). 1. Desiccation. J. Exp. Biol., 10:274–285. (*305*)

——— 1935. Oxygen consumption of the cockroach in relation to moulting. Nature, 135:434–435. (*31*)

Guth, G. 1919. Über den Kopfschild von *Leptodora* und *Polyphemus*. Zool. Anz., 50:285–286. (*194, 267*)

Hacker, H. P. 1925. How oil kills anopheline larvae. F. M. S. Malaria Bur. Rept., 3:1–62. (*137, 139*)

Hackman, R. H., M. G. M. Pryor, and A. R. Todd 1948. The occurrence of phenolic substances in arthropods. Biochem. J., 43:474–477. (*72, 74*)

Hadorn, E., and G. Frizzi 1949. Experimentelle Untersuchungen zur Melanophoren-Reaktion von *Corethra*. Rev. Suisse Zool., 56:306–316. (*93*)

Hadorn, E., and J. Neel 1938. Der hormonale Einfluss der Ringdrüse (Corpus allatum) auf die Pupariumbildung bei Fliegen. Arch. Entw.-Mech., 138:281–304. (*231*)

* Hadzi, J. 1938. Beitrag zur Kenntnis der adriatischen Folliculiden. Acta Adriatica Inst. Oceanogr. Split. Jugoslav., 1:1–46. (*254*)

Haeckel, E. 1857. Über die Gewebe des Flüsskrebses. Arch. Anat. Physiol. wiss. Med., pp. 469–568. (*159, 163, 182, 202, 220*)

——— 1864. Beiträge zur Kenntnis der Corycaeiden. Jena. Z. Med. Naturwiss., 1:61–112. (*192, 193, 196, 215*)

von Haffner, K. 1924a. Beiträge zur Kenntnis der Linguatuliden. 4. Die Körper muskulatur von *Porocephalus armillatus*. Zool. Anz., 59:270–276. (*160, 237, 238*)

——— 1924b. Beiträge zur Kenntnis der Linguatuliden. 5. Die Drüsen von *Porocephalus armillatus*. Zool. Anz., 60:126–136. (*160, 163, 182*)

Hagen, H. A. 1883. On the color and the pattern of insects. Proc. Amer. Acad. Arts Sci., ser. 2, 9:234–262. (*86*)

Hagmann, L. E. 1940. A method for injecting insect tracheae permanently. Stain Tech., 15:115–118. (*140*)

* Hahn, L. 1946. A method for the determination of glucosamine and N-acetylglucosamine in the presence of other sugars. Arkiv Kemi, Mineral Geol., ser. A, 22(12):1–12. (Chem. Abstr., 41:1006.) (*11*)

Haller, G. 1880. Beiträge zur Kenntnis der *Laemodipodes filiformes*. Z. wiss. Zool., 33:350–422. (*275*)

Halliburton, W. D. 1885a. On the chemical composition of the cartilage occurring in certain invertebrate animals. Proc. R. Soc. London, 38:75–76. (*12, 41*)

——— 1885b. On the occurrence of chitin as a constituent of the cartilages of *Limulus* and *Sepia*. Quart. J. Micr. Sci., 25:173–181. (*12, 38, 41*)

Hamamura, Y., S. Iida, and M. Otsuka 1940. (Enzymatic studies on exuvial fluid of *Bombyx mori.*) (In Japanese.) Bull. Agric. Chem. Soc. Japan, 16:905–909. (*12, 78, 112*)

Hamilton, A. G. 1936. The relation of humidity and temperature to the development of three species of African locusts. Trans. R. Ent. Soc. London, 85:1–60. (*92*)

Hammond, C. O. 1928. The emergence of *Erythromma maias* Haus. (Paraneuroptera.) Entomologist, 61:54–55. (*92*)

Hansen, E. L., J. W. Hansen, and R. Craig 1944. The distribution of a bromine homologue of DDT in insect tissue. J. Econ. Ent., 37:853. (*294*)

* Harder, S. 1937. Über das Vorkommen von Chitin und seine Bedeutung für die phylogenetische und systematische Beurteilung der Pilze. Nachr. Ges. Wiss. Göttingen, 3:1. (*45, 52*)

Harnisch, O. 1934. Osmoregulation und osmoregulatorischen Mechanismus der Larve von *Chironomus thummi.* Z. vergl. Physiol., 21:281–295. (*292*)

Harpster, H. T. 1941. An investigation of the gaseous plastron as a respiratory mechanism in *Helichus striatus* Leconte (Dryopidae). Trans. Amer. Micr. Soc., 60:329–358. (*276*)

——— 1944. The gaseous plastron as a respiratory mechanism in *Stenelmis quadrimaculata* Horn (Dryopidae). Trans. Amer. Micr. Soc., 63:1–26. (*276*)

* Harris, M., and T. B. Johnson 1930. Study of the fibroin from silk in the isoelectric region. Ind. Eng. Chem., 22:539–542. (Chem. Abstr., 24:3375.) (*121*)

Hase, A. 1929. Durch Quarzlichtbestrahlung erzwungene Pigmentveränderungen bei Insekten (Schlupfwespen). Arch. Dermatol. Syphilis, 157:437–445. (*126*)

Hasebroek, K. 1921–1926. Untersuchungen zum Problem des neuzeitlichen Melanismus der Schmetterlinge. Parts 1–10. Fermentforschung, 5:1–40, 1921; 5:297–333, 1922; 7:1–13, 138–142, 143–152, 182–194; 8:197–198, 199–226, 1925; 8:553–567, 568–573, 1926. (*89*)

Hass, W. 1914. Über das Zustandekommen der Flügeldeckenskulptur einiger Brachyceriden. Sitz.-Ber. Ges. Naturf. Freunde Berlin, 7:354–364. (*163, 246*)

——— 1916a. Über die Struktur des Chitins bei Arthropoden. Arch. Anat. Physiol., Physiol. Abt., pp. 295–338. (Cited by Wigglesworth, 1933.) (*163, 179, 180, 182, 192, 209*)

——— 1916b. Über Metallfarben bei Buprestiden. Sitz.-Ber. Ges. Naturf. Freunde Berlin, pp. 332–343. (*163*)

Hassan, A. A. G. 1944. The structure and mechanism of the spiracular regulatory apparatus in adult Diptera and certain other groups of insects. Trans. R. Ent. Soc. London, 94:103–153. (*222, 266*)

** Häuslmayer, W. 1937. Die chemische Entwicklung der Schmetterlingszeichnung. Anz. Akad. Wiss. Wien, 74:42–44. (*271*)

Haworth, W. N. 1946. The structure, function and synthesis of polysaccharides. Proc. R. Soc. London, ser. A, 186:1–19. (*9, 10, 12, 147, 255*)

———, W. H. G. Lake, and S. Peat 1939. The configuration of glucosamine (= chitosamine). J. Chem. Soc., pp. 271–274. (*11*)

Hay, W. P. 1904. The life history of the blue crab (*Callinectes sapidus*). Ann. Rpt. U. S. Bur. Fish., pp. 397–413. (*104, 105*)

Hayes, W. P., and Y. S. Liu 1947. Tarsal chemoreceptors of the housefly and their possible relation to DDT toxicity. Ann. Ent. Soc. Amer., 40:401–416. (*158*)

Hedicke, H. 1929. Arthropoden-Fette, Öle und Wachse und Shellack. Rohstoffe des Tierreiches, Berlin, 1:4–46. (*250*)

Heilbrunn, L. V. 1943. An Outline of General Physiology, 2d ed. Saunders, Philadelphia. (*291*)

Heinemann, C. 1872. Untersuchungen über die Leuchtorgane der bei Vera Cruz vorkommenden Leuchtkäfer. Arch. Mikr. Anat., 8:461–471. (*264*)

Helfer, H., and E. Schlottke 1935. Pantopoda. *In* Bronn, Klassen und Ordnungen des Tierreichs, vol. 5, Abt. 4, Buch 2, 314 pp. (*153, 161, 205, 207, 211, 226*)

* Heller, J. 1947. (Insect metamorphosis. 14. Regulation of the metabolism during the pupal stage. The role of tyrosinase.) Acta Biol. Exptl. (Warsaw), 14:229–237. (Chem. Abstr., 42:8980.) (*76*)

Henke, K. 1924. Die Färbung und Zeichnung der Feuerwanze (*Pyrrhocoris apterus* L.) und ihre experimentelle Beinflussbarkeit. Z. vergl. Physiol., 1:297–499. (*76, 88, 91, 191*)

——— 1946. Über die Verschiedenen Zellteilungsvorgänge in der Entwicklung des beschuppten Flügelepithels der Mehlmotte *Ephestia kühniella*. Biol. Zbl., 65:120–135. (*243, 245*)

Henrici, H. 1938. Die Hautdrüsen der Landwanzen (Geocorisae), ihre mikroskopische Anatomie, ihre Histologie und Entwicklung. 1. Die abdominalen Stinkdrüsen, die Drüsenpakete und die zerstreuten Hautdrüsen. Zool. Jahrb., Anat., 65:141–228. (*251*)

——— 1940. Die Hautdrüsen der Landwanzen (Geocorisae), ihre mikroskopische Anatomie, ihre Histologie und Entwicklung. 2. Die thorakalen Stinkdrüsen. *Ibid.*, 66:371–402. (*251*)

Henricksen, K. L. 1931. The manner of moulting in Arthropoda. Notul. Entomol., 11:103–127. (*234*)

Henseval, M. 1896. Étude comparée des glandes de Gilson, organes métamériques des larves d'insectes. La Cellule, 11:329–355. (*162, 251*)

Henson, H. 1931. The structure and postembryonic development of *Vanessa urticae*. 1. The larval alimentary canal. Quart. J. Micr. Sci., 74:321–360. (*278*)

Hering, M. 1939. Die peritrophischen Hüllen der Hönigbiene mit besonderer Berücksichtigung der Zeit während der Entwicklung des imaginalen Darmes. Ein Beitrag zum Studium der peritrophischen Membran der Insekten. Zool. Jahrb., Anat., 66:129–190. (*277, 278*)

Hermans, P. H. 1946. Contribution to the Physics of Cellulose Fibers. Elsevier, New York. (*118, 136*)

Herold, W. 1913. Beiträge zur Anatomie und Physiologie einiger Landisopoden. Häutung-Sekretion-Atmung. Zool. Jahrb., Anat., 35:457–526. (*106, 161, 163, 171, 182, 207, 209, 234, 253*)

Herrick, F. H. 1896. The American lobster: A study of its habits and development. Bull. U. S. Fish Comm., 15:1–252. (*101, 159, 161*)

——— 1911. Natural history of the American lobster. U. S. Bur. Fish., Bull. no. 29. (*161*)

Herrmann, F. 1931. Über den Wasserhaushalt des Flusskrebses (*Potamobius astacus* Leach). Z. vergl. Physiol., 14:479–524. (*292*)

Hers, M. J. 1942. Anaerobiose et régulation minérale chez les larves de *Chironomus*. Ann. Soc. Roy. Zool. Belg., 73:173–179. (*292*)

Herzog, R. O. 1924. Über den Feinbau der Faserstoffe. Naturwiss., 12:955–960. (*10, 17, 69*)

——— 1926. Fortschritte in der Erkenntnis der Faserstoffe. Z. angew. Chem., 39:297–302. (*29, 119, 120, 122*)

* Hess, E. 1937. Chitinovorous bacteria on live lobsters. Progress Rept. Biol. Board Canada, no. 19. (*57*)

Hess, W. N. 1922. Origin and development of the light organs of *Photurus pennsylvanica* de Geer. J. Morph., 36:245–277. (*126*)

——— 1941. Factors influencing moulting in the crustacean, *Crangon armillatus*. Biol. Bull., 81:215–220. (*232, 235*)

Heuschmann, O. 1929. Über die elektrischen Eigenschaften der Insektenhaare. Z. vergl. Physiol., 10:594–664. (*118*)

Hewitt, L. F. 1938. The polysaccharide content and reducing power of proteins and of their digestion products. Biochem. J., 32:1554–1560. (*12*)

Heyn, A. N. J. 1936a. Molecular structure of chitin in plant cell walls. Nature, 137:277–278. (*18, 39, 42, 45, 50*)

* ——— 1936b. X-ray investigations on the molecular structure of chitin in cell walls. Proc. Acad. Sci. Amsterdam, 39:132–135. (Chem. Abstr., 30:3438.) (*18, 39, 42, 45, 50*)

——— 1936c. Further investigations on the mechanism of cell elongation and the properties of the cell wall in connection with elongation. 4. Investigations on the molecular structure of chitin cell walls of sporangiophores of *Phycomyces* and its probable bearing on the phenomenon of spiral growth. Protoplasma, 25:372–396. (*18, 39, 42, 45, 50*)

Hickin, N. E. 1945. Mode of entry of contact insecticides. Nature, 156:753–754. (*313*)

Hill, D. L. 1945. Carbohydrate metabolism during embryonic development (Orthoptera). J. Cell. Comp. Physiol., 25:205–216. (*30*)

Hilpert, R. S., D. Becker, and W. Rossée 1937. Untersuchungen an Flechten, Pilzen und Algen. Biochem. Z., 289:179–192, 193–197. (*45*)

Hinton, H. E. 1947. On the reduction of functional spiracles in the aquatic larvae of the holometabola, with notes on the moulting process of spiracles. Trans. R. Ent. Soc. London, 98:449–473. (*223, 225, 261, 266*)

——— 1948. On the origin and function of the pupal stage. Trans. R. Ent. Soc. London, 99:395–409. (*240*)

Hirata, Y., K. Nakanishi, and H. Kikkawa 1950. Xanthopterin obtained from the skins of the yellow mutant of *Bombyx mori* (Silkworm). Science, 111:608–609. (*91*)

Ho, C. P., S. M. Shen, P. S. Tang, and S. H. Yu 1944. Physiology of the silkworm. 2. Mechanism of silk formation as revealed by X-ray analyses of the contents of the silk gland in *Bombyx mori.* Physiol. Zool., 17:78–82. (*67*)

Höber, R. 1936. Membrane permeability to solutes in its relations to cellular physiology. Physiol. Rev., 16:52–102. (*286, 287, 289*)

——— 1940. Correlation between the molecular configuration of organic compounds and their active transfer in living cells. Cold Spring Harbor Symp. Quant. Biol., 8:40–50. (*291*)

Hock, C. W. 1940. Decomposition of chitin (of *Limulus polyphemus*) by marine bacteria. Biol. Bull., 79:199–206. (*55, 56*)

——— 1941. Marine chitin-decomposing bacteria. J. Marine Res., 4:99–106. (*55–57, 77, 78*)

Hockenyos, G. L. 1933. The mechanism of absorption of sodium fluoride by roaches. J. Econ. Ent., 26:1162–1169. (*294, 313*)

——— 1939. Factors influencing the absorption of sodium fluoride by the American cockroach. *Ibid.*, 32:843–848. (*300, 315*)

Hoffbauer, C. 1892. Beiträge zur Kenntnis der Insektenflügel. Z. wiss. Zool., 54:579–630. (*246*)

Hollande, A. C. 1913. Les corps figurés du protoplasma des oenocytes des insectes. C. R. Acad. Sci., 156:636–638. (*217*)

——— 1914. Les Cérodécytes ou 'oenocytes' des insectes, considérés au point de vue biochimique. Arch d'Anat. Micr., 16:1–64. (*217, 219*)

——— 1920. Réactions des tissus du *Dytiscus marginalis* L. au contact de larves de distome enkystées et fixées aux parois du tube digestif de l'insecte. Arch. Zool. Exp. & Gen., 59:543–563. (*52, 222*)

——— 1943. Observations sur la structure du protoplasma et l'organisation de la cellule. *Ibid.*, 83:270–412. (*92, 205 206, 257*)

* Holliday, R. A. 1942. Some observations on Natal Onychophora. Ann. Natal Mus., 10:237–244. (*157*)

Holmgren, E. 1895. Die trachealen Endverzweigungen bei den Spinndrüsen der Lepidopterenlarven. Anat. Anz., 11:340–346. (*263, 264*)

Holmgren, N. 1902a. Über das Verhalten des Chitins und Epithels zu den unterliegenden Gewebearten bei Insekten. Anat. Anz., 20:480–488. (*159, 182, 183*)

——— 1902b. Über die morphologische Bedeutung des Chitins bei Insekten. *Ibid.*, 21:372–378. (*159, 180, 182*)

——— 1907. Monographische Bearbeitung einer schalentragenden Mycetophilidenlarve, *Mycetophila ancyliformans* n. sp. Z. wiss. Zool., 88:1–77. (*159, 161, 209, 222, 238, 264*)

——— 1910. Über die Muskelinsertion an das Chitin bei den Arthropoden. Anat. Anz., 36:116–122. (*238*)

Homann, H. 1949. Über das Wachstum und die mechanischen Vorgänge bei der Hautung von *Tegenaria agrestis* (Araneae). Z. vergl. Physiol., 31:413–440. (*119, 233*)

Hoop, M. 1933. Häutungshistologie einiger Insekten. Zool. Jahrb., Anat., 57:433–464. (*153, 157, 161, 209, 211, 213, 217, 225–229*)

Hoppe-Seyler, F. 1894. Über Chitin und Cellulose. Ber. dtsch. Chem. Ges., 27:3329–3331. (*27*)

——— 1895. Über Unwandlungen des Chitins. *Ibid.*, 28:82. (*27, 72*)

Hoskins, W. M. 1932. Toxicity and permeability. 1. The toxicity of acid and basic solutions of sodium arsenite to mosquito pupae. J. Econ. Ent., 25:1212–1224. (*288, 294*)

——— 1933. The penetration of insecticidal oils into porous solids. Hilgardia, 8:49–82. (*137*)

——— 1940. Recent contributions of insect physiology to insect toxicology and control. *Ibid.*, 13:307–386. (*137, 313*)

——— 1941. Some recent advances in the chemistry and physics of spray oil emulsions. J. Econ. Ent., 34:791–798. (*137*)

———, and Y. Ben-Amotz 1938. The deposit of aqueous solutions and of oil sprays. Hilgardia, 12:83–111. (*137*)

Hoskins, W. M., and R. Craig 1935. Recent progress in insect physiology. Physiol. Rev., 15:525–596. (*160*)

Hosselet, C. 1925. Les oenocytes de *Culex annulatus* et l'étude de leur chondriome au cours de la sécrétion. C. R. Acad. Sci., 180:399–401. (*217, 218*)

Hotchkiss, R. D. 1948. A microchemical reaction resulting in the staining of polysaccharide structures in fixed tissue preparations. Arch. Biochem., 16:131–141. (*37, 38*)

Hough, L., J. K. N. Jones, and W. H. Wadman 1948. Application of paper partition chromatography to the separation of the sugars and their methylated derivatives on a column of powdered cellulose. Nature, 162:448. (*11, 133*)

Hovanitz, W. 1945. The combined effects of genetic and environmental variations upon the composition of *Colias* populations. Ann. Ent. Soc. Amer., 38:482–502. (*201*)

Hövener, M. 1930. Der Darmtraktus von *Psychoda alternata* und seine Anhangsdrüsen. Z. Morph. Ökol. Tiere, 18:74–113. (*278*)

Hsü, F. 1938. Étude cytologique et comparée sur les sensilla des insectes. La Cellule, 47:5–60. (*183, 275*)

Hsu, W. S. 1948. Some observations on the Golgi material in the larval epidermal cells of *Drosophila melanogaster*. Biol. Bull., 95:163–168. (*206*)

Hsu, Y. C. 1933. Some new morphological findings in Ephemeroptera. 5th Congr. Int. Ent., Paris, 2:361–368. (*236, 261*)

Huet, E. L. L. 1883. Recherches sur les Isopodes. J. Anat. Physiol., 19:241–376. (*66, 159, 207, 216*)

Huf, E. 1936. Der Einfluss des mechanischen Innendruchs auf die Flüssigkeitsausscheidnung bei gepanzerten Süsswasser- und Meereskrebsen. Pflüger's Arch. ges. Physiol., 237:240–250. (*292*)

Hufnagel, A. 1918. Recherches histologiques sur le métamorphose d'un Lépidoptère *Hyponomeuta padella* L.). Arch. Zool. Exp. & Gen., 57:47–202. (*209, 216, 217*)

Humperdinck, I. 1924. Über Muskulatur und Endoskelett von *Polyphemus pediculus* de Geer. Topographisches und Embryologisches. Z. wiss. Zool., 121:621–655. (*237*)

Humphrey, J. H. 1946. Studies on diffusing factors. 1. Kinetics of the action of hyaluronidase from various sources upon hyaluronic acid, with a note upon anomalies encountered in the estimation of N-acetylglucosamine. Biochem. J., 40:435–441. (*12*)

Hurst, H. 1940. Permeability of insect cuticle. Nature, 145:462–463. (*294, 312*)

——— 1941. Insect cuticle as an asymmetrical membrane. *Ibid.*, 147:388–389. (*154, 289, 293, 294, 304, 305*)

——— 1943a. Permeability and molecular constitution as factors in drug action. *Ibid.*, 152:292–296. (*289, 304*)

——— 1943b. Principles of insecticidal action as a guide to drug reactivity-phase distribution relationships. Trans. Faraday Soc., 39:390–411. (*289, 304*)

——— 1945a. Enzyme activity as a factor in insect physiology and toxicology. Nature, 156:194–198. (*304*)

——— 1945b. Biophysical factors in drug action. Brit. Med. Bull., 3:132–137. (*289, 304*)

——— 1948. Asymmetrical behaviour of insect cuticle in relation to water permeability. Disc. Faraday Soc., no. 3, pp. 193–210. (*294, 304*)

Husain, M. A., and C. B. Mather 1936. Studies on *Schistocerca gregaria* Forsk. 3. Why locusts eat wool. A study in the hydromania of *Schistocerca gregaria*. Indian J. Agric. Sci., 6:263–267. (*305*)

Huttrer, K. 1932. Wege zur Analyse der Entstehung der Schmetterlingszeichnung. Anz. Akad. Wiss. Wien, 69:123–125. (*141*)

Hutzel, J. M. 1942. Action of pyrethrum upon the German cockroach. J. Econ. Ent., 35:933–937. (*317*)

* Huxley, T. H. 1880. The crayfish. Internat. Sci. Ser., vol. 28. Kegan-Paul, London. (*180, 182*)

* Ichikawa, C. 1938. (Biochemical studies on the locust. 4. Differences of proteins in the male and female.) J. Agric. Chem. Soc. Japan, 14:43–44. (*50*)

Ide, M. 1891. Glandes cutanées à canaux intracellulaires chez les crustacés Edriophthalmes. La Cellule, 7:345–372. (*207*)

** Ikeda, Y. 1911. (Dorsal glands at the time of moulting. Silkworm.) Tokyo Nip. Sanshi Kw. Ho., 230:3–7. (*209*)

* Iljiskaya, M. I. 1946. The mechanism of insecticidal action and the permeability of the cuticle of insects. C. R. Acad. Sci. URSS (Doklady), 51:557–560. (Chem. Abstr., 40:7504.) (*294, 314*)

* Ilkewitsch, K. 1908. (Fungal chitin named mycetin.) Bull. Acad. St. Petersburg, p. 571. (Cited by Rammelberg 1931.) (*14*)

Illig, K. G. 1903. Duftorgane der männlichen Schmetterlinge. Zoologica (Stuttgart), 15(37):1–34. (*275*)

Irvine, J. C. 1909. A polarimetric method of identifying chitin. J. Chem. Soc., 95:564–570. (*39, 132*)

Irvine, R., and G. S. Woodhead 1889. Secretion of carbonate of lime by animals. Proc. R. Soc. Edinburgh, 16:324–354. (*101*)

* Iseki, T. 1934. (Constitution of ovomucoids.) J. Biochem. (Japan), 19:1–5. (Chem. Abstr., 28:2378.) (*12*)

Issel, R. 1910. Ricerche intorno alla biologia ed alla morfologia dei crostacei decapodi. 1. Studi sui Paguridi. Arch. Zool. Napoli, 4:335–397. (*207, 213, 243*)

van Iterson, G., K. H. Meyer, and W. Lotmar 1936. Über den Feinbau des pflanzlichen Chitins. Rec. Trav. Chim. Pays-Bas Belg., 55:61–63, 130. (*18, 19, 39, 42, 45, 49*)

Ito, H. 1924. Contribution histologique et physiologique à l'étude des annexes des organes génitaux des orthoptères (tubes glandulaires ou glandes annexes, spermathèques, vésicules séminales, glandes prostatiques). Arch. Anat. Micr., 20:343–460. (*15, 161, 250*)

* Ito, T., and K. Komori 1936. (Sericine I and II.) J. Agric. Chem. Soc. Japan, 13:1195–1200, 1201–1207. (Chem. Abstr., 32:3160.) (*68*)

* ——— 1939. (Sericine. 3. Nitrogen distribution and the contents of sugars and amino sugars in sericine.) J. Agric. Chem. Soc. Japan, 15:50–52. (Chem. Abstr., 33:4793.) (*62, 64, 68*)

* Ivanova, P. G. 1937. (The permeability of the external covers of insects with regard to anabasine.) Bull. Inst. Zool. appl. Phytopath. (Izv. Kurs. prskl. Zool.), 6:25–32. (Cited by Brightwell 1938.) (*293*)

Jackson, H. G. 1913. *Eupagurus.* Liverpool Proc. Trans. Biol. Soc., 27:495–573. (*161*)

Jacobs, W. 1924. Das Duftorgan von *Apis mellifica* und ähnliche Hautdrüsenorgane sozialer und solitärer Apiden. Z. Morph. Ökol. Tiere, 3:1–80. (*37, 51, 161, 251, 252*)

Jacobsen, V. C. 1934. A review of the chemical aspects of the melanin problem. Arch. Path., 17:391–403. (*84*)

Jahn, T. L. 1934. Electro-measurements of the permeability of the grasshopper egg membrane. Anat. Rec., 60(suppl.):33. (*314*)

——— 1935a. The nature and permeability of the grasshopper egg membranes. 1. The e. m. f. across membranes during early diapause. J. Cell. Comp. Physiol., 7:23–46. (*121, 281, 293, 310, 314*)

——— 1935b. Nature and permeability of grasshopper egg membranes. 2. Chemical composition of membranes. Proc. Soc. Exp. Biol. Med., 33:159–163. (*50, 66, 281*)

——— 1936. Studies on the nature and permeability of the grasshopper egg membranes. 3. Changes in electrical properties of the membranes during development. J. Cell. Comp. Physiol., 8:289–300. (*282, 293, 310, 314*)

Janda, V. 1936. Über den Farbwechsel transplantierter Hautstücke und kunstlich verbundener Körperfragmente bei *Dixippus morosus.* Zool. Anz., 115:177–185. (*93*)

Janet, C. 1897. Limites morphologiques des anneaux post-cephaliques et musculature des anneaux post-thoracique chez la *Myrmica rubra.* Lille, Paris. 35 pp. (*241*)

——— 1907. Anatomie du corselet et histolyse des muscles vibrateurs, après le vol nuptial, chez la reine de la fourmi (*Lasius niger*). Limoges, Paris. 149 pp. (*161, 174, 175, 217, 242*)

——— 1909. Sur l'ontogénèse de l'insecte. Limoges, Paris. (*161, 201*)

——— 1911. Sur l'existence d'un organe chordotonal et d'une vésicule pulsatile antennaires chez l'abeille et sur la morphologie de la tête de cette espèce. C. R. Acad. Sci., 152:110–112. (*261*)

Janisch, E. 1923. Der Bau des Enddarm von *Astacus fluviatilis.* Ein Beitrag zur Morphologie der Dekapoden. Z. wiss. Zool., 121:1–63. (*161, 207, 237*)

Jaworowsky, A. 1885. Über die schlauchförmigen Anhänge bei den Nematocerenlarven. (In Polish.) Kosmos, Lemburg, 10:204–224. (*249*)

Jensen, H. L. 1932. The microbiology of farmyard manure decomposition in soil. J. Agric. Sci., 22:1–25. (*55*)
Johannsen, O. E., and F. H. Butt 1941. The Embryology of Insects and Myriapods. McGraw-Hill, New York. (*150, 280*)
Johansson, B. 1914. Zur Kenntnis der Spinndrüsen der Araneina. Lunds Univ. Arssk., N. F., Afd. 2, 10(5):1–12. (*251*)
Johnson, C. G. 1937. The absorption of water and the associated volume changes in the eggs of *Notostira erratica* L. (Hemiptera, Capsidae) during embryonic development under experimental conditions. J. Exp. Biol., 14:413–421. (*282, 298*)
Johnson, D. E. 1931. The antibiosis of certain bacteria to smuts and some other fungi. Phytopath., 21:843–863. (*45*)
——— 1932. Chitin destroying bacteria. J. Bact., 24:335–340. (*49, 56*)
Johnstone, J. 1908. Conditions of Life in the Sea. Cambridge Univ. Press. (*54*)
Joly, N. 1849. Mémoire sur l'existence supposée d'une circulation péritrachéenne chez les insectes. Ann. Sci. Nat., Zool., ser. 3, 12:306–316. (*256*)
Jones, B. M. 1950. Acarine growth: A new ecdysial mechanism. Nature, 166:908–909. (*236*)
* Jordan, H., and H. J. Lam 1918. Über die Durchlässigkeit bei *Astacus fluviatilis* und *Helix pomatia*. Tijdsch. Ned. Dierk Vereenig., 16:281–292. (Cited by Yonge 1924.) (*298*)
Jordan, R., J. Tischer, and E. Illner 1940. Vergleich des von altbienen Erzeugten Wachses mit "Jungfernwachs" und Gewöhnlichen Bienenwachs. Z. vergl. Physiol., 28:353–357. (*99*)
Jucci, C. 1936. Nuove ricerche sulla colorazione dei bozzoli nel baco da seta in rapporto ai pigmenti della foglia ingerita. Arch. Zool. Ital., Torino, 22:259–268. (*91*)
Junge, H. 1941. Über grüne Insektenfarbstoffe. Z. physiol. Chem., 268:179–186. (*91*)
Kalmus, H. 1941a. Physiology and ecology of cuticle color in insects. Nature, 148:428–431. (*154, 305*)
——— 1941b. Relation between color and permeability of insect cuticles. *Ibid.*, 147:455. (*154, 304*)
——— 1941c. The resistance to desiccation of *Drosophila* mutants affecting body color. Proc. R. Soc. London, ser. B, 130:185–201. (*154, 304*)
——— 1942. Differences in resistance to toxic substances shown by different body colour mutants in *Drosophila* (Diptera). Proc. R. Ent. Soc. London, ser. A, 17:127–133. (*313*)
——— 1944. Action of inert dusts on insects. Nature, 153:714–715. (*302*)
———, J. T. Martin, and C. Potter 1942. Differences in resistance to toxic substances of mutants of *Drosophila* of different body color. *Ibid.*, 149:110. (*313*)
Kapzov, S. 1911. Untersuchungen über den feineren Bau der Cuticula bei Insekten. Z. wiss. Zool., 98:297–337. (*159–161, 163, 179, 183, 192, 193*)
Karawaiew, W. 1898. Die Nachembryonale Entwicklung von *Lasius flavus*. Z. wiss. Zool., 64:385–478. (*217*)
Karlberg, O. 1936. The carbohydrate groups of some glucoproteids. Z. physiol. Chem., 240:55–58. (*12*)
Karrer, P. 1930. Der enzymatische Abbau von nativer und umgefällter Zellulose, von Kunstseiden und von Chitin. Kolloid Z., 52:304–319. (*11, 14, 17, 26, 27, 56, 57, 77*)
———, and G. V. François 1929. Polysaccharide. 40. Über den enzymatischen Abbau von Chitin. Helv. Chim. Acta, 12:986–988. (*11, 56, 77*)
Karrer, P., and A. Hoffmann 1929. Polysaccharide. 39. Über den enzymatischen

Abbau von Chitin und Chitosan. Helv. Chim. Acta, 12:616–637. (*11, 14, 56, 77, 78*)
Karrer, P., H. Koenig, and E. Usteri 1943. Zur Kenntnis blutgerinnungshemmender Polysaccharid-polyschwefelsäure-ester und ähnlicher Verbindungen. Helv. Chim. Acta, 26:1296–1315. (*28*)
Karrer, P., and J. Mayer 1937. Ein neuer Abbau der Glucosaminsäure. Die Konfiguration der Glucosamin- und Chondrosaminsäure. Helv. Chim. Acta, 20:407–417. (*11*)
Karrer, P., O. Schnider, and A. P. Smirnov 1924. Polysaccharide. 29. Zur Kenntnis des Chitins II und Konfiguration des Glucosamins. Helv. Chim. Acta, 7:1039–1045. (*11*)
Karrer, P., and A. P. Smirnoff 1922. Polysaccharide. 17. Beitrag zur Kenntnis des Chitins. Helv. Chim. Acta, 5:832–852. (*11*)
Karrer, P., and S. M. White 1930. Polysaccharide. 44. Weitere Beiträge zur Kenntnis des Chitins. Helv. Chim. Acta, 13:1105–1113. (*11, 12, 26, 27, 56, 77, 78*)
Kästner, A. 1929. Bau und Funktion der Fächertracheen einiger Spinnen. Z. Morph. Ökol. Tiere, 13:463–558. (*160, 174, 248, 255, 259*)
——— 1933. Verdauungs- und Atemorgane der Weberknechte *Opilio pariatinus* de Geer und *Phalangium opilio* L. Z. Morph. Ökol. Tiere, 27:587–623. (*161, 261*)
Kaston, B. J. 1935. The slit sense organs of spiders. J. Morph., 58:189–209. (*163, 172*)
Katz, J. R. 1933. The laws of swelling. Trans. Faraday Soc., 29:279–300. (*136, 287*)
* ———, and H. Mark 1924. (X-ray study of the swelling of various substances.) Verslag. Akad. Wetenschappen Amsterdam, 33:294–301. Proc. Acad. Sci. Amsterdam, 27:520–528. Physik. Z., 25:431–435. (*17, 136, 287*)
* Kawabe, K. 1934. (Fate of glucosamine in the animal body.) J. Biochem. (Japan), 20:293–310. (*78*)
* Kawakami, I. 1934. (Enzymic degradation of glucosamine.) J. Biochem. (Japan), 20:423–429. (Chem. Abstr., 29:825.) (*78*)
** Kawase, S. 1915. (Studies on the chitinous matter of silkworms.) Tokyo Ni. Sanshi Kw. Ho., 280:3–14.
Keeble, F., and F. W. Gamble 1904. On the presence of mobile fat in the chromatophores of the crustacea (*Hippolyte varians*). Zool. Anz., 27:262–264. (*205*)
Keilin, D. 1913. Sur diverses glandes des larves de Diptères: Glandes mandibulaires, hypodermique et péristigmatiques. Arch. Zool. Exp. & Gen., 51 (Not. & Rev.):1–8. (*215, 300*)
——— 1917. Recherches sur les Anthomyides à larves carnivores. Parasitology, 9:325–450. (*240, 241*)
——— 1921. On the calcium carbonate and the calcospherites in the malpighian tubes and the fat body of dipterous larvae and the ecdysial elimination of these products of excretion. Quart. J. Micr. Sci., 65:611–625. (*107*)
——— 1924. On the appearance of gas in the tracheae of insects. Biol. Rev., 1:63–70. (*307*)
——— 1944. Respiratory systems and respiratory adaptations in larvae and pupae of Diptera. Parasitology, 36:1–66. (*170, 215, 223, 257, 261, 266*)
———, and T. Mann 1938. Polyphenol oxidase: Purification, nature and properties. Proc. R. Soc. London, ser. B, 125:187–204. (*75*)
Keilin, D., and P. Tate 1943. The larval stages of the celery fly (*Acidia heraclei* L.) and of the braconid *Adelura apii* (Curtis), with notes upon an associated parasitic yeast-like fungus. Parasitology, 35:27–36. (*215*)

———, and M. Vincent 1935. The perispiracular glands of mosquito larvae. Parasitology, 1:257–262. (*215*)

Keister, M. L. 1948. The morphogenesis of the tracheal system of *Sciara*. J. Morph., 83:373–424. (*139, 140, 171, 235, 255, 257, 261–265*)

———, and J. B. Buck 1949. Tracheal filling in *Sciara* larvae. Biol. Bull., 97:323–330. (*307*)

Kelly, A. 1901. Beiträge zur mineralogischen Kenntnis der Kalkausscheidungen im Tierreich. Jena Z. Naturwiss., 35:429–494. (*101*)

Kemper, H. 1931. Beiträge zur Biologie der Bettwanze (*Cimex lectularius* L.). 2. Über die Häutung. Z. Morph. Ökol. Tiere, 22:53–109. (*232*)

Kendall, F. E., M. Heidelberger, and M. H. Dawson 1937. A serologically inactive polysaccharide elaborated by mucoid strains of group A hemolytic streptococcus. J. Biol. Chem., 118:61–69. (*12*)

Kennedy, C. H. 1927. The exoskeleton as a factor in limiting and directing the evolution of insects. J. Morph. Physiol., 44:267–312. (*6*)

Kennedy, J. S., M. Ainsworth, and B. A. Toms 1948. Laboratory studies on the spraying of locusts at rest and in flight. Anti-locust Res. Bull. (London), no. 2. 64 pp. (*290, 313*)

Kephart, C. F. 1914. The poison glands of the larva of the brown-tail moth (*Euproctis chrysorrhoea* Linn.). J. Parasitol., 1:93–103. (*276*)

Kerenski, J. 1930. Beobachtungen über die Entwicklung der Eier von *Anisoplia austriaca* Reitt. Z. angew. Ent., 16:178–188. (*282; 298*)

Kew, H. W. 1929. On the external features of the development of the pseudoscorpions, with observations on the ecdyses and notes on the immature forms. Proc. Zool. Soc. London, pp. 33–38. (*66*)

Khalifa, A. 1949a. The mechanism of insemination and the mode of action of the spermatophore in *Gryllus domesticus*. Quart. J. Micr. Sci., 90:281–292. (*52, 282*)

——— 1949b. Spermatophore production in Trichoptera and some other insects. Trans. R. Ent. Soc. London, 100:449–471. (*282*)

Khouvine, Y. 1932. Étude aux rayons X de la chitine d'*Aspergillus niger*, de *Psalliota campestris* et d'*Armillaria mellea*. C. R. Acad. Sci., 195:396–397. (*17, 18, 39, 42, 45, 49*)

Kielich, J. 1918. Beiträge zur Kenntnis der Insektenmuskeln. Zool. Jahrb., Anat., 40:515–556. (*263*)

Kikkawa, H. 1950. Tryptophane synthesis in insects. Science, 111:495–496. (*88*)

Kikkiwa, H. 1941. Mechanism of pigment formation in *Bombyx* and *Drosophila*. Genetics, 26:587–607. (*92*)

Kimus, J. 1898. Recherches sur les branchies des crustacés. La Cellule, 15:295–404. (*153, 161, 206, 246, 247*)

Kinder, E., and F. Süffert 1943. Über den Feinbau schillernder Schmetterlingsschuppen vom Morpho-Typ. Biol. Zbl., 63:268–288. (*140, 141, 150, 196, 272*)

King, G. 1944. Permeability of keratin membranes. Nature, 154:575–576. (*287, 295*)

King, H. 1943. Chemical structure of arsenicals and drug resistance of trypanosomes. Trans. Faraday Soc., 39:383–389. (*317*)

Kinsinger, W. G., and C. W. Hock 1948. Electron microscopical studies of natural cellulose fibers. Ind. Eng. Chem., 40:1711–1716. (*21*)

* Kinzig, H. 1918. Untersuchungen über den Bau der Statocysten einiger decapoder Crustaceen. Verh. Heidelberger Nat.-hist.-med. Ver., N. F., 14:1–90. (Cited by Balss 1927.) (*275*)

* Kirch, —— 1886. Das Glykogen in den Geweben des Flusskrebses. Bonner dissertation. (Cited by Zander 1897.) (*30, 31*)

Kitchener, J. A., P. Alexander, and H. V. A. Briscoe 1943. A simple method of protecting cereals and other stored foodstuffs against insect pests. Chem. & Ind. (London), 62:32–33. (*302*)

* Kiyomizu, S. —— (Exuvial fluid of silkworms.) Sericulture Bull. (Sanshi-ho), 13:103, 525. (Cited by Hamamura, Iida, and Otsuka 1940.) (*107, 229*)

Klatt, B. 1908. Die Trichterwarzen der Lipariden-Larven. Zool. Jahrb., Anat., 27:135–170. (*251, 276*)

Kleinholz, L. H. 1941. Molting and calcium deposition in decapod crustaceans. J. Cell. Comp. Physiol., 18:101–107. (*105*)

——— 1942. Hormones in crustacea. Biol. Rev., 17:91–119. (*93*)

Klein-Krautheim, F. 1936. Über das Chorion der Eier einiger Syrphiden. Biol. Zbl., 56:323–329. (*280*)

Klinger, H. 1936. Die Insektizidwirkung von Pyrethrum und Derrisgiften und ihre Abhängigkeit vom insekten Körper. Arb. Physiol. angew. Ent., 3:49–69, 115–151. (*153, 162, 290, 293, 313, 317*)

Knab, F. 1909. The role of air in the ecdysis of insects. Proc. Ent. Soc. Wash., 11:68–73. (*233*)

——— 1911. Ecdysis in the Diptera. Proc. Ent. Soc. Wash., 13:32–42. (*233*)

Knecht, E., and E. Hibbert 1926. Chitin. J. Soc. Dyers Colourists, 42:343–345. (*29*)

Knight, H. H. 1924. On the nature of the color patterns in Heteroptera with data on the effects produced by temperature and humidity. Ann. Ent. Soc. Amer., 17:258–272. (*92*)

Koch, A. 1918. Zur Physiologie des Tracheensystems der Larven von *Mochlonyx*. Mitt. Zool. Inst. Westfäl Wilhelms Univ. Münster, 1:11–13. (*255, 306*)

——— 1920. Messende Untersuchungen über den Einfluss von Sauerstoff und Kohlensäure auf *Culex*-larven bei der Submersion. Zool. Jahrb., allg. Zool., 37:361–492. (*306*)

——— 1921. Die Atmung der Culiciden-Larven (Weitere Studien an *Mochlonyx velutina* Rutke). Mitt. Zool. Inst. Westfäl Wilhelms Univ. Münster, 3:31–41. (*306, 310*)

Koch, C. 1932. Der Nachweis des Chitins in tierischen Skeletsubstanzen. Z. Morph. Ökol. Tiere, 25:730–756. (*32, 37, 42, 49–51, 111, 112*)

* Koch, H. 1934. Essai d'interpretation de la soi-disant "reduction vitale" de sels d'argent par certains organes d'Arthropodes. Ann. Soc. Sci. Bruxelles, 54:346–361. (*292*)

——— 1938. The absorption of chloride ions by the anal papillae of Diptera larvae. J. Exp. Biol., 15:152–160. (*292*)

* ———, and A. Krogh 1936. La fonction des papilles anals des larves de Diptères. Ann. Soc. Sci. Bruxelles, 56B:459–461. (*292*)

Koch, H. J. A. 1936. Recherches sur la physiologie du système trachéen clos. Mém. Acad. R. Belg., Cl. Sci., 16(1):1–98. (*93, 156, 161, 203, 205, 246, 262, 265, 307*)

Kodani, M. 1948. The protein of the salivary gland secretion in *Drosophila*. Proc. Nat. Acad. Sci., 34:131–135. (*12, 62, 64*)

Koehler, A. 1921. Über die chemische Zusammensetzung der Sporenschale von *Nosema apis*. Zool. Anz., 53:85–87. (*42*)

Koehring, V. 1930. The neutral red reaction. J. Morph., 49:45–137. (*311*)

——— 1931. Thermal relationships in the neutral-red reaction. J. Morph., 52:165–193. (*311*)

Köhler, W. 1932. Die Entwicklung der Flügel bei der Mehlmotte *Ephestia kühniella* Zeller mit besonderer Berücksichtung des Zeichnungsmusters. Z. Morph. Ökol. Tiere, 24:582–681. (*223, 227, 233, 235, 243, 270*)

* Koidsumi, K. 1934. Experimentelle Studien über die Transpiration und den

Wärmehaushalt bei Insekten. Mem. Fac. Sci. Agric. Taihoku, 12:1–380. (Cited by Wigglesworth 1945.) (*154, 305*)

Kolbe, H. J. 1893. Einführung in die Kenntnis der Insekten. Dümmler, Berlin. (*93, 265*)

Koller, G. 1929. Die innere Sekretion bei wirbellosen Tieren. Biol. Rev., 4:269–306. (*217*)

* Kölliker, A. 1857. Untersuchung zur vergleichenden Gewebelehre. Verh. phys.-med. Ges. Würzburg, 8:1–128. (Cited by Wigglesworth 1948b.) (*159, 194*)

——— 1889. Zur Kenntnis der Quergestreiften Muskelfasern. Z. wiss. Zool., 47:689–710. (*264*)

Komori, Y. 1926. Zur Kenntnis der Glukosaminverbindungen. J. Biochem. (Japan), 6:1–20. (*12, 112*)

Kopac, M. J. 1940. The physical properties of the extraneous coats of living cells. Cold Spring Harbor Symp. Quant. Biol., 8:154–170. (*216, 222*)

——— 1943. Micrurgical application of surface chemistry to the study of living cells. *In* Reyniers, Micrurgical and Germ-Free Methods. Thomas, Springfield, Illinois. (*222*)

——— 1948. Some cytochemical aspects of pigmented cells. *In* "Biology of Melanomas," Spec. Publ. N. Y. Acad. Sci., 4:423–432. (*88*)

Köppen, A. 1921. Die feineren Verästelungen der Tracheen nach Untersuchungen an *Dytiscus marginalis* L. Zool. Anz., 52:132–139. (*263, 264*)

Korschelt, E. 1923. Bearbeitung einheimischer Tiere. Der Gelbrand, *Dytiscus marginalis*. 2 vols. Engelmann, Leipzig. (*161, 217, 249*)

——— 1938a. Cuticularsehne und Bindegewebssehne. Eine vergleichend morphologischhistologische Betrachtung. Z. wiss. Zool., 150:494–526. (*240, 241*)

——— 1938b. Einige Bemerkungen zur Frage der Muskelausatzes und der Muskelsehnenverbindung. *Ibid.*, 151:286–290. (*240*)

Koschevnikov, G. A. 1900. Über den Fettkörper und die Oenocyten der Honigbiene. Zool. Anz., 23:337–353. (*217, 218*)

Kotake, J., and Y. Sera 1913. Über ein neue Glukosaminverbindungen, zugleich ein Beitrag zur Konstitutionsfrage des Chitins. Z. physiol. Chem., 88:56–72. (*11, 26, 28*)

* Kozhanchikov, I. V. 1934. (Water balance of the pupae of *Agrotis* and *Ephestia* as a reaction to the humidity of the environment.) C. R. Acad. Sci. URSS, 3:548–552. (*298*)

* Krafft, W. 1914. Die Versonsche Zelle des Mikrolepidopteren. Abh. Mus. Nat.-Heinmath. Magdeburg, 2:331–370. (*209*)

Kraft, P. 1923. Über die ontogenetische Entwicklung und die Biologie von *Diplograptus* und *Monograptus*. Zbl. f. Mineral., pp. 285–288. (*36, 37, 43, 54*)

——— 1926. Ontogenetische Entwicklung und Biologie von *Diplograptus* und *Monograptus*. Paleontol. Z., 7:207–249. (*38, 43*)

Kramer, S., and V. B. Wigglesworth 1950. The outer layers of the cuticle in the cockroach *Periplaneta americana* and the function of the oenocytes. Quart. J. Micr. Sci., 91:63–72. (*168, 177*)

Kratky, O., E. Schauenstein, and A. Sekora 1950. X-ray diagram and ultra-violet absorption spectrum of "renatured" silk-fibroin. Nature, 166:1031–1032. (*68*)

Krawkow, N. P. 1892. Über verschiedenartige Chitine. Z. f. Biol., 29:177–198. (*15, 24, 34, 42, 43, 47–51*)

Kremer, J. 1918. Beiträge zur Histologie der Coleopteren mit besondere Berücksichtigung des Flügeldeckengewebes und der auftretenden Farbstoffe. Zool. Jahrb., Anat., 40:105–154. (*161, 217, 245, 246*)

——— 1920. Die Flügeldecken der Coleopteren. Ein kritische Studie. Zool. Jahrb., Anat., 41:175–272. (*161, 164, 217, 245, 246*)

——— 1925. Die Oenocyten der Coleopteren. Z. mikr. Anat. Forsch., 2:536–581. (*209, 217, 218*)

Kreuscher, A. 1922. Die Fettkörper und die Oenocyten von *Dytiscus marginalis*. Z. wiss. Zool., 119:247–284. (*217–219, 221*)

Krishnan, G. 1950. The sinus gland and tyrosinase activity in *Carcinus maenas*. Nature, 165:364–365. (*232*)

Križenecký, I. 1914. Über die beschleunigende Einwirkung des Hungers auf die Metamorphose. Biol. Zbl., 34:46–59. (*232*)

Krogh, A. 1911. On the hydrostatic mechanism of the *Corethra* larva with an account of methods of microscopic gas analysis. Skand. Arch. Physiol., 28:183–203. (*307*)

——— 1914. Ethyl urethane as a narcotic for aquatic animals. Int. Rev. Hydrobiol., 7:42–47. (*294, 312*)

* ——— 1917. Injection preparation of the tracheal system of insects. Vid. Medd. Densk. Naturh. Forening, 68:319–322. (*140, 261*)

——— 1918. The rate of diffusion of gases through animal tissues, with some remarks on the coefficient of invasion. J. Physiol., 52:391–408. (*295, 307*)

——— 1920a. Studien über Tracheenrespiration. 2. Über Gasdiffusion in den Tracheen. Pflüger's Arch. ges. Physiol., 179:95–112.

——— 1920b. Studien über Tracheenrespiration. 3. Die Kombination von mechanischer Ventilation mit Gasdiffusion nach Versuchen an *Dytiscus* larven. *Ibid.*, pp. 113–120. (*261*)

——— 1938. The active absorption of ions in some freshwater animals. Z. vergl. Physiol., 25:335–350. (*291*)

——— 1939. Osmotic Regulation in Aquatic Animals. Cambridge Univ. Press. (*291*)

——— 1946a. The active and passive exchanges of inorganic ions through the surfaces of living cells and through living membranes generally. Proc. R. Soc. London, ser. B, 133:140–200. (*291, 292*)

——— 1946b. On the active and passive exchanges of ions through cell surfaces and membranes in general. Amer. Scientist, 34:415–423. (*291*)

Krugelis, E. J. 1946. Distribution and properties of intracellular alkaline phosphatases. Biol. Bull., 90:220–233. (*70, 252*)

* Krüger, E. 1898. Über die Entwicklung der Flügel der Insekten, besonders der Deckflügel der Käfer. Inaug. dissertation, Göttingen. (*246*)

Krüger, P. 1923. Studien an Cirripedien. 3. Die Zementdrüsen von *Scalpellum*. Über die Beteiligung des Zellkerns an der Sekretion. Arch. mikr. Anat., 97:839–872. (*207, 211, 252*)

Krukenberg, C. F. W. 1885a. Über das Conchiolin und über das Vorkommen des Chitins bei Cephalopoden. Ber. dtsch. Chem. Ges., 18:989–993. (*44, 46*)

* ——— 1885b. Vergleichend-Physiologische Vorträge. 4. Vergleichenden Physiologie der Thierischen Gerüstsubstanzen. Heidelberg. (*17*)

Krüper, F. 1930. Über Verkalkungserscheinungen bei Dipteren-Larven und ihre Ursachen. Arch. Hydrobiol., 22:185–220. (*106*)

Kudo, R. 1921. On the nature of structures characteristic of Cnidosporian spores. Trans. Amer. Micr. Soc., 40:59–74. (*38, 42*)

Kugler, O. E., and M. L. Birkner 1948. Histochemical observations of alkaline phosphatases in the integument, gastrolith sac, digestive gland and nephridium of the crayfish. Physiol. Zool., 21:105–110. (*79, 106*)

Kühn, A. 1939. Zur Entwicklungsphysiologie der Schmetterlingsmetamorphose. 7th Int. Kongr. Ent., Berlin, 2:780–796. (*162, 184, 196, 223, 226, 227, 270*)

——— 1941. Zur Entwicklungsphysiologie der Schmetterlingsschuppen. Biol. Zbl., 61:109–147. (*156, 196, 270, 271*)

——— 1946. Konstructionsprinzipien von Schmetterlingsschuppen nach electronenmikroskopischen Aufnahmen. Z. f. Naturf., 1:348–357. (*196, 272*)

———, and M. An (von Engelhardt) 1946. Elektronenoptische Untersuchungen über den Bau von Schmetterlingsschuppen. Biol. Zbl., 65:30–40. (*140, 150, 196, 272, 277*)

Kuhn, A., and H. Piepho 1938. Die Reaktionen der Hypodermis und der Versonschen Drüsen auf das Verpuppungshormon bei *Ephestia kühniella*. Z. Biol. Zbl., 58:13–51. (*76, 87, 89, 149, 162, 180, 182, 183, 190, 192, 203, 204, 206, 209–212, 220, 223–226*)

Kühnelt, W. 1928a. Ein Beitrag zur Histochemie des Insektenskelettes. Zool. Anz., 75:111–113. (*94, 163, 300*)

——— 1928b. Studien über den mikrochemischen Nachweis des Chitins. Biol. Zbl., 48:374–382. (*32, 33, 37, 47, 49, 51*)

——— 1928c. Über den Bau des Insektenskelettes. Zool. Jahrb., Anat., 50:219–278. (*6, 94, 107, 116, 148, 154, 160–164, 182, 192, 193, 203, 205, 206, 237, 238, 245, 267, 268*)

** ——— 1929. Der Aufbau des Insektenpanzers. Forsch. u. Fortschr., Berlin, 5:140.

——— 1939. Beiträge zur Kenntnis des Wasserhaushaltes der Insekten. 7th Int. Kongr. Ent. (1938), Berlin, 2:797–807. (*136, 154, 290, 294, 300, 305*)

* ——— 1949. Über Vorkommen und Verteilung reduzierender Stoffe im Integument der Insekten. Österr. Zool. Z., 2:223–241. (*115, 187*)

Kükenthal, W., and T. Krumbach 1926–1930. Handbuch der Zoologie. W. De Gruyten & Co., Berlin and Leipzig. (*6, 160, 275*)

** Kulagin, N. M. 1939. (On the structure of chitin in insects.) Proc. Lenin Acad. Agric. Sci. USSR, Moscow, no. 7, pp. 21–23.

Kunike, G. 1925. Nachweis und Verbreitung organischer Skeletsubstanzen bei Tieren. Z. vergl. Physiol., 2:233–253. (*32–35, 37, 39, 42–44, 47–51, 136, 194*)

* ——— 1926a. (Chitin and chitin-silk.) Chem. Zbl., 97:2129. (*29, 120*)

——— 1926b. Chitin und Chitinseide. Die Kunstseide, 8:182–183. (*112*)

Kunkel d'Herculais, J. 1890–1894. Mécanisme physiologique de l'éclosion, des mues et de la metamorphose chez les insectes orthoptères de la famille des Acridides. C. R. Acad. Sci., 110:657–659, 807–809; 119:244–247. (*233*)

Kupffer, C. 1873. Das Verhältniss von Drusennerven zu Drüsenzellen. Arch. mikr. Anat., 9:387–395. (*264*)

Kusmenko, S. 1940. Über die postembryonale Entwicklung des Darmes der Honigbiene und die Herkunft der larvalen peritrophischen Hüllen. Zool. Jahrb., Anat., 66:463–530. (*49, 277*)

Kuster, K. C. 1934. A study of the general biology, morphology of the respiratory system and respiration of certain aquatic *Stratiomyia* and *Odontomyia* larvae (Diptera). Pap. Mich. Acad. Sci. Arts Let., 19:605–658. (*295, 306*)

Kuwana, Z. 1932. Distribution density of nodules on the skin of the silkworm larva. Proc. Imp. Acad. Tokyo, 8:105–108. (*268*)

——— 1933. Notes on the growth of cuticle in the silkworm. Proc. Imp. Acad. Tokyo, 9:280–283. (*109, 113, 153, 192, 225, 229, 231*)

——— 1937. Reducing power of the body fluid of the silkworm. Jap. J. Zool., 7:273–303. (*76*)

——— 1940. Some histochemical characters of the cuticle of the larva of *Bombyx mori* L. Annot. Zool. Jap., Tokyo, 19:309–311. (*71, 94, 121, 163*)

Lacroix, E. 1923. Texture chitineuse fondamentale de la coquille des foraminifères porcelanés. C. R. Acad. Sci., 176:1673–1674. (*42*)

Lafon, M. 1941a. Sur la composition du tégument des crustacés. C. R. Soc. Biol., 135:1003–1007. (*25, 40, 48–50, 111*)

——— 1941b. Sur l'elytre de quelques coleoptères (Contribution a l'étude chimique de tégument des insectes). Bull. Soc. Zool., 66:173–182. (*25, 50, 65, 71, 94, 112–114*)

——— 1941c. Le puparium des muscides: Principaux constituents et évolution de la composition chimique. C. R. Acad. Sci., 212:456–458. (*25, 51, 71, 94, 114*)

——— 1943a. Sur la structure et la composition chimique du tégument de la Limule (*Xiphosura polyphemus* L.). Bull. l'Inst. Oceanogr., no. 850. 11 pp. (*25, 48, 82, 100, 110, 114, 115, 121, 132, 153, 160, 163, 164, 175, 182, 192*)

——— 1943b. Recherches biochimiques et physiologiques sur le squelette tégumentaire des arthropodes. Ann. Sci. Nat., ser. Bot. Zool., 11:113–146. (*25, 47–51, 85, 100, 101, 109–112, 201, 302*)

——— 1943c. Recherches sur le cycle de la chitine chez quelques coléoptères. Arch. Zool. Exp. & Gen., 83:58–70. (*31, 38, 50, 110, 112–114, 229*)

——— 1948. Nouvelles recherches biochimiques et physiologiques sur le squelette tégumentaire des crustacés. Bull. l'Inst. Oceanogr., 45:1–28. (*25, 40, 49–51, 65, 85, 94, 100, 111, 123, 229, 289, 304*)

Laing, J. 1935. On the ptilinum of the blowfly (*Calliphora erythrocephala*). Quart. J. Micr. Sci., 77:497–521. (*109, 229*)

Lamy, E. 1900. Note sur l'appareil respiratoire trachéen des Aranéides. Bull. Soc. Ent. France, pp. 267–270. (*255*)

——— 1901. Sur la terminaison des trachées chez les Aranéides. Bull. Soc. Ent. France, pp. 178–179. (*221, 255*)

——— 1902. Recherches anatomiques sur la trachées des Araignées. Ann. Soc. Nat. Zool., ser. 8, 15:149–280. (*255*)

Lang, D., and C. M. Yonge 1935. The function of the tegumental glands in the statocyst of *Homarus vulgaris*. J. Marine Biol. Assoc., N. S., 20:333–339. (*215*)

Lang, O. 1948a. Über die Zusammensetzung des Sericin. Biochem. Z., 319:283–289. (*62, 64, 68*)

——— 1948b. Über die Aminodicarbonsäurefällung nach Foremann in Sericinhydrolysaten. Biochem. Z., 319:290–294. (*62, 64, 68*)

Langmuir, I., and V. J. Schaefer 1943. Rates of evaporation of water through compressed monolayers on water. J. Franklin Inst., 235:119–162. (*287*)

Langner, E. 1937. Untersuchungen an Tegument und Epidermis bei Diplopoden (Mit Beiträgen zu Sehorganen und Hautdrüsen). Zool. Jahrb., Anat., 63:483–541. (*160, 163, 175, 180, 182, 192, 193, 195*)

Lankaster, E. R. 1884. On the skeletotrophic tissues and coxal glands. Quart. J. Micr. Sci., 24:129–162. (*52, 220*)

——— 1885. On the muscular and endoskeletal systems of *Limulus* and *Scorpio*. Trans. Zool. Soc. London, 11:311–384. (*220*)

Lassaigne, —— 1843a. Sur le tissu tégumentaire des insectes de différents ordres. C. R. Acad. Sci., 16:1087–1089. (*14, 43*)

* ——— 1843b. Über die Hautgewebe der Insekten verschiedener Ordnungen. J. Prakt. Chem., 29:323.

* Laszt, L., and H. Süllmann 1936. Einfluss der Narkose auf die Permeabilität der Kiemensäckchen von *Daphnia magna* für Säuren. Arb. Ung. Biol. Forsch. Inst., 8:341–344. (*298*)

Laubmann, A. L. 1912. Untersuchungen über die Hautsinnesorgane bei decapoden Krebsen aus der Gruppe der Carididen. Zool. Jahrb., Anat., 35:105–160. (*275*)

Lauger, P., H. Martin, and P. Muller 1944. Über Konstitution und toxische Wirkung von naturlichen und neuen synthetischen insektentotenden Stoffen. Helv. Chim. Acta, 27:892–928. (Also English translation privately printed and distributed by Geigy Co., New York.) (*313*)

Lazarenko, T. 1925. Die morphologische Bedeutung der Blut- und Bindegewebeelemente der Insekten. Z. mikr. anat. Forsch., 3:409–499. (*222*)

——— 1928. Experimentelle Untersuchungen über das Hypodermisepithel der Insekten. Z. mikr. anat. Forsch., 12:467–506. (*83, 161, 222, 232*)

Lea, A. J. 1945. A neutral solvent for melanin. Nature, 156:478. (*88*)

* Leao, M. A. 1941. O expurgo pelas ondas-curtas. Bol. Soc. Brasil. Agron., 4:319–334. (Biol. Abstr., 18:3697.) (*126*)

Lécaillon, A. 1906. Sur la structure de la couche chitineuse tégumentaire et sur les insertions musculaires de la larve de *Tabanus quatuornotatus*. C. R. Assoc. Anat., 8th session, pp. 68–70. (*238*)

——— 1907a. Sur la structure de la cuticle tégumentaire des insectes et sur la manière dont s'attachent les muscles chez ces animaux. C. R. Assoc. Anat., 9th session, pp. 73–75. (*237, 238*)

——— 1907b. Recherches sur la structure de la cuticle tégumentaire des insectes. Bibliogr. Anat., Nancy, 16:245–261. (*237, 238*)

Leclercq, J. 1950. Occurrence of pterin pigments in Hymenoptera. Nature, 165:367–368. (*92*)

Ledderhose, G. 1876. Über salzsäures Glycosamin. Ber. dtsch. Chem. Ges., 9:1200–1201. (*9*)

——— 1878/79. Über Chitin und seine Spaltungsprodukte. Z. physiol. Chem., 2:213–227. (*9*)

——— 1881. Über Chitin und seine Spaltungsprodukte. Z. physiol. Chem., 4:139–159. (*9*)

Lederer, E. 1935. Les Carotenoides des Animaux. Hermann, Paris. (*86, 90*)

——— 1940. Les pigments des invertébrés. Biol. Rev., 15:273–306. (*86*)

Lee, H. T. Y. 1950. A preliminary histological study of the insemination reaction in *Drosophila gibberosa*. Biol. Bull., 98:25–33. (*227*)

Lee, M. O. 1929. Respiration in the insects. Quart. Rev. Biol., 4:213–232. (*253, 255, 306*)

Lees, A. D. 1946. The water balance in *Ixodes ricinus* L. and certain other species of ticks. Parasitology, 37:1–20. (*161, 180, 182, 202, 207, 211, 213, 290, 298, 299*)

——— 1947. Transpiration and the structure of the epicuticle in ticks. J. Exp. Biol., 23:379–410. (*71, 85, 94, 97, 99, 123, 161, 163, 166, 170, 207, 213, 214, 290, 298–302*)

——— 1948. Passive and active water exchange through the cuticle of ticks. Disc. Faraday Soc., no. 3, pp. 187–192. (*202, 226, 298, 299*)

———, and J. W. L. Beament 1948. An egg-waxing organ in ticks. Quart. J. Micr. Sci., 89:291–332. (*48, 97–99, 251, 280, 314*)

Lees, A. D., and L. E. R. Picken 1945. Shape in relation to fine structure in the bristles of *Drosophila melanogaster*. Proc. R. Soc. London, ser. B, 132:396–423. (*23, 82, 84, 117, 121, 122, 130, 141, 145, 194, 276*)

Lees, A. D., and C. H. Waddington 1942. The development of the bristles in normal and some mutant types of *Drosophila melanogaster*. Proc. R. Soc. London, ser. B, 131:87–110. (*275, 276*)

Lehmann, F. E. 1926. Über die Entwicklung des Tracheensystems, nebst Beiträgen zur vergleichenden Morphologie des Insektentracheensystems. *In* Leuzinger, Wiesmann, and Lehmann, Zur Kenntnis der Anatomie und Entwicklungsgeschichte von *Carausius morosus* Br. (pp. 329–414), Fischer, Jena. (*255*)

von Lengerken, H. 1921. *Carabus auratus* L. und seine Larve. Arch. f. Naturges., 87(3):31–113. (*192*)

——— 1922. Über fossile Chitin-strukturen. Verh. dtsch. Zool. Ges., 27:73–75. (*54*)

——— 1923. Über Widerstandefähigkeit organischer Substanzen gegen natürliche Zersetzung. Biol. Zbl., 43:546–555. (*34, 48, 54*)

Lennox, F. G. 1940. The action of contact larvicides on *Lucilia cuprina.* Council Sci. Ind. Res. Australia, Pamph. no. 101, pp. 67–131. (*290, 294, 313*)

* Lepesme, P. 1937a. L'action externe des arsenicaux sur le criquet pélerin (*Schistocerca gregaria* Forsk.). Bull. Soc. d'hist. nat. Afr. Nord, 28:88. (*313*)

——— 1937b. De l'action externe arsenicaux sur les insectes. C. R. Acad. Sci., 204:717–719. (*313*)

* Lereboullet, A. 1853. Mémoire sur les crustacés de la famille des Cloportides. Mem. Soc. Nat. Hist. Strasb., 4:1–130. (Cited by Collinge 1921.) (*207*)

Lesperon, L. 1937. Recherches cytologiques et expérimentales sur la sécrétion de la soie et sur certains mecanismus excréteurs chez les insectes. Arch. Zool. Exp. & Gen., 79:1–156. (*66, 205, 206, 209, 211, 217, 218, 250–252*)

* Leuckart, R. 1847. Über die Morphologie und die Verwandtschafsverhältnisse der wirbellosen Tiere. Braunschweig. (Cited by Deegener 1913.) (*262*)

——— 1852. Über das Vorkommen und die Verbreitung des Chitins bei den wirbellosen Tieren. Arch. f. Naturges., 18:22–28. (*15, 42*)

Levene, P. A. 1921. Synthese von 2-hexosaminsäuren und 2-hexosaminen. Biochem. Z., 124:37–83. (*10*)

———, and C. C. Christman 1937. Catalytically induced reactions resembling the Cannizzaro reaction. J. Biol. Chem., 120:575–590. (*28*)

Lever, R. J. A. W. 1930. A new endoskeletal organ in the hind legs of the Halticinae. Zool. Anz., 92:287–288. (*242*)

Levereault, P. 1934. Iron haematoxylin stain for differentiation of sclerites from membrane areas. Ann. Ent. Soc. Amer., 27:313–314. (*184*)

Levy, M., and E. Slobodiansky 1948. The order of amino acids in silk: An application of isotopic derivative technic. Biol. Bull., 95:240. (*62, 64, 68*)

Lewkowitsch, J. I., and G. H. Warburton 1921. Chemical Technology of Oils, Fats and Waxes. Macmillan, New York. (*120*)

Leydig, F. 1851. Anatomisches und Histologisches über die Larve von *Corethra plumicornis.* Z. wiss. Zool., 3:435–451. (*159, 264*)

——— 1855. Zur feineren Bau der Arthropoden. Arch. Anat. Physiol., pp. 376–480. (*159, 182, 183*)

* ——— 1857. Traite d'histologie comparée. (Cited by Viallanes.) (*159*)

——— 1859. Zur Anatomie der Insekten. Arch. Anat. Physiol., pp. 33–89, 149–83. (*159, 207, 209, 215*)

——— 1860. Über Kalkablagerungen in der Haut der Insekten. Arch. f. Naturges., 26(1):157–160. (*106*)

* ——— 1864. Über den Bau des tierischen Körpers. Tübingen. (Cited by Wigglesworth 1933.) (*30, 159, 180, 182*)

——— 1878. Über Amphipoden und Isopoden. Z. wiss. Zool., 30(Suppl.):225–274. (*182, 244, 247*)

* ——— 1885. Zelle und Gewebe. Bonn. (See pp. 142–150.) (Cited by Wigglesworth 1931a.) (*264*)

van Lidth de Jeude, W. 1878. Zur Anatomie und Physiologie der Spinndrüsen der Seidenraupe. Zool. Anz., 1:100–102. (*68, 251, 264*)

Linderstrom-Lang, K., and F. Duspiva 1935. Beiträge zur enzymatischen Histochemie. 16. Die Verdauung von Keratin durch die Larven der Kleidermotte (*Tineola biselliella* Humm.). Z. physiol. Chem., 237:131–158. (*57*)

Lindquist, A. W., A. H. Madden, and H. O. Schroeder 1946. Effect of temperature on knock-down and kill of mosquitoes and bedbugs exposed to DDT. J. Kansas Ent. Soc., 19:13–15. (*318*)

———, H. G. Wilson, H. O. Schroeder, and A. H. Madden 1945. Effect of temperature on knockdown and kill of houseflies exposed to DDT. J. Econ. Ent., 38:261–264. (*318*)

Lison, L. 1936. Histochimie Animale. Méthodes et Problèmes. Gauthier-Villars, Paris. (*37, 71, 75, 165*)

Ljungdahl, D. 1917. Etwas über die Oberflächenskulptur einiger Schmetterlingspuppen. Ent. Tidskr., 38:217–228. (*267*)

Lloyd, A. J., and C. M. Yonge 1940. Correlation between the egg-carrying setae and cement glands in decapod crustacea. Nature, 146:334. (*214*)

* Locquin, M. 1943. (A new technique for the study of amyloid perispores.) Bull. mens. Soc. Linnéenne Lyon, 12:110–112, 122–128. (Chem. Abstr., 40:623.) (*45, 53*)

Loeb, J. 1922. Proteins and the Theory of Colloidal Behaviour. McGraw-Hill, New York. (*132*)

Looss, —— 1885. Neue Lösungsmittel des Chitins. Zool. Anz., 8:333–334. (*15*)

Lord, K. A. 1948. The sorption of DDT and its analogues by chitin. Biochem. J., 43:72–78. (*133, 319*)

Lotmar, W., and L. E. R. Picken 1950. A new crystallographic modification of chitin (polyacetylglucosamine) and its distribution. Experientia, 6:58. (*18, 24, 39, 44, 47–51, 120*)

Lowne, B. T. 1893–1895. The Anatomy, Physiology, Morphology and Development of the Blow-Fly (*Calliphora erythrocephala*). 2 vols. Porter, London. (*163, 222, 237, 238, 262, 265, 270*)

Löwy, E. 1909. Über kristallinisches Chitosansulfat. Biochem. Z., 23:47–60. (*22, 25–27*)

Lübben, H. 1907. Über die innere Metamorphose der Trichopteren. Zool. Jahrb., Anat., 24:71–128. (*153, 211, 227, 265*)

Ludwig, D. 1937. The effect of different relative humidities on respiratory metabolism and survival of the grasshopper *Chortophaga viridifasciata*. Physiol. Zool., 10:342–351. (*298*)

—— 1945. The effects of atmospheric humidity on animal life. *Ibid.*, 18:103–135. (*305, 314*)

—— 1948. Relation between lipid content of cuticle, duration of diapause, and resistance to desiccation of pupae of the cynthia moth. *Ibid.*, 21:252–257. (*94, 301*)

Lund, E. J. 1911. On the structure, physiology and use of photogenic organs with special reference to the Lampyridae. J. Exp. Zool., 11:415–468. (*262–264*)

Lundblad, O. 1930. Über die Anatomie von *Arrhenrus mediorotundatus* und die Hautdrüsen der *Arrhenrus*-Arten. Z. Morph. Ökol. Tiere, 17:302–338. (*161, 163*)

Lüscher, M. 1947. A method for observing growing epithelial tissue in *Rhodnius prolixus*. Nature, 160:873–874. (*233*)

Lutwak-Mann, C. 1941. Enzymic decomposition of amino sugars. Biochem. J., 35:610–626. (*78*)

LuValle, J. E., and D. R. Goddard 1948. The mechanism of enzymatic oxidations and reductions. Quart. Rev. Biol., 23:197–228. (*73*)

Lyonnet, P. 1762. Traite anatomique de la Chenille qui rouge les bois du Saule. Pierre Grosse Jr. & Daniel Pinet, La Haye. (*253, 256*)

MacGinite, G. E. 1945. The size of the mesh openings in mucous feeding nets of marine animals. Biol. Bull., 88:107–111. (*293, 311*)

Machatoschke, J. W. 1936. Des cuticulär Aufbau des Rhabdoms im Arthropodenauge. Vest. Ceskosl. zool. Spolec., 4:90–109. (*41, 52*)

MacLeod, G. F. 1941. Effects of infra-red irradiation on the American cockroach. J. Econ. Ent., 34:728–729. (*126*)

Macloskie, G. 1884. The structure of the tracheae of insects. Amer. Nat., 18:567–573. (*257*)

Mahdihassan, S. 1938. Die Struktur des Stocklacks und der Bau der Lackzelle. Z. Morph. Ökol. Tiere, 33:527–554. (*282*)

** Malaczynska-Suchcitz, Z. 1936. Zytologische Studien über die Hautdrüsen des Flusskrebses, nebst Erwagungen über die funktionelle Bedeutung des Plasmastrukturen. Mem. Akad. Polon. Cracovie, 10:1–64. (*214*)

** ——— 1949. Glycogen in the tegumental tissues of the crayfish. Exptl. Cell Res., Suppl. 1, pp. 388–389. (*30*)

Malloch, A. 1911. Note on the iridescent colours of birds and insects. Proc. R. Soc. London, ser. A, 85:598–605. (*196*)

Maloeuf, N. S. R. 1935a. The role of muscular contraction in the production of configurations in the insect skeleton. J. Morph., 58:41–86. (*5, 6, 122, 235, 242*)

——— 1935b. The postembryonic history of the somatic musculature of the dragonfly thorax. *Ibid.*, pp. 87–115. (*240*)

——— 1936. Quantitative studies on the respiration of aquatic arthropods and on the permeability of their outer integument to gases. J. Exp. Zool., 74:323–351. (*276, 306*)

——— 1937. The permeability of the integument of the crayfish (*Cambarus bartoni*) to water and electrolytes. Biol. Zbl., 57:282–287. (*290, 298*)

——— 1938. Secretions from ectodermal glands of arthropods. Quart. Rev. Biol., 13:169–195. (*250*)

——— 1940. The uptake of inorganic electrolytes by the crayfish. J. Gen. Physiol., 24:151–167. (*79, 105, 106, 229, 247, 292*)

Malpighi, M. 1669. Dissertatio Epistoloca de Bombyce. Regia Societati dicata. (*229, 253*)

Maluf, N. S. R., *see* Maloeuf, N. S. R.

Mann, H., and U. Pieplow 1938. Der Kalkhaushalt bei der Hautung der Krebse. Sitz.-ber. Ges. naturf. Freunde Berlin, pp. 1–17. (*100, 105*)

Manton, S. M., and J. A. Ramsay 1937. Studies on the Onychophora. 3. The control of water loss in *Peripatopsis*. J. Exp. Biol., 14:470–472. (*305*)

Manunta, C. 1939. Estrazione e cristallizzazione del pigmento che colora in rosso la pelle di certi acari del genera *Trombidium*. Helv. Chim. Acta, 22:1154–1155. (*91*)

* ——— 1942a. (Nitrogen metabolism in a "transparent-skinned" race of *Philosamia ricini.*) Scientia genetica (Torino), 2:252–272. (Biol. Abstr., 21:811.) (*205*)

* ——— 1942b. (The metabolism of carotenoids in the "transparent-skinned" race of *Philosamia ricini*, fed with *Ricinus* and *Ailanthus.*) *Ibid.*, pp. 273–279. (Biol. Abstr., 21:811; Chem. Abstr., 42:7452.) (*90*)

——— 1948. Astaxanthin in insects and other terrestrial arthropods. Nature, 162:298. (*91*)

Manzelli, M. A. 1941. Studies on the effect of reduction of surface tension on mosquito pupae. Proc. 28th Ann. Mtg. N. J. Mosq. Exterm. Comm., pp. 19–23. (*137*)

Marcu, O. 1929. Beiträge zur Kenntnis der Tracheen bei den Cerambyciden und Chrysomeliden. Zool. Anz., 85:329–332. (*259*)

——— 1930. Beitrag zur Kenntnis der Tracheen der Hymenopteren. Zool. Anz., 89:186–189. (*259*)

——— 1931. Beitrag zur Kenntnis der Tracheen der Insekten. Zool. Anz., 93:61–63. (*259*)

Marcus, E. 1927. Zur Ökologie und Physiologie der Tardigraden. Zool. Jahrb., allg. Zool., 44:323–370. (*47, 163*)

——— 1928. Zur vergleichenden Anatomie und Histologie der Tardigraden. Zool. Jahrb., allg. Zool., 45:99–158. (*47, 157, 160, 163, 164*)

——— 1929. Tardigrada. *In* Bronn, Klassen und Ordnungen des Tierreichs, vol. 5, Abt. 4, Buch 3. (*47, 160*)
——— 1935. Über die Verdauung bei den Tardigraden. Zool. Jahrb., allg. Zool., 54:385–404. (*235, 236*)
Margaria, R. 1931. The osmotic changes in some marine animals. Proc. R. Soc. London, ser. B, 107:606–624. (*292*)
Mark, H. 1943. The investigation of high polymers with x-rays. *In* Chemistry of Large Molecules, Interscience, New York. (*6, 20, 22, 68, 119, 122*)
Marsh, J. T., and F. C. Wood 1945. An Introduction to the Chemistry of Cellulose, 3d ed. Chapman and Hall, London. (*10*)
Marshall, J. F., and J. Staley 1929. A newly observed reaction of certain species of mosquitoes to the bites of larval hydrachnids. Parasitology, 21:158–160. (*52*)
Marshall, W. S. 1915. The formation of the middle membrane in the wings of *Platyphylax designatus* Wlk. Ann. Ent. Soc. Amer., 8:201–216. (*220, 227, 243*)
——— 1929–1930. The hypodermal glands of the black scale, *Saissetia oleae* (Bernard). Trans. Wisconsin Acad. Sci., 24:427–443; 25:255–272. (*209, 216, 251*)
Martynow, A. 1901. Über einige eigenthumliche Drüsen bei den Trichopterenlarven. Zool. Anz., 24:449–455. (*162, 209, 211, 265*)
Mason, C. W. 1926. Structural colors in insects. 1. J. Physical Chem., 30:383–395. (*136, 140, 196*)
——— 1927a. Structural colors in insects. 2. *Ibid.*, 31:321–354. (*136, 140, 196, 197, 199, 244*)
——— 1927b. Structural colors in insects. 3. *Ibid.*, pp. 1856–1872. (*120, 124, 136, 140, 181, 196, 197, 200, 244*)
——— 1929. Transient color changes in the tortoise beetles (Coleopt.: Chrysomelidae). Ent. News, 40:52–56. (*136, 140, 141, 196, 201*)
Mason, H. S. 1948a. Classification of melanins. *In* "Biology of Melanomas," Spec. Publ. N. Y. Acad. Sci., 4:399–404. (*75, 87*)
——— 1948b. Chemistry of melanins. 3. Mechanism of oxidation of 3,4-dihydroxyphenylalanine by tyrosinase. J. Biol. Chem., 172:83–99. (*75, 87, 88*)
Matheson, R. 1912. The structure and metamorphosis of the fore-gut of *Corydalis cornutus* L. J. Morph., 23:581–622. (*161, 216, 222*)
Mathews, A. P. 1923. Zusammensetzung des Knorpels eines wirbellosen Tieres, *Limulus*. Z. physiol. Chem., 130:169–175. (*41, 52*)
Matthée, J. J. 1948. Pore canals in the egg membranes of *Locustana paradalina* Walk. Nature, 162:226–227. (*182, 281, 298, 314*)
Mau, W. 1882. Über *Scoloplos armiger*. Z. wiss. Zool., 36:389–432. (*44*)
Maulik, S. 1929. On the structure of the hind femur in Halticine beetles. Proc. Zool. Soc. London, pp. 305–308. (*242*)
Mayer, A. G. 1896. The development of the wing scales and their pigment in butterflies and moths. Bull. Mus. Comp. Zool., 29:209–236. (*222*)
Mayer, F., and A. H. Cook 1943. The Chemistry of Natural Coloring Matter. Reinhold, New York. (*86, 90*)
Maziarski, S. 1911. Recherches cytologiques sur les phénomènes sécrétoires dans les glandes filières des larves des Lépidoptères. Arch. Zellforsch., 6:397–442. (*252*)
McIndoo, N. E. 1916. The reflex bleeding of the coccinellid beetle, *Epilachna borealis*. Ann. Ent. Soc. Amer., 9:201–223. (*213, 216*)
McLintock, J. 1945. The insect cuticle – a review. Proc. Ent. Soc. Manitoba, 1:16–29. (*289*)
* Meinert, F. 1886. De encephale Myggelarver. Vidensk. Selek. Skr. 6te Raehke, nat. og math. afd., 4:476–493. (Cited by Keister 1948.) (*255*)

Melander, A. L., and C. T. Brues 1906. The chemical nature of some insect secretions. Bull. Wisconsin Nat. Hist. Soc., n. s., 4:22–36. (*250*)
Mellanby, K. 1932. The effect of atmospheric humidity on the metabolism of the fasting mealworm (*Tenebrio molitor* L., Coleoptera). Proc. R. Soc. London, ser. B, 111:376–390. (*298*)
——— 1934a. The site of loss of water from insects. *Ibid.*, 116:139–149. (*299, 305*)
——— 1934b. Effects of temperature and humidity on the clothes moth larva, *Tineola biselliella* Humm. Ann. Appl. Biol., 21:476–482. (*299, 305*)
——— 1935. The structure and function of the spiracles of the tick, *Ornithodorus moubata* Murray. Parasitology, 27:288–290. (*266, 299, 305*)
——— 1936. The evaporation of water from insects. Biol. Rev., 10:317–333. (*299, 300, 305*)
Mercer, E. H., and A. L. G. Rees 1946. Structure of the cuticle of wool. Nature, 157:589–590. (*254*)
Mercer, W. F. 1900. The development of the wings in the Lepidoptera. J. New York Ent. Soc., 8:1–20. (*150, 220, 227, 243, 264*)
Merker, E. 1929a. Die Durchlässigkeit des Chitins für ultravioletten Licht. Verh. dtsch. Zool. Ges., 33:181–186. (*120, 121*)
——— 1929b. Die Fluoreszenz im Insektenauge, die Fluoreszenz des Chitins der Insekten und seine Durchlässigkeit für ultraviolettes Licht. Zool. Jahrb., allg. Zool., 46:483–574. (*121*)
——— 1931. Die Fluoreszenz und die Lichtdurchlässigkeit der bewohnten Gewässer. *Ibid.*, 49:69–104. (*121, 129*)
——— 1939. Chitin als Lichtschutz. 7th Int. Kongr. Ent. Berlin, 2:827–845. (*87, 120, 125, 126*)
Merlin, A. A. 1901. Note on the tracheal tubes of insects. J. Quekett Club, ser. 2, 7:405–406. (*257*)
* Merrill, W. J. 1936. (Water resistant binders from chitin.) U.S. Patent No. 2,047,218. (Chem. Abstr., 30:6097.) (*29*)
Metcalf, R. L. 1943. Isolation of a red-fluorescent pigment, lampyrine, from the Lampyridae. Ann. Ent. Soc. Amer., 36:37–40. (*92*)
——— 1945. The physiology of the salivary glands of *Anopheles quadrimaculatus*. J. Nat. Malaria Soc., 4:271–278. (*39, 121, 130, 251*)
Metcalfe, M. E. 1932. The structures and development of the reproductive system in Coleoptera with notes on its homologies. Quart. J. Micr. Sci., 75:49–129. (*250*)
Metz, C. W. 1935. Structure of the salivary gland chromosomes in *Sciara*. J. Hered., 26:177–188, 491–501. (*252*)
———, and E. G. Lawrence 1937. Studies on the organization of the giant gland chromosomes of Diptera. Quart. Rev. Biol., 12:135–151. (*252*)
Meyer, H. 1842. Über den Bau der Hornschale der Käfer. Arch. Anat. Physiol. wiss. Med., pp. 12–16. (*192*)
——— 1849. Über die Entwicklung des Fettkörpers, der Tracheen und der keimbereitenden Geschlechtstheile bei den Lepidopteren. Z. wiss. Zool., 1:175–197. (*257, 264*)
* Meyer, J. A. 1914. Beiträge zur Kenntnis der chemischen Zusammensetzung wirbelloser Tiere. Wiss. Meeresuntersuchungen, Abt. Kiel, N. F., vol. 16. (*110*)
Meyer, Karl 1938. The chemistry and biology of mucopolysaccharides and glycoproteins. Cold Spring Harbor Symp. Quant. Biol., 6:91–102. (*13, 81*)
———, E. M. Smyth, and J. W. Palmer 1934. Glucoproteins. 3. The polysaccharides from pig gastric mucosa. J. Biol. Chem., 119:73–84. (*12*)
Meyer, Kurt H., and P. Bernfeld 1946. The potentiometric analysis of membrane

structure and its application to living animal membranes. J. Gen. Physiol., 29:353–378. (*288*)
Meyer, Kurt H., and H. Mark 1928a. Über den Aufbau des Seiden-Fibroins. Ber. dtsch. Chem. Ges., 61:1932–1936. (*68, 69*)
——— 1928b. Über den Aufbau des Chitins. *Ibid.*, pp. 1936–1939. (*10, 13, 17*)
——— 1930. Der Aufbau der hochpolymeren organischen Naturstoffe. auf Grund Molekular-Morphologischer Betrachtungen. Akad. Verlagsges., Leipzig. (*68, 69*)
Meyer, Kurt H., and G. W. Pankow 1935. Sur la constitution et la structure de la chitine. Helv. Chim. Acta, 18:589–598. (*10, 17, 18*)
Meyer, Kurt H., and J. F. Sievers 1936. La perméabilité des membranes. 1–4. Helv. Chim. Acta, 19:649–664, 665–677, 948–962, 987–995. (*317*)
Meyer, Kurt H., and H. Wehrli 1937. Comparaison chimique de la chitine et de la cellulose. Helv. Chim. Acta, 20:353–362. (*11, 17, 19, 26–28, 119, 121*)
Miall, L. C., and A. Denny 1886. The Structure and Life-History of the Cockroach (*Periplaneta orientalis*). L. Reeve & Co., London. (*114, 251, 254, 265*)
Miall, L. C., and A. R. Hammond 1900. The Structure and Life History of the Harlequin Fly (*Chironomus*). Clarendon Press, Oxford. (*161, 204, 249*)
* Michael, A. D. 1901. British Tyroglyphidae. Ray Soc. (Cited by Murray 1907.) (*236*)
Michaelis, L. 1935. Semiquinones, the intermediate steps of reversible organic oxidation-reduction. Chem. Rev., 16:243–286. (*73*)
——— 1946a. Fundamentals of oxidation and reduction. *In* Currents in Biochemical Research. Interscience, New York. (*73*)
——— 1946b. Fundamentals of oxidation and respiration. Amer. Scientist, 34:573–596. (*73*)
——— 1949. Fundamental principles in oxidation-reduction. Biol. Bull., 96:293–295. (*73*)
Michelbacher, A. E. 1938. The biology of the garden centipede, *Scutigerella immaculata*. Hilgardia, 11:55–148. (*66, 231–233*)
Mickel, C. E., and J. Standish 1946. Susceptibility of edible Soya products in storage to attack by *Tribolium confusum* Duv. Minnesota Agric. Exp. Sta., Tech. Bull., 175. (*232*)
Miller, A. 1939. The egg and early development of the stonefly, *Pteronarcys proteus*. J. Morph., 64:555–609. (*280*)
Millot, J. 1926a. La sécrétion de la soie chez les Araignées. C. R. Soc. Biol., 94:10–11. (*67, 160, 205*)
——— 1926b. Contribution à l'histo-physiologie des Aranéides. Bull. Biol. Fr. Belg., Suppl., 8:1–238. (*67, 92, 160, 205*)
——— 1931. Les glandes venimeuses des aranéides. Ann. Sci. Nat. Zool., ser. 10, 14:113–147. (*250*)
———, and M. Fontaine 1938. Le taux de chitine chez *Schistocerca gregaria*. Bull. Soc. Zool., 63:123–124. (*110, 113, 154*)
———, and R. Jonnart 1933. Sur la présence de corps à fonction phénolique libre dans le sang des araignées. C. R. Acad. Sci., 197:1002–1003. (*72*)
Minchin, E. A. 1888. Note on a new organ, and on the structure of the hypodermis, in *Periplaneta orientalis*. Quart. J. Micr. Sci., 29:229–233. (*217*)
* Mingazzini, P. 1889. Ricerche sulla struttura dell'ipodermide nella *Periplaneta orientalis*. R. C. Accad. Lincei, 5:573–578. (Cited by Wigglesworth 1948b.) (*217*)
Minot, C. S. 1876. Recherches histologiques sur les trachées de l'*Hydrophilus piceus*. Arch. Physiol. Expt., norm. & path., ser. 2, 3:1–10. (*256, 257, 265*)
Mirande, M. 1905a. Sur la présence d'un "corps reducteur" dans le tégument chitineux des arthropodes. Ach. Anat. Micr., Paris, 7:207–231. (*30, 115, 187*)

——— 1905b. Sur une nouvelle fonction du tégument des arthropodes considéré comme organe producteur du sucre. *Ibid.*, pp. 232–238. (*30, 115, 187*)
——— 1906. Sur la fonction glycogénique du tégument. C. R. Assoc. Fr. Av. Sc. Sess., 34:572. (*30*)
Misra, A. B. 1939. The structure and secretion of the ovisac by the female of *Drosichiella (Monophlebus) quadricaudata*. 7th Int. Kongr. Ent. Berlin, 2:872–876. (*216*)
Mitchell, J. S. 1939. The colloidal properties of the cell. Tab. Biol., 19:276–345. (*287*)
* Möhring, A. 1922. (Birefringence and refractive index of chitin.) Wiss. u. Ind. (Hamburg), 1:51, 68, 90. (Cited by Ambronn and Frey 1926.) (*120*)
——— 1926. Zur Doppelbrechung natürlicher Zellulosefasern und des Chitins. Kolloid-Chem. Beihefte, 23:162–188. (*121, 131*)
Montalenti, G. 1931a. Sulla permeabilità della membrana peritrofica dell' intestino degli insetti. Boll. Soc. Ital Biol. Sper., Naples, 6:89–94. (*279*)
——— 1931b. Gli enzimi digerenti e l'assorbimento delle sostanze solubili nell'intestino delle termiti. Arch. Zool. Ital., Torino, 16:859–870. (*279*)
Montgomery, T. H. 1900. On nucleolar structures of the hypodermal cells of the larva of *Carpocapsa*. Zool. Jahrb., Anat., 13:385–392. (*159, 162, 183, 203, 206*)
Mooney, R. C. L. 1941. An x-ray study of the structure of polyvinyl alcohol. J. Amer. Chem. Soc., 63:2828–2832. (*22, 35*)
* Moreau, L. 1931. La sécrétion du *Blaps gigas*. Bull. Soc. Linn. Provence, Marseille, 5:34–37. (*74*)
Morgan, W. T. J., and L. A. Elson 1934. A colorimetric method for the determination of N-acetylglucosamine and N-acetylchondrosamine. Biochem. J., 28:988–995. (*12*)
Morgulis, S. 1916. The chemical constitution of chitin. Science, 44:866–867. (*15*)
——— 1917. An hydrolytic study of chitin. Amer. J. Physiol., 43:328–342. (*15*)
** Morimoto, S. 1936. (Notes on the etching figures that appear on the elytra of some species belonging to Scarabaeidae when Schultze's mixture is applied.) Kontyu, 10:297–301. (*267*)
Morison, G. D. 1927. The muscles of the adult honey-bee (*Apis mellifica* L.). Quart. J. Micr. Sci., 71:395–463. (*262–264*)
** Moriyama, T. 1939. (Morphological studies on the integuments of insect larvae, with special reference to the effect of insecticides.) Bot. Zool., Tokyo, 7:1391–1394. (*313*)
Morozov, S. F. 1935. (Penetration of contact insecticides. 1. Methods of investigation and general properties of the cuticle with regard to its permeability.) Plant Prot., 6:38–58. (*290, 293*)
Morrison, P. R. 1946. Physiological observations on water loss and oxygen consumption in *Peripatus*. Biol. Bull., 91:181–188. (*298*)
Moscona, A. 1948. Utilization of mineral constituents of the egg shell by the developing embryo of the stick insect. Nature, 162:62–63. (*107*)
——— 1950. Studies on the egg of *Bacillus libanicus* (Orthoptera, Phasmida). Quart. J. Micr. Sci., 91:183–194, 195–204. (*107*)
Mou, Y. C. 1938. Morphologische und histologische Studien über Paussidendrüsen. Zool. Jahrb., Anat., 64:287–346. (*251*)
Müller, Adolf 1924. Zur Anatomie einiger Arten des Genus *Ischyropsalis* C. L. Koch nebst vergleichend-anatomischen Betrachtungen. Zool. Jahrb., Anat., 45:405–518. (*266*)
Müller, Alex 1928. Further x-ray investigation of long-chain compounds (n-hydrocarbons). Proc. R. Soc. London, ser. A, 120:437–459. (*98*)
——— 1929. The connection between the zig-zag structure of the hydrocarbon

chain and the alterations in the properties of odd- and even-numbered chain compounds. *Ibid.*, 124:317–321. (*98*)

——— 1930. Crystal structure of the normal paraffins at temperatures ranging from that of liquid air to the melting point. *Ibid.*, 127:417–430. (*98*)

——— 1932. X-ray investigation of normal paraffins near their melting point. *Ibid.*, 138:514–530. (*98, 300*)

Müller, G. W. 1925. Kalk in der Haut der Insekten und die Larve von *Sargus cuprarius* L. Z. Morph. Ökol. Tiere, 3:542–566. (*106, 162*)

——— 1927. Crustacea Entomostraca, Ostracoda. *In* Kukenthal and Krumbach, Handbuch der Zoologie, 3(1):399–434. (*180, 206, 269*)

Munscheid, L. 1933. Die Metamorphose des Labiums der Odonata. Z. wiss. Zool., 143:201–240. (*237, 238, 240*)

Murlin, J. R. 1902. Absorption and secretion in the digestive system of the land isopods. Proc. Acad. Nat. Sci. Philadelphia, 54:284–359. (*223*)

Murray, F. V., and O. W. Tiegs 1935. The metamorphosis of *Calandra oryzae*. Quart. J. Micr. Sci., 77:405–495. (*217*)

Murray, J. 1907. Encystment in Tardigrada. Trans. R. Soc. Edinburgh, 45:837–854. (*236*)

Nabel, K. 1939. Über die Membran niederer Pilze, besonders von *Rhizidiomyces bivellatus* nov. spec. Arch. Mikrobiol., 10:515–541. (*45, 53*)

Nagel, H. 1934. Die Aufgaben der Exkretionsorgane und der Kiemen bei der Osmoregulation von *Carcinus maenas*. Z. vergl. Physiol., 21:468–491. (*292*)

* Nakamura, T. 1940. The phosphorus metabolism during the growth of the animal. The behaviour of various phosphatases and phosphoric acid compounds of *Bombyx mori* L. during growth. Mitt. Med. Akad. Kioto, 28:387–416, 590–592. (*252*)

Nasmith, F. 1926. Artificial Silk Handbook. Heywood, London. (*29*)

Nasse, O. 1886. Über Verbindungen der Glykogen nebst Bemerkungen über die mechanische Absorption. Pflüger's Arch. ges. Physiol., 37:582–606. (*35*)

* Nastyukov, A. M., and A. A. Nikol'skii 1935. (Plastic masses from chitin.) Russian Patent no. 44,679. (Chem. Abstr., 32:3050.) (*29*)

Nebeski, O. 1880. Beiträge zur Kenntnis der Amphipoden der Adria. Arb. Zool. Inst. Wien, 3:111–163. (*215*)

Needham, A. E. 1946. Ecdysis and growth in crustacea. Nature, 158:667–668. (*153, 226, 227, 234*)

Needham, J. 1942. Biochemistry and Morphogenesis. Cambridge Univ. Press. (*6*)

Nelson, F. C. 1927. The penetration of a contact oil spray into the breathing system of an insect. J. Econ. Ent., 20:632–635. (*140*)

Nelson, J. M., and C. R. Dawson 1944. Tyrosinase. Adv. Enzymol., 4:99–152. (*75, 76*)

Nettovich, L. V. 1900. Neue Beiträge zur Kenntnis der Arguliden. Arb. Inst. Wien, 13:1–32. (*207, 209, 211*)

Nicholls, A. G. 1931a. Studies on *Ligia oceanica*. 1. A. Habitat and effect of change of environment on respiration. B. Observations on moulting and breeding. J. Marine Biol. Assoc., n. s., 17:655–673. (*106, 234, 306*)

——— 1931b. Studies on *Ligia oceanica*. 2. The process of feeding, digestion and absorption, with a description of the structure of the foregut. *Ibid.*, pp. 675–707. (*203, 310*)

Nicolet, B. H., and L. J. Saidel 1941. The hydroxyamino acids of silk proteins. J. Biol. Chem., 139:477–478. (*62, 64*)

* Nikol'skii, A. A. 1936. (Utilization of chitin for the manufacture of plastic masses.) J. Applied Chem., USSR, 9:1308–1315. (*29*)

Nilsson, J. 1936. Zur Bestimmung von Glucosamin in Proteinstoffen. Biochem. Z., 285:386–389. (*12*)

* Nitsche, G. 1933. Methoden zur Prüfung von pflanzenschitzmitteln. 3. Die Bestimmung des Wachslösungsvermogens von Blutlausmitteln. Nachr. Bl. dtsch. Pfl. Sch. Dienst., 13:9, 18. (*137*)

Noël, R., and A. Paillot 1927. Sur la participation du noyau à la sécrétion dans les cellules des tubes séricigènes chez le Bombyx du mûrier. C. R. Soc. Biol., 97:764–766. (*250*)

Nordenskiöld, E. 1908. Zur Anatomie und Histologie von *Ixodes reduvius*. Zool. Jahrb., Anat., 25:637–674. (*161, 180, 182, 207, 251, 254*)

——— 1909. Zur Anatomie und Histologie von *Ixodes reduvius. Ibid.*, 27:449–464. (*159*)

——— 1911. Zur Anatomie und Histologie von *Ixodes reduvius. Ibid.*, 32:77–106. (*159, 174, 206*)

Norman, A. G. 1937. The Biochemistry of Cellulose, the Polyuronides, Lignin, Etc. Clarendon Press, Oxford. (*39, 52, 53, 116*)

———, and W. H. Peterson 1932. The chemistry of mould tissue. 2. The resistant cell wall material. Biochem. J., 26:1946–1953. (*25, 45*)

Northrop, J. H. 1929. The permeability of dry collodion membranes. J. Gen. Physiol., 12:435–461. (*295*)

Nouvel, L. 1933a. Sur la mue des *Leander serratus* parasités par *Bopyrus fougerouxi*. C. R. Acad. Sci., 196:811–812. (*236*)

——— 1933b. Sur la croissance et la frequence des mues chez les crustacés décapodes Natantia. Bull. Soc. Zool. France, 58:71–75. (*236*)

Novikoff, M. 1905. Untersuchungen über den Bau der *Limnadia lenticularia* L. Z. wiss. Zool., 78:561–619. (*159, 161, 195, 204, 222, 237, 244*)

* Numanoi, H. 1934a. Calcium in the blood of *Ligia exotica* during non-moulting and moulting phases. J. Fac. Sci. Tokyo Univ., ser. 4, 3:351–358. (Cited by Robertson 1941.) (*234*)

* ——— 1934b. Calcium contents of the carapace and other organs of *Ligia exotica* during non-moulting and moulting phases. *Ibid.*, pp. 359–364. (Cited by Robertson 1941.) (*100*)

——— 1937. Migration of calcium through blood in *Ligia exotica* during its moulting. Japan. J. Zool., 7:241–249. (*100*)

——— 1939a. Behaviour of blood calcium in the formation of gastrolith in some decapod crustacea. *Ibid.*, 8:357–363. (*105*)

——— 1939b. Hepatopancreas in relation to moulting in *Ligia exotica. Ibid.*, pp. 365–369. (*105*)

* ——— 1943. (Migration of calcium during molting in some crustaceans.) Sigenkagaku Kenkysuyo Iho, 10:1–25. (Chem. Abstr., 42:3088.) (*100, 105, 106*)

Ochmann, A. 1933. Aus der Spinnstube einiger heimischer Raupen. Int. Ent. Z., Guben, 27:249–252. (*67*)

Ochsé, W. 1946. Über Vorkommen und Funktion von argyrophilen Bindegewebe bei Insekten. Rev. Suisse Zool., 53:534–547. (*221, 238*)

Odier, A. 1823. Mémoire sur la composition chimique des parties cornées des insectes. Mém. Soc. Hist. Nat. Paris, 1:29–42. (*5, 14, 59, 94, 114, 159, 163*)

Offer, T. R. 1908. Über Chitin. Biochem. Z., 7:117–127. (*15*)

Oguma, K. 1913. On the rectal tracheal gills of a libellulid nymph, and their fate during the course of metamorphosis. Berlin Ent. Z., 58:211–225. (*205, 206*)

* Ohara, K. 1933a. (The optics of silk fibers.) Sci. Pap. Inst. Phys. Chem. Res. Tokyo, 21:104. (Cited by Frey-Wyssling 1938.) (*67, 131*)

* ——— 1933b. (The swelling of silk.) *Ibid.*, 22:216. (Cited by Frey-Wyssling 1938.) (*67, 131*)

O'Kane, W. C., and W. C. Baker 1934. Studies on contact insecticides. 8. Some determinations of oil penetration into insect eggs. New Hampshire Agric. Exp. Sta., Bull. no. 60, 12 pp. (*290, 293, 314*)

——— 1935. Studies on contact insecticides. 9. Further determinations of oil penetration into insect eggs. New Hampshire Agric. Exp. Sta., Bull. no. 62, 8 pp. (*290, 293, 314*)

O'Kane, W. C., and L. C. Glover 1935. Studies on contact insecticides. 10. Penetration of arsenic into insects. New Hampshire Agric. Exp. Sta., Bull. no. 63, 8 pp. (*294, 313*)

——— 1936. Studies on contact insecticides. 11. Further determinations of the penetration of arsenic into insects. New Hampshire Agric. Exp. Sta., Bull. 65, 8 pp. (*294, 313*)

———, R. L. Blickle, and B. M. Parker 1940. Studies on contact insecticides. 14. Penetration of certain liquids through the pronotum of the American roach. New Hampshire Agric. Exp. Sta., Bull. no. 74, 16 pp. (*293, 295*)

O'Kane, W. C., L. C. Glover, and W. A. Westgate 1937. Studies of contact insecticides. 12. The performance of certain contact agents on various plant surfaces. New Hampshire Agric. Exp. Sta., Bull. no. 68, 22 pp. (*138*)

O'Kane, W. C., W. A. Westgate, and L. C. Glover 1932. Studies of contact insecticides. 5. The performance of certain contact agents on various insects. New Hampshire Agric. Exp. Sta., Bull. no. 51, 20 pp. (*138*)

———, and P. R. Lowry 1930. Studies of contact insecticides. 1. Surface tension, surface activity, and wetting ability as factors in the performance of contact insecticides. New Hampshire Agric. Exp. Sta., Bull. no. 39, 44 pp. (*137, 138*)

* Okay, S. 1947a. (Pigments of the blue, red, and yellow posterior wings of acridians.) Rev. fac. sci. Univ. Istanbul, ser. B, 12:1–8. (Chem. Abstr., 42:2683.) (*91*)

* ——— 1947b. (The green pigment of insects.) *Ibid.*, pp. 89–106. (*91*)

——— 1949. Sur les pigments des ailes postérieures rouges, bleues et jaunes des Acrididae. Bull. Soc. Zool. France, 74:11–15. (*91*)

* Oku, M. 1929–1935. On the natural pigments of raw silk fiber of the domestic cocoon. 1–11. Bull. Agric. Chem. Soc. Japan, 1929:81; 1930:104; 1931:8; 1932:8; 1933:9, 93; 1934:158, 164; 1935:8, 10, 1253. (Cited by Maloeuf 1938.) (*91*)

Olmsted, J. M. D., and J. P. Baumberger 1923. Form and growth of grapsoid crabs. A comparison of the form of three species of grapsoid crabs and their growth at molting. J. Morph., 38:279–294. (*104*)

* Ongaro, D. 1933. Una paraffina nell 'uovo die *Bombyx mori.* Ann. Chimica Applicata, 23:567–572. (Chem. Abstr., 28:3469; see also Bergmann 1938.) (*98, 280, 314*)

Onslow, H. 1916. On the development of the black markings on the wings of *Pieris brassicae.* Biochem. J., 10:26–30. (*74, 76, 77, 88, 191*)

——— 1920. The iridescent colours of insects. 1. The colours of thin films. 2. Diffraction colours. 3. Selective metallic reflection. Nature, 106:149–152, 181–183, 215–218. (*196*)

——— 1921. On a periodic structure in many insect scales and the cause of their iridescent colours. Phil. Trans. R. Soc. London, ser. B, 211:1–74. (*196*)

Onslow, M. W. 1923. Oxidising enzymes. 6. A note on tyrosinase. Biochem. J., 17:217–219. (*72*)

———, and M. E. Robinson 1925. Oxidising enzymes. 8. The oxidation of certain parahydroxy compounds by plant enzymes and its connection with "tyrosinase." *Ibid.*, 19:420–423. (*72*)

* Oort, A. J. P., and P. A. Roelofsen 1932. Spiralwachstum, Wandbau und Plasmaströmung bei *Phycomyces.* Proc. R. Soc. Amsterdam, 35:898. (Cited by Castle 1940.) (*176*)

Osterhout, W. J. V. 1949. Transport of water from concentrated to dilute solutions in cells of *Nitella.* J. Gen. Physiol., 32:559–566. (*292*)

Osterloh, A. 1922. Beiträge zur Kenntnis des Kopulationsapparates einiger Spinnen. Z. wiss. Zool., 119:326–421. (*160*)

Ott, E. 1943. Chemistry of cellulose and cellulose derivatives. *In* The Chemistry of Large Molecules, pp. 243–308. Interscience, New York. (*10, 15*)

* Ozaki, G. 1936. The carbohydrate complex of serum mucoid. J. Biochem. (Japan), 24:73–79. (*12*)

Packard, A. S. 1883. Moulting of the shell in *Limulus*. Amer. Nat., 17:1075–1076. (*241*)

——— 1886. On the nature and origin of the so-called "spiral thread" of tracheae. *Ibid.*, 20:438–442. (*257*)

——— 1898. A Textbook of Entomology. Macmillan, New York. (*14, 67*)

Pagast, F. 1936. Über Bau und Funktion der Analpapillen bei *Aedes aegypti*. Zool. Jahrb., allg. Zool., 56:183–218. (*249, 293, 310–312*)

Paillot, A. 1920. Sur les oenocytoides et les teratocytes. C. R. Acad. Sci., 171:192–193. (*217*)

——— 1938. La glycogène chez le Bombyx du mûrier. C. R. Soc. Biol., 127:1502–1504. (*30*)

——— 1939. Contribution à l'étude cytologique et histophysiologique du Bombyx du mûrier pendant la mue. Ann. Epiphyt., Paris, 5:339–386. (*30, 205, 209, 217, 225*)

———, and R. Noël 1926. Sur l'origine des pigments dans les cellules hypodermiques de *Pieris brassicae*. C. R. Soc. Biol., 95:1372–1374. (*86, 205*)

——— 1929. Histo-physiologie des glandes séricigènes du Ver à soie pendant la mue. *Ibid.*, 101:1153–1155. (*252*)

Pal, R. 1947. Permeability of insect cuticle. Nature, 159:400. (*291*)

——— 1950. The wetting of insect cuticle. Bull. Ent. Res., 41:121–139. (*139*)

Palmén, J. A. 1877. Zur Morphologie des Tracheensystems. J. C. Frenckell & Sohn, Helsingfors. (*253, 255, 261*)

Palmer, L. S., and H. H. Knight 1924a. Carotin – the principal cause of the red and yellow colors in *Perillus bioculatus* (Fab.), and its biological origin from the lymph of *Leptinotarsa decemlineata* Say. J. Biol. Chem., 59:443–449. (*91*)

——— 1924b. Anthocyanin and flavone-like pigments as cause of red colorations in the hemipterous families Aphididae, Coreidae, Lygaeidae, Miridae and Reduviidae. *Ibid.*, pp. 451–455. (*91*)

Pantel, J. 1898. Le *Thrixion halidayanum* Rond. Essai monographique sur les caractères extérieurs, la biologie et l'anatomie d'une larve parasite du groupe des tachinaires. La Cellule, 15:1–290. (*159, 162, 191, 217, 255, 262, 264, 265, 270*)

——— 1901. Sur quelques détails de l'appareil respiratoire et de ses annexes dans les larves des muscides. Bull. Soc. Ent. France, pp. 57–61. (*215, 255, 264*)

——— 1919. Le calcium dans la physiologie normale des phasmides: Oeuf et larve éclosante. C. R. Acad. Sci., 168:127–129. (*66, 85, 107*)

Pantin, C. F. A., and T. H. Rogers 1925. An amphoteric substance in the radula of the whelk (*Buccinum undatum*). Nature, 115:639–640. (*44, 116, 121*)

Pardi, L. 1938. Glicogeno degli enociti e suo significato. Monit. Zool. Ital., Florence, 49:108–115. (*30, 217, 219*)

——— 1939. Osservazioni di istofisiologia su *Melasoma populi* L. (Copeoptera – Chrysomelidae). Enociti e mute. *Ibid.*, 50:88–93. (*30, 31, 205, 217, 219*)

Parkin, E. A. 1944. Control of the granary weevil with finely ground mineral dusts. Ann. Appl. Biol., 31:84–88. (*302*)

Passonneau, J. V., and C. M. Williams. (Unpublished data on molting fluid of pupa of cecropia moth.) (*78, 229, 230*)

dos Passos, C. F. 1948. Occurrence of anthoxanthins in the wing pigments of some nearctic *Oeneis*. Ent. News, 59:92–96. (*91*)

Patanè, L. 1936a. Prime ricerche sulla struttura degli oostegiti die *Porcellio laevis*. Boll. Zool., Torino, 7:161–165. (*161, 244*)

——— 1936b. Ricerche sul sistema tegumentale degli Isopodi. Arch. Zool. Ital., Torino, 23:209–240. (*161*)

Patten, W. 1893. On the morphology and physiology of the brain and sense organs of *Limulus*. Quart. J. Micr. Sci., 35:1–96. (*160, 205*)

* Patterson, G. D., and J. H. Peterson 1936. (Chitin suspension for washable wallpaper.) U.S. Patent no. 2,047,220. (Chem. Abstr., 30:6094.) (*29*)

Paul, J. H., and J. S. Sharpe 1916. Studies in calcium metabolism. 1. The deposition of lime salts in the integument of decapod crustacea. J. Physiol., 50:183–192. (*104, 106*)

Pautel, P. 1898. Sur la clivage de la cuticule, en tant que processus temporaire ou permanent. C. R. Acad. Sci., 126:850–853. (*159*)

Pavlowsky, E. 1913. Ein Beitrag zur Kenntnis des Baues der Giftdrüsen von *Scolopendra morsitans*. Zool. Jahrb., Anat., 36:91–112. (*250*)

——— 1927. Gifttiere und ihre Giftigkeit. Fischer, Jena. (*160, 163*)

Payen, —— 1843. Propriétés distinctives entre les membranes végétales et les enveloppes des insectes et des crustacés. C. R. Acad. Sci., 17:227–231. (*9*)

Pearce, G. W., P. J. Chapman, and A. W. Avens 1942. The efficiency of dormant type oils in relation to their composition. J. Econ. Ent., 35:211–220. (*137*)

Pearson, J. 1908. *Cancer* (the edible crab). Liverpool Marine Biol. Ct. Mem., 16:1–209. (*159, 161*)

Pearson, J. C. 1939. The early life histories of some American Penaeidae, chiefly the commercial shrimp *Penaeus setiferus* (Linn.). Bull. U.S. Bur. Fish., 49:1–73. (*225*)

Pepper, J. H., and E. Hastings 1943. Age variations in exoskeletal composition of the sugar beet webworm and their possible effect on membrane permeability. J. Econ. Ent., 36:633. (*40, 51, 84, 112–114, 290, 317*)

Pérez, C. 1901a. Sur les oenocytes de la fourmi rousse. Bull. Soc. Ent. France, pp. 351–353. (*217*)

——— 1901b. Sur quelques phénomènes de nymphose chez la fourmi rousse. C. R. Soc. Biol., 53:1046–1049. (*217*)

——— 1910. Recherches histologiques sur la métamorphose des muscides, *Calliphora erythrocephala* Mg. Arch. Zool. Exp. & Gen., ser. 5, 4:1–274. (*162, 204, 217, 221, 237, 238, 240, 243, 264*)

** Perfiljev, P. 1926. Über den Kiemenbau einiger Insektenlarven. Bull. Acad. Sci. URSS, Leningrad, 20:1599–1618. (*246*)

Peschen, K. E. 1939. Untersuchungen über das Vorkommen und den Stoffwechsel des Guanins im Tierreich. Zool. Jahrb., allg. Zool., 59:429–462. (*92*)

Petersen, W. 1907. Über die Spermatophoren der Schmetterlinge. Z. wiss. Zool., 88:117–130. (*52, 282*)

Petrunkewitsch, A. 1899. Die Verdauungsorgane von *Periplaneta orientalis* und *Blatta germanica*. Zool. Jahrb., Anat., 13:171–190. (*161, 205, 311*)

Pflugfelder, O. 1935. Experimentelle Erzeugung von Chitinperlen bei Insekten. Zool. Anz., 109:131–134. (*236*)

——— 1939. Beeinflussung von Regenerationsvorgängen bei *Dixippus morosus* Br. durch Exstirpation und Transplantation der Corpora allata. Z. wiss. Zool., 152:159–184. (*223*)

Philip, B., and F. O. Fournier 1946. Technique for the detection of insect moulting. Ann. Rpt. Ent. Soc. Ontario, 75:10–13. (*230*)

Philiptschenko, J. 1906. Anatomische Studien über Collembola. Z. wiss. Zool., 85:270–304. (*209*)

Phillips, M. E. 1939. The anterior peristigmatic glands in trypetid larvae. Ann. Ent. Soc. Amer., 32:325–328. (*215*)

Phisalix, C. 1900. Un venin volatil. Sécrétion cutanée du *Iulus terrestris*. C. R. Soc. Biol., pp. 1033–1036, 1036–1038. (*74*)

Picken, L. E. R. 1940. The fine structure of biological systems. Biol. Rev., 15:133–167. (*6, 23, 193*)

——— 1949. Shape and molecular orientation in lepidopteran scales. Phil. Trans. R. Soc. London, ser. B, 234:1–28. (*39, 42, 44, 46, 51, 120, 130–132, 142, 147, 157, 220, 271, 272*)

———, and W. Lotmar 1950. Oriented protein in chitinous structures. Nature, 165:599–600. (*47*)

Picken, L. E. R., M. G. M. Pryor, and M. M. Swann 1947. Orientation of fibrils in natural membranes. Nature, 159:434. (*21, 50, 67, 132, 141, 142, 174, 175*)

Pictet, F. J. 1841. Histoire naturelle générale et particulière des insectes neuroptères. 1. Perlides. Kessmann, Genève. (*261*)

Pieh, S. 1936. Über die Beziehungen zwischen Atmung, Osmoregulation und Hydration der Gewebe bei euryhalinen Meeresvertebraten. Zool. Jahrb., allg. Zool., 56:129–160. (*292, 298*)

Piepho, H. 1938a. Wachstum und totale Metamorphose an Hautimplantaten bei der Wachsmotte *Galleria mellonella*. Biol. Zbl., 58:356–366. (*223*)

——— 1938b. Über die Auslösung der Raupenhautung, Verpuppung und Imaginalentwicklung an Hautimplantaten von Schmetterlingen. *Ibid.*, pp. 481–495. (*223*)

Pigman, W. W., and M. L. Wolfrom 1945. Advances in Carbohydrate Chemistry. Academic Press, New York. (*10*)

Pinhey, K. G. 1930. Tyrosinase in crustacean blood. J. Exp. Biol., 7:19–36. (*76*)

* Piper, J. 1946. The anticoagulant effect of heparin and synthetic polysaccharide-polysulfuric acid esters. Acta Pharmacol. & Toxicol., 2:138–148, 317–328. (Chem. Abstr., 40:7415; 41:3866.) (*29*)

Piper, S. H., A. C. Chibnall, S. J. Hopkins, A. Pollard, J. A. B. Smith, and E. F. Williams 1931. Synthesis and crystal spacings of certain long-chain paraffins, ketones and secondary alcohols. Biochem. J., 25:2072–2094. (*98*)

Piper, S. H., A. C. Chibnall, and E. F. Williams 1934. Melting points and long crystal spacings of the higher primary alcohols and n-fatty acids. Biochem. J., 28:2175–2188. (*98*)

Platania, E. 1938. Ricerche sulla struttura del tubo digerente di *Reticulitermes lucifugus* (Rossi), con particolare riguardo alla nature, origine e funzione della peritrofica. Arch. Zool. Ital., Torino, 25:297–328. (*278*)

Plate, L. H. 1888. Beiträge zur Naturgeschichte der Tardigraden. Zool. Jahrb., Anat., 3:487–550. (*160, 205*)

Plateau, F. 1876. Note sur une sécrétion propre aux Coléoptères Dytiscides. Ann. Soc. Ent. Belg., 19:1–10. (*116, 164, 170*)

Platner, E. A. 1844. Die Respirationsorgane und die Haut bei den Seidenraupen. Arch. Anat. Physiol. wiss. Med., pp. 38–48. (*262*)

Plotnikow, W. 1904. Über die Häutung und über einige Elemente der Haut bei den Insekten. Z. wiss. Zool., 76:333–366. (*159, 161, 163, 179, 180, 182, 192, 209, 213*)

Poisson, R. 1924. Contribution à l'étude des Hémiptères aquatiques. Bull. Biol. Fr. Belg., 58:49–204. (*161, 170, 180, 182, 209, 216–219, 228*)

——— 1925. Sur un processus particulier d'élimination des produits uriques chez certains Hémiptères. Bull. Soc. Zool. Fr., 50:116–124. (*161, 205*)

——— 1926. L'*Anisops producta* Fieb. (Hémiptèra Notonectidae). Observations sur son anatomie et sa biologie. Arch. Zool. Exp. & Gen., 65:181–208. (*264*)

Pollard, A., A. C. Chibnall, and S. H. Piper 1931. The wax constituents of forage grasses. 1. Cocksfoot and perennial ryegrass. Biochem. J., 25:2111–2122. (*95*)

Pollister, P. F. 1937. The structure and development of wax glands of *Pseudococcus maritimus*. Quart. J. Micr. Soc., 80:127–152. (*250*)

Polson, A., V. M. Mosley, and R. W. G. Wyckoff 1947. The quantitative chromatography of silk hydrolysate. Science, 105:603–604. (*62, 64*)

Portier, P. 1911. Recherches physiologiques sur les insectes aquatiques. Arch. Zool. Exp. & Gen., ser. 5, 8:89–379. (*261, 264*)

———, and F. Emmanuel 1932. Sur l'absorption des radiations calorifiques par les ailes des Lépidoptères. C. R. Acad. Sci., 194:568–569. (*120*)

Potter, C., and E. M. Gillham 1946. Effects of atmospheric environment, before and after treatment, on the toxicity to insects of contact poisons. Ann. Appl. Biol., 33:142–159. (*318*)

Potts, W. H., and F. L. Vanderplank 1945. Mode of entry of contact insecticides. Nature, 156:112. (*313*)

Powell, P. B. 1905. The development of wings of certain beetles, and some studies of the origin of the wings of insects. J. New York Ent. Soc., 12:237–243; 13:5–22. (*227*)

Poyarkoff, E. 1910. Recherches histologiques sur la metémorphose d'un coléoptère (la Galéruque de l'orme). Arch. d'Anat. Micr., 12:333–474. (*161, 209, 213, 216, 228*)

——— 1914. Essai d'une théorie de la nymphe des insectes holométaboles. Arch. Zool. Exp. & Gen., 54:221–265. (*238, 240*)

Pratt, J. J., and H. L. House 1949. A qualitative analysis of the amino acids in royal jelly. Science, 110:9–10. (*63, 64*)

Prenant, A. 1900. Cellules trachéales des Oestres. Arch. d'Anat. Micr., 3:293–336. (*264*)

——— 1911. Problèmes cytologiques généraux soulevés par l'étude des cellules musculaires. J. Anat. et Physiol., 47:601–680. (*264*)

Prenant, M. 1925. Notes sur les parties calcifiées des téguments chez *Pollicipes cornucopiae*. Bull. Soc. Zool. France, 49:611–621. (*48, 161*)

——— 1927a. La stabilité du calcaire amorphe et le tégument des crustacés. Ann. Physiol. Physico-Chim. Biol., 3:818–843. (*100, 104*)

——— 1927b. Les formes minéralogiques du calcaire chez les êtres vivants et le problème de leur déterminisme. Biol. Rev., 2:364–393. (*100, 101*)

Preston, R. D. 1939. The molecular chain structure of cellulose and its botanical significance. Biol. Rev., 14:281–313. (*10*)

——— 1948. Spiral growth and spiral structure. 1. Spiral growth in sporangiophores of *Phycomyces*. Biochim. Biophys. Acta, 2:155–166. (*258*)

———, E. Nicolai, R. Reed, and A. Millard 1948. An electron microscope study of cellulose in *Valonia ventricosa*. Nature, 162:665–667. (*21*)

Priebatsch, I. 1933. Der Einfluss des Lichtes auf Farbwechsel und Phototaxis von *Dixippus (Carausius) morosus*. Z. vergl. Physiol., 19:453–488. (*93*)

Prochnow, O. 1907. Die Lautapparate der Insekten. Scholz, Guben. (*161*)

——— 1927. Die Farbung der Insekten. *In* Schröder, Handbuch der Entomologie, 2:230–572. (*86, 196*)

Proskuriakow, N. J. 1925. Über die Beteiligung des Chitins am Aufbau der Pilzzellwand. Biochem. Z., 167:68–76. (*25, 26, 28, 45, 53*)

Pryor, M. G. M. 1940a. On the hardening of the ootheca of *Blatta orientalis*. Proc. R. Soc. London, ser. B, 128:378–393. (*50, 59, 71, 73, 80, 81, 279*)

——— 1940b. On the hardening of the cuticle of insects. *Ibid.*, pp. 393–407. (*59, 71, 73, 80, 85, 95, 121, 130, 139, 157, 164, 171, 182, 192, 201*)

——— 1948. Hardness and colour of insect cuticle. Proc. R. Ent. Soc. London, ser. A, 23:96–97. (*76*)

———, P. B. Russell, and A. R. Todd 1946. Protocatechuic acid, the substance responsible for the hardening of the cockroach ootheca. Biochem. J., 40:627–628. (*72*)

——— 1947. Phenolic substances concerned in hardening the insect cuticle. Nature, 159:399–400. (*72, 80*)

Przibram, H. 1922. Die Ausfärbung der Puppenkokone gewisser Schmetterlinge (*Eriogaster, Saturnia*) eine typische Dopareaktion. Biochem. Z., 127:286–292. (*72*)

——— 1924. Die Rolle der Dopa in den Kokonen gewisser Nachtfalter und Blattwespen mit Bemerkungen über die chemischen Orte der Melaninbildung. Arch. mikr.-anat. Entw., 102:624–634. (*72*)

———, and L. Brecher 1922. Die Farbmodifikationen der Stabheuschrecke *Dixippus morosus* Br. et Redt. Arch. Entw.-Mech., 50:147–185. (*93*)

Przibram, H., and H. Schmalfuss 1927. Das Dioxyphenylalanin in den Kokons des Nachtpfauenauges *Samia cecropia*. Biochem. Z., 187:467–469. (*72*)

Purcell, W. F. 1909. Development and origin of the respiratory organs in Araneae. Quart. J. Micr. Sci., 54:1–110. (*248, 255*)

——— 1910. The phylogeny of the tracheae in Araneae. *Ibid*., pp. 519–564. (*255*)

Purser, G. L. 1915. Preliminary notes on some problems connected with respiration in insects generally and in aquatic forms in particular. Proc. Cambr. Phil. Soc., 18:63–70. (*93, 205, 246, 265*)

Racovitza, E. G. 1919. Notes sur les Isopodes. Arch. Zool. Exp. & Gen., 58(Not. & Rev.):31–116. (*38*)

Radlkofer, L. 1855. Über die Darstellung der Chlorzinkjodlösung als Reagens auf Zellstoff für mikroskopische Untersuchungen. Arch. Chem. Pharm., 94:332–336. (*36*)

Radu, V. 1930a. Le noyau générateur de mitochondries dans les cellules glandulaires du canal déférent chez *Armadillidium vulgare* Latr. C. R. Soc. Biol., 103:285–288. (*205*)

——— 1930b. Structure histologique et cytologique du canal déférent chez *Armadillidium vulgare* Latr. Arch. Zool. Exp. & Gen., 70(Not. & Rev.):1–14. (*161, 205, 206*)

Rammelberg, G. 1931. Beitrag zur Kenntnis des Chitins der Pilze und Krabben. Bot. Arch., 32:1–37. (*25, 42, 45, 49, 56, 57*)

Ramsay, J. A. 1935. The evaporation of water from the cockroach. J. Exp. Biol., 12:373–383. (*168, 300*)

Ramsden, W. 1938. Coagulation by shearing and by freezing. Nature, 142:1120–1121. (*68, 141*)

Raper, H. S. 1926. The tyrosinase-tyrosine reaction. 5. Production of l–3,4-dihydroxyphenylalanine from tyrosine. Biochem. J., 20:735–742. (*72*)

von Rath, O. 1895. Über den feineren Bau der Drüsenzellen des Kopfes von *Anilocra mediterranea* Leach im Speciellen und die Amitosenfrage im Allgemeinen. Z. wiss. Zool., 60:1–89. (*251*)

Rayleigh, Lord 1923. Iridescent beetles. Proc. R. Soc. London, ser. A, 103:233–239. (*196*)

——— 1930. The iridescent colors of birds and insects. *Ibid*., 128:624–641. (*196*)

Reckie, J., and J. Aird 1945. Flow of water through very narrow channels and attempts to measure thermomechanical effects in water. Nature, 156:367–368. (*295, 302*)

Reed, R., and K. M. Rudall 1948. Electron microscope studies on the structure of earthworm cuticles. Biochim. Biophysica Acta, 2:7–18. (*44, 47, 176*)

van Rees, J. 1889. Beiträge zur Kenntnis der inneren Metamorphose von *Musca vomitoria*. Zool. Jahrb., Anat., 3:1–134. (*203*)

Regen, J. 1924. Anatomisch-physiologische Untersuchungen über die Spermatophore von *Liogryllus campestris* L. Sitz.-Ber. Akad. wiss. Wien, Math.-naturwiss. Kl., 133:347–359. (*282*)

* Reichard, A. 1903. Über Cuticular- und Gerüstsubstanzen bei wirbellosen Tieren. Inaug. dissertation, Heidelberg. (Cited by Biedermann 1914, Schulze 1924.) (*44*)

Reichelt, M. 1925. Schuppentwicklung und Pigmentbildung auf den Flügeln von *Lymantria dispar* unter besonderer Berücksichtigung des sexuellen Dimorphismus. Z. Morph. Ökol. Tiere, 3:477–525. (*271*)

Reid, D. M. 1943. Occurrence of crystals in the skin of Amphipoda. Nature, 151:504–505. (*101, 104, 105*)

Reinders, D. E. 1933. Die Funktion der corpora alba bei *Porcellio scaber*. Z. vergl. Physiol., 20:291–298. (*253, 306*)

Remy, P. 1925a. Contribution à l'étude de l'appareil respiratoire et de la respiration chez quelques invertébrés. Vagner, Nancy. (*93, 253, 264, 265*)

——— 1925b. Sur la structure de l'appareil aérifère chez les Monoantennés et les Chélicérés. C. R. Soc. Biol., 92:44–46. (*264*)

Rengel, C. 1903. Über den Zusammenhang von Mitteldarm und Enddarm bei den Larven der aculeaten Hymenopteren. Z. wiss. Zool., 75:221–232. (*278*)

Reuter, E. 1937. Elytren und Alae während der Puppen- und Käferstadien von *Calandra granaria* und *Calandra oryzae*. Zool. Jahrb., Anat., 62:449–506. (*161, 193, 243, 244, 246*)

Richards, A. G. 1937. Insect development analyzed by experimental methods. 2. Larval and pupal stages. J. New York Ent. Soc., 45:149–210. (*154, 202, 233*)

——— 1938. The remarkable setae on the male genitalia of the North American species of the genus *Amyna* (Lepidoptera). Ent. News, 49:91–96. (*275*)

——— 1941. Differentiation between toxic and suffocating effects of petroleum oils on larvae of the house mosquito (*Culex pipiens*). Trans. Amer. Ent. Soc., 67:161–196. (*139, 301, 306, 317*)

——— 1943. Lipid nerve sheaths in insects and their probable relation to insecticide action. J. New York Ent. Soc., 51:55–69. (*316, 317*)

——— 1944a. The structure of living insect nerves and nerve sheaths as deduced from the optical properties. *Ibid.*, 52:285–310. (*52, 130, 317*)

——— 1944b. Electron micrographs of mosquito microtrichiae. Ent. News, 55:260–262. (*141, 201, 270*)

——— 1947a. The organization of arthropod cuticle: A modified interpretation. Science, 105:170–171. (*5, 32, 81, 84, 145, 157*)

——— 1947b. Studies on arthropod cuticle. 1. The distribution of chitin in lepidopterous scales, and its bearing on the interpretation of arthropod cuticle. Ann. Ent. Soc. Amer., 40:227–240. (*5, 24, 27, 28, 32–34, 38, 50, 51, 81, 84, 109, 114, 141, 145, 146, 157, 271*)

——— 1949. Studies on arthropod cuticle. 3. The chitin of *Limulus*. Science, 109:591–592. (*18, 24, 25, 39, 40, 48, 82, 110, 116*)

———, and T. F. Anderson 1942a. Electron microscope studies of insect cuticle with a discussion of the application of electron optics to this problem. J. Morph., 71:135–183. (*50, 119, 124, 137, 141, 153, 157, 161–164, 167, 168, 171, 175–177, 179–183, 209, 213, 287, 290*)

——— 1942b. Electron micrographs of insect tracheae. J. New York Ent. Soc., 50:147–167. (*234, 259, 262*)

——— 1942c. Further electron microscope studies on arthropod tracheae. *Ibid.*, pp. 245–247. (*259, 262*)

Richards, A. G., and L. K. Cutkomp 1945. Neuropathology in insects. J. New York Ent. Soc., 53:313–355. (*316, 317*)

——— 1946. Correlation between the possession of a chitinous cuticle and sensitivity to DDT. Biol. Bull., 90:97–108. (*43–46, 48, 49, 116, 133, 134, 314, 318*)

Richards, A. G., and H. Y. Fan 1949. Studies on arthropod cuticle. 5. The variation in permeability of larval cuticles of the blowfly, *Phormia regina*. J. Cell. Comp. Physiol., 33:1–22. (*54, 124, 154, 156, 270, 293, 294, 297, 298, 308–312*)

Richards, A. G., and F. H. Korda 1947. Electron micrographs of centipede setae and microtrichia. Ent. News, 58:141–145. (*47, 141, 183, 254, 269, 270, 275, 276*)

——— 1948. Studies on arthropod cuticle. 2. Electron microscope studies of extracted cuticles. Biol. Bull., 94:212–235. (*21–24, 28, 36, 42, 47, 49, 51, 54, 82, 83, 132, 157, 160, 171, 183, 193, 209, 244, 245, 255, 257–259, 267, 268, 278, 279, 294, 301*)

——— 1950. Studies on arthropod cuticle. 4. An electron microscope survey of the intima of arthropod tracheae. Ann. Ent. Soc. Amer., 43:49–71. (*49, 51, 117, 122, 132, 157, 160, 183, 235, 255, 257–263, 268–270*)

Richards, A. G., and J. L. Weygandt 1945. The selective penetration of fat solvents into the nervous system of mosquito larvae. J. New York Ent. Soc., 53:153–165. (*140, 261, 291, 293, 311, 317*)

Ricks, M., and W. M. Hoskins 1948. Toxicity and permeability. 2. The entrance of arsenic into larvae of the flesh fly, *Sarcophaga securifera*. Physiol. Zool., 21:258–272. (*54, 156, 288, 290, 291, 293, 294, 308–310, 313*)

Riede, E. 1912. Vergleichende Untersuchung der Sauerstoffversorgung in den Insektenovarien. Zool. Jahrb., allg. Zool., 32:231–310. (*93, 264, 265*)

* Rigby, G. W. 1936. (Various patents on chitin derivatives used as binders for treating paper, fabrics, concrete, etc.) U.S. Patents nos. 2,047,225; 2,047,226; 2,040,879; 2,040,880. (Chem. Abstr., 30:4598, 6093, and 6097.) (*27, 29, 49*)

Rigden, P. J. 1946. Flow of fluids through porous plugs and the measurement of specific surface. Nature, 157:268. (*295, 302*)

Riley, W. A. 1908. Muscle attachment in insects. Ann. Ent. Soc. Amer., 1:265–269. (*237, 240*)

Rippel, A. 1937. Chitin bei Mikroorganismen. Eine Richtigstellung. Biochem. Z., 290:444. (*45*)

Ripper, W. 1931. Versuch einer Kritik der Homologiefrage der Arthropodentracheen. Z. wiss. Zool., 138:303–369. (*253*)

Rittenberg, S. C., D. G. Anderson, and C. E. Zobell 1937. Studies on the enumeration of marine anaerobic bacteria. Proc. Soc. Exp. Biol. Med., 35:652–653. (*55*)

Robertson, J. D. 1937. Some features of the calcium metabolism of the shore crab. Proc. R. Soc. London, ser. B, 124:162–182. (*79, 292*)

——— 1939. The inorganic composition of the body fluids of three marine invertebrates. J. Exp. Biol., 16:387–397. (*292*)

——— 1941. The function and metabolism of calcium in the invertebrates. Biol. Rev., 16:106–133. (*100, 107*)

Robinson, E. S., and J. M. Nelson 1944. The tyrosine-tyrosinase reaction and aerobic plant respiration. Arch. Biochem., 4:111–117. (*76*)

Robinson, G. G. 1942. The penetration of pyrethrum through the cuticle of the tick *Ornithodorus moubata* Murray (Argasidae). Parasitology, 34:113–121. (*290, 294, 312, 315*)

Roche, J., and C. Dumazert 1940. Sur les glucides de l'hémolymphe de *Cancer pagurus*. Nature et rôle physiologue. Ann. Inst. Oceanogr., Paris, 20:87–95. (*12, 31, 38*)

Roewer, C. F. 1934. Solifugae. *In* Bronn, Klassen und Ordnungen des Tierreichs, vol. 5, Abt. 4, Buch 4. (*160*)

Rogick, M. D., and H. Croasdale 1949. Studies on marine Bryozoa. Biol. Bull., 96:32–69. (*254*)

Rohwer, C. 1931. Evaporation from free water surfaces. U.S. D. A., Tech. Bull. no. 271, 96 pp. (*299*)

Roman, W. 1938. The electric theory of the two-step oxidation and some constants of the semiquinones. Tab. Biol., 16:110–115. (*73*)

Rome, D. R. 1936. Note sur la microstructure de l'appareil tegumentaire de *Phacops (Ph.) accipitrinus maretiolensis* R. & E. Richter. Bull. Mus. Hist. Nat. Belg., 12(31):1–7. (*160, 175*)

Rome, R. 1947. *Herpetocypris reptans* (Ostracode). 1. Morphologie externe et système nerveux. La Cellule, 51:51–152. (*275*)

Rosedale, J. L. 1945a. Some aspects of insect metabolism. J. South Afric. Chem. Inst., 28:3–9. (*17*)

——— 1945b. On the composition of insect chitin. J. Ent. Soc. S. Africa, 8:21–23. (*17*)

——— 1946. Synthesis of fat in locusts. *Ibid.*, 9:36–38. (*94, 234*)

Rosenheim, O. 1905. Chitin in the carapace of *Pterygotus osiliensis*, from the Silurian rocks of Oesel. Proc. R. Soc. London, ser. B, 76:398–400. (*48, 54*)

Ross, E. B. 1939. The post-embryonic development of the salivary glands of *Drosophila melanogaster.* J. Morph., 65:471–496. (*252*)

* Rossi, G. 1902. Sulla organizzazione del Miriapodi. Ricerche Lab. Anat. Univ. Roma, 9:5–88. (Cited by Silvestri 1903.) (*101, 160*)

* ——— 1903. A proposito del tegumento dei Diplopodi. Napoli. (Abstract in Zool. Jahresber., 1903, Arthrop., p. 45.) (*160*)

Rössig, H. 1904. Von welchen Organen der Gallwespenlarven geht der Reiz zur Bildung der Pflanzengalle aus? Zool. Jahrb., Syst., 20:19–90. (*217, 218*)

Roth, L. M. 1942. The oenocytes of *Tenebrio.* Ann. Ent. Soc. Amer., 35:81–84. (*217, 218*)

——— 1943. Studies on the gaseous secretion of *Tribolium confusum* Duval. 2. The odoriferous glands of *Tribolium confusum. Ibid.*, 36:397–424. (*209, 213*)

Rothera, C. H. 1904. Zur Kenntnis der Stickstoffbindung im Eiweiss. Beitr. Chem. Physiol. Path., 5:442–448. (*15*)

* Rotman, M. N. 1929. Contribution to the study of the chitin of the migratory locust (*Locusta migratoria* L.) in its different stages and phases. Plant Prot., Leningrad, 6:369–378. (Cited by Uvarov 1948.) (*110, 113*)

Rouget, C. 1859. Des substances amylacées dans les tissus des animaux, spécialement des Articulés (chitine). C. R. Acad. Sci., 48:792–795. (*26–28, 32, 36*)

Rücker, F. 1934. Über die Ultrarot-Reflexion tierischer Körperoberflächen. Z. vergl. Physiol., 21:275–280. (*127*)

Rudall, K. M. 1947. X-ray studies on the distribution of protein chain types in the vertebrate epidermis. Biochim. Biophysica Acta, 1:549–562. (*60*)

Rühle, H. 1932. Das larvale Tracheensystem von *Drosophila melanogaster* Meigen und seine Variabilität. Z. wiss. Zool., 141:159–245. (*254*)

Ruser, M. 1933. Beiträge zur Kenntnis des Chitins und der Muskulatur der Zecken (Ixodidae). Z. Morph. Ökol. Tiere, 27:199–261. (*153, 156, 161, 163, 182, 206, 229, 238, 240, 251, 254*)

Sadones, J. 1896. L'appareil digestif et respiratoire larvaire des odonates. La Cellule, 11:273–325. (*161, 182*)

* Sadov, F. I. 1941. (Chitosan as textile dressing.) Tekstil Prom., pp. 52–54. (Chem. Abstr., 38:2215.) (*29*)

Saint-Hilaire, K. 1927. Histo-physiologische Studien über die Spinndrüsen der Tenthredinidenlarven. Z. Zellforsch. Mikr. Anat., 5:449–494. (*251*)

Sakurai, M. 1928. Sur la glande trachéale de quelques insectes. C. R. Acad. Sci., 187:614–615. (*211*)

Salfi, M. 1937. La membrana peritrofica osservata alla "luce di Wood." Boll. Zool., Torino, 8:147–149. (*121, 130, 278*)

Sanford, E. W. 1918. Experiments on the physiology of digestion in the Blattidae. J. Exp. Zool., 25:355–401. (*290, 293, 311*)

Sarkaria, D. S., and R. L. Patton 1949. Histological and morphological factors in the penetration of DDT through the pulvilli of several insect species. Trans. Amer. Ent. Soc., 75:71–82. (*157, 158*)

Schäffer, C. 1889. Beiträge zur Histologie der Insekten. Zool. Jahrb., Anat., 3:611–652. (*251, 262, 268*)

Scharrer, B. 1939. The differentiation between neuroglia and connective tissue sheath in the cockroach (*Periplaneta americana*). J. Comp. Neurol., 70:77–88. (*52*)

Schatz, L. 1950. The finer structure of the tarsal integument of Orthoptera. Thesis, Cornell University. (*158, 180*)

Schepotieff, A. 1903. Untersuchungen über den feineren Bau der Borsten einiger Chaetopoden und Brachiopoden. Z. wiss. Zool., 74:656–710. (*47*)

Scheuring, L. 1912. Über ein neues Sinnesorgan bei *Heterometrus longimanus*. Zool. Anz., 40:370–374. (*178, 182*)

Schimkewitsch, W. 1884. Étude sur l'anatomie de l'Epeire. Ann. Sci. Nat. Zool., ser. 6, 17:1–94. (*160*)

Schleip, W. 1910. Der Farbwechsel von *Dixippus morosus*. Zool. Jahrb., allg. Zool., 30:45–132. (*93, 161, 205*)

Schlieper, C. 1929. Über die Einwirkung niederer Salzkonzentrationen auf marine Organismen. Z. vergl. Physiol., 9:478–514. (*292*)

Schlossberger, J. 1856. Zur näheren Kenntnis der Muskelschalen, des Byssus und der Chitinfrage. Ann. d. Chem. & Pharm., 98:99–120. (*54, 55, 101*)

Schlottke, E. 1934. Histologische Beobachtungen am Darmkanal von *Limulus* und Vergleich seines Zwischengewebes mit dem von Spinnen. Z. mikr. anat. Forsch., 35:57–70. (*52, 220*)

——— 1938a. Die Häutung der Spinnenlungen und die dabei zu Beobachtende Grössenänderung der Zellkerne. Z. Morph. Ökol. Tiere, 34:207–220. (*30, 160, 205–207, 228, 229, 248, 259*)

——— 1938b. Versuche über die Bildung des schwarzen Pigments bei *Habrobracon*. Biol. Zbl., 58:261–268. (*76, 88, 191*)

Schlüter, J. 1933. Die Entwicklung der Flügel bei der Schlupfwespe *Habrobracon juglandis* Ash. Z. Morph. Ökol. Tiere, 27:458–517. (*220, 227, 243*)

Schmalfuss, H., and H. Barthmeyer 1929. Einwirkung von Licht auf Melanin und o-dioxybenzolstoff im Hautskelett von Käfern. Biochem. Z., 215:79–84. (*72*)

——— 1930a. Postmortale Melaninbildung beim Mehlkäfer *Tenebrio molitor* L. *Ibid.*, 223:457–469. (*192*)

——— 1930b. Vererbungstheoretische Betrachtungen, nebst entwicklungschemische Untersuchungen über Verbreitung, Entstehung und Bedeutung von Melanogen, insonderheit von o-dioxybenzol-Stoff, im Organismenreich. Z. indukt. Abstamm. Vererb. Lehre, 53:67–132.

——— 1931. Same title. *Ibid.*, 58:332–371. (*71*)

Schmalfuss, H., and G. Bussmann 1935. 3,4-dioxyphenylessigsäure, ein Stoffwechselerzeugnis des Mehlkäfers (*Tenebrio molitor*) und ihr Feinnachweis. Z. physiol. Chem., 232:161–166. (*72*)

———, H. Schmalfuss, and H. Pohl 1939. Das Dunkeln des lebenden Mehlkäfers, *Tenebrio molitor*. 2. Der Säurestoffverbrauch des Mehlkäfers. Z. vergl. Physiol., 27:434–442. (*74*)

Schmalfuss, H., A. Heider, and K. Winkelmann 1933. 3,4-dioxyphenylessigsäure,

Farbvorstufe der Flügeldecken des Mehlkäfers, *Tenebrio molitor* L. Biochem. Z., 257:188–193. (*72*)

Schmalfuss, H., and H. P. Müller 1927. Über das Hautskelett von Insekten. Über Dioxyphenylalanin in der Flügeldecken von Maikäfern. Biochem. Z., 183:362–368.

Schmalfuss, H., and H. Werner 1926. Studien über die Bildung von Pigmenten. Fermentforschung, 8:116–134. (*72*)

Schmid, L., A. Waschkau, and E. Ludwig 1928. Alkaliverbindungen von mehrwertigen Alkoholen und Kohlenhydraten. Monatschr. f. Chem., 49:107–110. (*28*)

Schmidt, C. 1845a. Zur vergleichenden Physiologie der wirbellosen Thiere. Ann. Chem. & Pharm., 54:284–330. (*101, 202*)

* ——— 1845b. Zur vergleichenden Physiologie der wirbellosen Thiere. Braunschweig. (*159, 202*)

Schmidt, C. L. A. 1944. Chemistry of the Amino Acids and Proteins. Thomas, Springfield, Illinois. (*57, 62, 64*)

Schmidt, E. 1931. Über die chemische Zusammensetzung des Holzes der Rotbache (*Fagus silvatica*). Zusammenfassen der Bericht über die Ergebnisse von E. Schmidt und Mitarbeitern bis zum Jahre 1931. Cellulosechemie, 12:62–67. (*36, 39*)

———, and E. Graumann 1921. Zur Kenntnis pflanzlicher Inkrusten. 1. Methode zur Reindarstellung pflanzlicher Skeletsubstanzen. Ber. dtsch. Bot. Ges., 54:1860–1873. (*36*)

Schmidt, M. 1936. Makrochemische Untersuchungen über das Vorkommen von Chitin bei Mikroorganismen. Arch. Mikrobiol., 7:241–260. (*45*)

Schmidt, U. 1935. Beiträge zur Anatomie und Histologie der Hydracarinen, besonders von *Diplodontus despiciens* O. F. Müller. Z. Morph. Ökol. Tiere, 30:99–177. (*161*)

Schmidt, W. J. 1920. Über Chromatophoren bei Insekten. Arch. Mikr. Anat., 93:118–136. (*93*)

——— 1924. Die Bausteine des Tierkörpers im polarisierten Lichte. Bonn. (*104*)

——— 1926. Ergebnisse einer Untersuchungen über das Glanzepithel und die Schillerfarben der Sapphirinen nebst Bemerkungen über die Erzeugung von Strukturfarben durch Guanin bei anderen Tieren. Biol. Zbl., 46:314–318 (also in Verh. Nat. Ver. Bonn, 82:227–300, 1926). (*92, 196*)

——— 1928. Der submikroskopische Bau der tierischen Gewebe erschlossen aus der Polarisationsoptik. Arch. Exp. Zellforsch., 6:350–366. (*130, 131*)

——— 1929. Submikroskopischer Bau und Farbung des Chitins. 3 Wanderversammlung dtsch. Ent. Giesen, pp. 100–103. (*121, 131, 133, 134*)

——— 1934a. Der Wandel der Doppelbrechung bei der Nitrierung des Chitins. Z. wiss. Mikrosk., 50:296–304. (*121, 131*)

——— 1934b. Polarizationsoptische Analyse des submikroskopischen Baues von Zellen und Geweben. *In* Abderhalden, Handbuch Biol. Arbeitensmethoden, Abt. 5, 10:435–665. (*121, 131, 175*)

——— 1936a. (Review of Castle's 1936 paper on chitin birefringence.) Z. wiss. Mikrosk., 53:229–231. (*121, 131, 133*)

——— 1936b. Doppelbrechung und Feinbau der Eischale von *Ascaris megalocephala.* Ein Vergleich des Feinbaues faserigen und filartigen Chitins. Z. Zellforsch. mikr. Anat., 25:181–203. (*23, 43, 131, 132*)

——— 1937a. Die Doppelbrechung von Karyoplasma, Zytoplasma und Metaplasma. Protoplasma Monographien, vol. 11, 388 pp. Bornträger, Berlin. (*84, 131, 133, 134*)

——— 1937b. Über Schillerfarben bei Käfern, inbesondere des Prismentyp der farberzeugenden Lage. Verh. dtsch. Zool. Ges., 39:111–118. (*194, 196*)

——— 1939a. Über physikalische und chemische Eigenschaften des Sekretes, mit dem *Pediculus capitis* seiner Eier ankittet. Z. Parasitenkunde, 10:729–736. (*50, 132, 280*)
——— 1939b. Über das Vorkommen von Wachs im Lumen der Chitinhaare von *Bombus*. Zool. Anz., 128:270–273. (*94*)
——— 1939c. Über den Wandel der Doppelbrechung bei der Acetylierung des Chitins. Z. wiss. Mikrosk., 56:52–56. (*131*)
——— 1940. Zur Morphologie, Polarisationsoptik und Chemie der Greifhaken von *Sagitta hexaptera*. Z. Morph. Ökol. Tiere, 37:63–82. (*43, 46*)
——— 1941a. Bemerkungen über den blauen Chitinfarbstoff in den Schuppen der Nymphaliden *Nassaea obrinus* L. Zool. Anz., 139:70–72. (*92, 201*)
——— 1941b. Über die Metallfarben der Schildkäfers *Aspidomorpha*. Z. Morph. Ökol. Tiere, 38:85–95. (*201*)
——— 1942a. Die Mosaikschuppen des *Teinopalpus imperialis* Hope, ein neues Muster schillernder Schmetterlingsschuppen. *Ibid.*, 39:176–216. (*23, 132, 201*)
——— 1942b. Die Farberzeugende Struktur der Schillerschuppen von *Ornithoptera arruana* Fldr. Zool. Anz., 137:30–33. (*132, 201*)
Schmiedeberg, O. 1891. Über die chemische Zusammensetzung der Knorpels. Arch. exp. Path. Pharm., 28:355–404. (*12*)
——— 1920. Über Chitin und Chitinabkömmlinge des Tier- und Pflanzenreichs. *Ibid.*, 87:76–85. (*11, 17*)
Schmitt, J. B. 1938. The feeding mechanism of adult Lepidoptera. Smithsonian Misc. Coll., 97(4):1–28. (*119*)
Schnelle, H. 1923. Über den feineren Bau des Fettkörpers der Honigbiene. Zool. Anz., 57:172–179. (*211, 217–219*)
Schofield, R. K. 1947. Calculation of surface areas from measurements of negative adsorption. Nature, 160:408–410. (*134*)
———, and E. K. Rideal 1926. The kinetic theory of surface films. 2. Gaseous, expanded and condensed films. Proc. R. Soc. London, ser. A, 110:167–177. (*98*)
Scholl, E. 1908. Die Reindarstellung des Chitins aus *Boletus edulis*. Monatschr. f. Chem., 29:1023–1036. (*42*)
Schön, A. 1911. Bau und Entwicklung des tibialen Chordotonalorgans bei der Honigbiene und bei Ameisen. Zool. Jahrb., Anat., 31:439–472. (*251*)
von Schönborn, E. G. 1911. Beiträge zur Kenntnis des Kohlehydratstoffwechsels bei *Carcinus maenas*. Z. Biol., 55:70–82. (*30, 110, 113*)
——— 1912. Weitere Untersuchungen über den Stoffwechsel der Krustazeen. *Ibid.*, 57:534–544. (*113*)
Schreiber, E. 1922. Beiträge zur Kenntnis der Morphologie, Entwicklung und Lebensweise der Süsswasser-Ostracoden. Zool. Jahrb., Anat., 43:485–538. (*161, 237, 238, 240, 251*)
van Schreven, A. C. 1938. Über die sogenannten Tracheenlungen von *Gryllus domesticus*. Zool. Anz., 121:263–264. (*235*)
Schuch, K. 1915. Beiträge zur Kenntnis der Schalendrüse und der Geschlechtsorgane der Cumaceen. Arb. Zool. Inst. Wien, 20:7–22. (*161, 207*)
Schultze, M. 1865. Zur Kenntnis der Leuchtorgane von *Lampyris splendidula*. Arch. mikr. Anat., 1:124–139. (*264*)
———, and M. Rudneff 1865. Weitere Mittheilungen über die Einwirkung der Überosmiumsäure auf thierische Gewebe. Arch. mikr. Anat., 1:299–304. (*264*)
Schulz, F. N. 1900. Kommt in der Sepiaschulpe Cellulose vor? Z. physiol. Chem., 29:124–128. (*44*)
——— 1922. Über Farbstoff und Wachs der Blutlaus (*Schizoneura lanigera*). Biochem. Z., 127:112–119. (*95*)
——— 1930. Zur Biologie des Mehlwurms (*Tenebrio molitor*). 1. Der Wasserhaushalt. *Ibid.*, 227:340–353. (*94, 300*)

———, and M. Becker 1931a. Zur Biologie des Mehlwurms (*Tenebrio molitor*). 2. Tenebrioglykol, ein wachsartiger Stoff. *Ibid.*, 232:189–195. (*94*)

——— 1931b. Über Insektenwachse. 3. Über das Wachs der Wollaus (*Pemphigus xylostei*). *Ibid.*, 235:233–239. (*94–97*)

Schulze, K. 1934. Die Hautdrüsen der Odonaten: Bau, Verteilung, Entwicklung und Funktion. Zool. Jahrb., Anat., 58:239–274. (*161, 163, 170, 207, 209*)

Schulze, P. 1912. Über Versondrüsen bei Lepidopteren. Zool. Anz., 39:433–444. (*209, 213*)

——— 1913a. Chitin- und andere Cuticularstrukturen bei Insekten. Verh. dtsch. Zool. Ges., 23:165–195. (*164, 170, 193, 244, 246*)

——— 1913b. Zur Flügeldeckenstruktur der Cicindelen und über ein in dieser Beziehung interessantes Exemplar von *Cicindela campestris* L. Berlin. Ent. Z., 58:242–243. (*161, 164, 170, 207, 209, 246, 267*)

——— 1913c. Studien über tierische Körper der Carotingruppe. 1. Insecta. Sitz.-Ber. Ges. Naturf. Freunde Berlin, pp. 1–22. (*92*)

——— 1915. Die Flügeldeckenskulptur der *Cicindela hybrida*-Rassen. Dtsch. Ent. Z., pp. 247–255. (*161, 164, 170, 246, 267*)

——— 1921. Ein neues Verfahren zum Bleichen und Erweichen tierischer Hartgebilde. Sitz.-Ber. Ges. Naturf. Freunde Berlin, pp. 135–139. (*36, 37*)

——— 1922a. Über Beziehungen zwischen pflanzlichen und tierischen Skelettensubstanzen, über eine neue Chitinreaktion und eine Methode zur Bleichen und Erweichen tierischer Hartgebilde. Verh. dtsch. Zool. Ges., 27:71–73. (*37*)

——— 1922b. Über Beziehungen zwischen pflanzlichen und tierischen Skelettsubstanzen und über Chitinreaktionen. Biol. Zbl., 42:388–394. (*33, 37*)

——— 1924. Der Nachweis und die Verbreitung des Chitins mit einem Anhang über das komplizierte Verdauungssystem der Ophryoscoleciden. Z. Morph. Ökol. Tiere, 2:643–666. (*37, 42*)

——— 1926. Das Chitin, sein Aufbau, seine Verbreitung, sein Nachweis und seine Behandlung bei der entomologischen Präparation. Ent. Mitt., 15:420–423. (*37*)

——— 1927. Der chitinige Gespinstfaden der Larve von *Platyderma tricuspis* Motsch. (Col. Tenebr.). Z. Morph. Ökol. Tiere, 9:333–340. (*50, 67*)

** ——— 1927–1928. Zur Einbettungstechnik nach Diaphanolbehandlung. Sitz.-Ber. ber. Abh. Naturf. Ges. Rostock, vol. 3.

——— 1932. Über das Zustandekommen des Zeichnungsmuster und der Schmelzfärbung in der Zeckengattung *Amblyomma* Koch, nebst Bemerkungen über die Gliederung des Ixodidenkörpers. Z. Morph. Ökol. Tiere, 25:508–533. (*132, 161, 175*)

———, and G. Kunike 1923. Zur Mikrochemie tierischer Skelettsubstanzen. Biol. Zbl., 43:556–559. (*15, 38, 39*)

Schumann, F. 1928. Experimentelle Untersuchungen über die Bedeutung einiger Salze, insbesondere des Kohlensäuren Kalkes, für Gammariden und ihren Einfluss auf deren Hautungsphysiologie und Lebensmöglichkeit. Zool. Jahrb., allg. Zool., 44:623–704. (*290, 292*)

Schürfeld, W. 1935. Die physiologische Bedeutung der Versondrüsen, untersucht im Zusammenhang mit ihrem feineren Bau. Arch. Entw. Mech., 133:728–759. (*162, 209*)

Schutts, J. H. 1949. An electron microscope study of the egg membranes of *Melanoplus differentialis*. Biol. Bull., 97:100–107. (*82, 281*)

Schuurman, J. J. 1937. Contribution to the genetics of *Tenebrio molitor* L. Genetica, 19:273–355. (*75*)

* Schwenk, H. 1947. Untersuchungen über die Entwicklung der Borsten bei *Drosophila*. Nachr. Ges. wiss. Göttingen, Math.-Phys. Kl., pp. 14–16. (Cited by Wigglesworth 1948.) (*275*)

Sciacchitano, I. 1933. Ricerche chimiche sui Lepidotteri. Boll. Zool., Torino, 4:179–186. (*72*)

Scudamore, H. H. 1948. Factors influencing molting and the sexual cycles in the crayfish. Biol. Bull., 95:229–237. (*235*)

Seagren, G. W., M. H. Smith, and G. H. Young 1945. The comparative antifouling efficacy of DDT. Science, 102:425–426. (*314*)

Sebba, F., and H. V. A. Briscoe 1940. The evaporation of water through unimolecular films. J. Chem. Soc., pp. 106–114. (*287, 289*)

** Semichon, L. 1939. Modifications du tégument chitineux pendant la diapause larvaire des insectes. Bull. Soc. Fr. Micr., Paris, 8:145–146. (*154*)

Semper, C. 1857. Über die Bildung der Flügel, Schuppen und Haare bei den Lepidopteren. Z. wiss. Zool., 8:326–339. (*243*)

Sen, H. K. 1937. Indian lac industry. Sci. & Culture, 2:454–459. (*282*)

Sewell, M. T. (Unpublished data on integument of spiders.) (*85, 156, 163, 172, 303*)

Shafer, G. D. 1923. The growth of dragonfly nymphs at the moult and between moults. Stanford Univ. Publ. Biol. Sci., 3:307–338. (*229, 233*)

Shepard, H. H., and C. H. Richardson 1931. A method of determining the relative toxicity of contact insecticides, with special reference to the action of nicotine against *Aphis rumicis*. J. Econ. Ent., 24:905–914. (*294*)

Shimizu, S. 1931. On the origin of the crystals in the exuvial fluid of the silkworm larva. Proc. Imp. Acad., Japan, 7:361–362. (*107*)

Shorey, E. C. 1930. Some methods for detecting differences in soil organic matter. U.S. D. A., Tech. Bull. 211, 25 pp. (*55*)

Shorigin, P. P., and E. Hait 1934. Über die Nitrierung von Chitin. Ber. dtsch. Chem. Ges., 67:1712–1714. (*28*)

——— 1935. Über die Acetylierung des Chitins. *Ibid.*, 68:971–973. (*11*)

Shorigin, P. P., and N. N. Makorowa-Semljanskaja 1935. Über des Desaminerung von Chitin und Glucosamin. Ber. dtsch. Chem. Ges., 68:965–969. (*28*)

———, and V. Anur'eva 1935. Über die Methyläther des Chitins. Ber. dtsch. Chem. Ges., 68:969–971. (*28*)

Sihler, H. 1924. Die Sinnesorgane au den Cerci der Insekten. Zool. Jahrb., Anat., 45:519–580. (*275*)

Silvestri, F. 1902. Acari, Myriopoda et Scorpiones hucusque in Italia reperta. Ordo Pauropoda. 85 pp. Vesuviana, Portici. (*161*)

——— 1903. Acari, Myriopoda et Scorpiones hucusque in Italia reperta. Classis Diplopoda. Vol. 1: Segmenta, Tegumentum, Musculi. 272 pp. Vesuviana, Portici. (*101, 155, 160, 163, 182, 207, 213, 238, 251, 267, 268, 270, 275*)

de Sinéty, R. 1901. Recherches sur la biologie et l'anatomie des Phasmes. La Cellule, 19:119–278. (*161, 217, 237, 242, 264*)

Singh-Pruthi, H. 1925. Studies on insect metamorphosis. Influence of starvation. Brit. J. Exp. Biol., 3:1–8. (*232*)

* Skvortzov, A. A. 1946. (On the permeability of insect integuments for contact insecticides.) (In Russian.) Adv. Mod. Biol., 21:249–256. (Rev. Appl. Ent., 37A:43.) (*293, 310*)

Slifer, E. H. 1935. Morphology and development of the femoral chordotonal organs of *Melanoplus differentialis*. J. Morph., 58:615–637. (*221, 238, 277*)

——— 1936. The scoloparia on *Melanoplus differentialis* (Orthoptera, Acrididae). Ent. News, 47:174–180. (*277*)

——— 1937. The origin and fate of the membranes surrounding the grasshopper egg; together with some experiments on the source of the hatching enzyme. Quart. J. Micr. Sci., 79:493–506. (*50, 52, 227, 281, 282*)

——— 1938. The formation and structure of a special water-absorbing area in the membranes covering the grasshopper egg. *Ibid.*, 80:437–458. (*298, 314*)

——— 1945. Removing the shell from living grasshopper eggs. Science, 102:282. (*281*)

——— 1946. The effects of xylol and other solvents on diapause in the grasshopper egg; together with a possible explanation for the action of these agents. J. Exp. Zool., 102:333–356. (*314*)

——— 1948. Isolation of a wax-like material from the shell of the grasshopper egg. Disc. Faraday Soc., no. 3, pp. 182–187. (*96–98, 281*)

——— 1949a. Changes in certain of the grasshopper egg coverings during development as indicated by fast green and other dyes. J. Exp. Zool., 110:183–204. (*182, 281, 282, 293, 311, 314*)

——— 1949b. Variations, during development, in the resistance of the grasshopper egg to a toxic substance. Ann. Ent. Soc. Amer., 42:134–140. (*294, 310, 314*)

——— 1950. Vulnerable areas on the surface of the tarsus and pretarsus of the grasshopper (Acrididae, Orthoptera); with special reference to the arolium. *Ibid.*, 43:173–188. (*158, 290, 302, 311*)

———, and R. L. King 1934. Insect development. 7. Early stages in the development of grasshopper eggs of known age with a known temperature history. J. Morph., 56:593–601. (*50, 280*)

Slifer, E. H., and B. P. Uvarov 1938. Brunner's organ; a structure found on the jumping legs of grasshoppers (Orthoptera). Proc. R. Ent. Soc. London, ser. A, 13:111–115. (*270*)

Smallman, B. N. 1942. Quantitative characters of the growth and development of a paurometabolous insect, *Dixippus morosus* Br. & Redt. 1. The loss of water in relation to ecdysis. Proc. R. Soc. Edinburgh, ser. B, 61:167–185. (*290*)

Smith, E. H., and G. W. Pearce 1948. The mode of action of petroleum oils as ovicides. J. Econ. Ent., 41:173–180. (*314*)

Smith, S. L. 1943. A survey of plastics from the viewpoint of the mechanical engineer. Engineer, 176:491–515. (*83*)

Snethlage, E. 1905. Über die Frage von Muskelansatz und der Herkunft der Muskulatur bei den Arthropoden. Zool. Jahrb., Anat., 21:495–514. (*159, 160, 237, 238*)

Snodgrass, R. E. 1924. Anatomy and metamorphosis of the apple maggot, *Rhagoletis pomonella.* J. Agric. Res., 28:1–36. (*231*)

——— 1925. Anatomy and Physiology of the Honey Bee. McGraw-Hill, New York. (*161*)

——— 1926. The morphology of insect sense organs and the sensory nervous system. Smithsonian Miscl. Coll., 77(8):1–80. (*275*)

——— 1935. Principles of Insect Morphology. McGraw-Hill, New York. (*5, 6, 160, 243, 275*)

——— 1947. The insect cranium and the "epicranial suture." Smithsonian Miscl. Coll., 107(7):1–52. (*234*)

Sollas, I. B. J. 1907. On the identification of chitin by its physical constants. Proc. R. Soc. London, ser. B, 79:474–481. (*39, 44, 47–51, 120*)

Sollner, K., I. Abrams, and C. W. Carr 1941. The structure of the collodion membrane and its electrical behavior. 1. The behavior and properties of commercial collodion. J. Gen. Physiol., 24:467–482. (*288*)

Spek, J. 1919. Beiträge zur Kenntnis der chemischen Zusammensetzung und Entwicklung der Radula der Gasteropoden. Z. wiss. Zool., 118:313–363. (*33, 44*)

* Spitzer, K. 1926. Der Gehalt von Kokonen der Nachtpfauenaugen (*Saturnia*) an Orthodioxybenzolderivaten. Anz. Akad. Wiss. Wien, 63:71–73. (72)

Sprung, F. 1932. Die Flügeldecken der Carabiden. Z. Morph. Ökol. Tiere, 24:435–490. (*164, 192, 244, 246*)

Stacey, M. 1943. Mucopolysaccharides and related substances. Chem. & Ind., 62:110–112. (*12, 81*)
Städeler, G. 1859. Untersuchungen über das Fibroin, Spongin und Chitin, nebst Bemerkungen über den thierischen Schleim. Ann. Chem. & Pharm., 111:12–28. (*17*)
Stair, R., and W. W. Coblentz 1935. Infrared absorption spectra of plant and animal tissues and of various other substances. J. Res. Nat. Bur. Standards, 15:295–316. (*120, 128*)
Stallberg-Stenhagen, S., and E. Stenhagen 1945. Phase transitions in condensed monolayers of normal chain carboxylic acids. Nature, 156:239–240. (*300, 302*)
Stamm, R. H. 1909. Über die Muskelinsertionen an das Chitin bei den Arthropoden. Anat. Anz., 34:337–349. (*237*)
——— 1910. Die Muskelinsertionen an das Chitin bei den Arthropoden. *Ibid.*, 37:82–83. (*237*)
Stanier, R. Y. 1947. The non-fermenting myxobacteria. *Cytophaga johnsonae* n. sp., a chitin-decomposing myxobacterium. J. Bact., 53:297–315. (*55, 56, 77*)
Steding, E. 1924. Zur Anatomie und Histologie von *Halarachne otariae* n. sp. Z. wiss. Zool., 121:442–493. (*161, 182*)
Stegemann, F. 1929a. Ist die Insektenkutikula wirklich einheitlich gebaut? Untersuchungen an Cicindeliden. Zool. Jahrb., Anat., 50:571–580. (*164, 170, 246*)
——— 1929b. Die Flügeldecken der Cicindelinae. Ein Beitrag zur Kenntnis der Insektenkutikula. Z. Morph. Ökol. Tiere, 18:1–73. (*161, 164, 170, 192, 209, 244, 246*)
Stein, R. S., and R. E. Rundle 1948. On the nature of the interaction between starch and iodine. J. Chem. Physics, 16:195–207. (*35*)
Steinhaus, E. A. 1949. Principles of Insect Pathology. McGraw-Hill, New York. (*57, 315*)
Stellwaag, F. 1923. Die Benetzungsfähigkeit flüssiger Pflanzenschutzmittel und ihre Messbarkeit nach einem neuen Verfahren. Z. angew. Ent., 10:163–176. (*137*)
Stendell, W. 1911. Über Drüsenzellen bei Lepidopteren. Zool. Anz., 38:582–585. (*217*)
——— 1912. Beiträge zur Kenntnis der Önocyten von *Ephestia kühniella*. Z. wiss. Zool., 102:136–168. (*217, 218*)
Stobbe, R. 1912. Die abdominalen Duftorgane der männlichen Sphingiden und Noctuiden. Zool. Jahrb., Anat., 32:493–532. (*275*)
Stokes, A. C. 1893. The structure of insect tracheae, with special reference to those of *Zaitha fluminea*. Science, 21:44–46. (*257, 259*)
Stossberg, M. 1937. Über die Entwicklung der Schmetterlingschuppen. Biol. Zbl., 57:393–402. (*270*)
——— 1938. Die Zellvorgänge bei der Entwicklung der Flügelschuppen von *Ephestia kühniella*. Z. Morph. Ökol. Tiere, 34:173–206. (*162, 227, 243, 270*)
Strasburger, E. H. 1935. *Drosophila melanogaster* Meig. Eine Einführung in den Bau und die Entwicklung. Springer, Berlin. (*216, 220*)
Straus-Durckheim, H. 1828. L'anatomie comparée des animaux articulés. Paris. (*6, 159, 163, 184, 253*)
Stuart, L. S. 1936. A note on halophilic chitinovorous bacteria. J. Amer. Leather Chem. Assoc., 31:119–120. (*55–57*)
Stübel, H. 1911. Die Fluoreszenz tierischer Gewebe in ultravioletten Licht. Pflüger's Arch. ges. Physiol., 142:1–14. (*121, 129*)
Subklew, W. 1934. Physiologisch-experimentelle Untersuchungen an einigen Elateriden. Z. Morph. Ökol. Tiere, 28:184–228. (*294, 302, 310*)
Süffert, F. 1924. Morphologie und Optik der Schmetterlingsschuppen, insbeson-

dere die Schillerfarben der Schmetterlinge. Z. Morph. Ökol. Tiere, 1:171–308. (*140, 196*)

** ——— 1926. Die Flügelschuppen der Schmetterlinge, ihr Bau und ihre Farbe. Mikr. f. Naturfreunde (Bermuhler), vol. 4.

Sukatschoff, B. 1899. Über den feineren Bau einiger Cuticulae und der Spongienfasern. Z. wiss. Zool., 66:377–406. (*44, 222*)

——— 1901. Nochmals über das chemische Verhalten des Cocons von *Hirudo.* Zool. Anz., 24:604–608. (*44*)

Sulc, K. 1911. Über Respiration, Tracheensystem und Schaumproduktion der Schaumzikadenlarven (Aphrophorinae – Homoptera). Z. wiss. Zool., 99:147–188. (*206, 251*)

Sumner, F. B., and P. Doudoroff 1943. An improved method of assaying melanin in fishes. Biol. Bull., 84:187–194. (*87*)

Sun, Y. P. 1947. An analysis of some important factors affecting the results of fumigation tests on insects. Minnesota Agric. Exp. Sta., Tech. Bull. no. 177. 104 pp. (*307, 313*)

Sundermeier, W. 1940. Der Hautpanzer des Kopfs und des Thorax von *Myrmeleon europaeus* und seine Metamorphose. Zool. Jahrb., Anat., 66:291–348. (*243*)

Sundwik, E. E. 1881. Zur Konstitution des Chitins. Z. physiol. Chem., 5:384–394. (*17*)

——— 1893. Psyllostearylalkohol, ein neuer Fettalkohol im Thierreiche. *Ibid.*, 17:425–430. (*95*)

——— 1898a. Über Psyllostearylalkohol. *Ibid.*, 25:116–121. (*95*)

——— 1898b. Über das Wachs der Hummeln (*Bombus* sp.). *Ibid.*, 26:56–59. (*95*)

——— 1901. Über Psyllawachs, Psyllostearylalkohol und Psyllostearylsäure (Psyllalkohol, Psyllasäure). *Ibid.*, 32:355–360. (*95*)

——— 1907. Über das Wachs der Hummeln. 2. Mitt. Psyllaalkohol, ein Bestandteil des Hummelwachses. *Ibid.*, 53:365–369. (*95*)

——— 1908. Über das Psyllawachs. 4. Mitt. Die Psyllasäure und einige ihrer Salze. *Ibid.*, 54:255–257. (*95*)

——— 1911. Über das Wachs der Hummeln. 3. Mitt. Sind die Alkohole des Psyllawachses und des Hummelwachses identisch? *Ibid.*, 72:455–458. (*95*)

Swammerdamm, J. 1752. Bibel der Natur. (*253*)

Symposium. 1948. Interaction of Water and Porous Materials. Disc. Faraday Soc. no. 3, 294 pp. (*299, 305*)

Szalay, L. 1926. Bemerkungen über die Körperhaut von *Mideopsis orbicularis.* Ann. Hist.-Nat. Mus. Nat. Hung., Budapest, 23:258–262. (*154*)

* Tadokoro, T., and M. Nisida 1940. (Strength of artificial fibers containing fish proteins.) J. Soc. Chem. Ind., Japan, 43:347. (Chem. Abstr., 35:1998.) (*29*)

Tait, J. 1916. Experiments and observations on crustacea. 2. Moulting of isopods. Proc. R. Soc. Edinburgh, 37:59–68. (*234*)

* Takata, R. 1929. The utilization of microorganisms for human food materials. 10. Carbohydrates of the mycelium of *Aspergillus oryzae.* J. Soc. Chem. Ind., Japan, 32:245–247. (Chem. Abstr., 24:2206.) (*53*)

Tänzer, E. 1921. Die Zellkerne einiger Dipterenlarven und ihre Entwicklung. Z. wiss. Zool., 119:114–153. (*206, 251, 254*)

Tauber, O. E. 1934. The distribution of chitin in an insect. J. Morph., 56:51–58. (*40, 50, 110, 111, 114*)

Teorell, T. 1949. Permeability. Ann. Rev. Physiol., 9:545–564. (*286, 288*)

Theodor, O. 1936. On the relation of *Phlebotomus papatasii* to the temperature and humidity of the environment. Bull. Ent. Res., 27:653–671. (*289, 298, 301*)

Thomas, H. J. 1944. Tegumental glands in the Cirripedia thoracica. Quart. J. Micr. Sci., 84:257–282. (*94, 121, 161, 163, 207, 215*)

Thomas, R. C. 1942. Composition of fungus hyphae. 3. The Pythiaceae. Ohio J. Sci., 42:60–62. (*45, 53*)

Thompson, W. R. 1920. Recherches sur les Diptères parasites. 1. Les larves des Sarcophagidae. Bull. Biol. Fr. Belg., 54:313–463. (*262*)

——— 1929. A contribution to the study of morphogenesis in the muscoid Diptera. Trans. R. Ent. Soc. London, 77:195–244. (*122, 162, 204, 235, 238, 240, 257, 270*)

* Thor, C. J. B. 1939. (Chitin compounds and regenerated chitin products such as filaments, films, tubes or straws.) U.S. Patents nos. 2,168,374; 2,168,375. (Chem. Abstr., 33:9671.) (*29*)

———, and W. F. Henderson 1940. The preparation of alkali chitin. Amer. Dyestuff Reporter, 29:461–464, 489–491 (and U.S. Patent no. 2,217,823.) (*25, 29, 40, 82, 119, 120*)

Thor, S. 1902. Untersuchungen über die Haut verschiedener dickhäutiger Acarina. Arb. Inst. Wien, 14:291–306. (*161, 179, 182, 204*)

Thorpe, W. H. 1930a. The biology, postembryonic development and economic importance of *Cryptochaetum iceryae* parasitic on *Icerya purchasi*. Proc. Zool. Soc. London, pp. 929–971. (*139, 217, 301*)

——— 1930b. The biology of the petroleum fly (*Psilopa petrolei* Coq.). Trans. Ent. Soc. London, 78:331–343. (*95, 139, 157, 261, 301*)

——— 1931. The biology of the petroleum fly. Science, 123:101–103. (*95, 139, 157, 301*)

——— 1936. On a new type of respiratory interrelation between an insect (Chalcid) parasite and its host (Coccidae). Parasitology, 28:517–540. (*52, 66, 261*)

——— 1941. The biology of *Cryptochaetum* (Diptera) and *Eupelmus* (Hymenoptera) parasites of *Aspidoproctus* (Coccidae) in East Africa. *Ibid.*, 33:149–168. (*261*)

———, and D. J. Crisp 1947. Studies on plastron respiration. 1. The biology of *Aphelocheirus* and the mechanism of plastron retention. J. Exp. Biol., 24:227–269. (*126, 171, 181, 266, 269, 276*)

——— 1949. Studies on plastron respiration. 4. Plastron respiration in the Coleoptera. *Ibid.*, 26:219–260. (*276*)

Thulin, I. 1908. Studien über den Zusammenhang granulärer interstitieller Zellen mit den Muskelfasern. Anat. Anz., 33:193–205. (*264*)

Tichomiroff, A. 1885. Chemische Studien über Entwicklung der Insekteneier. Z. physiol. Chem., 9:518–532, 566–567. (*30. 50, 66*)

Tiegs, O. W. 1922. Researches on the insect metamorphosis. 1. On the structure and postembryonic development of a Chalcid wasp, *Nasonia*. 2. On the physiology and the interpretation of the insect metamorphosis. Trans. R. Soc. S. Australia, 46:319–527. (*161, 257, 261, 270*)

Tiemann, F., and R. H. Landolt 1886. Über Glucosamin. Ber. dtsch. Chem. Ges., 19:49–53, 155–157. (*9*)

Timm, R. 1883. Beobachtungen an *Phreoryctes menkeanus* und *Nais*. Arb. Zool.-zootom. Inst. Würzburg, 6:109–157. (*44*)

Timon-David, J. 1947. Pigments des insectes. L'Année Biol., 23:237–271. (*86, 91*)

Tirelli, M. 1931. Il comportamente der glicogeno durante lo sviluppo embryionale del *Bombyx mori*. Z. vergl. Physiol., 15:148–158. (*30*)

Titschack, E. 1926. Untersuchungen über das Wachstum, den Nahrungsverbrauch und die Eierzeugung. 2. *Tineola biselliella* Hum. Gleichzeitig ein Beitrag zur Klärung der Insektenhäutung. Z. wiss. Zool., 128:509–569. (*232*)

Tobias, J. M., J. J. Kollros, and J. Savit 1946. Relation of absorbability to the comparative toxicity of DDT for insects and mammals. J. Pharm. Exp. Ther., 86:287–293. (*314*) di Tocco, R. 1927. Bibliografia del filugello (*Bombyx mori* L.) et del gelso (*Morus alba* L.). Padova, Milan. (*67*)

Tomita, M. 1921. Über die chemische Zusammensetzung der Eischale des Seidenspinners. Biochem. Z., 116:40–47. (*62, 63, 66*)

Tonner, F. 1936. Das Hautnervensystem der Arthropoden. Zool. Anz., 113:125–136. (*275*)

* Törne, O. 1911. Untersuchungen über die Insertion der Muskeln am Chitinskelett bei Insekten. Jurjev Schrift. Naturf. Ges., 20:1–94. (*238*)

Tóth, G. 1940. Über den präparativen Nachweis von Chitin in Mollusken. Z. physiol. Chem., 263:224–226. (*13, 42, 44, 46*)

Toth, L. 1937. Entwicklungszyklus und Symbiose von *Pemphigus spirothecae*. Z. Morph. Ökol. Tiere, 33:412–437. (*217, 219*)

Tower, W. L. 1902. Observations on the structure of the exuvial glands and the formation of the exuvial fluid in insects. Zool. Anz., 25:466–472. (*159*)

——— 1903a. The origin and development of the wings of Coleoptera. Zool. Jahrb., Anat., 17:517–572. (*159, 243*)

——— 1903b. The development of the colors and color patterns of Coleoptera, with observations upon the development of color in other orders of insects. Univ. Chicago Decenn. Publ., 10:31–70. (*38*)

——— 1906a. Observations on the changes in the hypodermis and cuticula of Coleoptera during ecdysis. Biol. Bull., 10:176–192. (*77, 88, 153, 157, 161, 178, 180, 183, 184, 209, 211, 226, 229, 237*)

——— 1906b. An investigation of evolution in chrysomelid beetles of the genus *Leptinotarsa*. Carnegie Inst. Wash., Publ. no. 48, 320 pp. (*76, 77, 86, 88, 161, 184, 205, 213*)

Townsend, A. B. 1904. The histology of the light organs of *Photinus marginellus*. Amer. Nat., 38:127–151. (*263, 264*)

Tozzetti, A. T. 1870. Sull'organo che fa'lume nelle lucciole volanti di Italia (*Luciola italica*). Bull. Soc. Ent. Ital., 2:177–189. (*264*)

Trager, W. 1935. The relation of cell size to growth in insect larvae. J. Exp. Zool., 71:489–508. (*204, 225*)

——— 1937. Cell size in relation to the growth and metamorphosis of the mosquito, *Aedes aegypti*. *Ibid.*, 76:467–491. (*204, 227*)

Trim, A. R. H. 1941a. The protein of insect cuticle. Nature, 147:115–116. (*59, 61–63, 65, 81, 83*)

——— 1941b. Studies in the chemistry of the insect cuticle. 1. Some general observations on certain arthropod cuticles with special reference to the characterization of the proteins. Biochem. J., 35:1088–1098. (*59, 61–63, 65, 69, 79, 81–84, 100, 114, 115, 188*)

Trogus, C., and K. Hess 1933. Zur Kenntnis der natürlichen Seiden und ihres Verhaltens gegen Säuren und Basen. Biochem. Z., 260:376–394. (*69*)

Tshirvinsky, P. 1926. Einige optische Beobachtungen an den Schuppen der Schmetterlinge. Zool. Jahrb., Anat., 48:1–18. (*120, 121, 132*)

Tsimehc, A. 1938. Chitin. Rayon & Silk J., 14(166):26–28; 14(167):27–28. (*29*)

Tuft, P. H. 1950. The structure of the insect egg-shell in relation to the respiration of the embryo. J. Exp. Biol., 26:327–334. (*307*)

Tullberg, T. 1882. Studien über den Bau und das Wachsthum des Hummerpanzers. Sv. Ak. Handl., 19:5–12. (*180, 182*)

Tulloch, G. S. 1936. The metasternal glands of the ant, *Myrmica rubra*, with special reference to the Golgi bodies and the intracellular canaliculi. Ann. Ent. Soc. Amer., 29:81–84. (*251*)

Tyzzer, E. E. 1907. The pathology of the brown-tail moth dermatitis. J. Med. Res., 16:43–64. (*276*)

Ulrich, W. 1924. Die Mundwerkzeuge der Spheciden. Beitrag zur Kenntnis der Insektenmundwerkzeuge. Z. Morph. Ökol. Tiere, 1:539–636. (*268*)

* Umbach, W. 1934. Untersuchungen über die Wirkungsweise der Kontactgifte. Mitt. a. Forstwirtschaft u. Forstwissenschaft, 5:216–218. (*293, 294*)

Upholt, W. M. 1947. The inactivation of DDT used in anopheline mosquito larvicides. U.S. Publ. Health Rpts., 62:302–309. (*319*)

Uvarov, B. P. 1933. Preliminary experiments on the annual cycle of the red locust. Bull. Ent. Res., 24:419–420. (*92*)

——— 1948. Recent advances in acridology: Anatomy and physiology of Acrididae. Trans. R. Ent. Soc. London, 99:1–75 (also printed and distributed as Anti-Locust Bull. no. 1, London). (*86*)

* Valentin, G. 1837. Über die Organisation des Hautskelettes der Krustaceen. Repertor f. Anat. u. Physiol., 1:122–126. (*159, 178, 182*)

Vaney, C. 1902. Contributions à l'étude des larves et des métamorphoses des Diptères. Ann. Univ. Lyon, n. s., 1, fasc. 9, 178 pp. (*106, 162, 216*)

———, and F. Maignon 1905. Variations subies par le glucose, le glycogène, la graisse et les albumines solubles au cours des métamorphoses du ver à soie. C. R. Acad. Sci., 140:1192–1195. (*30*)

von Veimarn, P. P. 1926a. Universal method for converting fibroin, chitin, casein and similar substances into the ropy-plastic state, and into the state of colloidal solution by means of concentrated aqueous solutions of readily soluble salts, capable of strong hydration. J. Textile Ind., 17:T-642–644. (*15, 136*)

* ——— 1926b. (Filament production from complex plastic masses.) Can. Chem. Met., 10:227–228. (*15, 136*)

——— 1927a. Conversion of fibroin, chitin, casein and similar substances into the ropy-plastic state and colloidal solution. Ind. Eng. Chem., 19:109–110. (*15, 136*)

——— 1927b. Solution of colloids of large molecular compounds by a very easily soluble strongly hydrolyzed material. Kolloid Z., 42:134–140. (*15, 136*)

* ——— 1928. Dispersoidological investigations on latex. Bull. Chem. Soc. Japan, 3:157–168. (*15, 136*)

Vejdovsky, F. 1925. Quelques remarques sur la structure et le dévelopment des cellules adipeuses et des oenocytes pendant la nymphose de l'abeille. La Cellule, 35:63–97. (*217*)

Verhoeff, K. W. 1901a. Einige Mittheilungen über Land-Isopoden. Berlin Ent. Z., 46:17–20. (*270*)

* ——— 1901b. Über den Häutungsvorgang der Diplopoden. Nova Acta Leop. Carol Akad. Wiss., 77:467–485. (*106*)

——— 1916. Zur Kenntnis der Ligiden, Porcellioniden und Onisciden. Arch. Naturges., ser. A, 82(10):108–169. (*270*)

——— 1917a. Zur Kenntnis der Atmung und der Atmungsorgane der Isopoda Oniscoidea. Biol. Zbl., 37:113–127. (*253*)

——— 1917b. Zur Kenntnis der Entwicklung der Trachealsysteme und der Untergattungen von *Porcellio* und *Trecheoniscus.* Sitz.-Ber. Ges. Naturf. Freunde, Berlin, pp. 195–223. (*253*)

——— 1919. Über die Atmung der Landasseln, zugleich ein Beitrag zur Kenntnis der Entstehung der Landtiere. Z. wiss. Zool., 118:365–447. (*106, 253*)

——— 1926–1932. Diplopoda. *In* Bronn, Klassen und Ordnungen des Tierreichs, vol. 5, Abt. 2, Buch 3. (*142, 160, 176, 249, 261*)

——— 1933. Symphyla. *Ibid.* (*161*)

——— 1934. Pauropoda. *Ibid.* (*161*)

——— 1937. Die Perioden der Häutungszeit bei den Chilognathen. Z. Morph. Ökol. Tiere, 33:438–444. (*226*)

——— 1939. Wachstum und Lebensverläugerung bei Blaniuliden und über die Periodomorphose. *Ibid.*, 36:21–40. (*106, 226*)
——— 1940. Über die Doppelhäutung der Land-Isopoden. *Ibid.*, 37:126–143. (*106, 234*)
Verne, J. 1921. Sur la nature ciliaire de la cuticule tégumentaire des crustacés. C. R. Ass. Anat. 16me réunion, Paris, pp. 17–20. (*161, 175, 178, 180, 182*)
* ——— 1923. Essai histo-chimique sur les pigments tégumentaires des crustacés décapodes. Arch. Morph. Gen. Exp., Paris, no. 16, 168 pp. (Gaston Doin, Paris.) (*86, 91*)
——— 1924. Note histochimique sur le métabolisme du glycogène pendant la mue chez les crustacés. C. R. Soc. Biol., 90:186–188. (*30*)
——— 1926. Les Pigments dans l'Organisme Animal. Gaston Doin, Paris. (*86*)
Versluys, J., and R. Demoll 1922. Das Limulus-Problem. Die Verwandtschaftsbeziehungen der Merostomen und Arachnoideen unter sich und mit anderen Arthropoden. Ergebn. Fortschr. Zool., Jena, 5:67–388. (*160, 220, 247*)
Verson, E. 1890. Hautdrüsensystem bei Bombyciden. Zool. Anz., 13:118–120. (*217*)
——— 1900. Beitrag zur Önocytenliteratur. *Ibid.*, 23:657–661. (*217*)
——— 1902. Observations on the structure of the exuvial glands and the formation of the exuvial fluid in insects. *Ibid.*, 25:652–654. (*209, 213*)
——— 1911. Beitrag zur näherer Kenntnis der Häutung und der Häutungsdrüsen bei *Bombyx mori.* Z. wiss. Zool., 97:457–480. (*209, 213*)
———, and E. Bisson 1891. Cellule glandulari ipostigmatische nel *Bombyx mori.* Bull. Soc. Ent. Ital., 23:3–20. (*217*)
Viallanes, H. 1882. Recherches sur l'histologie des insectes et sur les phénomènes histologiques qui accompagnent le développement post-embryonnaire de ces animaux. Ann. Sci. Nat. Zool., ser. 6, 14:1–348. (*106, 194, 217*)
Vickery, R. K. 1915. Evidence of a protoplasmic network in the oenocytes of the silkworm. Ann. Ent. Soc. Amer., 8:285–289. (*217*)
Vieweger, T. 1912. Les cellules tracheáles chez *Hypocrita jacobeae.* Arch. d. Biol., 27:1–25. (*264*)
* Viktorov, P. P., and I. M. Maiofis 1940. (Utilization of chitin in textile industry.) Khlopchatobumazhnaya Prom, no. 11/12, pp. 52–53. (Chem. Abstr., 38:874.) (*29*)
Vitzou, A. N. 1881. Recherches sur la structure et la formation des téguments chez les crutacées décapodes. Arch. Zool. Exp. & Gen., 10:451–576. (*30, 159, 163, 179, 182, 194, 207*)
Vogel, R. 1911. Über die Innervierung der Schmetterlingsflügel und den Bau und die Verbreitung der Sinnesorgane auf denselben. Z. wiss. Zool., 98:68–134. (*270*)
Voges, E. 1916. Myriapodenstudien. Z. wiss. Zool., 116:75–135. (*261*)
Vogt, M. 1948. Fettkörper und Önocyten der *Drosophila* nach Exstirpation der adulten Ringdrüse. Z. Zellforsch. mikr. Anat., 34:160–164. (*217*)
Voigt, W. 1886. Beiträge zur feineren Anatomie und Histologie von *Branchiobdella varians.* Arb. Zool.-zootom. Inst. Würzburg, 8:102–128. (*43, 44*)
Volmer, M. 1932. The migration of adsorbed molecules on surfaces of solids. Trans. Faraday Soc., 28:359–363. (*134, 287, 319*)
* ——— 1938. Oberflachendiffusion. Ver. dtsch. Ing. 74 Hauptversamml. Darmstadt u. 80-Jahrfeier, pp. 163–167. (Chem. Abstr., 34:5717.) (*134*)
Vonk, H. J. 1931. Quellungsminimum und isoelektrischer Punkt des Fibrins. Z. physiol. Chem., 198:201–218. (*136, 287*)
Vouk, V. 1915. Zur Kenntnis der mikrochemischen Chitin-Reaktion. Ber. dtsch. Bot. Ges., 33:413–415. (*33*)

Wachter, S. 1930. The moulting of the silkworm and a histological study of the moulting gland. Ann. Ent. Soc. Amer., 23:381–389. (*209, 229*)

Waddington, C. H. 1941. Body-color genes in *Drosophila*. Proc. Zool. Soc. London, ser. A, 111:173–180. (*88*)

Wahl, B. 1899. Über das Tracheensystem und die Imaginalscheiben der Larve von *Eristalis tenax* L. Arb. Zool. Inst. Wien, 12:45–98. (*215, 253, 263, 265*)

Wajda, S. 1931. Cytologische Untersuchungen über die Spinnstoffsekretion der Trichopterenlarven. Bull. Int. Akad. Cracovie, pp. 307–319. (*251*)

Wallengren, H. 1901. Über das Vorkommen und die Verbreitung der sogenannten Intestinaldrüsen bei den Decapoden. Z. wiss. Zool., 70:321–345. (*207*)

——— 1914a. Physiologisch-biologische Studien über die Atmung bei den Arthropoden. 2. Die Mechanik der Atembewegungen bei *Aeschna*larven. Lund Univ. Arssk., N. F., Afd. 2, 10(4):1–24. (*119*)

——— 1914b. Physiologisch-biologische Studien über die Atmung bei den Arthropoden. 3. Die Atmung der *Aeschna*larven. *Ibid.*, 10(8):1–28. (*119*)

——— 1915. Physiologisch-biologische Studien über die Atmung bei den Arthropoden. 5. Die Zusammensetzung der Luft der grossen Tracheenstämme bei den *Aeschna*larven. *Ibid.*, 10(11):1–12. (*307*)

Waloff, N. 1941. The mechanisms of humidity reactions of terrestrial isopods. J. Exp. Biol., 18:115–135. (*298*)

* Watanabe, K. 1936. (Chemistry of assimilation and disintegration of N-acetylglucosamine.) J. Biochem. (Japan), 24:287–295. (Chem. Abstr., 31:1054.) (*36*)

Waterhouse, D. F. 1945. A quantitative investigation of the copper content of *Lucilia cuprina*. Council Sci. Ind. Res. Australia, Bull. 191, pp. 21–39. (*281*)

Waterman, T. H. 1950. A light polarization analyzer in the compound eye of *Limulus*. Science, 111:252–254. (*132*)

Way, M. J. 1948. (Unpublished data on the moth *Diataraxia*, cited by Wigglesworth 1948b.) [See Quart. J. Micr. Sci., 91:145–182, 1950.] (*162, 163, 166, 180, 209, 213*)

Webb, D. A. 1940. Ionic regulation in *Carcinus maenas*. Proc. R. Soc. London, ser. B, 129:107–136. (*246, 247, 290, 292, 295, 298, 309, 310*)

Webb, J. E. 1946. Spiracle structure as a guide to the phylogenetic relationships of the Anoplura (Biting and Sucking Lice), with notes on the affinities of the mammalian hosts. Proc. Zool. Soc. London, 116:49–119. (*266*)

——— 1947. The structure of the cuticle in *Eomenacanthus stramineus* (Nitzsch.) (Mallophaga). Parasitology, 38:70–71. (*161, 163, 164, 166, 182*)

———, and R. A. Green 1945. On the penetration of insecticides through the insect cuticle. J. Exp. Biol., 22:8–20. (*289, 317*)

Weber, H. 1931. Lebensweise und Umweltbeziehungen von *Trialeurodes vaporariorum*. Z. Morph. Ökol. Tiere, 23:575–753. (*99, 300*)

——— 1933. Lehrbuch der Entomologie. Fischer, Jena. (*6, 159, 160, 243, 275*)

——— 1934. Die postembryonale Entwicklung der Aleurodinen. Ein Beitrag zur Kenntnis der metamorphosen der Insekten. Z. Morph. Ökol. Tiere, 29:268–305. (*163, 170*)

Weber, Max. 1881. Anatomisches über Trichonisciden. Arch. mikr. Anat., 19:579–648. (*207*)

Wege, W. 1909. Über die Insertionsweise der Arthropodenmuskeln nach Beobachtungen an *Asellus aquaticus*. Zool. Anz., 35:124–129. (*238*)

Weidner, H. 1934. Beiträge zur Morphologie und Physiologie des Genitalapparates der weiblichen Lepidopteren. Z. angew. Ent., 21:239–290. (*52, 282*)

Weinland, E. 1909. Chemische Beobachtungen an der Fliege *Calliphora*. Biol. Zbl., 29:564–577. (*31*)

Weismann, A. 1863. Die Entwicklung der Diptera im Ei. Z. wiss. Zool., 13:107–220. (*150, 255, 262, 264*)

——— 1864. Die Nachembryonale Entwicklung der Musciden nach Beobachtungen an *Musca vomitoria* und *Sarcophaga carnaria*. *Ibid.*, 14:187–336. (*264*)

Weiss, H. B. 1944. Insect responses to color. J. New York Ent. Soc., 52:267–271. (*120*)

——— 1946. Insects and the spectrum. *Ibid.*, 54:17–30. (*120, 126*)

Weissenberg, R. 1907. Über die Önocyten von *Torymus nigricornis* Boh. mit besonderen Berücksichtigung der Metamorphose. Zool. Jahrb., Anat., 23:231–268. (*217*)

Wergin, W. 1943. Über den Feinbau der Zellwande höherer Pflanzen. Biol. Zbl., 63:350–370. (*10*)

Werner, F. 1935. Scorpiones, Pedipalpi. *In* Bronn, Klassen und Ordnungen des Tierreichs, vol. 5, Abt. 4, Buch 8. (*160*)

Wester, D. H. 1909. Studien über das Chitin. Arch. d. Pharm., 247:282–307. (*17*)

——— 1910. Über die Verbreitung und Lokalisation des Chitins im Tierreiche. Zool. Jahrb., Syst., 28:531–558. (*42–44, 47–51, 261*)

——— 1913a. Chemischer Beitrag zur *Limulus*-Frage. Zool. Jahrb., Syst., 35:637–639. (*47–49*)

** ——— 1913b. Staat *Limulus* chemisch het dichtst bij de Arachnoidea of bij de Crustacea? Helder Tijdschr. Ned. Dierk. Ver., ser. 2, 12:222–224. (*47, 48*)

von Wettstein, F. 1921. Das Vorkommen von Chitin und seine Verwertung als systematisch-phylogenetischen Merkmal im Pflanzenreich. Sitz.-Ber. Akad. Wiss. Wien, Math. Naturwiss. Kl., Abt. 1, 130:3–20. (*42*)

Wheeler, B. M. 1947. The iodine metabolism of *Drosophila gibberosa* studied by means of radioiodine I^{131}. Proc. Nat. Acad. Sci., 33:298–302. (*66*)

——— 1950. Halogen metabolism of *Drosophila gibberosa*. I. Iodine metabolism studied by means of I^{131}. J. Exp. Zool., 115:83–107. (*66*)

Wheeler, W. M. 1892. Concerning the blood tissue of Insecta. Psyche, 6:216–220, 233–236, 253–258. (*217, 219*)

Whitcomb, W., and H. F. Wilson 1929. Mechanics of digestion of pollen by the adult honey bee and the relation of undigested parts to dysentery of bees. Wisconsin Agric. Exp. Sta., Res. Bull. no. 92, 27 pp. (*277*)

White, T. 1938. Amino sugars. 1. A case of acyl migration. J. Chem. Soc., pp. 1498–1500. (*28*)

——— 1940. Amino sugars. 2. Action of dilute alkali solutions on N-acylglucosamines. *Ibid.*, pp. 428–437. (*28*)

Wieland, H., and A. Tartter 1940. Über die Flügelpigmente der Schmetterlinge. 8. Pterobilin, der blaue Farbstoff der Pieridenflügel. Ann. d. Chem., 545:197–208. (*92*)

von Wielowiejski, H. R. 1882. Studien über Lampyriden. Z. wiss. Zool., 37:354–428. (*263*)

——— 1886. Über das Blutgewebe der Insekten. *Ibid.*, 43:512–536. (*217*)

——— 1889. Beiträge zur Kenntnis der Leuchtorgane der Insekten. Zool. Anz., 12:594–600. (*264*)

Wiesmann, R. 1938. Untersuchungen über die Struktur der Kutikula des Puppentönnchens der Kirschfliege, *Rhagoletis cerasi* L. Vjschr. naturf. Ges. Zürich, Beiblatt, 83:127–136. (*107, 108, 167, 187, 189*)

——— 1946. Untersuchungen über die Eintrittspforten des Dichlordiphenyltrichlorethan (DDT) in den Insektenkörper. Verh. schweiz. naturf. Ges., 126:166–167. (Rev. Appl. Ent., 37A: 115.) (*290*)

Wiggins, L. F. 1946. Reversible conversion of amino- into anhydro-sugars. Nature, 157:300. (*28*)

Wigglesworth, V. B. 1929. Digestion in the tsetse fly: A study of structure and function. Parasitology, 21:288–321. (*264, 278, 279*)
——— 1930a. A theory of tracheal respiration in insects. Proc. R. Soc. London, ser. B, 106:229–250. (*139*)
——— 1930b. The formation of the peritrophic membrane in insects, with special reference to the larvae of mosquitoes. Quart. J. Micr. Sci., 73:593–616. (*47, 49, 51, 277, 278*)
——— 1931a. The respiration of insects. Biol. Rev., 6:181–220. (*253, 306*)
——— 1931b. A curious effect of desiccation on the bedbug (*Cimex lectularius*). Proc. Ent. Soc. London, ser. B, C6:25–26. (*298*)
——— 1932a. The function of the anal gills of the mosquito larva. J. Exp. Biol., 10:16–26. (*249, 298*)
——— 1932b. On the function of the so-called "rectal glands" of insects. Quart. J. Micr. Sci., 75:131–150. (*249, 292, 298*)
——— 1933. The physiology of the cuticle and of ecdysis in *Rhodnius prolixus* (Triatomidae, Hemiptera); with special reference to the function of the oenocytes and of the dermal glands. *Ibid.*, 76:269–318. (*50, 92, 94, 146, 148, 154, 161, 179, 180, 182, 189–191, 202–205, 208, 209, 211, 213, 217–222, 225–229, 232, 275, 290*)
——— 1937. Wound healing in an insect (*Rhodnius prolixus* Hemiptera). J. Exp. Biol., 14:364–381. (*52, 66, 156, 202, 203, 222, 233*)
——— 1938. Absorption of fluid from the tracheal system of mosquito larvae at hatching and moulting. *Ibid.*, 15:248–254. (*307*)
——— 1939. The Principles of Insect Physiology. Dutton, London. (*6, 160, 182, 217, 278*)
——— 1940a. Local and general factors in the development of "pattern" in *Rhodnius prolixus* (Hemiptera). J. Exp. Biol., 17:180–200. (*76, 161, 191, 202*)
——— 1940b. The determination of characters at metamorphosis in *Rhodnius prolixus*. *Ibid.*, pp. 201–222. (*76, 191, 223, 227*)
——— 1941. Permeability of insect cuticle. Nature, 147:116. (*137, 140, 312, 315*)
——— 1942a. The significance of "chromatic droplets" in the growth of insects. Quart. J. Micr. Sci., 83:141–152. (*161, 216*)
——— 1942b. The storage of protein, fat, glycogen and uric acid in the fat body and other tissues of mosquito larvae. J. Exp. Biol., 19:56–77. (*30, 205*)
——— 1942c. Some notes on the integument of insects in relation to the entry of contact insecticides. Bull. Ent. Res., 33:205–218. (*94, 137, 140, 161, 179, 290, 291, 301, 312*)
——— 1944a. Action of inert dusts on insects. Nature, 153:493–494. (*123, 302*)
——— 1944b. Abrasion of soil insects. *Ibid.*, 154:333–334. (*123, 296, 302*)
——— 1945. Transpiration through the cuticle of insects. J. Exp. Biol., 21:97–114. (*71, 94, 99, 123, 137, 139, 157, 202, 287, 289, 290, 294, 295, 297, 299, 300–303, 314, 316*)
——— 1946. Water relations in insects. Experientia, 2:210–214. (*123, 300*)
——— 1947a. The site of action of inert dusts on certain beetles infesting stored products. Proc. R. Ent. Soc. London, ser. A, 22:65–69. (*71, 123, 296, 302*)
——— 1947b. The epicuticle in an insect, *Rhodnius prolixus*. *Ibid.*, ser. B, 134:163–181. (*71, 76, 85, 116, 148, 161, 163–165, 182, 207, 213, 219, 290*)
——— 1948a. The insect cuticle as a living system. Disc. Faraday Soc., no. 3, pp. 172–177. (*156*)
——— 1948b. The insect cuticle. Biol. Rev., 23:408–451. (*6, 30, 42, 71, 76, 82, 85, 92, 94, 139, 145, 147, 156, 160, 161, 174, 182, 206, 213, 219, 231, 300, 313–315*)
——— 1948c. The insect as a medium for the study of physiology. Proc. R. Soc. London, ser. B, 135:430–446.

——— 1948d. The structure and deposition of the cuticle in the adult mealworm, *Tenebrio molitor*. Quart. J. Micr. Sci., 89:197–217. (*154, 161, 163, 164, 166, 178–180, 183, 189, 193, 206, 209, 214, 226–228, 250, 290*)
——— 1949. Insect biochemistry. Ann. Rev. Biochem., 18:595–614. (*86*)
———, and J. D. Gillett 1936. The loss of water during ecdysis in *Rhodnius prolixus* Stal (Hemiptera). Proc. R. Ent. Soc. London, ser. A, 11:104–107. (*290*)
Wilcoxon, F., and A. Hartzell 1931. Some factors affecting the efficiency of contact insecticides. 1. Surface forces as related to wetting and tracheal penetration. Contrib. Boyce Thomp. Inst., 3:1–12. (*131, 140*)
Willers, W., and B. Dürken 1916. Celluläre Vorgänge bei der Häutung der Insekten. Z. wiss. Zool., 116:43–74. (*153, 159, 160, 203, 217, 219, 226, 227*)
Williams, C. M. 1949. The prothoracic glands of insects in retrospect and in prospect. Biol. Bull., 97:111–114. (*223*)
Williams, L. W. 1907a. The significance of the grasping antennae of Harpacticoid copepods. Science, 25:225–226. (*236*)
——— 1907b. The function of the gastrolith of the lobster. Science, 25:783. (*195*)
* Williamson, H. C. 1901. Contributions to the life-history of the edible crab (*Cancer pagurus* L.). Rep. Fish Board Scotland, 18(3):77–143.
Williamson, W. C. 1860. On some histological features in the shells of the crustacea. Quart. J. Micr. Sci., 8:35–47. (*159, 161, 163, 195*)
Winterstein, E. 1893. Zur Kenntnis der Pilzcellulose. Ber. dtsch. Bot. Ges., 11:441–445. (*10*)
——— 1894a. Über ein stickstoffhaltiges Spaltungsproduct der Pilzcellulose. Ber. dtsch. Chem. Ges., 27:3113–3115. (*10*)
——— 1894b. Zur Kenntnis der in den Membranen der Pilze enthaltenen Bestandtheile. I. Z. physiol. Chem., 19:521–562. (*10*)
——— 1895a. Zur Kenntnis der in den Membranen der Pilze enthaltenen Bestandtheile. II. *Ibid.*, 21:134–151. (*10*)
——— 1895b. Über Pilzcellulose. Ber. dtsch. Bot. Ges., 13:65–70. (*10, 42*)
——— 1895c. Über die Spaltungsproducte der Pilzcellulose. Ber. dtsch. Chem. Ges., 28:167–169. (*10, 42*)
——— 1899. Über die stickstoffhaltigen Stoffe der Pilze. Z. physiol. Chem., 26:438–441. (*10, 42*)
van Wisselingh, C. 1898. Mikrochemische Untersuchungen über die Zellwände der Fungi. Jahrb. wiss. Bot., 31:619–687. (*32, 34, 42, 44, 48, 49, 51, 261*)
——— 1910. (Appendix to Wester 1910.) Zool. Jahrb., Syst., 28:554. (*32, 34, 49*)
* ——— 1914. Über die Anwendung der in der organischen Chemie gebräulichen Reaktionen bei der phytomikrochemischen Untersuchungen. Folia Mikrobiol., Delft, 3:165–198. (*32, 38*)
——— 1925. Die Zellmembran. *In* Linsbauer, Handbuch der Pflanzenanatomie, III, 2:170–192. (*32, 37–39, 42, 45, 52*)
Wisselingh, E. 1916. Over het onderzoek naar het voorkomen von Chitine en Cellulose bij bacterien. Pharmac. Weekbl., 53:1069–1078, 1102–1107. (*45*)
von Wistinghausen, C. 1890. Über Tracheenendigungen in den Sericterien der Raupen. Z. wiss. Zool., 49:565–582. (*264*)
Wodsedalek, J. E. 1912. Life history and habits of *Trogoderma tarsale*, a museum pest. Ann. Ent. Soc. Amer., 5:367–382. (*232*)
Wolf, H. 1935. Das larvale und imaginale Tracheensystem der Odonaten und seine Metamorphose. Z. wiss. Zool., 146:591–620. (*93, 256, 259, 265*)
Wolff, E., W. Funke, and G. Dittmann 1876. Versuche über das Verdauungsvermögen der Schweine für verschiedene Futtermittel und Futtermischungen. Landw. Vers. Sta., 19:241–313. (*54, 110*)

Wolsky, A. 1929. Untersuchungen an Cornealinsen der Land-Isopoden in polarisiertem Lichte. Zool. Anz., 80:56–64. (*105*)

Woods, W. C. 1929. The integument of the larva of the alder flea beetle. Bull. Brook. Ent. Soc., 24:116–123. (*209, 211, 213, 221, 238, 267, 300*)

Woodworth, C. W. 1908. The leg tendons of insects. Amer. Nat., 42:452–456. (*241*)

Worden, E. C. 1940–1941. Developments in organic noncellulosic fibrous materials. Rayon Textile Monthly, 21:527–528, 609–610, 680–682, 733–735; 22:17–18, 85–86, 147–148, 225–226 (silk fibroin), 290–291, 354–356, 455–456, 517–518 (chitin), 603–604, 663. (*17, 29*)

Wottge, K. 1937. Die stofflichen Veränderung in der Eizelle von *Ascaris megalocephala* nach der Befruchtung. Protoplasma, 29:31–59. (*30, 43, 46, 281*)

Yalvac, S. 1939. Histologische Untersuchungen über die Entwicklung des Zeckenadultes in der Nymphe. Z. Morph. Ökol. Tiere, 35:535–585. (*161, 163, 182, 204–206, 227–229, 237, 240, 241*)

Yeager, J. F. 1945. The blood picture of the southern armyworm (*Prodenia eridania*). J. Agric. Res., 71:1–40. (*226*)

Yokoyama, T. 1936. Histological observations on a non-moulting strain of silkworms. Proc. Ent. Soc. London, ser. A, 11:35–44. (*217, 219, 231*)

Yonge, C. M. 1924. Studies on the comparative physiology of digestion. 2. The mechanism of feeding, digestion and assimilation in *Nephrops norvegicus*. Brit. J. Exp. Biol., 1:343–389. (*161, 163, 207, 298*)

——— 1932. On the nature and permeability of chitin. 1. The chitin lining the foregut of decapod crustacea and the function of the tegumental glands. Proc. R. Soc. London, ser. B, 111:298–329. (*47, 49, 56, 57, 94, 112, 161, 163, 169, 207, 211, 213, 214, 226, 230*)

——— 1935. Origin and nature of the egg-case in crustacea. Nature, 136:67–68. (*49, 52, 214, 280, 281*)

——— 1936. On the nature of the permeability of chitin. 2. The permeability of the uncalcified chitin lining the foregut of *Homarus*. Proc. R. Soc. London, ser. B, 120:15–41. (*294, 295, 305, 310*)

——— 1938a. Recent work on the digestion of cellulose and chitin by invertebrates. Sci. Progress, London, 32:638–647. (*78*)

——— 1938b. The nature and significance of the membranes surrounding the developing eggs of *Homarus vulgaris* and other Decapoda. Proc. Zool. Soc. London, ser. A, 107:499–517. (*52, 214, 280, 281*)

Zacker, F. 1937. Neue Untersuchungen über die Einwirkung oberflachenaktiver Pulver auf Insekten. Verh. dtsch. Zool. Ges., 39:264–271. (*302*)

———, and G. Kunike 1930. Beiträge zur Kenntnis der Vorratsschädlinge. 5. Untersuchungen über die insektizide Wirkung von Oxyden und Karbonaten. Arb. biol. Abt. (Anst.-Reichanst.), Berlin, 18:201–231. (*302*)

Zaitschek, A. 1904. Versuche über die Verdaulichkeit des Chitins und den Nachwert der Insekten. Pflüger's Arch. ges. Physiol., 104:612–623. (*50, 54, 110*)

Zamecnik, P. C., R. B. Lotfield, M. L. Stephenson, and C. M. Williams 1949. Biological synthesis of radioactive silk. Science, 109:624–626. (*67*)

Zander, E. 1897. Vergleichende und kritische Untersuchungen zum Verstandnisse der Jodreaktion des Chitins. Pflüger's Arch. ges. Physiol., 66:545–573. (*32, 35, 36, 39, 42, 45, 47–50*)

Zarapkin, S. R. 1930. Über gerichtete Variabilität bei Coccinelliden. 1. Allgemeine Einleitung und Analyse der ersten Pigmentierungsetappe bei *Coccinella 10-punctata*. Z. Morph. Ökol. Tiere, 17:719–736. (*244*)

——— 1934. Analyse der genotypisch und durch Aussenfaktoren bedingten Grössenunterschiede bei *Drosophila funebris*. Z. ind. Abstamm. Vererb.-Lehre, 68:163–171. (*204*)

Zavřel, J. 1920. Über Atmung und Atmungsorgane der Chironomidenlarven. Bull. Int. Acad. Sci. Prague, 22:120–129. (*261*)

* ——— 1935. Endokrine Hautdrüsen von *Syndiamesa branicki*. Publ. Fac. Sci. Univ. Masaryk, Brno, no. 213, 18 pp. (*217, 228*)

Zechmeister, L., W. Grassmann, G. Tóth, and R. Bender 1932. Über die Verknüpfungsart der Glucosamin-Reste im Chitin. Ber. dtsch. Chem. Ges., 65:1706–1708. (*13, 14*)

Zechmeister, L., and I. Pinczési. 1936. Octaacetyl-chitobiose aus Käfern. Z. physiol. Chem., 242:97–99. (*13, 38, 50*)

Zechmeister, L., and G. Tóth 1931. Zur Kenntnis der Hydrolyse von Chitin mit Salzsäure. Ber. dtsch. Chem. Ges., 64:2028–2032. (*11, 14, 38*)

——— 1932. Zur Kenntnis der Hydrolyse von Chitin mit Salzsäure. *Ibid.*, 65:161–162. (*14*)

——— 1933. Ein Beitrag zur Desamidierung des Glucosamins. *Ibid.*, 66:522–525. (*13*)

——— 1934. Vergleich von pflanzlichem und tierischem Chitin. Z. physiol. Chem., 223:53–56. (*13, 38, 42, 45, 49*)

——— 1939a. Chromatographischer Analyse Chitinreihe wirksamen Enzyme. Naturwiss., 27:367. (*38, 77*)

——— 1939b. Chromatographie der in der Chitinreihe wirksamen Enzyme des Emulsins. Enzymologia, 7:165–169. (*38, 77*)

——— 1939c. Chitin und seine Spaltprodukte. Fortschr. Chem. organ. Naturstoffe, 2:212–247. (*77*)

———, and M. Bálint 1938. Über die chromatographische Trennung einiger Enzyme der Emulsins. Enzymologia, 5:302–306. (*77*)

Zechmeister, L., G. Tóth, and É. Vajda. 1939. Chromatographie der in der Chitinreihe wirksamen Enzyme der Weinbergschmecke (*Helix pomatia*). Enzymologia, 7:170–175. (*77*)

Ziegler, H. E. 1907. Die Tracheen bei *Julus*. Zool. Anz., 31:776–782. (*261*)

Zilch, A. 1936. Zur Frage des Flimmerepithels bei Arthropoden. Z. wiss. Zool., 148:89–132. (*206*)

Zobell, C. E., and S. C. Rittenberg 1937. The occurrence and characteristics of chitinoclastic bacteria in the sea. J. Bact., 35:275–287. (*55–57, 77*)

Zograf, N. 1919. Zum Bau, zur Konservierung und Bearbeitung der Hautdrüsen von *Chirocephalus (Branchipus) josephinae* Grube, *Chirocephalus carnuntans* Brauer und *Streptocephalus auritus* Koch. Zool. Anz., 50:139–143. (*207*)

* von Zopf, —— 1888. (Fungal chitinase.) Nova Acta, 11:330. (Cited by Benecke 1905.) (*57*)

Zschorn, J. 1937. Beiträge zur Skelettbildung bei Arthropoden. Zool. Jahrb., Anat., 62:323–348. (*113, 160–162, 175, 203, 232, 233, 267*)

Zuckerkandl, F., and L. Messiner-Klebermass 1931. Eine Methode zum Nachweis und zur Bestimmung von Glucosamin. Biochem. Z., 236:19–28. (*11*)

Zuelzer, M. 1907. Über den Einfluss der Regeneration auf die Wachstumsgeschwindigkeit von *Asellus aquaticus* L. Arch. Entw.-Mech., 25:361–397. (*233*)

Zwack, A. 1905. Der feinere Bau und die Bildung des Ephippiums von *Daphnia hyalina*. Z. wiss. Zool., 79:548–573. (*244*)

SUBJECT INDEX